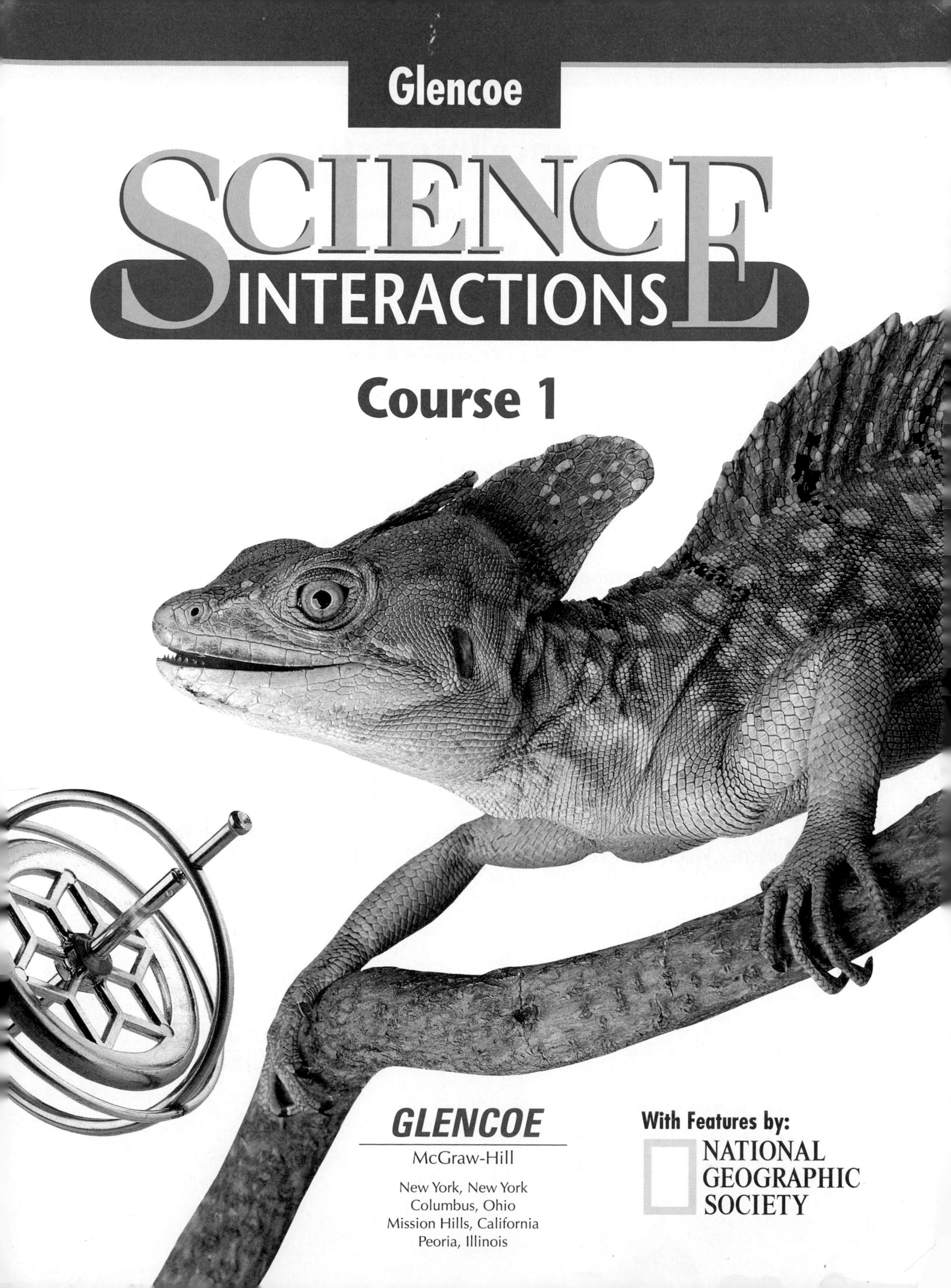
Glencoe
SCIENCE
INTERACTIONS
Course 1
GLENCOE
McGraw-Hill
New York, New York
Columbus, Ohio
Mission Hills, California
Peoria, Illinois
With Features by:
NATIONAL
GEOGRAPHIC
SOCIETY

Science Interactions

Science Interactions
Student Edition
Teacher Wraparound Edition
Science Discovery Activities
Teacher Classroom Resources
Laboratory Manual
Study Guide
Section Focus Transparencies
Teaching Transparencies
Performance Assessment
Performance Assessment in the Science Classroom
Computer Test Bank: IBM and Macintosh Versions
Spanish Resources
English/Spanish Audiocassettes
Science and Technology Videodisc Series
Integrated Science Videodisc Program
MindJogger Videoquizzes

Glencoe/McGraw-Hill
A Division of The McGraw-Hill Companies

Series Design: DECODE, Inc.

Send all inquiries to:
Glencoe/McGraw-Hill
936 Eastwind Drive
Westerville, OH 43081

ISBN 0-02-828054-7

Printed in the United States of America.

2 3 4 5 6 7 8 9 10 071/043 06 05 04 03 02 01 00 99 98 97

With Features by:

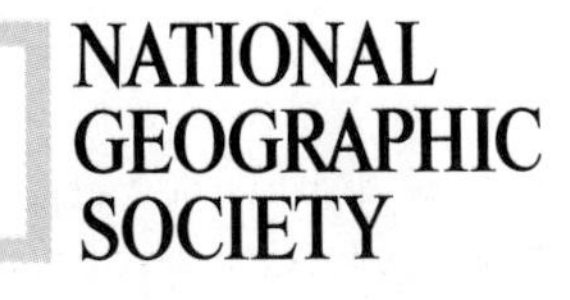

Authors

Bill Aldridge, M.S.
Director—Division of Science Education Solutions
Airborne Research and Services, Inc.
Fredericksburg, Virginia

Russell Aiuto, Ph.D.
Education Consultant
Frederick, Maryland

Jack Ballinger, Ed.D.
Professor of Chemistry
St. Louis Community College at Florissant Valley
St. Louis, Missouri

Anne Barefoot, A.G.C.
Physics and Chemistry Teacher, Emeritus
Whiteville High School
Whiteville, North Carolina

Linda Crow, Ed.D.
Associate Professor
University of Houston—Downtown
Houston, Texas

Ralph M. Feather, Jr., M.Ed.
Science Department Chair
Derry Area School District
Derry, Pennsylvania

Albert Kaskel, M.Ed.
Biology Teacher, Emeritus
Evanston Township High School
Evanston, Illinois

Craig Kramer, M.A.
Physics Teacher
Bexley High School
Bexley, Ohio

Edward Ortleb, A.G.C.
Science Consultant
St. Louis Board of Education
St. Louis, Missouri

Susan Snyder, M.S.
Earth Science Teacher
Jones Middle School
Upper Arlington, Ohio

Paul W. Zitzewitz, Ph.D.
Professor of Physics
University of Michigan-Dearborn
Dearborn, Michigan

With Features by:

NATIONAL GEOGRAPHIC SOCIETY

The National Geographic Society, founded in 1888 for the increase and diffusion of geographic knowledge, is the world's largest nonprofit scientific and educational organization. Since its earliest days, the Society has used sophisticated communication technologies, from color photography to holography, to convey geographic knowledge to a worldwide membership. The Education Products Division supports the Society's mission by developing innovative educational programs—ranging from traditional print materials to multimedia programs including CD-ROMs, videodiscs, and software.

Consultants

Chemistry

Richard J. Merrill
Director,
Project Physical Science
Associate Director,
Institute for Chemical
Education
University of California
Berkeley, California

Robert W. Parry, Ph.D.
Dist. Professor of Chemistry
University of Utah
Salt Lake City, Utah

Earth Science

Allan A. Ekdale, Ph.D.
Professor of Geology
University of Utah
Salt Lake City, Utah

Janifer Mayden
Aerospace Education Specialist
NASA
Washington, DC

James B. Phipps, Ph.D.
Professor of Geology
and Oceanography
Gray's Harbor College
Aberdeen, Washington

Life Science

David M. Armstrong, Ph.D.
Professor of Environmental,
Population, and
Organismic Biology
University of Colorado-Boulder
Boulder, Colorado

David Futch, Ph.D.
Professor of Biology
San Diego State University
San Diego, California

Richard D. Storey, Ph.D.
Associate Professor of Biology
Colorado College
Colorado Springs, Colorado

Physics

David Haase, Ph.D.
Professor of Physics
North Carolina State University
North Carolina

Patrick Hamill, Ph.D.
Professor of Physics
San Jose State University
San Jose, California

Middle School Science

Garland E. Johnson
Science and Education Consultant
Fresno, California

Barbara Sitzman
Chatsworth High School
Tarzana, California

Multicultural

Thomas Custer
Coordinator of Science
Anne Arundel County Schools
Annapolis, Maryland

Francisco Hernandez
Science Department Chair
John B. Hood Middle School
Dallas, Texas

Carol T. Mitchell
Instructor
Elementary Science Methods
College of Teacher Education
University of Omaha at Omaha
Omaha, Nebraska

Karen Muir, Ph.D.
Lead Instructor
Department of Social and
Behavioral Sciences
Columbus State
Community College
Columbus, Ohio

Reading

Elizabeth Gray, Ph.D.
Reading Specialist
Heath City Schools
Heath, Ohio
Adjunct Professor
Otterbein College
Westerville, Ohio

Timothy Heron, Ph.D.
Professor, Department
of Educational
Services & Research
The Ohio State University
Columbus, Ohio

Barbara Pettegrew, Ph.D.
Director of Reading
Study Center
Assistant Professor of Education
Otterbein College
Westerville, Ohio

LEP

Ross M. Arnold
Magnet School Coordinator
Van Nuys Junior High
Van Nuys, California

Linda E. Heckenberg
Director
Eisenhower Program
Van Nuys, California

Harold Frederick Robertson, Jr.
Science Resource Teacher
LAUSD Science Materials Center
Van Nuys, California

Safety

Robert Tatz, Ph.D.
Instructional Lab Supervisor
Department of Chemistry
The Ohio State University
Columbus, Ohio

Reviewers

Lillian Valeria Jordan Alston
Science Consultant
Institute of Government
University of North Carolina
Chapel Hill, North Carolina

Jamye Barnes
Science Teacher
Prescott Middle School
Prescott, Arkansas

Betty Bordelon
Science Teacher
Haynes Middle School
Metairie, Louisiana

James Carbaugh
Science Teacher
Greencastle Middle School
Greencastle, Pennsylvania

Nancy Donohue
General Science Teacher
Emerson Junior High School
Yonkers, New York

Melville Fuller
Professor of Science Education
Department of Teacher Education
University of Arkansas
at Little Rock
Little Rock, Arkansas

Joanne Hardy
7th Grade Science/Social
Studies/Language Arts Teacher
Memorial Middle School
Conyers, Georgia

Nancy J. Hopkins
Gifted/Talented Coordinating
Teacher for Middle School Science
Morrill Elementary
San Antonio, Texas

Rebecca King
Chemistry Teacher
New Hanover High School
Wilmington, North Carolina

Kenneth Krause
Science Teacher
Harriet Tubman Middle School
Portland, Oregon

Martha Scully Lai
Science Teacher
Department Chairperson
Highland High School
Medina, Ohio

William E. Lavinghousez, Jr.
MAGNET Program Director
Ronald McNair MAGNET School
Cocoa, Florida

Norman Mankins
Science Specialist (Curriculum)
Canton City Schools
Canton, Ohio

John Maxwell
7th Grade Life Science Teacher
Claremont Middle School
Claremont, New Hampshire

Fred J. Mayberry
Earth/Life Science Teacher
Department Chairperson
Vernon Junior High School
Harlingen, Texas

Susan Middlebrooks
7th Grade Science Teacher
Pulaski Heights Jr. High
Little Rock, Arkansas

Judith Lee Nielsen
Middle School Science Teacher
Nyssa Middle School
Nyssa, Oregon

Michael Parry
Science Supervisor
Boyerstown Area School District
Boyerstown, Pennsylvania

Chuck Porrazzo
Science Department Chairperson
Bronx Career Technical
Assistance Center
Junior High 145
New York, New York

James Stewart
Life Science Teacher
W.E. Greiner Middle School
Dallas, Texas

James Todd
7th/8th Grade Science Teacher
East Hardin Middle School
Glendale, Kentucky

Deborah Tully
8th Grade Earth Science Teacher
Department Chairperson
Winburn Middle School
Lexington, Kentucky

Kim Lee Turbyfill
Computer Coordinator
Erwin Middle School
Salisbury, North Carolina

Marianne Wilson
Science-Health-Drug
Coordinator
Pulaski County Special Schools
Sherwood, Arkansas

Ronald Wolfe
8th Grade Science Teacher
Project Discovery Teacher Leader
Beachwood Middle School
Beachwood, Ohio

Maurice Yaggi
Instructional Leader for Science
Science Teacher
Wilton Public Schools
Wilton, Connecticut

Course 1

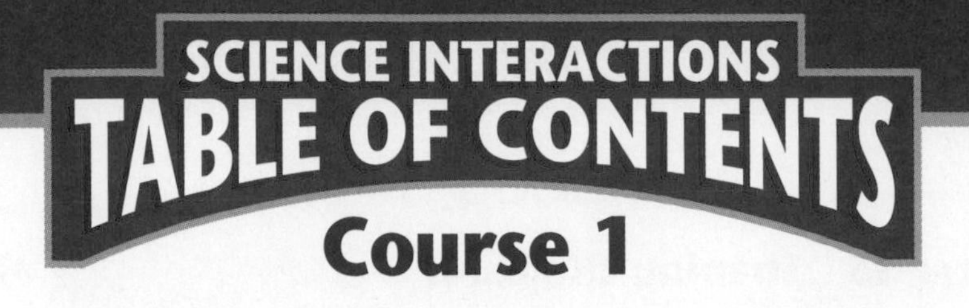
SCIENCE INTERACTIONS
TABLE OF CONTENTS
Course 1

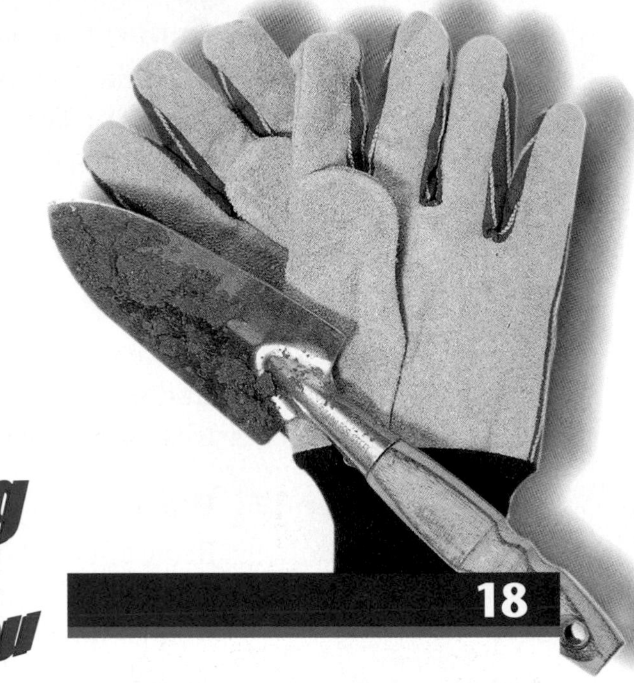

UNIT 1
Observing the World Around You

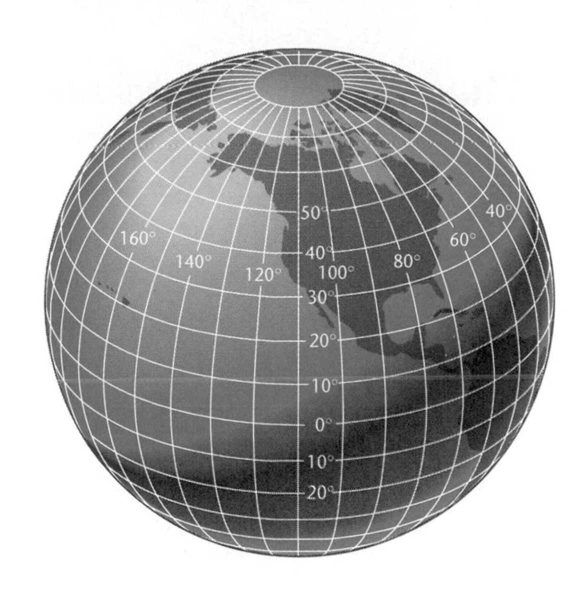

50°
40°
160°
140°
120°
40°
100°
80°
60°
30°
20°
10°
0°
10°
20°

UNIT
2

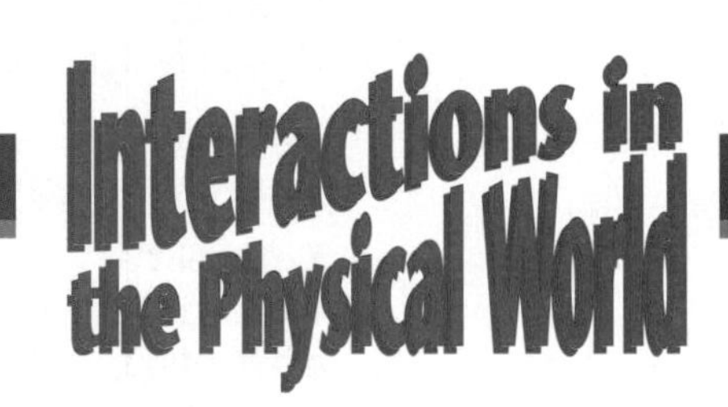

Interactions in the Physical World

UNIT
3

Interactions
In the Living World

214

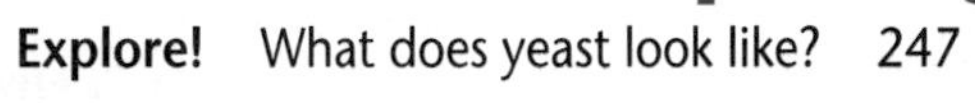

Country Style

UNIT
4
Changing Systems
378

Chapter 13 Motion Near Earth 412

Chapter 14 Moving Water 442

Wave Motion

Chapter 19 The Earth-Moon System 600

SCIENCE CONNECTIONS

Can you talk about the speed at which an animal runs without mentioning velocity? Is one science related to another? Expand your view of science through A CLOSER LOOK and Science Connections features in each chapter.

Earth Science

Life Science

Physics and Chemistry

SCIENCE CONNECTIONS

Science is something that refuses to stay locked away in a laboratory. In both the Science and Society and the Technology features, you'll learn how science impacts the world you live in today. You will also be asked to think about science-related questions that may affect your life fifty years from now.

Science and Society

Technology Connection

With the EXPAND YOUR VIEW features at the end of each chapter, you'll quickly become aware that science is an important part of every subject you'll ever encounter in school. Read these features to learn how science has affected history, health, and the ground you stand on.

As you begin each unit of Science Interactions, start by envisioning the big picture with the help of an exciting National Geographic photograph. Then look for the National Geographic SciFacts article in each unit to enrich and extend your understanding of science in the real world.

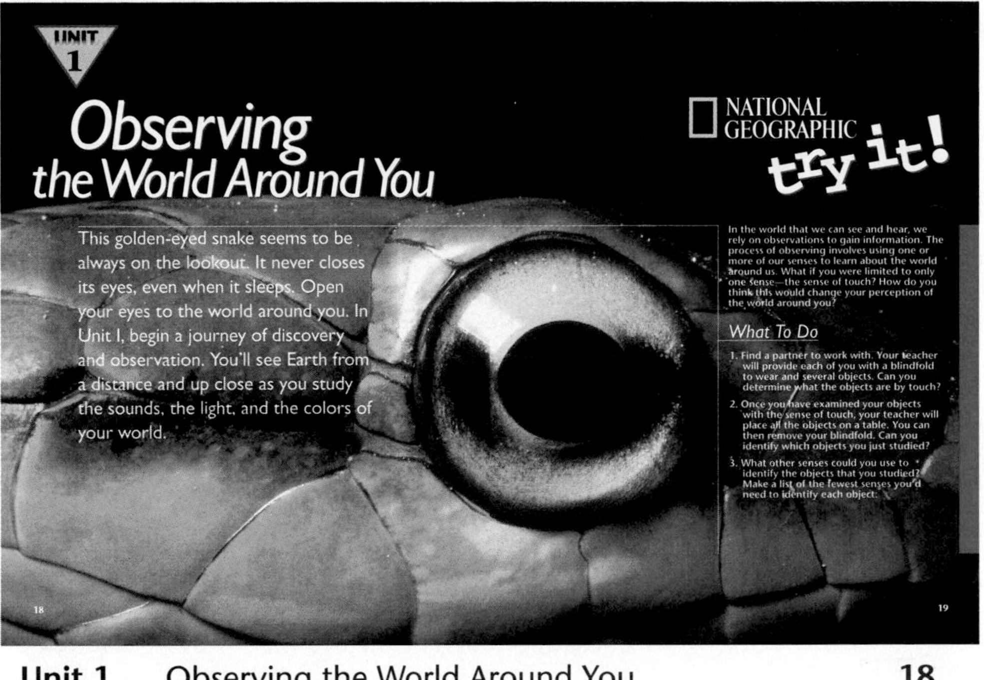

UNIT 1

Observing the World Around You

This golden-eyed snake seems to be always on the lookout. It never closes its eyes, even when it sleeps. Open your eyes to the world around you. In Unit I, begin a journey of discovery and observation. You'll see Earth from a distance and up close as you study the sounds, the light, and the colors of your world.

NATIONAL GEOGRAPHIC try it!

In the world that we can see and hear, we rely on observations to gain information. The process of observing involves using one or more of our senses to learn about the world around us. What if you were limited to only one sense—the sense of touch? How do you think this would change your perception of the world around you?

What To Do

1. Find a partner to work with. Your teacher will provide each of you with a blindfold to wear and several objects. Can you determine what the objects are by touch?
2. Once you have examined your objects with the sense of touch, your teacher will place all the objects on a table. You can then remove your blindfold. Can you identify which objects you just studied?
3. What other senses could you use to identify the objects that you studied? Make a list of the fewest senses you'd need to identify each object.

18 19

NATIONAL GEOGRAPHIC SCIFACTS

How bad is battery pollution?

Electronic-gadget-loving Americans buy approximately 2.5 billion batteries a year and throw away more than 90 percent of them. Disposable batteries contain toxic materials such as mercury. These harmful materials can leak from landfills or fall to the ground from incinerator stacks.

Can this problem be remedied easily? Most new single-use disposable batteries are designed to work with little or no mercury. Smaller button-size batteries, which power watches and cameras, are made with silver oxide or lithium. But most rechargeable batteries contain nickel and cadmium. These batteries, which can be recharged between 300 and 1000 times, have reduced landfill waste; however, they put more than a million kg of highly toxic cadmium into the environment each year once they are discarded.

Science Journal

In your Science Journal, plan a public service brochure aimed at encouraging consumers to make use of rechargeable batteries and write a rough draft.

Expand Your View 209

NATIONAL GEOGRAPHIC SOCIETY

SCIENCE: A Tool for Solving Problems

What is science? Can ordinary people use it? Or do all real scientists look a little like Albert Einstein and spend all their time in laboratories? Do scientists ever guess at something—or make discoveries by accident?

How do scientists do their work? What kinds of tools do they use? You probably know about microscopes and telescopes, but there are other tools scientists use also—tools that help them put their investigations into order. These thought-tools help scientists solve problems and find answers to new questions. How could you use these tools?

Come along with Leticia, Alberto, and the rest of their science class as they explore the nature and uses of science. As their class plans how to use a vacant lot, they learn that science is not just something you study at school. The tools of science can go with you out of the classroom and into the rest of your life!

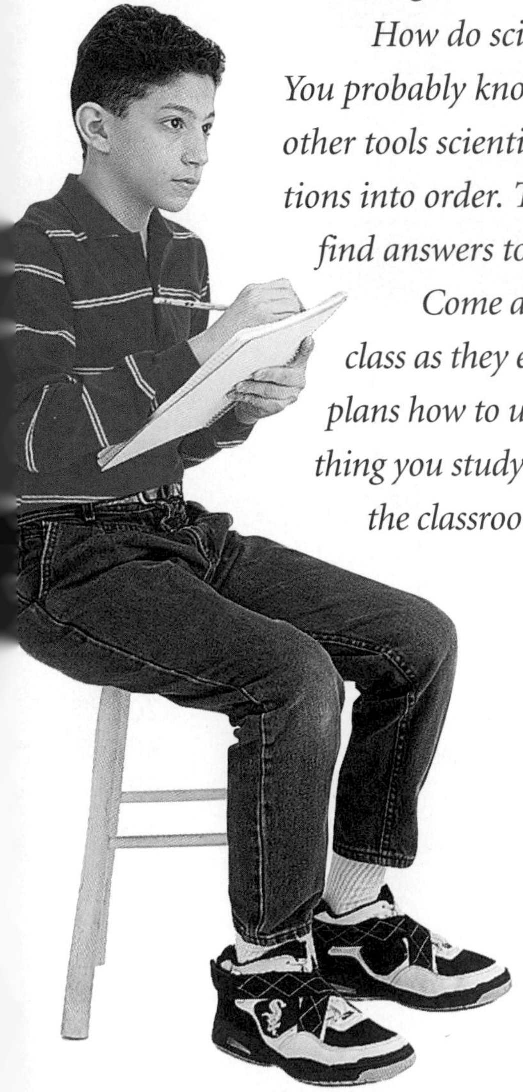

What Questions Can Science Answer?

Leticia was surprised. "Mr. Steinmetz, did you just say our science class is going to clean up the empty lot next to the school?" she said. What does science have to do with cleaning up that mess, she wondered.

"Are we going to put all that trash in test tubes and study it?" Alberto asked. "And then fill out a million tables and graphs?"

Mr. Steinmetz smiled. "Maybe only two or three hundred tables and graphs. Actually, we're going to let science help us find a use for the lot. Scientific tools will help us figure out what to do and how to do it."

"What to do is easy," Jennifer said. "We'll just pick up all the garbage and make the lot into a softball diamond. This school needs another one, since the boys always hog the one we have!"

"What about using the lot for a garden?" Kevin suggested.

"Or we could make it into a park or a playground for the kids in the neighborhood," Hiroko said. "Or..."

Leticia raised her hand. "Mr. Steinmetz, you said we'd use science to figure out what to do. How can it help us decide what to do with the lot?"

"Well, science can help us answer a lot of questions, but not all of them," he explained. "Science can help us learn the facts about a situation, but the answers to some questions depend on what we value or think is important.

"For example, we can use science to learn what kind of soil is in that lot, but science won't make the decision as to whether we should use the lot for a garden or a softball diamond. What are some other questions that you think science can help us answer? What are some questions you think science can't answer?"

Explore! ACTIVITY

Sorting Out Questions

Have you ever stopped to think about what kinds of questions science can answer? This activity will give you an opportunity to do so.

What To Do

1. Work in small groups to make two lists of questions: those you think science can answer and those you think science cannot answer.
2. Aim for at least five questions in each list. Your questions can relate to cleaning up a vacant lot or other topics. Record your lists of questions *in your Journal.*
3. Each group will take turns sharing its questions with the class. Be ready to explain the reasons for your choices.

How Does Science Help Answer Questions?

Hiroko said. "Michael and I thought of a good example of the two types of questions. Suppose a company dumped toxic chemicals into a river. Science could help us find out how much of the river was polluted and exactly what was killing the fish. And science could probably tell us how to clean up the pollution. But what if the company would go out of business if it had to spend a lot of money cleaning up the river? And what if most of the people in the town worked for that company? They would lose their jobs if the company closed."

"So we can't decide whether the company should clean up the river based just on scientific information," Michael added. "We have to decide what's more important to us: clean water or jobs."

After the class had discussed the two kinds of questions, Alberto raised his hand. "I think I can see the difference now. Science can help us find out facts about our world and understand why something happens, but it can't answer questions that depend on what we think is important."

"In that case, how can we figure out what to do with the empty lot?" Leticia asked. "Choosing between a garden or a softball diamond may depend on what's important to us."

Beginning the Investigation

"Why don't we ask our friends and see how many want a garden and how many want a softball field?" Jennifer suggested.

"Oh, sure! You'd just ask the girls on your softball team," Kevin teased. "We know what they'd say!"

Leticia had been thinking. "Maybe we could take a survey of everyone in the school and neighborhood. We could list the choices we've thought of and have them pick the one they want."

Mr. Steinmetz agreed. "A survey is a good way to gather information. Then we can analyze our findings. But we don't want our opinions to influence the results of the survey. So, we need to survey as many people as possible, not just the softball team or the garden club. Scientists do the same thing when they collect and study many samples before they analyze their findings and draw conclusions."

"We have to be careful how we list the choices," Hiroko pointed out, "because that could influence the results, too. For example, if we ask 'Wouldn't a garden be better than a softball diamond?' people would know which one we like better. We wouldn't find out what they really wanted."

"We could leave a space on the survey so people can write in their own ideas for ways to use the lot," Michael suggested.

"Then we could count up the votes for each choice," Alberto said, "and put them in a table." He smiled. "I knew there would be a table in here somewhere!"

Find Out! ACTIVITY

Survey Service

How is a survey an example of scientific study? How can a survey help you find answers? Find out how by doing the activity.

What To Do

1. Work as a class or in small groups to create and carry out a survey.
2. For example, you might survey parents to find out which fund-raising activities they would be willing to support. You might ask students which afterschool activities should be added or discontinued. These are only two ideas. Base your survey on questions that are important to you and your community.
3. Describe each choice so that your opinion does not affect the outcome of the survey.
4. Decide which groups of people should be included in your survey in order to get a wide sampling of opinions.
5. Show your teacher your survey and get your teacher's approval. Then, carry out the survey.
6. Afterward, make a table and bar graph of the results *in your Journal*.
7. As the last step, let others know what you've found out by writing a report describing your survey procedure and your conclusions.

Conclude and Apply

1. How did the results of your survey differ from that of other groups? How were they similar?
2. If the whole class did a survey on the same question, try combining your group's results with the results from all the other groups. Compare and contrast the class results and your individual results. Which gave you a better idea of what people think? Why?
3. How would you redesign your survey to get more accurate results?

Analyzing Data

"Here's what the survey says people are interested in," Kevin announced. "There were two main ideas. Over 44 percent of the people thought we should use the lot for a garden. But 21 percent thought it should be used as a softball field."

"Well," Jennifer said, "21 percent is a lot."

"Yes," Hiroko said, "But many of those votes came from outside the neighborhood. More than half of them."

"What about those who wanted a garden?" Jennifer asked.

"About 88 percent of those people lived in the neighborhood," Hiroko said. "Some said they'd even help clean up and take care of the garden."

"Then maybe we should build something everyone can contribute to," Jennifer said, smiling.

Observations: Defining the Problem

The school building next door shaded one side of the lot. A cement wall ran along the back of the lot. The back half of the lot was higher than the front half, so the ground sloped down toward the street. Erosion was a big problem. The students could see deep cracks in the soil, from the middle of the lot all the way to the street. It hadn't rained for a while, so some of the cracks looked like tiny, dry creek beds.

The students decided to hold a workday that weekend, when they and their families would get rid of the trash. They wanted to reuse or recycle as much as possible. For example, they decided to keep the old tires and plant flowers in them.

When the class visited the lot the following Monday, everyone agreed that it looked much better. But now the erosion was even more noticeable.

We sure are going to need a lot of science to stop this erosion," Leticia said. "I wonder how we can do it."

"Let's just fill in the cracks with dirt and plant seeds," suggested Hiroko. "The roots will hold the dirt in place and stop the erosion."

"I think the rain would wash away the dirt and the seeds before the plants could grow," Kevin said. "Let's use these rocks to build a wall across the lot, like a dam, to keep the water from running off."

Mr. Steinmetz looked at the dry soil. "We could try that or several other methods. Let's think about how we can approach this problem."

Thinking About the Problem

When they had returned to the classroom, Mr. Steinmetz posted a large form.

"This *Flex Your Brain* form is sort of an outline about how to think about a problem. It's a step by step procedure to help you develop a procedure for finding an answer. So let's give it a try."

Leticia raised her hand and said, "Well, the problem seems to be erosion."

Mr. Steinmetz smiled and wrote the word erosion into the blank near the word topic. "We're off to a great start; we've identified the problem."

Alberto said, "Well, we already know that plant growth can stop erosion, but that takes a while. Maybe our question should be something like, 'Besides plants, what's the most effective way to stop erosion?'"

The class had several possible answers for how to control erosion. "Okay," Mr. Steinmetz said, "when you have several possible answers to a question, what do you do with each possibility?"

Jennifer suggested, "You test them?" Mr. Steinmetz said, "Great, but how do you test them?"

Hiroko said, "You look at it. You test it by observing."

"Good idea. But in this case we need results that are a little faster."

Kevin said, "Experiment."

Mr. Steinmetz said, "Yes, you can experiment, but it seems like that might be difficult here. How are we going to erode a land area like our garden?"

Alberto said, "Well, maybe we can experiment using models."

"That sounds like a good idea. We can experiment and make our observations all in a day or two. Let's plan our models," Mr. Steinmetz said.

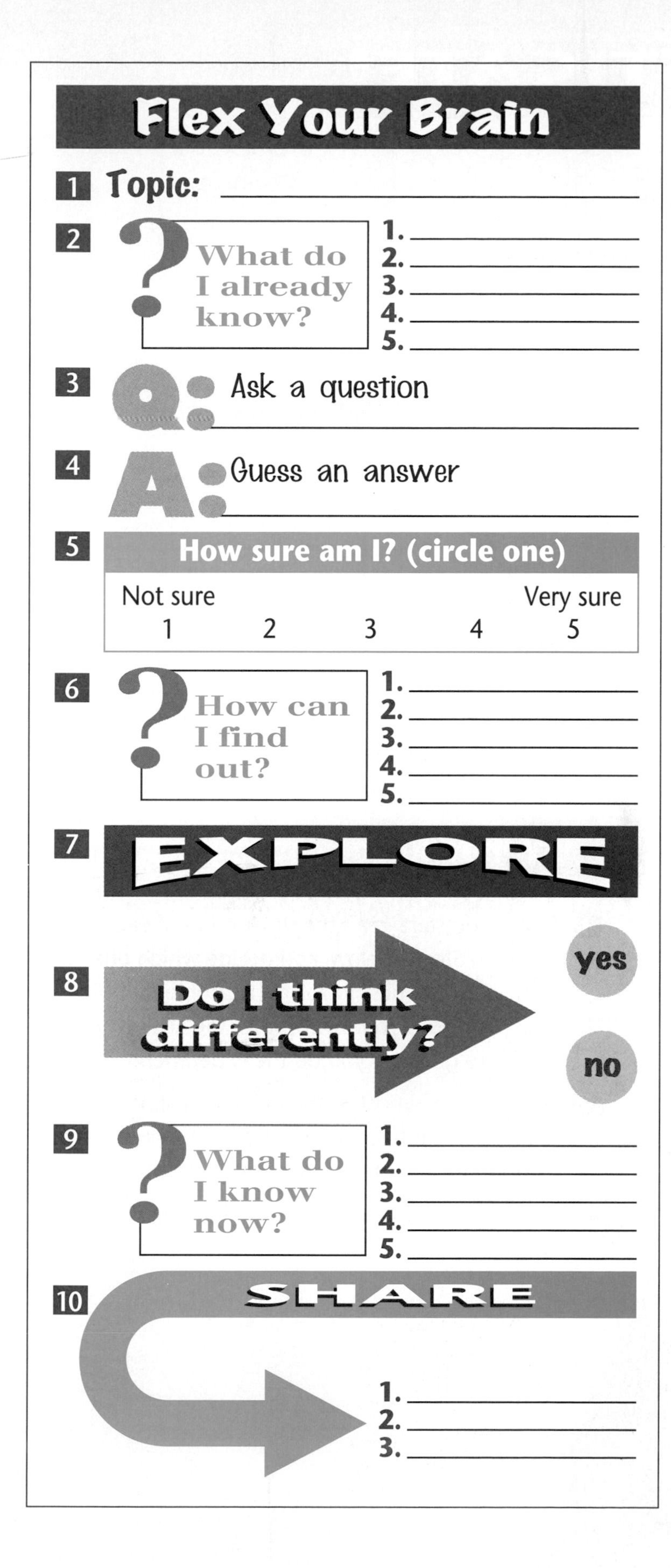

1 Fill in the topic.

2 Jot down what you already know about the topic.

3 Using what you already know (Step 2), form a question about the topic. Are you unsure about one of the items you listed? Do you want to know more? Do you want to know what, how, or why? Write down your question.

4 Guess an answer to your question. In the next few steps, you will be exploring the reasonableness of your answer. Write down your guesses.

5 Circle the number in the box that matches how sure you are of your answer in Step 4. This is your chance to rate your confidence in what you've done so far and, later, to see how your level of sureness affects your thinking.

6 How can you figure out more about your topic? You might want to read a book, ask an expert, or do an experiment. Write down ways you can find out more.

7 Make a plan to explore your answer. Use the resources you listed in Step 6. Then, carry out your plan.

8 Now that you've explored, go back to your answer in Step 4. Would you answer differently? Mark one of the boxes.

9 Considering what you learned in your exploration, answer your question again, adding new things you've learned. You may completely change your answer.

10 It's important to be able to talk about thinking. Choose three people to tell about how you arrived at your response in every step. For example, don't just read what you wrote down in Step 2. Try to share how you thought of those things.

INVESTIGATE!

Saving the Soil

You've seen eroded soil and you're probably aware of the problems erosion can cause. But how do you begin to explore how to solve these problems?

Problem

Which of five methods is the best way to control soil erosion?

Safety Precautions

Materials

- 5 aluminum 8 or 9-inch pie pans
- leaves or grass clippings
- 500-mL beaker
- water
- metric ruler
- newspaper
- pebbles
- potting soil
- watering can
- dishpan

What To Do

1. Before you start, read the description of each model in Step 4 below, and decide which one you think will work best to solve the problem above. That method is your hypothesis, the answer you expect to get after you do the experiment.
2. Fill each pan almost to the rim with soil. Pat the soil until the surface is firm and flat. Soak the soil by pouring 100 mL of water into each pan.
3. Set one pan aside as the control for this experiment.

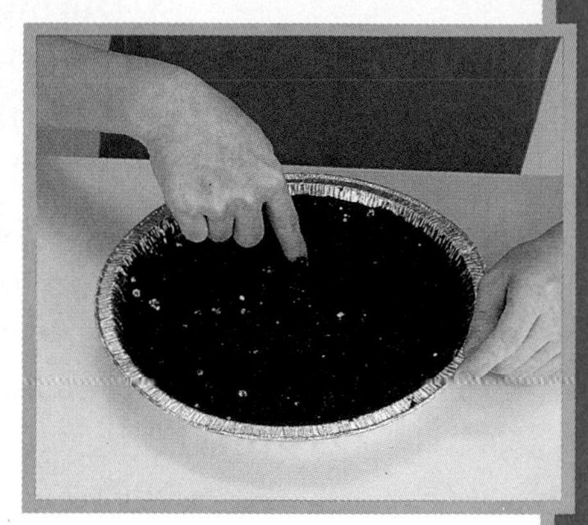

A B C

4 Use the other four pans to set up these conditions:
   a. Mulching: Cover the surface with a layer of grass clippings or leaves.
   b. Other soil cover: Tear the newspaper into small strips. Lay the strips across the surface, leaving about 5 mm between each strip.
   c. Terracing: Build two small walls of pebbles.
   d. Contour plowing: Use your finger to make a curved groove across the surface.

5 Follow this procedure with all five pans, starting with the control:
   a. Measure 200 mL of water into the watering can.
   b. Hold the pan so that one side touches the edge of the dishpan and the opposite edge is about 10 cm higher.
   c. Slowly pour the water onto the soil at the top of the pan. Wait until the excess water runs across the soil and into the dishpan. Note: Be sure to hold the terracing and contour plowing pans so the water runs across the pebble walls and the grooves.
   d. Pour the water and soil from each pie pan into the beaker. Measure it and record the results. When the soil settles to the bottom, measure and record its height in the beaker.

6 As a class, decide which method was most effective at preventing erosion.

Analyzing

1. Construct a graph to show results for all five pans.
2. Compare and contrast the results for the pans.
3. Was your hypothesis correct?

Concluding and Applying

4. **Going Further** One test or experiment isn't enough to prove a hypothesis. Most scientists perform numerous tests. Write an outline for another test of this hypothesis that does not use a model.

■ Making Discoveries—Accidents in Science

During the experiment, Alberto accidentally let a whole pie pan of soil slide into the dishpan. "Some scientist you are!" Jennifer teased.

"You never know," Mr. Steinmetz said. "Some of science's most important discoveries were made by accident, including the discovery of penicillin. When Sir Alexander Fleming was growing dishes of bacteria for an experiment, some mold accidentally got into one dish. Lucky for us, Fleming didn't just throw that dish away because it was contaminated. He noticed that the mold had killed the bacteria around it. The penicillin he accidentally discovered has helped cure millions of people worldwide."

Alberto nodded. "So maybe we should save this muddy mess!" he told Jennifer.

"And maybe not," she said with a smile.

■ Expanding What You Know

After analyzing the results of the experiment, the class planned how they could use the method that worked the best. They hoped it would slow down the erosion in the lot until the garden was planted.

Hiroko was getting impatient. "Let's start planting!"

"Okay," Mr. Steinmetz said. "Let's plant a garden of bananas." He looked around the classroom. "I see some puzzled faces. What's the problem?"

"Bananas don't grow here," Michael said. "It's not warm enough."

"I see," Mr. Steinmetz said slowly. "So what do we need to do before we start our garden?"

"Figure out what will grow there," Leticia said. Then she smiled at Mr. Steinmetz. "I bet science can help us do that, right?"

"Right! We need to do some scientific observing and analyzing before we decide what to plant in our

Science on the Run

Can you imagine playing basketball or running track in a pair of loafers? We can wear sneakers instead, thanks to two accidental discoveries, one by a scientist and one by a track coach. Charles Goodyear had been trying for nine years to make rubber that would stay flexible at both high and low temperatures. One day in 1839, he accidentally allowed some rubber and sulfur to touch on a hot stove. He had discovered a flexible rubber that had all kinds of uses!

In the 1960s, a college track coach wanted his runners to get more traction from their rubber-soled shoes. He put a piece of rubber on a waffle iron and got a pattern that may have changed the history of track!

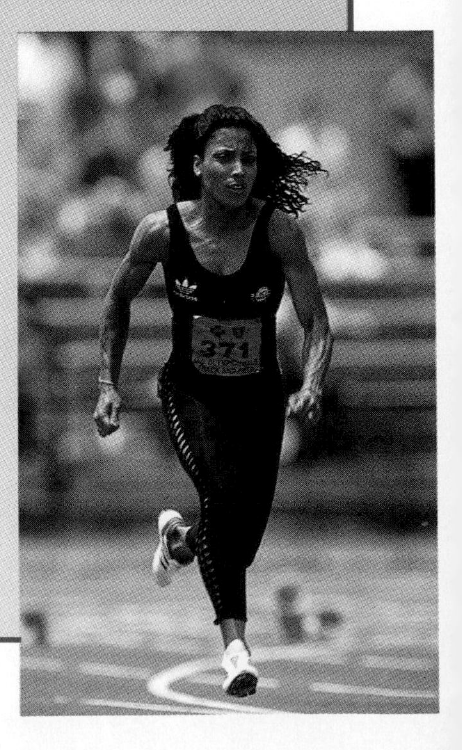

Thanks to two accidental discoveries, athletes today, such as Florence Griffith-Joyner, pictured here, have running shoes that help improve traction.

garden," he said. "Science has helped us understand how different plants grow. We can gather and analyze this information and choose plants that will grow best in that lot. What if no one before us had done any observing or experimenting, and we didn't know anything about how plants grow?"

Kevin shook his head. "I guess we'd have to do a lot of experimenting ourselves before we discovered which plants will grow best on that lot."

"True! Now, what kind of growing conditions will our plants have?" Mr. Steinmetz asked.

"Well, the soil is kind of hard and rocky and dry," Jennifer offered. "But after we stop the erosion, maybe the soil will be able to soak up more water. And I noticed a definite wet area back by the wall."

"Part of the lot is in the sun and part is in the shade," Alberto added. "You know, these growing conditions are getting complicated. Maybe we could make a big table." He started smiling again. "We could fill it in with plants that grow in different kinds of soil and light. Then we could decide what to grow."

"You're starting to think like a scientist!" Mr. Steinmetz said. "A lot of science begins with careful observation, and your table will give us a good start. We can use it to analyze information, draw conclusions, and make our decisions based on facts. Now let's divide into groups and see how many ways we can think of to plan this garden!"

Find Out! ACTIVITY

Planning Before Planting

Use the information in the table below to plan a garden 60 feet long and 40 feet wide.

What To Do

Begin by drawing a diagram that shows the different conditions in the garden. (Make 1 inch equal 1 foot.)

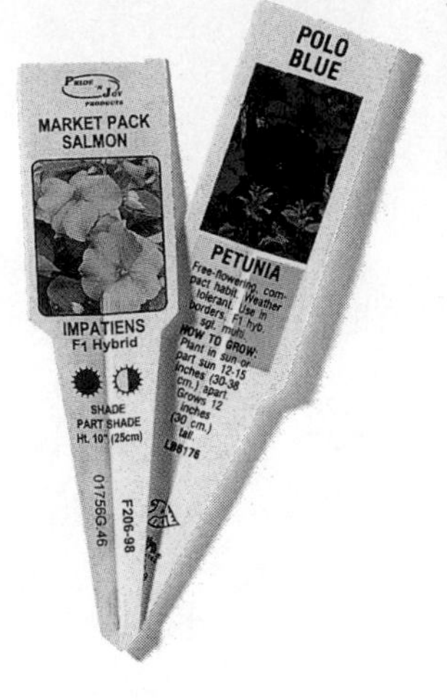

1. Keep in mind that a 10-foot-wide strip along the left side of the garden is shaded during most of the day by the school building next door. Most of the soil will have average moisture after the erosion is stopped. However, the wall along the back of the lot traps rain water, so a 15-foot-wide section there is a lot wetter.
2. Be sure to take into account the way your class has decided to cut down on erosion.
3. Then, plan your garden. Some of the possible choices for your garden are available in the chart.
4. Copy the chart *into your Journal.* Leave enough space for everyone in your group to add one kind of plant. Use reference books to find the needed information.
5. Be prepared to share with the class your group's plan and the reasons for your choices. You'll need to explain how each of your selections is based on scientific reasoning.

Conclude and Apply

1. How important was each factor (sunlight/soil and plant height) in helping you make your decision?
2. How did you use other people's observations in planning your garden?
3. What did you already know about the garden that helped you plan? What other information would have been helpful to know in making your plan?

	Plant height			Light/soil requirements			
Plant	6-12"	1-3'	over 3'	sun/ average	sun/ moist	shade/ average	shade/ moist
wax begonia	✓			✓		✓	
sunflower			✓	✓			
petunia	✓	✓		✓		✓	
impatiens	✓	✓				✓	✓
butterfly flower	✓	✓		✓	✓	✓	✓
black-eyed Susan vine			✓	✓	✓	✓	✓
peas			✓	✓			
peppers		✓		✓			
lettuce	✓			✓		✓	
cucumbers	✓			✓			
corn			✓	✓			

■ A Solution to the Problem

After each group presented its plan for the garden, the class combined the best ideas.

Michael and Hiroko showed the class a diagram of paths the class could build. They wanted to line the paths with rocks cleared out of the areas where the plants would go.

Leticia and Kevin thought of planting ivy and ferns in the area at the back of the lot to take advantage of the wet conditions and to cover the ugly cement wall. Alberto and Jennifer suggested setting aside part of the garden in full sunlight for tomatoes, corn, and green peppers, which could be donated to the food bank. Hiroko suggested planting herbs to take advantage of the full sunlight and to attract butterflies.

The garden took a lot of work—on the part of the class and the neighborhood. Finally there was little to do but wait for the plants to grow. A photographer from the local newspaper came to take pictures as the first tiny leaves broke through the ground. The class posed around a sign they had posted: "A Garden Built with Science!"

Alberto, Leticia, and their classmates learned some of the processes of science to help solve a problem. As you study this book, you can use similar processes to solve problems. But remember, scientific thinking is not just for the classroom, it can be used in your everyday life as well!

REVIEWING MAIN IDEAS

Science Journal

Review the statements below about the big ideas presented in this chapter, and try to answer the questions. Then, re-read your answers to the Did You Ever Wonder questions at the beginning of the chapter. *In your Science Journal*, write a paragraph about how your understanding of the big ideas in the chapter has changed.

1. **Science can help us answer questions and make decisions.** ***Describe a specific way someone your age can use science in everyday life.***

2. **Scientists use many methods to increase knowledge. They observe, experiment, make models, and apply old observations to new situations to help solve problems.** ***What are two specific things scientists have learned about the natural world as a result of observing it?***

3. **Sometimes scientists perform experiments under different conditions to see which condition works best.** ***Why is it important, whenever possible, to have a control in your experiments?***

CHAPTER REVIEW

Critical Thinking

In your Journal, *answer each of the following questions.*

1. Why is an open mind essential for a scientist?
2. When do scientists make guesses? How do they test their guesses?
3. Why are tables and graphs used so often in science?
4. How could scientists apply observations and information learned during space shuttle flights to building a space station on the moon? What other observations might help?

Problem Solving

Read the following problem and explain your answers.

The deer population at a certain park has greatly increased. The deer have eaten most of the vegetation and are beginning to starve. One group of people wants to shoot some of the deer. That way, the remaining deer will have enough to eat. The deer meat will be given to a homeless shelter. Another group wants to pay $1000 each to move some of the deer to another park. Some deer, maybe half of them, will die from stress during the move.

1. What are at least two questions science can answer relating to this problem?
2. What is at least one question science cannot answer?
3. What would you do in this situation? Explain the reasons for your decision. Discuss which of your reasons is based on science and which is based on what you value.

Understanding Ideas

1. When would you choose to make a model to find the solution to a problem?
2. How can observation be a scientific method?
3. Why is it important to plan your investigation before doing it?
4. Compare and contrast observation and experimentation as scientific methods.

UNIT 1

Observing the World Around You

This golden-eyed snake seems to be always on the lookout. It never closes its eyes, even when it sleeps. Open your eyes to the world around you. In Unit 1, begin a journey of discovery and observation. You'll see Earth from a distance and up close as you study the sounds, the light, and the colors of your world.

try it!

In the world that we can see and hear, we rely on observations to gain information. The process of observing involves using one or more of our senses to learn about the world around us. What if you were limited to only one sense—the sense of touch? How do you think this would change your perception of the world around you?

What To Do

1. Find a partner to work with. Your teacher will provide each of you with a blindfold to wear and several objects. Can you determine what the objects are by touch?
2. Once you have examined your objects with the sense of touch, your teacher will place all the objects on a table. You can then remove your blindfold. Can you identify which objects you just studied?
3. What other senses could you use to identify the objects that you studied? Make a list of the fewest senses you'd need to identify each object.

CHAPTER 1

Viewing Earth & Sky

Did you ever wonder...

- ✓ How high the mountains are?
- ✓ What the surface of the moon looks like?
- ✓ What the Big Dipper is?

Science Journal

Before you begin to study what's under your feet and over your head, think about these questions and answer them *in your Science Journal*. When you finish the chapter, compare your journal write-up with what you have learned.

Have you ever taken a long trip by car, bus, train, or plane? If so, then you know there's not much to do while traveling except look out the window. But when you do, what a view! You can see miles and miles of sweeping fields or desert areas; high, snow-capped mountains; green, rolling hills; gentle valleys; and deep canyons. You might ask yourself how so many different landscapes can exist!

Making observations and asking questions about them is an excellent way to learn about your world. When you are traveling, it's easy to sit back and observe the world going by you. But you don't have to travel to observe. You can start right where you are—at home, in your classroom, around your neighborhood.

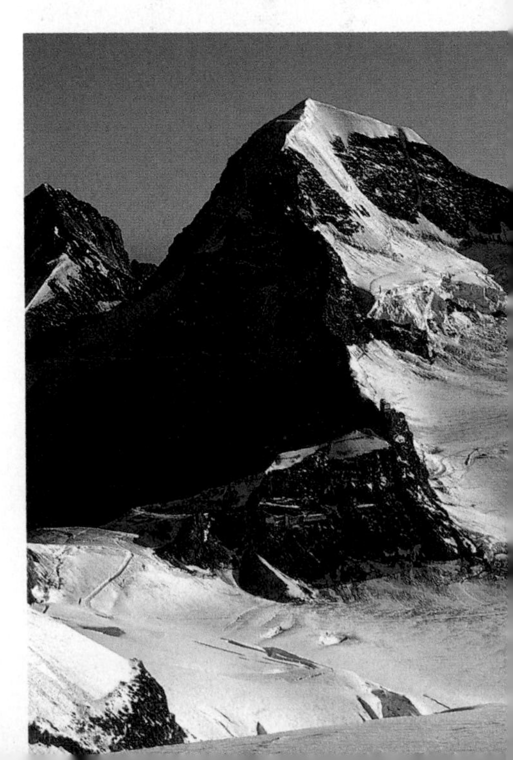

▶ ***In the next activity, you will be looking up, down, and all around as you observe your physical surroundings.***

Explore! ACTIVITY

What do the landscape and sky look like where you live?

What To Do

1. Find a spot outdoors, and sit and make yourself comfortable. Facing west, draw *in your Journal* what you see on the land and in the sky. Pay attention to any shadows cast by the objects in your view.
2. Then, face north and draw what you see.
3. Continue on until you have drawn the east and south views as well. What features are in your drawings?

Viewing Earth

Section Objectives

- Describe basic landforms such as mountains, plains, and plateaus.
- Recognize the kind of landform on which you live.

Key Terms

landforms

Over the Plains, Mountains, and Plateaus

Imagine that you have tickets for an early morning flight from Washington, D.C. to California. You will be flying for about six hours. Thank goodness you were able to get a window seat! You want to see the land unfold beneath you. What will you observe as you fly over the United States? The Explore activity will give you some clues.

Explore! ACTIVITY

What does a profile of the United States look like?

1. Find a physical map of the United States that shows its land features.
2. Use the map to guide you as you draw *in your Journal* a cross-section profile of the United States. A profile shows the surface features as they would look if you cut the United States along a line from Washington, D.C. to San Francisco, California and looked at the surface from the cut edge.
3. Mark and label the different features. What do you think those features would look like from the air?

Now that you have drawn a profile, you will see how your profile compares with the surface as seen from the air. The surface features you will see are called **landforms**. Mountains, plains, and plateaus are three common landforms in the United States.

The big day for your airplane trip arrives. You board the plane, settle yourself into your window seat, and fasten your seat belt. You're eager to compare your profile with the landforms you see on the trip. The plane taxis down the runway, and soon you're in the air. Good-bye, Washington! California, here you come!

Across the Low Plains

What do you think of when you hear the word plains? You might think of endless flat fields of wheat or grass. That's often what plains look like because many of them are used to grow crops. Plains are large, low, mostly flat areas. In fact, about half of all the land in the United States is plains.

You will see plains along many of the coastlines and in the interior of the country. The lowland areas along the coastlines are called coastal plains. These areas are characterized by low, rolling hills, swamps, and marshes. One coastal plain is the Gulf Coastal Plain. It includes the lowlands surrounding the Gulf of Mexico. Look at **Figure 1-1**. Where do you think this area is?

As you fly, you see that a large part of the middle of the United States is also made up of plains. They are called the interior plains. You may remember from the Explore activity you just did that the interior plains extend from the Appalachian Mountains in the east, to the Rocky Mountains in the west, and to the Gulf Coastal Plain in the south. The first interior plains you see are the very low, rolling hills of the Great Lakes area and the lowlands around the Mississippi and Missouri rivers.

To the west of the Mississippi lowlands, you see the Great Plains. These are flat, grassy, dry plains with few trees. The Great Plains are covered with nearly horizontal layers of dirt and small rocks. Where did these sediments come from? They washed down from the landform that you will fly over next on your trip.

Connect to... Life Science

Different plants and animals live in coastal and interior plains. Select one animal that lives in each type of plain. Prepare a poster that shows the food, dwelling, and habitat of each animal.

Figure 1-1

This map shows the location of the coastal plains and the interior plains.

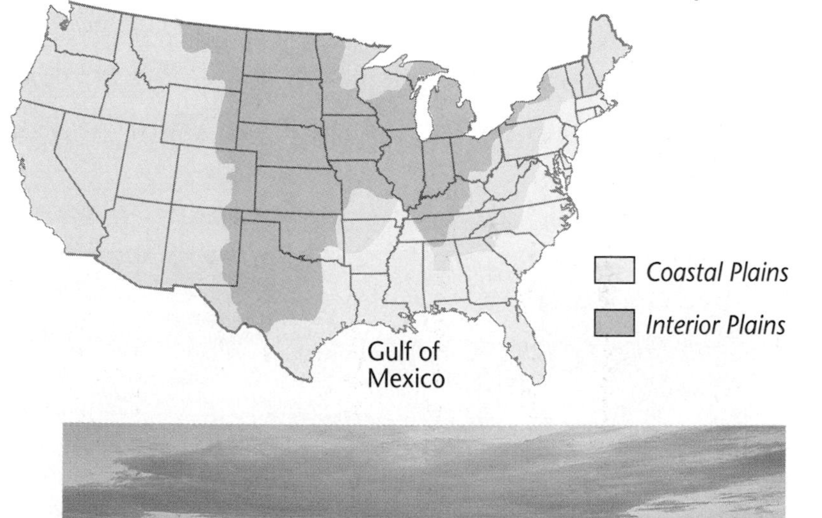

Coastal plains on the east coast

Interior plains in southeast Colorado

Mountains

Much of the dirt and rock that helped form the Great Plains washed down from the Rocky Mountains, pictured in **Figure 1-2** below. Mountains tower above the surrounding land, providing a spectacular view of Earth. The world's highest mountain peak, however, is not in the Rockies, or even in the United States. It is Mount Everest in the Himalaya in Asia, which rises more than 8800 meters above sea level. Mountain peaks in the part of the United States that you are traveling over reach just a little more than 4000 meters high.

As you might expect, mountains vary greatly in size and shape. Look at all the pictures of mountains in **Figure 1-2**, and you will see that they appear different. This is because they were formed in different ways. Also, some mountains are older than

Figure 1-2

This map shows the location of the Appalachian, Rocky, and Pacific Mountains.

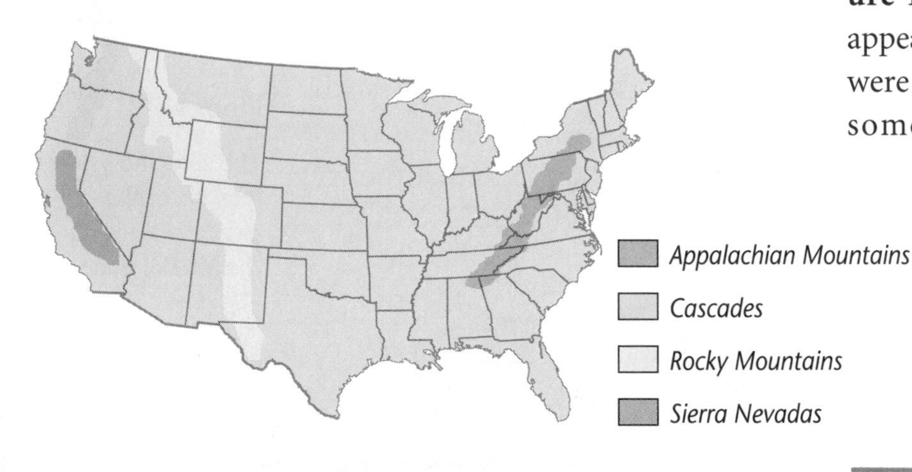

Cascades in Washington

Sierra Nevadas in California

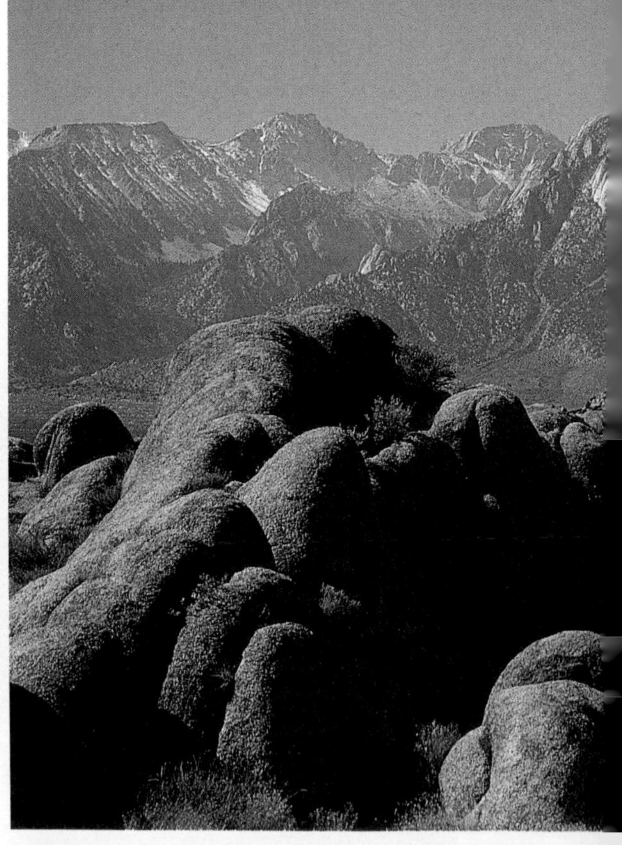

others. The older ones are often more like large hills, rounder and lower in comparison with younger mountains. They have been worn down to some degree by wind, rain, and running water. Which of the mountains shown in **Figure 1-2** are older mountains?

Appalachian Mountains in West Virginia and Tennessee

Rocky Mountains in Colorado

Some landforms are made by humans. The Bingham mine near Salt Lake City, Utah, is the largest hole ever made by humans. The Bingham mine is an open-pit copper mine that is almost 800 m deep and 4 km wide at the surface.

On the Flat Plateaus

As you continue your trip west, you see other highlands. These raised areas of fairly flat land are plateaus. Plateaus are made up of nearly horizontal rock layers. Unlike the plains, they rise steeply from the land around them. Long ago, plateaus were plains. But over time, they were pushed upward by forces inside Earth.

Figure 1-3 shows the Colorado Plateau, which lies just west of the Rocky Mountains. The Colorado River has cut deep into the rock layers of this plateau, forming the Grand Canyon. Other rivers, such as the Green River and the San Juan River, have also created canyonlands on the vast Colorado Plateau.

Plateaus are often found near mountains and can have very high altitudes. The Plateau of Tibet borders the Himalaya in Asia. Its elevation is about 4300 meters above sea level! Plateaus with lower elevations are often used as pasture lands for livestock.

Life Science CONNECTION

Just the Right Conditions

If you flew around the borders of our country, you would see many distinctly different farms growing a variety of crops in each area.

For instance, passing over North Carolina, you would notice a lot of tobacco farms. Farther up the coast, in New Jersey, farmers are growing vegetables such as tomatoes and green beans. Crossing the northern parts of the states, you see apple orchards on the interior plains around the Great Lakes, wheat on the Great Plains, potatoes in Idaho, and more (and different kinds of) apples in Washington State. In California, citrus fruit trees—grapefruit, oranges, lemons, and limes—would be plentiful, while in Arizona and Texas, there would be cotton farms.

Why is there such diversity over the continental United States? Why are many crops grown in one place but not another? Crops need a growing season, a time free from frost. It takes a certain amount of time for an apple, an orange, or a cotton plant to grow. If the weather does not act as expected, something will

The Colorado Plateau

Figure 1-3

This map shows the location of the Colorado Plateau and the Ozark Plateau.

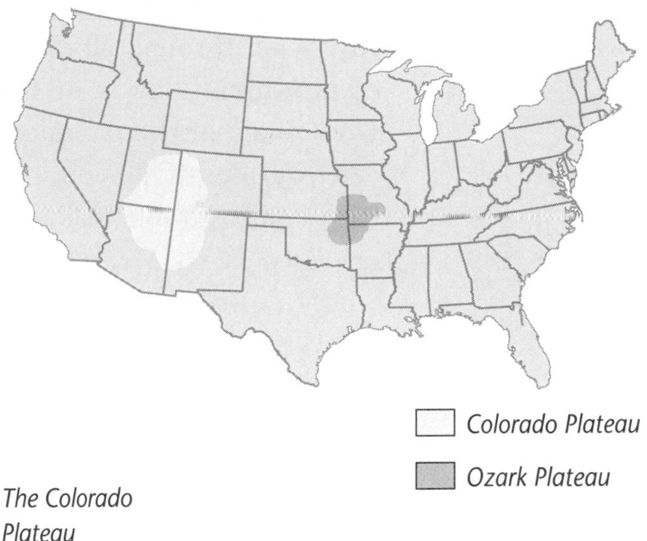

probably happen to the crops. If it is too hot or too cold for too long, or if there is not enough rain or too much rain, crops will die.

Soil and land formation are as important as climate in growing crops. Mountains are rocky and steep, with a thin layer of soil. They are not good for growing food or grazing cattle. Desert plains or plateaus have little vegetation because of little rain, but they can often produce crops if water is provided through irrigation.

You Try It!

Imagine that you are going to start a farm. Choose a plant or crop and find out about its ideal growing conditions. For instance, corn needs a lot of water, and tomatoes need sun. Would you start your farm in central Arizona, which has desert conditions, or in northern Ohio, bordering the Great Lakes? Back up your choice with details about the plants and the conditions in the area you choose.

Rivers

One feature that mountains and plains share with plateaus is rivers. Rivers cut through all different kinds of landforms. Look at **Figure 1-4**. How many of the rivers on the map can you identify? Some rivers curve back and forth like snakes, while others flow fairly straight. Some run wildly down mountain slopes, while others move slowly along.

It's time to prepare for landing. Your flight is nearly over. It was great seeing landforms from the airplane, but such a view is not usually possible. You can't often observe land directly. Most of the time, you use maps to identify landforms. Can a map show how high a mountain is or how flat a plain is? You will find out that maps can do these things and even more.

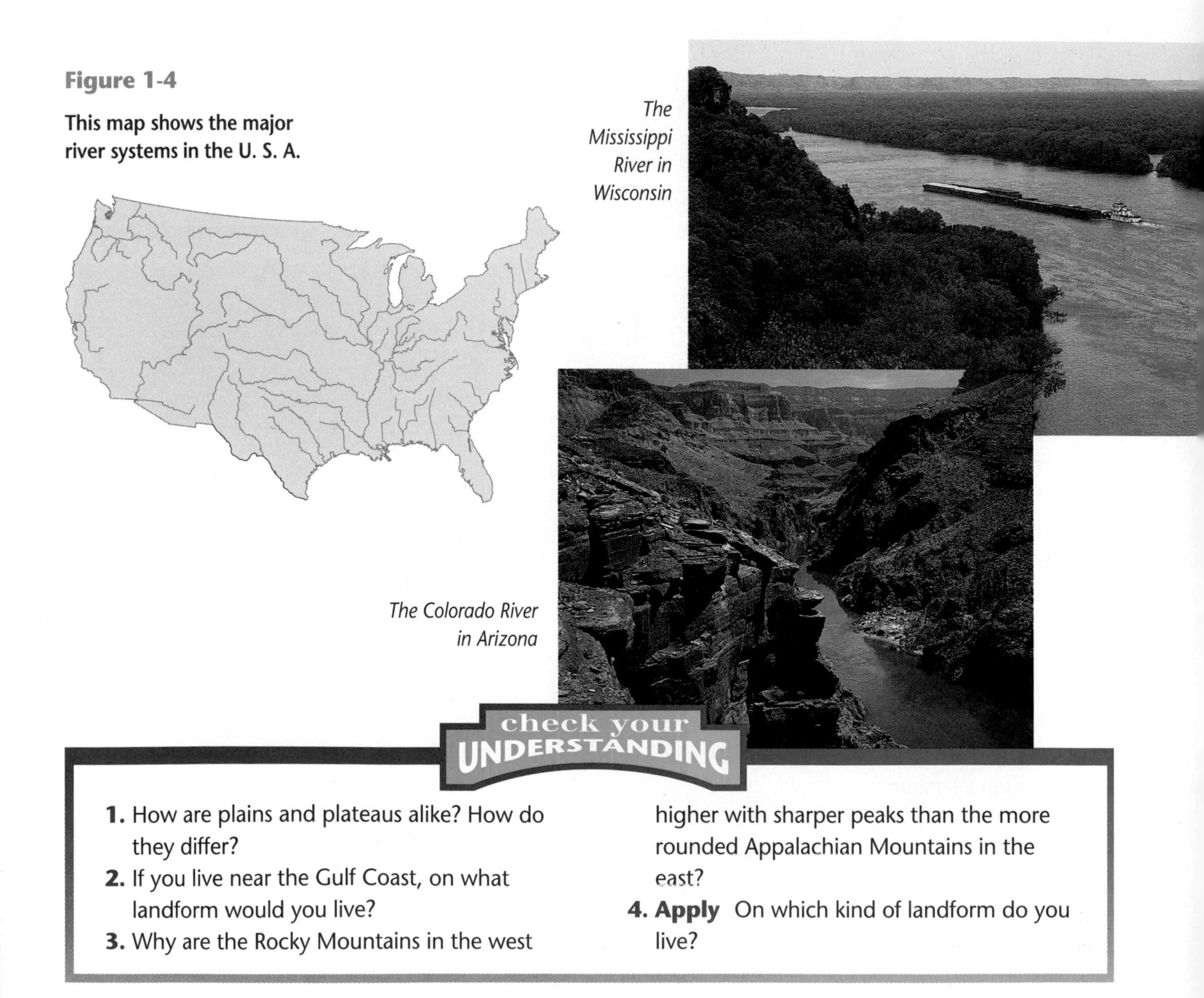

Figure 1-4

This map shows the major river systems in the U. S. A.

The Mississippi River in Wisconsin

The Colorado River in Arizona

check your UNDERSTANDING

1. How are plains and plateaus alike? How do they differ?
2. If you live near the Gulf Coast, on what landform would you live?
3. Why are the Rocky Mountains in the west higher with sharper peaks than the more rounded Appalachian Mountains in the east?
4. **Apply** On which kind of landform do you live?

1-2 Using Maps

Road Maps

Your plane has landed in California, where a good friend has moved, and you'd like to visit him at his school. You find your way from the airport to a beautiful city park, but you wonder where your friend's school is. You know a map would be useful to you. Maps are useful for locating places, finding your way around, and getting a clearer picture of an area. How have you used maps to help you? Use the map in the Find Out activity to help you find your friend's school.

Section Objectives

- Identify landforms using a topographic map.
- Demonstrate how elevation is shown on a topographic map.
- Compare and contrast latitude and longitude.

Key Terms

elevation, contour lines, latitude, longitude

Find Out! ACTIVITY

Where is Central School located?

You can find the school by studying the map. You're at the city park, Balmoral Park, right now. How can you get to the school?

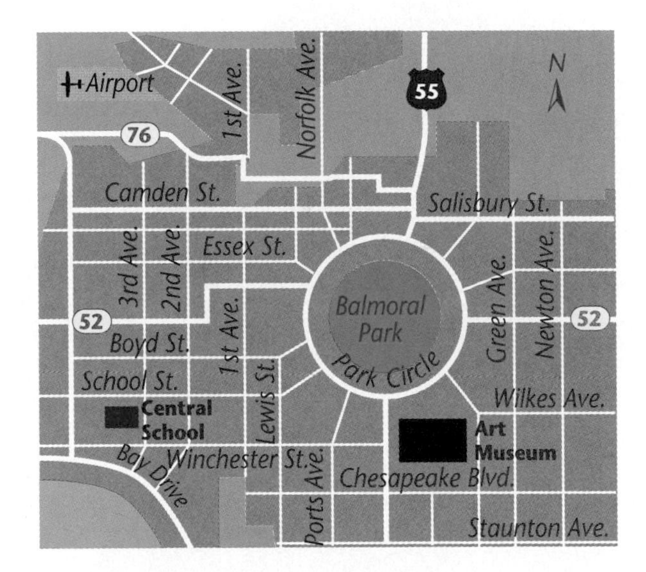

What To Do

1. Look at the different names of the streets and avenues on the map shown on the right. Now notice the location of the city park. *In your Journal,* describe the location of the park.
2. Next, notice the location of Central School. How would you describe its location?

Conclude and Apply

1. Suppose you wanted to get from the park to the school. *In your Journal,* describe how you would do it.

With the road map, you were able to get from the park to the school. Does the map tell you anything about landforms in the area? Are you able to find the highest and lowest points in the city? No, you need a different kind of map to get this information. One kind of map that shows landforms is a topographic map. As you'll discover in the next Investigate, showing hills and valleys on a flat map isn't as hard as it may seem.

INVESTIGATE!

Using Contour Lines

How can a map show the shape of a landform? In the following activity, you will show the elevations of a landform by drawing contour lines, which are lines of equal elevation that show the shape of the landform.

Problem

How can elevation of a landform be indicated on a map?

Safety Precautions

Materials

metric ruler
clear plastic box and lid
model landform
water
transparency marker
transparency
tape
beaker

What To Do

1. Using the ruler and the transparency marker, measure and mark 2-cm lines up the side of the box.
2. Secure the transparency to the outside of the box lid with tape (see photo ***A***).
3. Place the plastic model in the box. The bottom of the box will be zero elevation.
4. Using the beaker, pour water into the box to a height of 2 cm (see photo ***B***). Place the lid on the box.
5. Looking down at the top of the box, use the transparency marker to trace the top of the water line on the transparency.

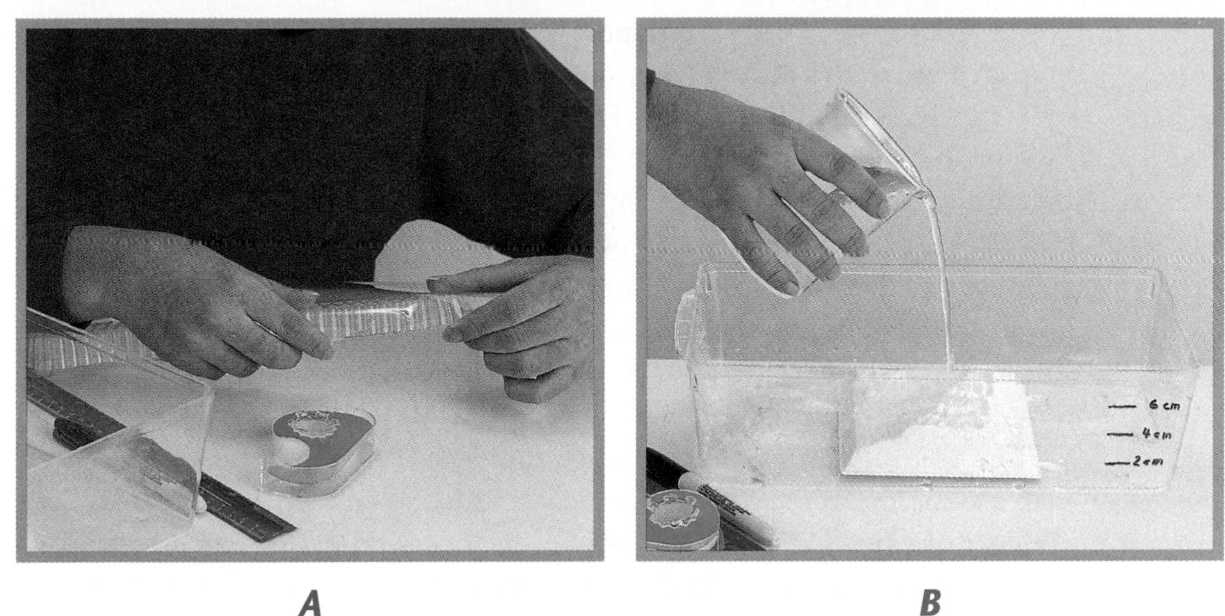

A *B*

6 Using the scale 2 cm = 5 ft, mark the elevation on the line.

7 Repeat Steps 4–6, adding water to the next 2-cm level and tracing until you have mapped the landform by means of contour lines.

8 Transfer the tracing of the contours of the landform onto paper.

Analyzing

1. What is the contour interval of this topographic map?
2. ***Interpret*** the relationship between contour lines on the map and the steepness of the slope on the landform.
3. ***Calculate*** the total elevation of the landform.

Concluding and Applying

4. How are elevations shown on topographic maps?
5. ***Explain*** whether all topographic maps must have a 0-ft elevation contour line.
6. **Going Further** How would the contour interval of an area of steep mountains ***compare*** with the interval of an area of flat plains?

Topographic Maps

As you can see, the topographic map in **Figure 1-5** differs from the map in the Find Out activity. The topographic map shows the shape of the area by giving information about elevation. **Elevation** is the height above sea level or the depth below sea level. With a topographic map, you can tell how steep a mountain is or how deep a canyon is.

The thin lines on a topographic map are contour lines. **Contour lines** are lines of equal elevation that show the shapes, or contours, of landforms. The contour lines represent three-dimensional contours on a two-dimensional map. They show the vertical rise and fall of the land.

Before the use of contour lines, mapmakers used shading to suggest the contours of the land. While shading can give you a good idea of surface contours, contour lines are based on elevation data and are more accurate.

Mapmakers today use contour lines to show differences in elevation on Earth's surface. Each contour line connects points of equal elevation. Between every two contour lines, the land changes elevation.

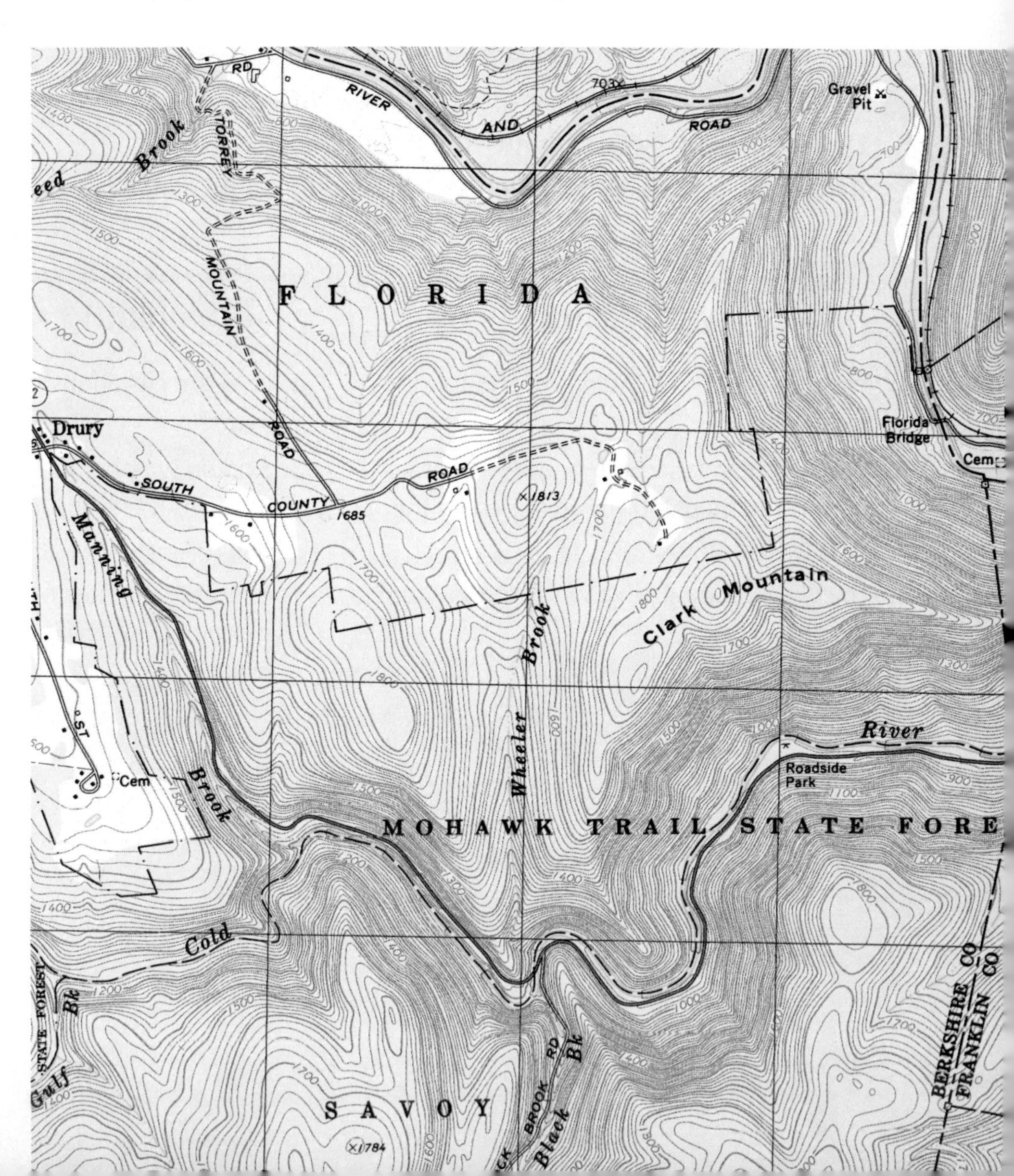

Figure 1-5

A This topographic map shows a portion of northwestern Massachusetts near the Vermont border. The contour interval on this map is 20 feet. In other words, there is a 20-foot change in elevation between lines.

B If you went from the top of Clark Mountain to the Florida Bridge on the Deerfield River, you would walk down a 1280-foot drop.

C The closer the lines, the steeper the change in elevation. Where is the steepest area on the map? Where is the land flattest?

Explore! ACTIVITY

How can you identify a landform without actually seeing it?

What To Do

1. Study the topographic map in **Figure 1-5** and notice its contour interval.
2. *In your Journal,* describe the kind of landform you think occurs where the contour lines are close together. What kind of landform occurs where the lines are far apart?

The difference in elevation from one contour line to the next contour line is the contour interval, and it is the same on the entire topographic map. In **Figure 1-5** the contour interval is given as 20 feet. This means that there is a 20-foot rise or drop in elevation from a place crossed by one thin contour line to a place crossed by the next thin contour line.

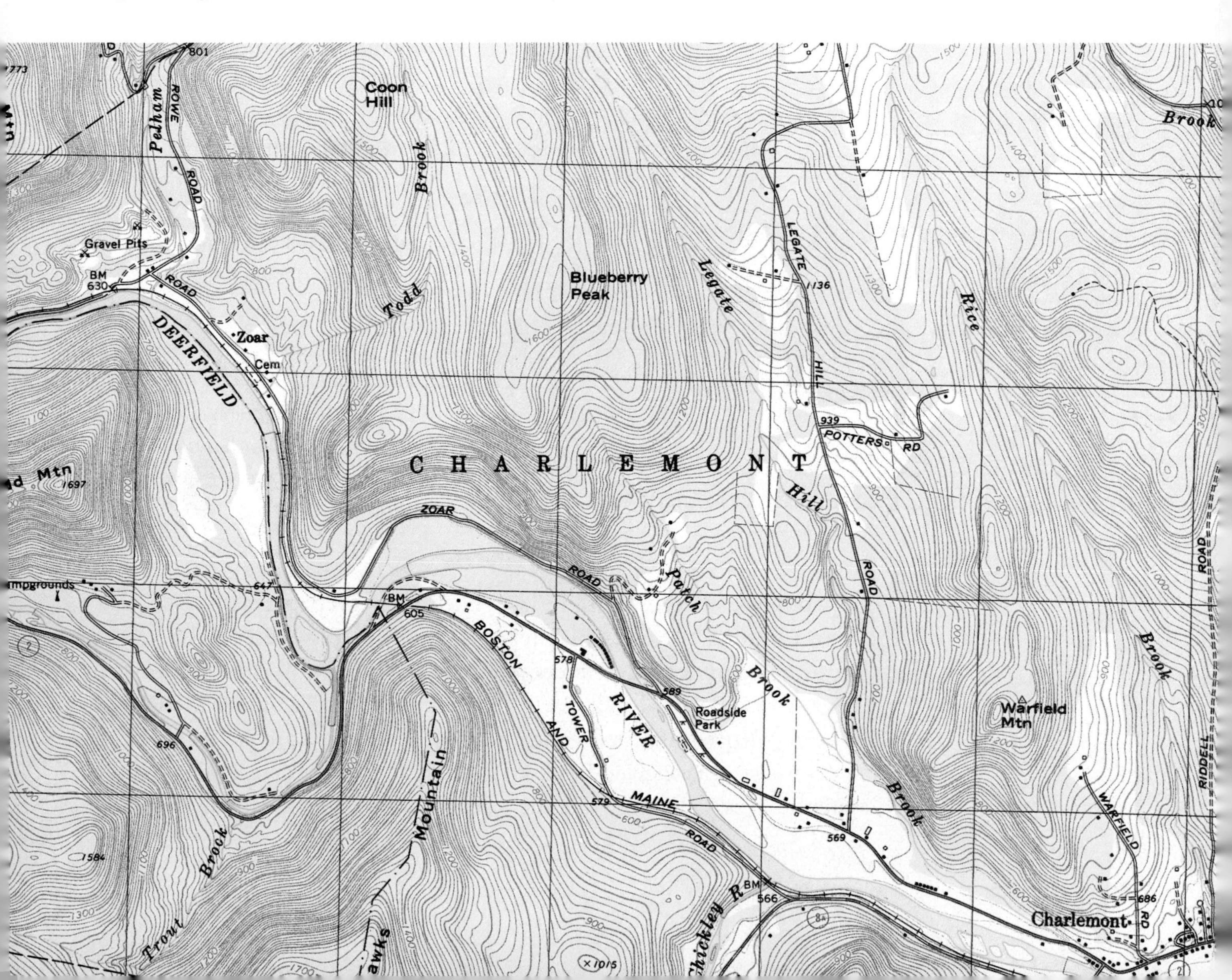

Latitude

Recall how you reached your friend's school from the park. You used a road map. The road map gave you the reference points of streets and avenues to help you get to the school. But suppose you wanted to get from one place on Earth to another. What reference points would you use? Do the following Explore activity to discover just how difficult it would be to describe a place without the use of reference points.

Can you describe the location of a dot on a ball?

Work with a friend to do this activity.

What To Do

1. Obtain a ball that does not have any markings on it. Use a marker to place a black dot on the ball.
2. Now, without showing the ball to your friend, try to describe the location of the dot. Can your friend tell you where the dot is located from your description?
3. With your partner, think of a way to make it easier to describe where the point on the ball is. Describe your system *in your Journal.* Test your system to see how well it works.

As you have discovered, it is almost impossible to describe the location of a dot on a ball. Reference points are needed. Like the ball, Earth is a sphere. To provide reference points, mapmakers have given Earth a grid system that is something like the lines on graph paper.

Look at **Figure 1-6.** The North Pole is the northernmost point on Earth; the South Pole is the southernmost. The equator is an imaginary line that circles Earth exactly halfway between the North and South poles. It

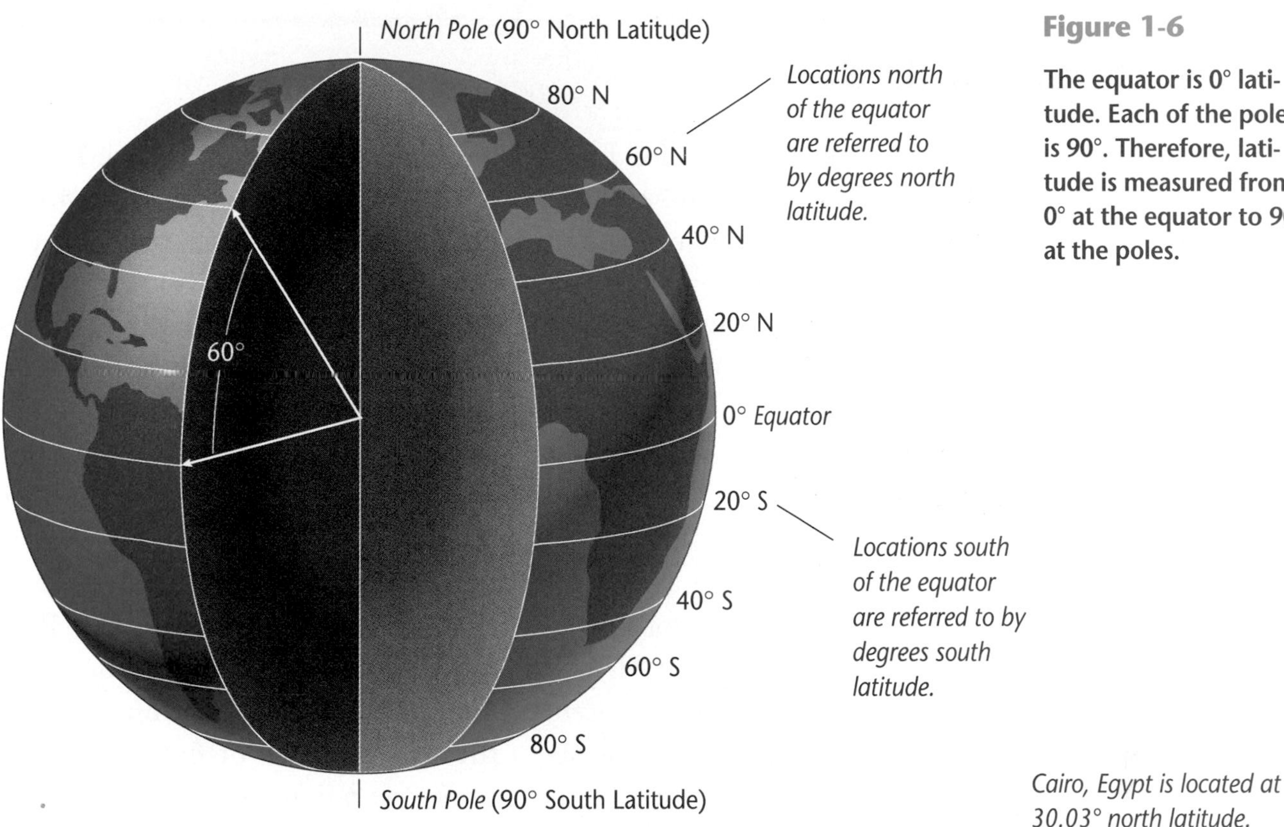

Figure 1-6

The equator is 0° latitude. Each of the poles is 90°. Therefore, latitude is measured from 0° at the equator to 90° at the poles.

separates Earth into two equal halves called the Northern Hemisphere and the Southern Hemisphere.

The lines circling Earth parallel to the equator are lines of latitude. **Latitude** refers to distance in degrees either north or south of the equator. These degrees are not like the degrees of temperature. Instead, the degree value used for the latitude of a place is the measurement of the imaginary angle created by the equator, the center of Earth, and the location of that place.

Look at **Figure 1-6**. What do you notice about the distance between each of the lines? All of the lines of latitude are parallel to each other. That means each line is always the same distance from the next line. Use a map or globe to find the approximate latitude of where you live. Follow that latitude around the world to find other places that are at the same latitude as you.

Cairo, Egypt is located at 30.03° north latitude.

Longitude

Latitude lines are used for locations north and south of the equator, but what reference points do mapmakers use for directions east and west? Vertical lines called meridians indicate east and west directions.

Just as the equator is used as a reference point for north-south grid lines, there's also a reference point for east-west grid lines. This reference point, known as the prime meridian, is shown in **Figure 1-7**. In 1884, scientists agreed that the prime meridian should pass through the Greenwich Observatory near London, England. This imaginary line represents 0° longitude. **Longitude** refers to distance in degrees east or west of the prime meridian.

Look at **Figure 1-7** again. Notice that the prime meridian does not circle Earth as the equator does. Instead, it extends from the North Pole through Greenwich, England, to the South Pole. The line of longitude on the opposite side of Earth from the prime meridian—where east lines of longitude meet west lines of longitude—is the 180° meridian.

Interpreting Scientific Illustrations

Use a world map that shows latitude and longitude to identify the cities that have the following coordinates:

1. 56° N; 38° E
2. 34° S; 18° E
3. 23° N; 82° W
4. 13° N; 101° E
5. 38° N; 9° W

Compare your answers with those of your classmates. If you need help, refer to the **Skill Handbook** on page 667.

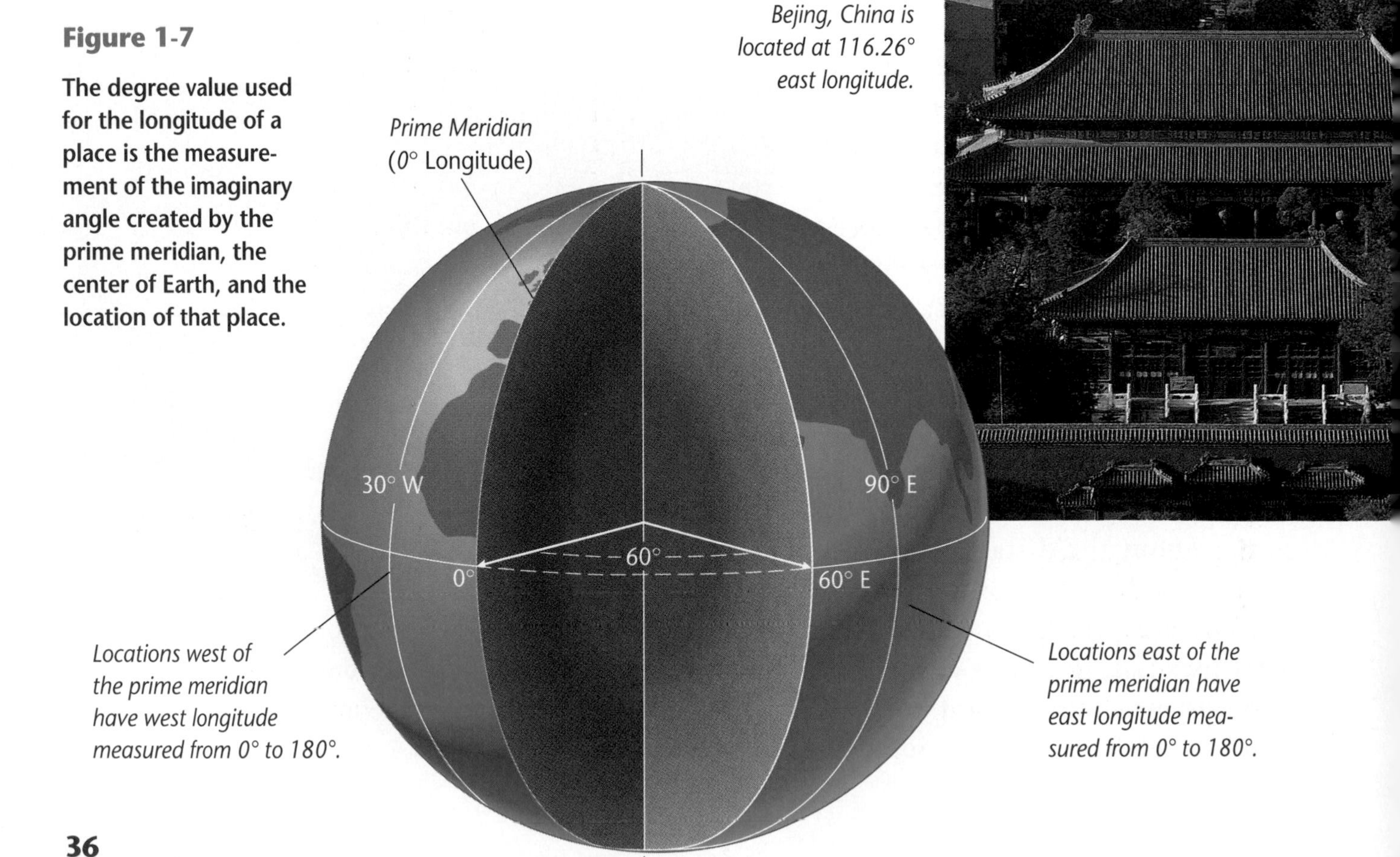

Figure 1-7

The degree value used for the longitude of a place is the measurement of the imaginary angle created by the prime meridian, the center of Earth, and the location of that place.

Figure 1-8

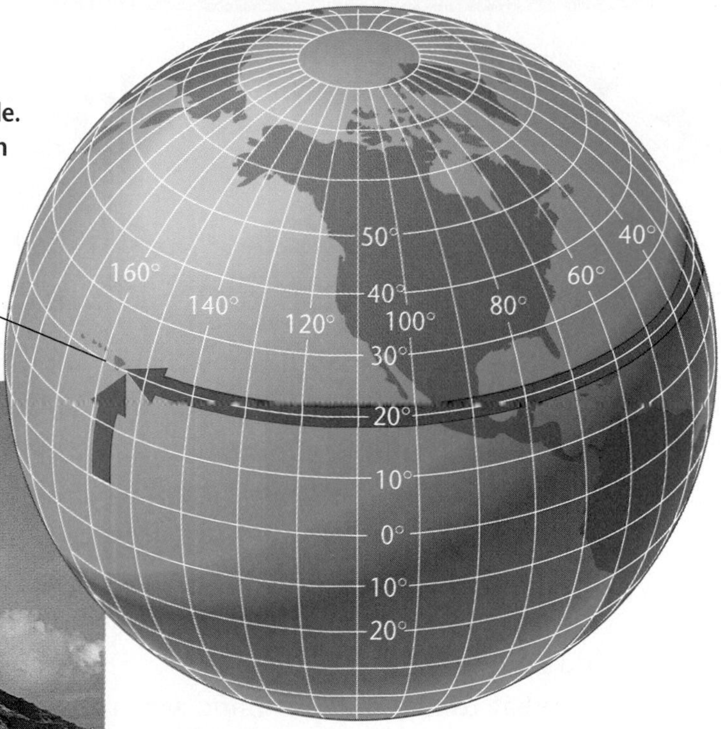

A **Hawaii is located at 20° north latitude and about 155° west longitude. How could you describe its location without lines of latitude and longitude?**

Hawaii

50°
40°
160°
60°
140°
40°
80°
120°
100°
30°
20°
10°
0°
10°
20°

B **Diamond Head is a famous extinct volcano located in Honolulu, the capital city and chief port of Hawaii. Honolulu's location is 21.19° N and 157.52° W. Which figure depicts longitude?**

Think about locating a spot on a ball again. Using the lines of latitude and longitude, you could locate that spot easily.

As you found out, maps can be informative and helpful if you know how to use them. Maps are tools for observing the world at a distance. They are particularly helpful when you cannot visit or observe the locations directly. In this section, you have learned about road maps, topographic maps, and world maps with latitude and longitude. How do you think this information can be useful to you in the future?

check your UNDERSTANDING

1. Suppose you are looking for an easy hiking route through a particular area. As you look at a topographic map, you notice the area has many closely spaced brown lines. How would you describe the area? Would it be a good place for an easy hike?
2. How would a plateau be represented on a topographic map?
3. Which lines are parallel to the equator?
4. **Apply** How can the approximate elevation of a place be obtained by looking at the contour lines on a topographic map?

1-3 Viewing the Sky

Section Objectives

- Describe the position and appearance of the sun and the moon as viewed from Earth.
- Explain the use of a star map in locating stars in the sky.

Key Terms

phase
constellations

Look Up in the Sky! It's a ...

So far, you've learned about many of the features of Earth's surface. It's fascinating to observe the beautiful rivers, plains, and mountains that shape the land we live on. Now, let's look a little higher. We're going to explore a couple of things you can find in the sky.

What things come to mind when you think about the sky? When you look up, do you see the same thing during the day as you do at night? Does the sky always look the same from day to day?

Puffy clouds, lightning, the sun, and the moon, as shown in **Figure 1-9**, are just a few of the things you might observe when you gaze upward. They are probably so familiar to you, that you don't always notice them. But how much do you really know about the sun and the moon? What causes their movements across the sky? Why does the moon appear to change shape?

Ancient cultures explained the movements and changes in the moon and sun through various myths and legends involving gods, heroes, and monsters. Today, through the observations of many astronomers, we know there are different reasons behind these phenomena.

Figure 1-9

The Moon

On your cross-country plane trip, you would probably notice the sky as well as the landforms below. What things in the sky do you notice? Perhaps you see white clouds or the bright sun. At nighttime, you might observe the stars twinkling in the sky. You might notice the position and shape of Earth's moon, too.

You've probably observed these objects in the sky before, but you may not have taken the time to notice how they change. Do the following activity to observe the changes in the moon.

Explore! ACTIVITY

What can you find out by observing the moon?

What To Do

1. Observe the moon at the same time every night for a week.
2. Record *in your Journal* as many observations as you can about the moon. Here are some questions you should try to answer: What does the moon look like? Describe it in detail. In what general direction do you see the moon? How does the moon's position change? Does the shape of the moon appear to change? Describe any changes.

Because the moon is easy to see, it has been observed throughout human history. These observations have led to many interesting stories and superstitions about the moon.

What do you see when you look at the moon? Do you see a "man in the moon," as some people do? Look at the picture of the moon in **Figure 1-9**. You can see dark areas, which may sometimes create a pattern that looks like a face. What are these dark spots, and what are some of the other features that people have discovered on the moon?

DESIGN YOUR OWN
INVESTIGATION

Formation of Moon Craters

A crater is made when an object from space strikes the surface of Earth, the moon, or another planet, leaving a dent behind. Before you begin this investigation, make a few craters in a mixture of flour and salt as described under materials. Observe what happens when you drop different "celestial objects" from different heights.

Preparation

Problem

What factors determine how deep a crater will be?

Form a Hypothesis

A hypothesis is a prediction or explanation that can be tested. From your observations, have your group list factors that might determine how deep a crater will be. Each group should make a hypothesis about one factor. A hypothesis might be that a heavier ball will make a deeper crater.

Objectives

- Observe what factors are important in creating a deep crater.
- Analyze your data to find what factors determine the depth of a crater.

Materials

25 × 30-cm pan, one-third full of table salt and two-thirds full of flour
marbles and small balls
metric ruler
pan balance
string

Safety

DESIGN YOUR OWN
INVESTIGATION

Plan the Experiment

1. Your group should test only one hypothesis. List specific steps needed to test it. Each experiment should test only one variable. A variable is the one factor that changes in each experiment, such as the size of the marbles.
2. Examine the materials provided. Decide which balls and marbles to use.
3. Design data tables *in your Science Journal* or on a computer word processor or database. Record information about each object before you start the test. What is it? How heavy is it? What height will it be dropped from?

Check the Plan

1. In what order will you test the variables? Does your data table match the test order?
2. Make sure your teacher approves your experiment before you proceed.
3. Carry out your experiment. Record your observations.

The Barringer Meteorite Crater in Arizona is 1300 m in diameter and nearly 200 m deep.

Analyze and Conclude

1. **Observe and Infer** Was your hypothesis supported by the data? Use your data to explain why or why not.
2. **Interpret Data** What factors proved most important in determining how deep a crater could be? What factors did not seem to matter?
3. **Draw a Conclusion** From the information in question 2, make a general statement about how to make the deepest crater.

Going Further

Design a similar investigation to find out what determines the diameter of a crater.

Moon Features

If you could look through a telescope at the moon, you would observe depressions called craters. In fact, there are so many craters that some of them overlap. **Figure 1-10B** shows what these craters look like.

How is a crater formed? As you might guess, the craters on the moon were formed in much the same way as you formed craters in the Investigate. The craters were formed by large objects striking the surface of the moon. In space, rock fragments called meteorites sometimes hit other objects, such as the moon. Meteorites also strike Earth.

Few craters remain visible on Earth because they are worn away by wind, rain, and water. Because these forces do not exist on the moon, craters remain for very long periods of time. Some of the moon's craters are also very large—one moon crater has a diameter of 226 kilometers.

The large dark areas on the moon, called maria, are very flat, low-lying areas. Maria formed when very large meteorites collided with the moon, forming very large depressions that have been filled with lava. If water existed in great amounts on the moon, as it does on Earth, the maria would be covered by water.

Craters and maria are prominent features of the moon. Next, you'll read about one of the more interesting aspects of the moon—its phases.

Figure 1-10

A The moon's surface is covered by a layer of dust and rocks. This is a rock obtained during the *Apollo 16* lunar landing mission.

This lunar rock weighs 443 grams and measures 11 x 7.5 x 5 centimeters.

B Craters in the moon were formed by rock fragments, called meteorites, striking the surface of the moon.

C Maria are flat areas on the moon's surfaces. Because these areas do not reflect as much sunlight as the lighter-colored rough areas do, they appear as dark spots when viewed from Earth.

D In July 1969, Neil Armstrong climbed down from the *Apollo 11* lunar module to become the first person to step onto the moon. In July 1971, astronaut David R. Scott, shown in the photograph to the right, was one of the first U.S. astronauts to walk on the moon.

Moon Phases

Sometimes the moon looks like a thin wedge of melon. At other times it looks like a silver disc. If you have observed the moon over a period of time, you have noticed such changes in its shape. You may have noticed that the changes occur in a cycle. That is, it slowly changes from a silver disc to a black disc and then back again to a silver disc.

Each stage in the cycle is known as a **phase**. Each cycle from full moon to new moon and back to full moon again takes a little over four weeks, or about a month. You'll discover in Chapter 19 why the moon appears to change. Until then, observe the moon periodically to see how it changes. Try to develop a hypothesis to explain your observations.

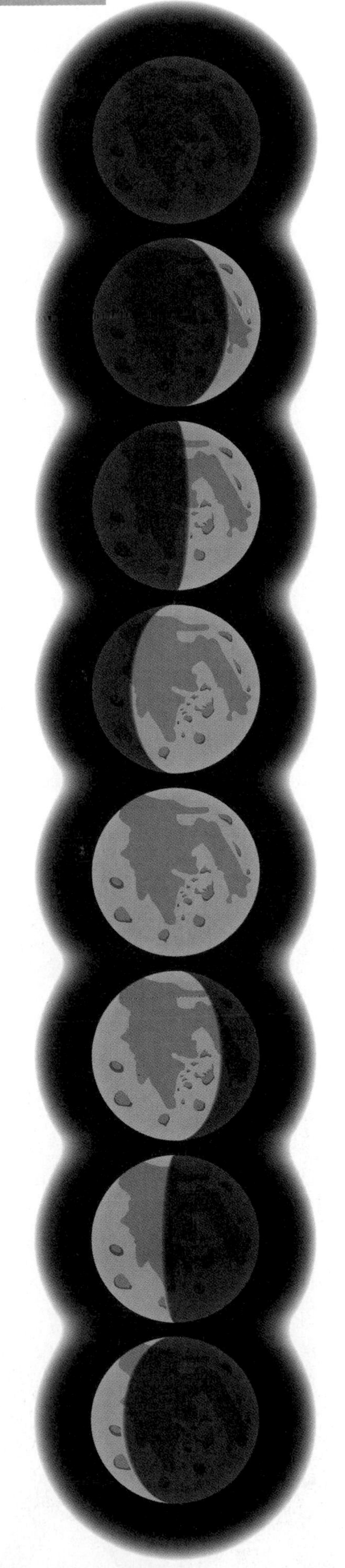

Figure 1-11

A The moon has no light of its own. What we call moonlight is simply sunlight reflected from the moon's surface. As the moon revolves around Earth, various portions of the moon's surface appear to be lighted to an observer on Earth. During a new moon, none of the moon's surface is visible.

B The lighted portion visible on Earth starts as a small slice and grows larger over two weeks until a full circle of light or full moon can be seen.

C During the next two weeks, the circle of visible light grows smaller until no reflected light can be seen. Then the cycle begins again. The changing pattern of moonlight visible on Earth repeats every 29.5 days.

The Sun's Apparent Movement

The stars and moon are visible in the night sky. What do you see in the daytime sky? You see the sun, of course. How does the sun move during the day? Do the following activity to find out.

Explore! ACTIVITY

What can you learn by observing the sun?

What To Do

1. Observe the sun every hour or so from sunrise to sunset. **CAUTION:** *Do not look directly at the sun. The brightness of the sun will damage your eyes. Make general observations of the sun based on shadows or reflections.*
2. Record *in your Science Journal* as many observations as you can about the sun. Here are some questions you should try to answer. What are the shadows like at various times during the day? In what direction do you see the sun? How does the sun's position change?

a CLOSER LOOK

Starry, Starry Night

Have you ever spent a summer afternoon gazing up at the clouds, imagining them as faces, or sailing ships slowly drifting by? If you have, you know it can be quite an entertaining display. But did you know there's an equally impressive show on a clear night? The night sky is full of wonders such as meteors and planets, and if you use your imagination, the stars can become an endless parade of people and objects.

Throughout human history, people have been enjoying the night sky. As they connected the stars with imaginary lines, the characters of myths and legends earned a place in the starry sky.

The patterns formed by groups of stars are called **constellations**. Cultures in China, the Middle East, Europe, and North and South America each have their own collection of constellations and legends to accompany them. A constellation may represent a hero, maiden, animal, or simply a common object such as a broken pot, or scales.

The patterns in the night sky have also served a more practical purpose. Sailors use them to easily recognize certain stars to help them in navigation. They relate the changing position of their ship to the position

The sun looks as if it rises in the east and sets in the west. It appears to move through the sky because Earth is spinning. As the seasons change in the Northern Hemisphere from summer, to autumn, and into winter, the sun appears to set farther south. Also, the sun doesn't get as high in the winter sky as it does in the summer, and the length of time that the sun is visible is shorter in the winter.

Viewing Earth and the sky is just the beginning of your study of the world around you. In the next chapter, you will find out about light—which helps you make observations.

1. Why does the moon appear to change its shape?
2. What is the difference in the position of the sun in the sky between winter and summer?
3. **Apply** You've just received a telescope and you want to view the full moon to see as many maria and craters as possible. Tonight there will be a new moon. About how long will you have to wait to observe the full moon with your telescope?

of certain constellations.

To learn what some constellations are, you need a star map. Just as maps of Earth are useful in locating cities, star maps are helpful in finding the locations of stars. Star maps show where stars, constellations and planets are at certain times of the year.

You Try It!

At night, go outside and look up at the night sky. Find a pattern of stars and record the pattern *in your Journal.* Now connect the stars in different ways, trying to imagine what the shapes could represent. Decide the one you like best and make a drawing of your constellation, and name it.

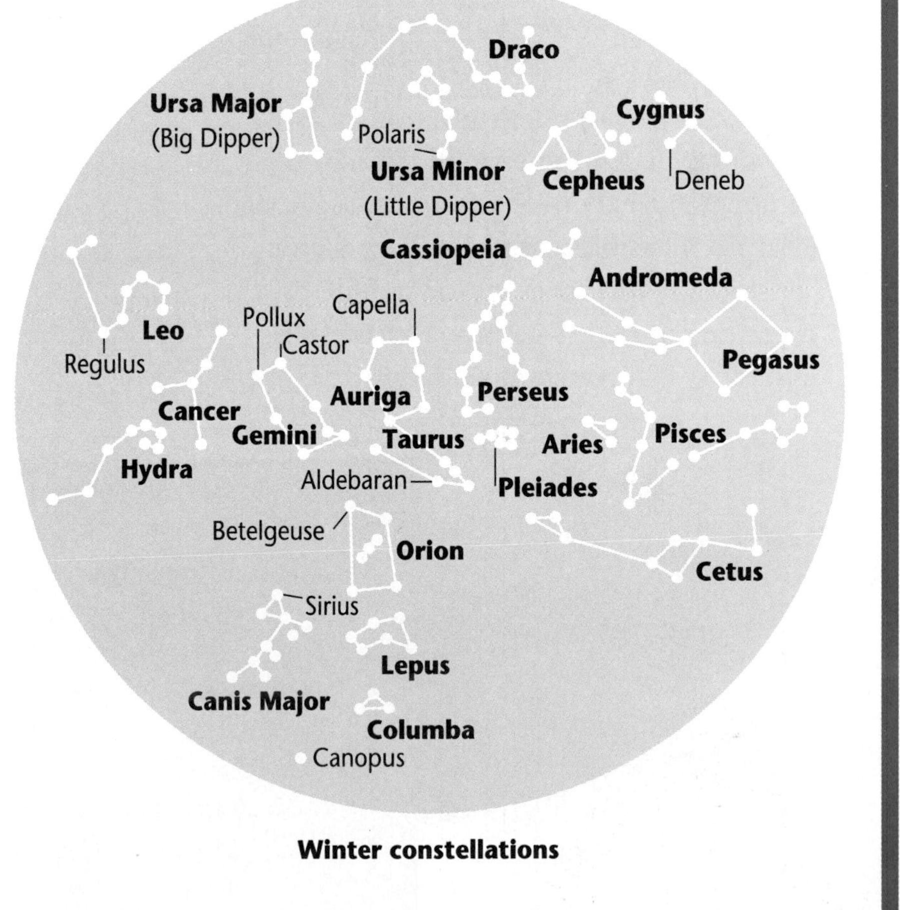

Winter constellations

Science *and* Society

What To Do with All That Garbage?

Until the mid-1960s, most communities disposed of waste in the town dump—an open, smelly place. Today, the sanitary landfill has taken the place of the dump. It's more than just a fancy new name for a familiar place. Modern engineering and construction techniques are used to confine wastes to the smallest possible space. Even so, a sanitary landfill can cover acres of land.

Dangerous Dumps

Once seen as a major advance, today we question whether sanitary landfills are safe. Although buried under layers of soil, garbage is far from harmless. Because there is little control over what goes into a landfill, toxic chemicals and other hazardous wastes seep into the soil, threatening underground water supplies. This risk has closed many landfills, while many communities are refusing to allow landfills to be constructed near them. This has led to a shortage of sites for new landfills.

Using Computers

As a society, we produce huge amounts of garbage every day. Imagine you are part of a community that's forming on a small island. With a group, come up with a plan for dealing with the garbage your community will produce. Consider the long-term effects of your actions, such as the impact your solution has on food sources and water supplies. Also consider how much you think it might cost and whether your community would be willing to pay that amount. Prepare a word-processed report describing your plans.

The Fresh Kills Landfill in New York

Technology Connection

Franklin Ramon Chang-Diaz

Franklin Ramon Chang-Diaz was born April 5, 1950, in San Jose, Costa Rica. As early as age seven he remembers wanting to go into space. In grade school, he wrote to Dr. Werner von Braun of the United States Space Program asking how to become an astronaut. Dr. von Braun wrote back that Franklin should come to the United States and study science. Franklin Chang-Diaz did just that in 1967. He moved in with distant relatives in Hartford, Connecticut. Chang-Diaz spoke no English when he arrived, and had no money, but he didn't let either of these things stop him. He attended public school to learn English. He studied hard in school to get a college scholarship and worked odd jobs to make extra money.

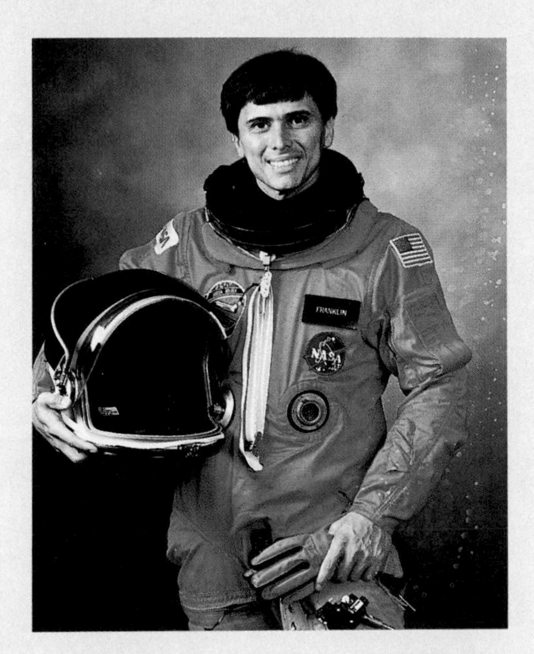

The "Right Stuff"

In 1973, Franklin Chang-Diaz received a degree in mechanical engineering from the University of Connecticut. Later, in 1977, he obtained a doctorate from the Massachusetts Institute of Technology (MIT) in applied plasma physics. After graduation, he worked on fusion reactor projects at a lab in Cambridge, Massachusetts. In 1978, he applied for astronaut selection but did not even receive a response. But Dr. Chang-Diaz was not about to give up. In 1980, he was selected as one of 19 astronauts admitted to the NASA program. He completed his mission specialist training in 1981 and began working on various research projects. On January 12, 1986, Franklin Chang-Diaz finally journeyed into space on the Space Shuttle *Columbia.*

Help Wanted: Astronauts

Dr. Chang-Diaz believes there is a need for astronauts who can do their own research as well as carrying out someone else's experiments. He sees space as an opportunity for everyone. "In 20 to 30 years, there will be all kinds of people in space and that makes a lot of sense."

interNET CONNECTION

Use the World Wide Web to find out what research will be carried out on upcoming shuttle missions. Select a research problem that you would like to help solve.

NATIONAL GEOGRAPHIC

SCIFACTS

Where is the largest crater on Earth?

Buried on Mexico's Yucatán Peninsula is the Chicxulub crater, whose diameter measures 300 kilometers at its widest point. It is thought to be the largest crater on Earth.

Geologists hypothesize that the Yucatán crater was formed about 65 million years ago, possibly by the same asteroid or comet that led to the extinction of the dinosaurs. At the time of impact, the Gulf of Mexico was much larger than it is now, and that portion of the Yucatán Peninsula was a shallow sea.

Chicxulub crater was discovered in the early 1980s when geologists detected a circular pattern of gravitational irregularities beneath more than one kilometer of sediment. About 130 other major impact craters have been discovered on Earth, most of them in Canada, the United States, Europe, and Australia. Chicxulub's closest rival in size is the Sudbury crater, located far to the north in the Canadian province of Ontario.

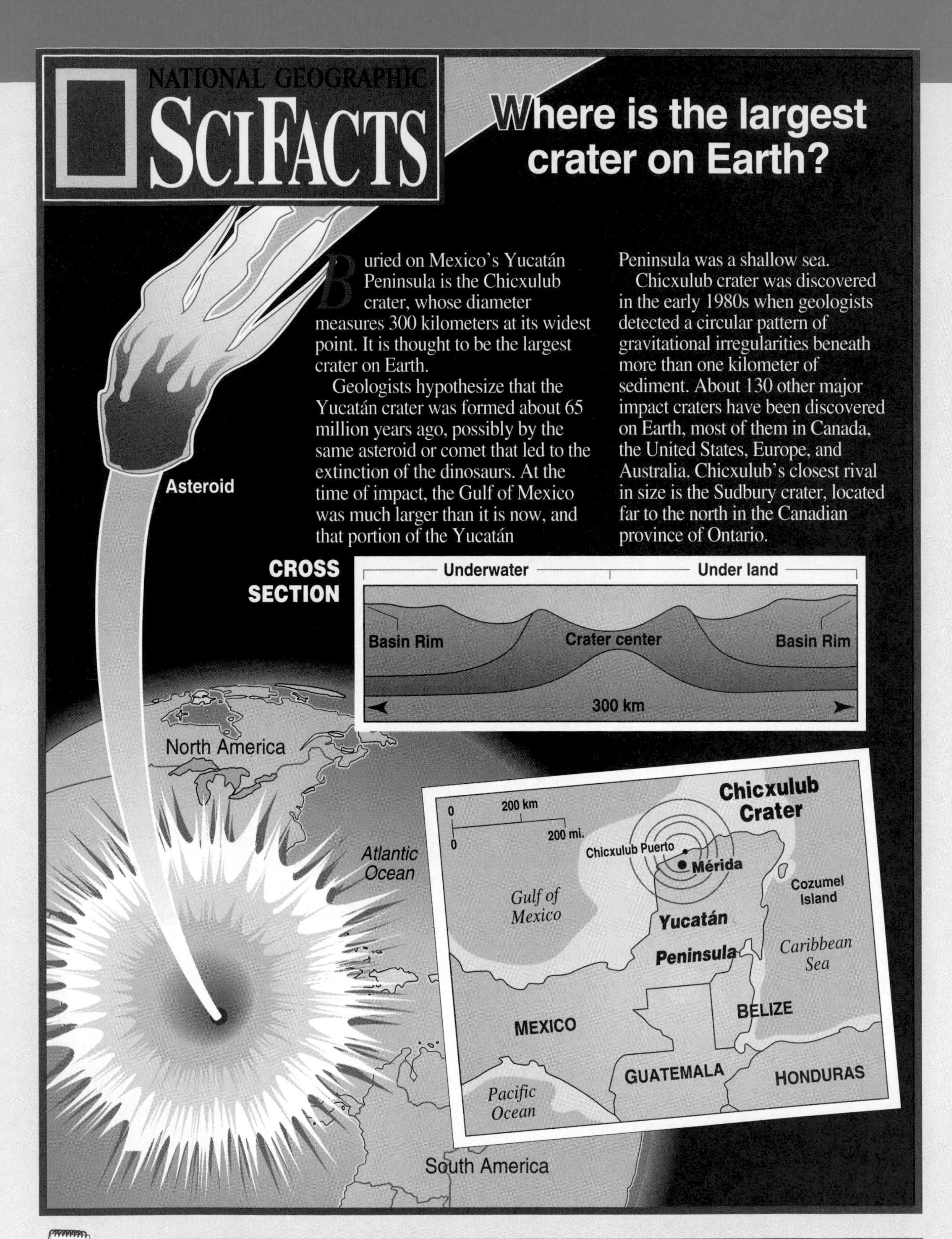

Science Journal

Research information about meteorites that are thought to have caused major craters on Earth, and write your findings *in your Science Journal.*

chapter 1 REVIEWING MAIN IDEAS

Science Journal

Review the statements below about the big ideas presented in this chapter, and answer the questions. Then, re-read your answers to the Did You Ever Wonder questions at the beginning of the chapter. *In your Science Journal,* write a paragraph about how your understanding of the big ideas in the chapter has changed.

1 When we observe our surroundings, we see landforms such as mountains, plains, and plateaus. We also see the sun appear to move through the sky. ***What landforms are found in your area?***

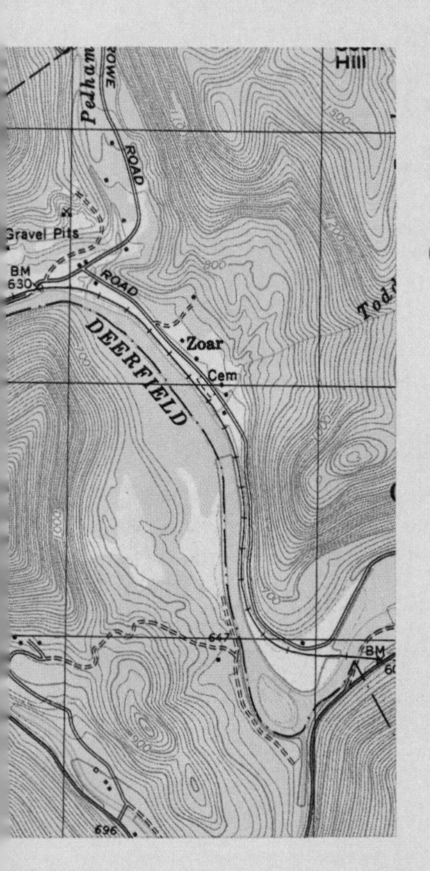

2 Topographic maps record our observations about landforms and their elevations through the use of contour lines. ***What does it mean when the contour lines on part of a topographic map are very close together?***

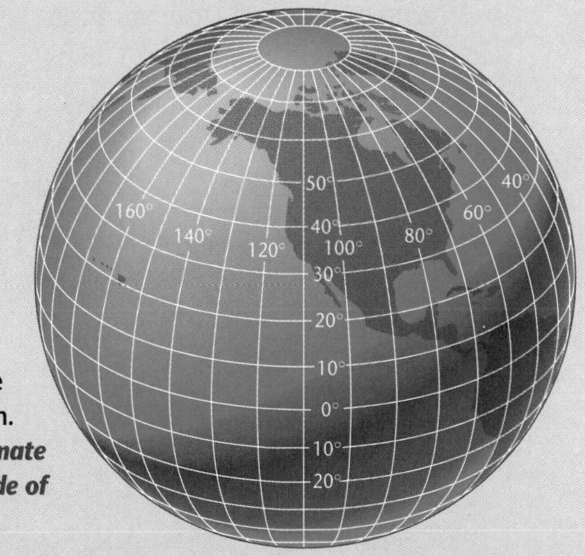

3 Lines of latitude and longitude were created as reference points to help people locate places on Earth. ***What is the approximate latitude and longitude of where you live?***

4 From Earth, we can observe large dark areas on the moon called maria. With a telescope, we can observe smaller depressions called craters. The moon's shape appears to change during a cycle that lasts about a month. ***Why do craters remain on the moon for a very long time?***

chapter 1

CHAPTER REVIEW

Using Key Science Terms

constellations
contour lines
elevation
landform
latitude
longitude
phase

An analogy is a relationship between two pairs of words generally written in the following manner: a:b::c:d. The symbol : is read "is to," and the symbol :: is read "as." For example, cat:animal::rose:plant is read "cat is to animal as rose is to plant." In the analogies that follow, a word is missing. Complete each analogy by providing the missing word from the list above.

1. Big Dipper: ________ ::Pacific:oceans
2. east:longitude::north: ________
3. houses:building::mountains: ________
4. degrees:temperature::meters: ________
5. innings:baseball game:: ________ :moon cycle
6. equator:latitude::prime meridian: ________
7. latitude and longitude:direction:: ________ :elevation

Understanding Ideas

Answer the following questions in your Journal *using complete sentences.*

1. List three common landforms and give a brief description of each.
2. Describe how contour lines are used on a topographic map.
3. How do latitude and longitude lines help describe location?
4. Explain how constellations are used.

Developing Skills

Use your understanding of the concepts developed in this chapter to answer each of the following questions.

1. **Concept Mapping** Using the following terms, complete the concept map of landforms: *mountains, plains, plateaus, Rocky, Great Plains*

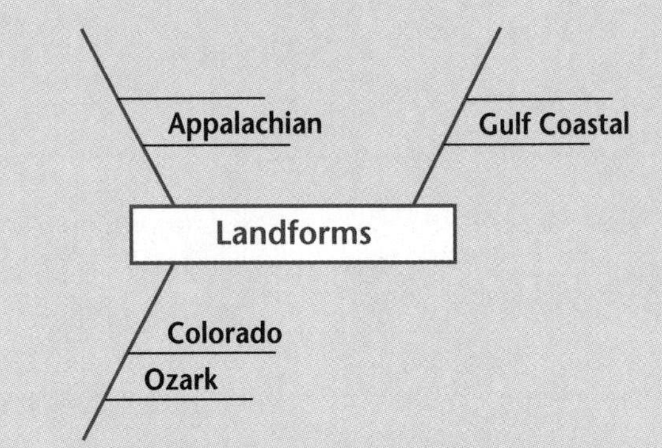

2. **Using Models** After doing the Investigate on pages 30-31, select a specific area in your community and create a topographic map of the area. Exchange maps with a classmate and try to identify this new location.
3. **Observing** After doing the Explore activity on page 39, repeat the activity for a two-week period observing and recording the moon changes.

Critical Thinking

In your Journal, *answer each of the following questions.*

1. Suppose you knew there was a new moon last night. What kind of a moon would you expect to see tonight? Why?

2. Study the topographic map of a hill below. Then, fill in the blanks in this sentence: The elevation at the top of the hill is between _____ and _____. Explain your answers.

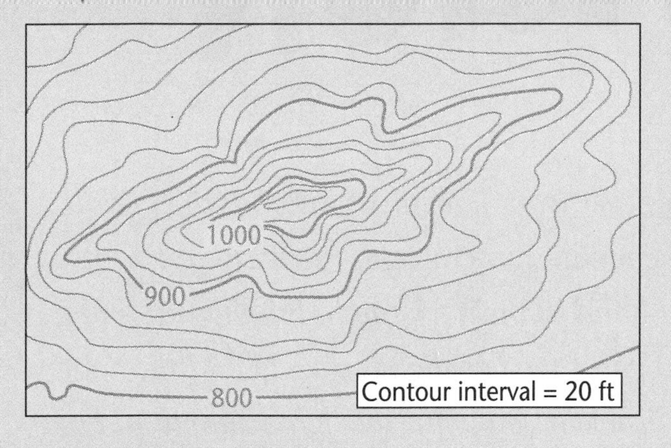

Problem Solving

Read the following problem and discuss your answers in a brief paragraph.

The North Star can be seen from most places in the United States in the night sky when you look north. At different latitudes, the North Star appears at different heights in the sky. The angle between the surface of Earth at your location and the position of the North Star is equal to your latitude. This angle can be found by using an instrument called a sextant. You can make a sextant with a protractor and straw. Hold or pin the straw so that it pivots at the center point of the protractor. Hold the protractor up close to your eyes, so its base is parallel to the ground. Sight along the straw to find the North Star. Keep the base of the protractor parallel to the ground.

1. Why do you think the base has to be horizontal?
2. What is your latitude?

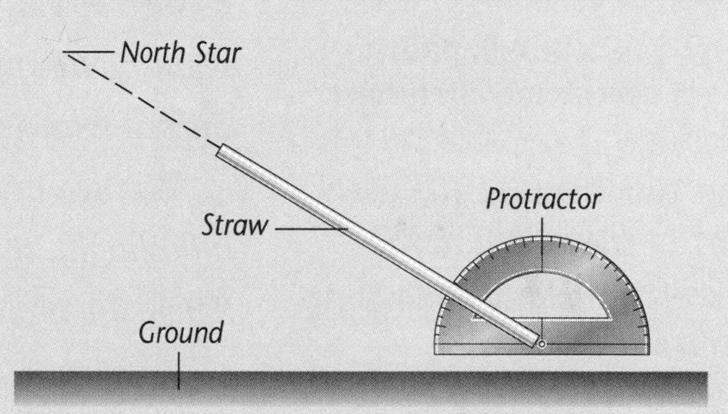

CONNECTING IDEAS

Discuss each of the following in a brief paragraph.

1. **Theme—Scale and Structure** Suppose that you want to find the approximate elevation and location of a place. What kind of map would you use? Why?
2. **Theme—Scale and Structure** How could all latitudes in the continental United States be north and all longitudes be west?
3. **Theme—Scale and Structure** Two craters overlap. How can you determine which crater is the younger?
4. **Science and Society** What are two environmental problems caused by sanitary landfills?
5. **Life Science Connection** Name three factors that are important in determining where crops can be grown.

CHAPTER 2

LIGHT and VISION

Did you ever wonder...

- ✓ **Why you can mix paints to get completely different colors?**
- ✓ **How long it takes for sunlight to travel to Earth?**
- ✓ **Why it's hard to distinguish different colors in moonlight?**

Science Journal

Before you begin to study about light and vision, think about these questions and answer them *in your Science Journal.* When you finish the chapter, compare your journal write-up with what you have learned.

Do you ever want a drink of water in the middle of the night? You grope for the flashlight with your hand in the dark room. Finally you find it, turn it on, and point the flashlight beam to find the door. The dresser is visible if you point the light beam at it, but as soon as you move the light toward the door, the dresser seems to disappear. The only objects you can see are the ones at which you point the flashlight beam.

Seeing any object requires light. Light may come from a flashlight, the light bulbs in your house, or from the sun. There are probably other sources of light in your home as well. Can you name them? How does light allow you to see the world around you? In this chapter, you'll learn about light and how it affects what you see.

▸ ***In the activity on the next page, explore some characteristics of light and shadows.***

Explore! ACTIVITY

What do shadows tell you about light?

What To Do

1. Use a flashlight, tape, a drinking straw, construction paper, and white paper for this activity.
2. Cut a shape from construction paper and tape it to the end of a drinking straw. Tape the white paper to the chalkboard or wall. Dim the lights in the room.
3. *In your Journal*, draw a diagram to predict how a shadow will appear when the shape attached to the straw is an inch from the flashlight and when it is a foot from the paper.
4. Test your prediction.
5. Vary the distance of the shape between the flashlight and the paper.
6. How does the shadow change as the shape is moved closer to the paper?
7. *In your Journal*, draw a diagram to explain how the light is traveling from the flashlight to the paper in order for the shape to make a shadow.

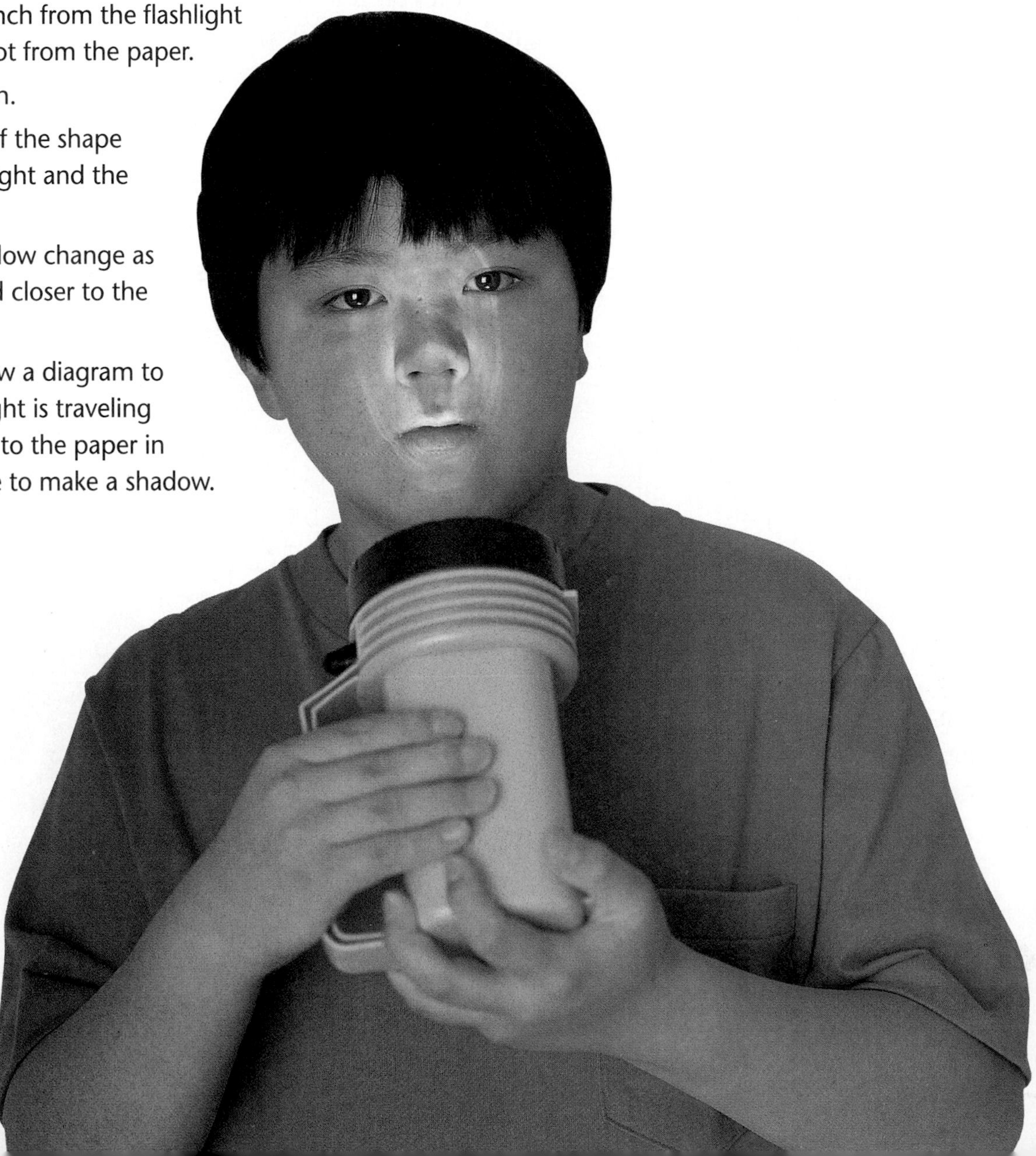

The Nature of Light

Section Objectives
- Identify how light travels.
- Distinguish between objects that create light and those that only reflect light.
- Compare and contrast opaque, translucent, and transparent materials.

Key Terms
reflection, opaque, transparent, translucent

Light and Reflection

Every day, all day long, light gives you information about the world around you. During the day, the sun is often your primary source of light. You also receive light from light bulbs, fire, and even from the television. Most things that you see are visible because light from somewhere else bounces off them. You can read this page because light is reflecting off it to your eyes. Light bouncing off something is **reflection**. You see your bedroom door when you shine a flashlight on it because the door reflects some of the light from the flashlight. You see your clothes in front of you in your closet because they reflect some of the light from your bedroom lamp directly back to your eye. You are unable to see these things when there is no source of light.

Exactly how does light travel from its source to objects and then to your eye?

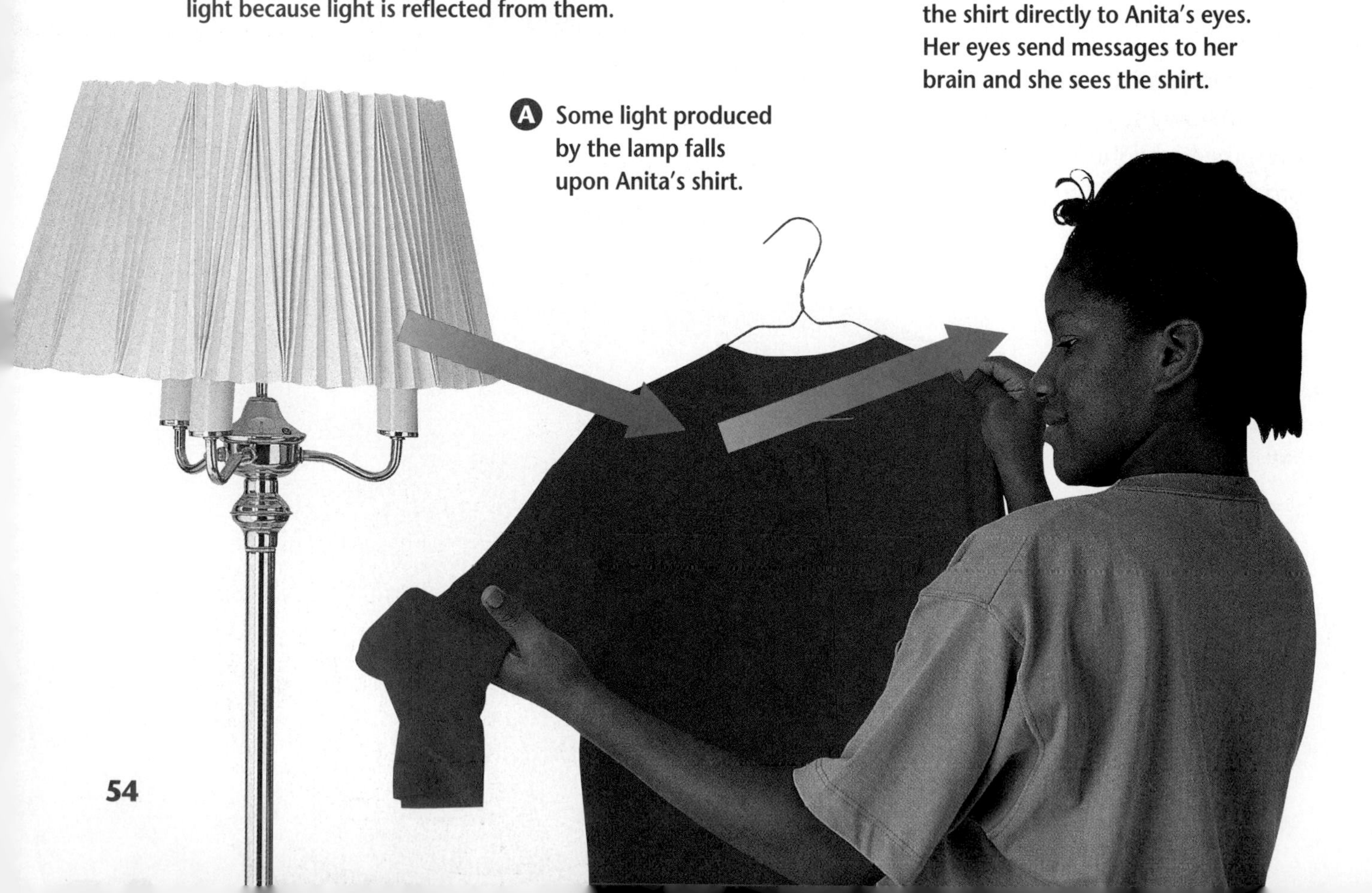

Figure 2-1

Without light, there is no vision. You are able to see objects that are not sources of light because light is reflected from them.

How Light Travels

You saw from the Explore activity that when an object blocks light, a shadow is produced. The appearance of the shadow depends on the positions of the light source and the object blocking the light. When the object was closer to the light source, the shadow was large and fuzzy. When the object was closer to the paper, the shadow was smaller, darker, and sharper. But, a shadow was always produced. The light did not reach every part of the paper. Are shadows alone enough proof that light travels in straight lines? Look at the Find Out activity and **Figure 2-2** for more evidence.

Find Out! ACTIVITY

How does light travel?

It appears that light does not travel around corners. We can observe a beam of light to determine how it travels.

What To Do

1. Stack three index cards together. Carefully punch a hole through the middle of all three cards with the point of a compass.
2. Using small pieces of clay to support them, stand the cards about 2.5 cm apart, with the holes lined up.
3. Place a light bulb about 5 cm behind the hole in the back index card.

Conclude and Apply

1. What do you see when you look through the holes in the index cards?
2. Move the center card slightly out of line. What do you see now?
3. Based on what you have observed, *in your Journal*, describe how light travels.

Figure 2-2

Light travels in a straight line. When an object blocks the passage of light, the area behind the object is not lit—it is in shadow.

A **The raised part of a sundial, the gnomon, blocks the sun's rays and casts a shadow on the sundial surface. Because Earth rotates, the position of the sundial in relation to the sun keeps changing as the day progresses.**

B **As the sundial's position changes, the angle of the shadow changes, marking the passing hours of the day.**

In the Find Out activity you discovered the light did not curve around through the second hole when you moved the card. The light was blocked. Let's take one more look at a beam of light to determine how light travels.

Explore! ACTIVITY

What does a beam of light look like?

You can observe white light traveling from its source.

What To Do

1. Choose an area that is not brightly lit. Smack two chalky chalkboard erasers together.
2. Shine a flashlight into the cloud of chalk dust.
3. *In your Journal,* describe what the beam of light looks like.
4. Shine the flashlight in another area, away from the chalk dust, and observe the light beam. Why do you think you can see the beam of light better in the chalk dust?
5. *In your Journal,* suggest other properties of light that you observe.

When you observed the light beam in the chalk dust, you saw a straight beam of light. You could see the beam because it bounced or reflected off the chalk dust particles. It didn't matter how you turned the flashlight, the light beam always traveled in a straight line.

■ The Speed of Light

Whichever type of light source you have, it seems that light zips instantly from it to the object and back to you. It appears that you can see everything immediately. Light travels much faster than anything else we know of, but it does take some time for it to travel from place to place. How fast does light travel?

Throughout history, many people have tried to measure how fast light travels, but it wasn't until the late 1800s that scientists found that light travels at about 300 000 kilometers per second. That's fast enough to go from the sun to you in about eight minutes. It's so fast that a beam of light could cross your bedroom several million times before you can let go of the light switch.

Light at Different Speeds

Light travels through air at about 300 000 kilometers per second. Light travels through other materials at different speeds. The speed at which light travels through any material depends on the nature of the material. For example, light travels more slowly in water than in air. **Figure 2-3** illustrates the speed of light through several common materials. Using the information provided in the figure below, determine whether light travels faster through diamond or glass.

How Do We Know?

How was the speed of light first timed?

One of the most famous experiments to time light speed was performed in 1926 by an American, Albert Michelson, on Mount Wilson in California. Using two large mirrors 22 miles apart and a rotating mirror with eight sides, he was able to bounce light beams between the mirrors and make the most precise measurements of the speed of light ever made with mechanical methods.

Figure 2-3

The speed of light is dependent upon the material through which it travels. Light travels faster through some materials than it does through others.

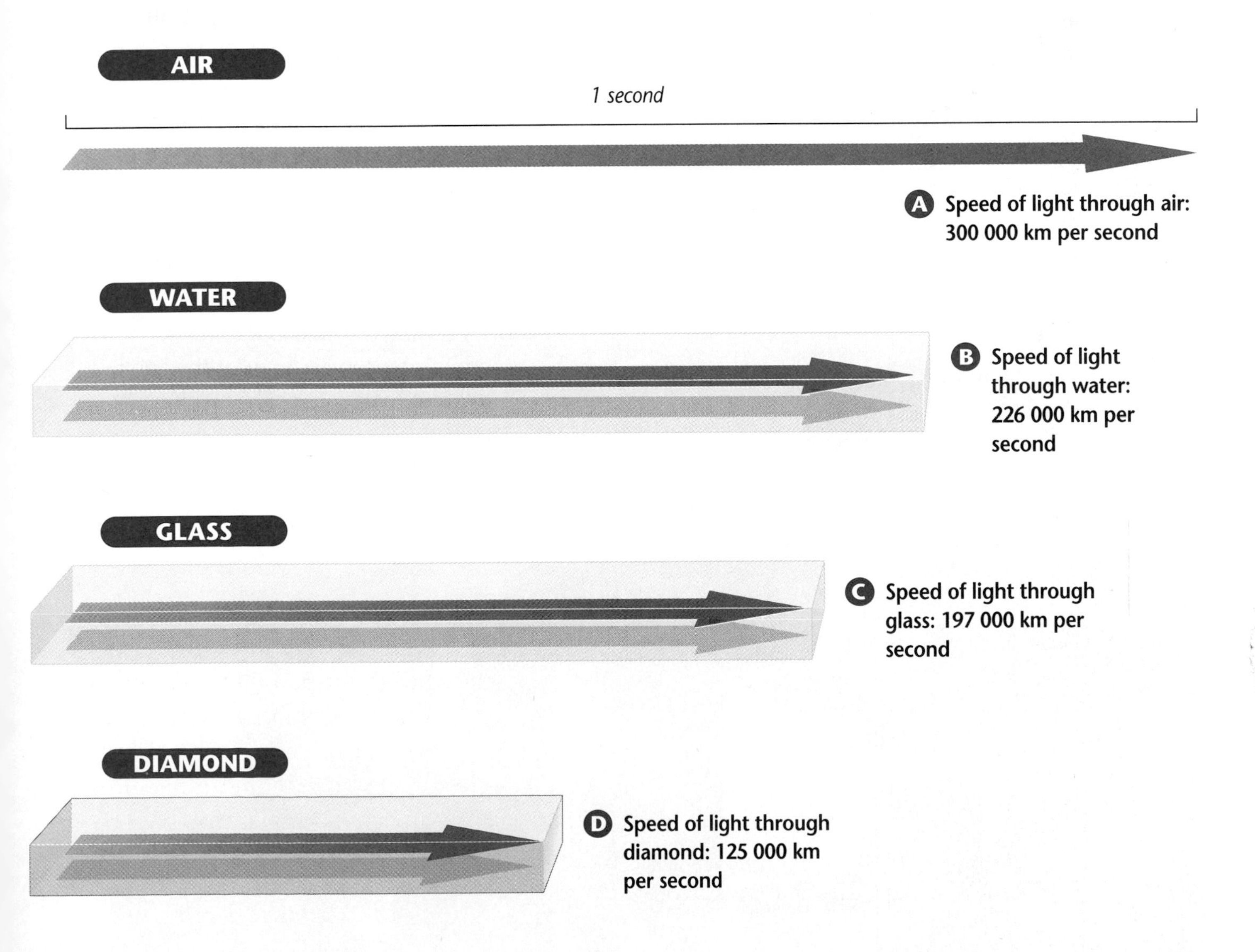

Opaque, Transparent, and Translucent

In the last three activities, you observed that light travels in straight lines. Several different things can happen when light hits an object. The nature of the object will determine what happens when light hits it. You've learned that light reflects off objects. The same objects also absorb some of the light that strikes them and can allow light to pass through. Collect several objects made of different materials for the Explore activity that follows to see what happens when light hits them.

What happens to light when it hits different objects?

Try shining light on different kinds of objects to see what happens to the light.

What To Do

1. Obtain a flashlight, a piece of clay, and a piece of white cardboard. Anchor the cardboard vertically on your desk using the clay.
2. Gather a variety of objects such as a piece of plate glass, a piece of frosted glass, cellophane, a book, waxed paper, sunglasses, tissue paper, an article of clothing, a notebook, and a printed page.
3. Select one object and place it in front of the cardboard. Shine the flashlight on the object and observe what you see on the white cardboard.
4. Record *in your Journal* what happened to the light as it hit each object.
5. Try sorting the objects into three groups depending on what the light did as it came into contact with each object.

Figure 2-4 shows three different things that can happen when light hits an object. Light can pass directly through some objects. Other objects scatter light that passes through, while others completely block the light.

Objects that reflect or absorb light but do not allow light to pass through them are **opaque**.

When something allows enough light to pass through so that you can clearly see objects on the other side, it is **transparent**.

Any materials that let light through, but do not allow objects on the other side to be clearly seen are called **translucent**.

Whether the sun, a flashlight, or a candle is your source of light, you can see the objects around you. You can see yourself in a mirror, find your way with a flashlight, or see your family sitting at the dinner table because all of these objects reflect light back to your eyes. Light travels fast and in straight lines.

Figure 2-4

A This candle holder is opaque. It reflects or absorbs all of the light that hits it, allowing none to pass through. You can see light from the candle escaping from the open top, but not through the sides of this holder.

B This candle holder is translucent. It allows light through, but bends the light in so many different directions that all you see are fuzzy images. Are most things that you see opaque, transparent, or translucent?

C This clear glass candle holder is transparent. Like window glass, it allows light to travel directly through so that you clearly see what's on the other side of the glass.

check your UNDERSTANDING

1. Name two items not discussed in this section that you could see without reflected light.
2. The moon is about 387 000 kilometers from Earth. How long does it take light to get from the moon to Earth?
3. How do transparent, opaque, and translucent objects differ? Give an example of each.
4. **Apply** Imagine a star that is four light-years away. That is, it takes four years for light from the star to reach us. Do we see the star as it is now or as it was?

Reflection and Refraction

Section Objectives
- Discuss the different types of reflection.
- Describe what happens to light during refraction.

Key Terms
refraction

When Light Bounces and Bends

We've discussed the nature of light—light travels in straight lines; light can be reflected; and light can travel at different speeds through different materials. In this section, you'll take a closer look at what happens when light bounces or reflects and learn about another property of light. In the Find Out activity you'll learn more about reflection.

Find Out! ACTIVITY

How does light reflect on smooth and bumpy surfaces?

The type of surface reflecting the light is important when you are trying to see yourself. You can compare how light reflects off different surfaces.

What To Do

1. Observe your reflection in a piece of smooth aluminum foil.
2. Crumple the foil, spread it out, and observe your reflection again.

Conclude and Apply

1. Which piece of foil reflected more clearly?
2. How does the reflection on the smooth foil differ from the reflection on the crumpled foil?
3. What do you think happens to light that is reflected from any rough surface?

Figure 2-5

A When light reflected from an object reaches a mirror, the smooth surface of the mirror reflects light back to your eyes in orderly, straight lines. If you look at a mirror, such as the mirror-tiled surface of the building on the far right of this photo, you see a reflected image of everything facing the mirror.

B When light reflected from an object reaches an uneven surface, the light scatters, bouncing every which way. If you look at the rough stone walls of the older building on the left side of the photo, you see no reflected image. Why?

Regular Reflection

If you were holding a mirror in place of this book, some of the light around you would reflect off you into the mirror, then bounce straight back to you. When a reflection is very clear and looks just like the object, it is called a regular reflection. Smooth surfaces, such as mirrors, produce regular reflections.

Diffuse Reflection

When you crumple a piece of foil, the foil changes from one mirror into thousands of tiny mirrors. Each surface reflects light, but the light bounces in many different directions. The crumpled foil produces a diffuse reflection.

Why can't you see yourself on the smooth surface of this page? If you were to look at this page under a microscope, you would see that the surface of this paper is extremely rough. Light reflecting off this page is also producing a diffuse reflection.

Figure 2-6

A Smooth aluminum foil is a mirror. When light is reflected from the vase of flowers to the foil, the foil reflects the light to your eyes in orderly, straight lines. You see a reflected image of the vase and flowers. The reflection produced by the smooth foil is regular reflection.

B Crumpling the aluminum foil changes the one large mirror into thousands of tiny mirrors, facing in various directions. Light reflected from the vase of flowers is reflected from the tiny mirrors in straight lines, but the lines go in many different directions. This type of reflection is diffuse reflection.

C Some diffuse reflections produce no reflected image at all. When light reflected from the flowers hits the relatively rough white paper, the light scatters in many more directions and does not produce a reflected image.

INVESTIGATE!

Mirror Reflections

When you see light reflected from a mirror, you see an entire object—your head, a car, or a chair, for example. You probably don't think about what happens when light reflects in a mirror. You can easily discover how mirrors reflect light in this activity.

Problem

How does light reflect in a mirror and how can this be used?

Materials

4 pocket mirrors
book
flashlight

What To Do

1. With a partner in a darkened room, use the mirrors and the flashlight to experiment with a beam of light.
2. Using as many mirrors as necessary, first reflect a light beam onto the ceiling.

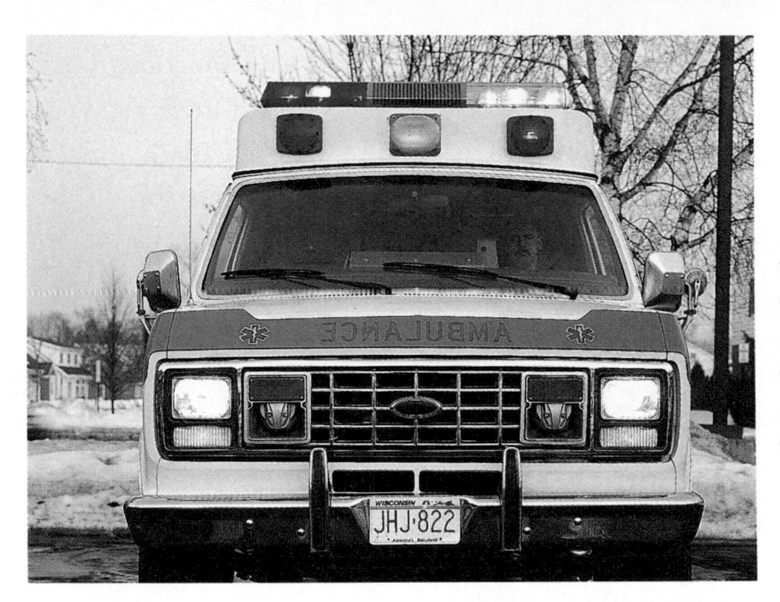

Why do you think that the front of some emergency vehicles, like this one, have backwards writing on the front?

3 Now, place a book upright on a desk.

4 Position the mirrors so that a light beam striking a mirror placed in front of the book is reflected to the back of the book.

5 Now, use your mirrors to reflect light into another room.

6 Using descriptions and diagrams, record the different positions of the mirrors, the flashlight, and the light beam for each trial *in your Journal.*

Analyzing

1. Make a statement that tells how light is reflected from a mirror.
2. What must you do to make the light beam change direction?
3. If you reversed the positions of the flashlight and the point at which the reflected beam strikes an object, how would the path of the light be affected?

Concluding and Applying

4. When might it be necessary to bounce light with mirrors? Name some situations in which a mirror would be more convenient than a light source.
5. ***Predict*** how you would arrange your flashlight and mirrors to get an image of the flashlight that would continue to be reflected from one mirror to the other. Write your prediction *in your Journal* and then try it.
6. **Going Further** Construct a periscope to see around corners or over fences using what you have learned in this activity. Draw a diagram to show how the light enters the periscope and reaches the viewer's eye.

Refraction

We started out this chapter by talking about how light always travels in straight lines. Now you've made light change direction by bouncing it off objects—by reflecting it. This doesn't mean that we were wrong. Light always does travel in straight lines, but you can change its direction.

Are there other ways to make light change direction besides reflection? You can find out for yourself in the next activity.

Explore! ACTIVITY

Why does light refract?

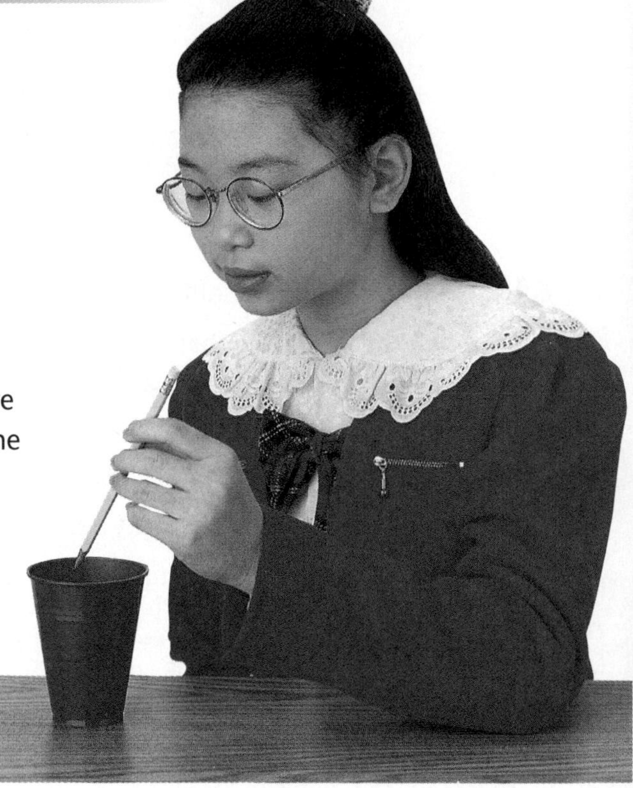

What To Do

1. Fill an opaque cup with water.
2. Place a pencil in the cup. The pencil should extend out of the water and the cup.
3. Stand directly over the cup and observe the pencil in the area where it leaves the water. What do you see?
4. Continue to observe the pencil and the water as you slowly back away from the cup. How does the pencil look now?
5. *In your Journal*, describe how the pencil appeared to change as you moved away from it.

Comparing and Contrasting

Compare and contrast reflection and refraction. Provide an example of each. If you need help, refer to the **Skill Handbook** on page 659.

In the Explore activity, you saw that your view of a pencil changed as you moved away from the water. We know that light changes speed as it moves through different substances. When light moves through water and then through air to your eyes it changes speed and direction. **Refraction** is the process of bending light when it passes from one material to another. Imagine a toy truck being pushed on a hard surface. The right wheels encounter a rug and the truck suddenly slows and turns to the right, toward the slower wheels. When light rays pass from one substance to another and change speed, they turn or bend like the toy truck. The light rays reflected from the pencil bent as they moved from the water to the air. They changed direction by changing the angle of the straight line. The light did not travel in a curved pathway.

Light travels in straight lines. You can change its direction by reflecting it with mirrors or refracting it by passing it through different materials. The way light reflects and refracts determines how you see the world.

Figure 2-7

A **The beam of light passing through this glass block refracts when it enters the glass and again when it leaves. Notice that the angle of the line in which the light travels has changed but the light still moves only in a straight line.**

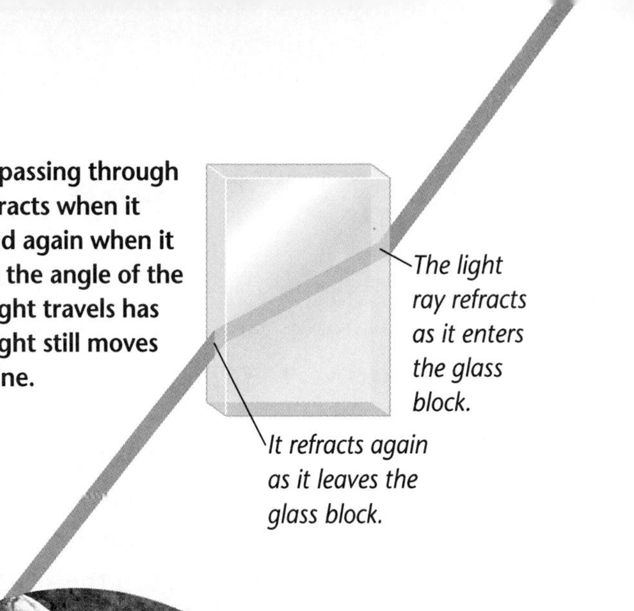

B **When you look at a fish through water, the light reflected from the fish changes direction as it moves from the water to the air. Your eyes, however, follow the light back as though it had traveled in a straight line. Refraction makes the fish appear closer to the surface than the fish really is.**

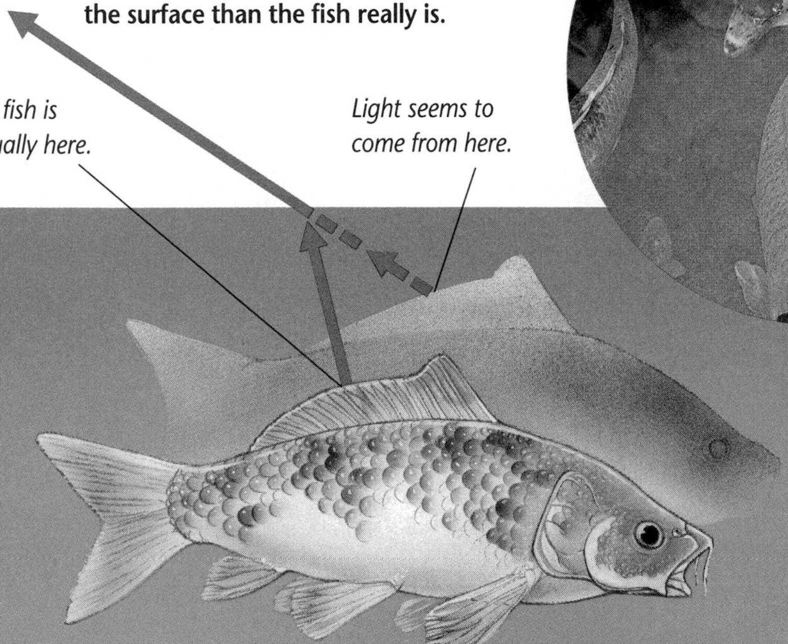

check your UNDERSTANDING

1. Draw diagrams showing how light is reflected from a dark, still pool of water and a rushing stream. Label the diagrams diffuse reflection and regular reflection.
2. Draw a diagram of light rays bending as they move from one material to another material.
3. Draw a diagram of how light would travel from a coin on the bottom of a swimming pool to your eyes if you were standing by the side of the pool.
4. **Apply** Draw a diagram showing how you might be able to see light from a room around a corner.

2-3 Color

Section Objectives

- Examine white (visible) light.
- Explain the difference between pigment color and light color.
- Describe the functions of the parts of the eye.
- Describe how light and color are sensed.

Key Terms

spectrum, retina, receptors, rods, cones

White Light

One morning, as you dress for school, you notice that your new green sweater does not look the same as it did in the store when you bought it. It's too late to change, so you wear it to school. Your classmates compliment you as soon as they see it. You look at your sweater and it looks different from the way it did at home! What's happening here? Shouldn't everything look the same when you see it in any light? Isn't all light white? Do the Explore activity to learn more about white light.

Explore! ACTIVITY

What colors are in sunlight or light from a light bulb?

What To Do

1. Place a prism between a light source and a piece of white paper.
2. Move the prism until you observe a spectrum of colors on the paper.
3. *In your Journal*, record the colors you observe. Make a sketch of what you see and label it.
4. What is white light made of?

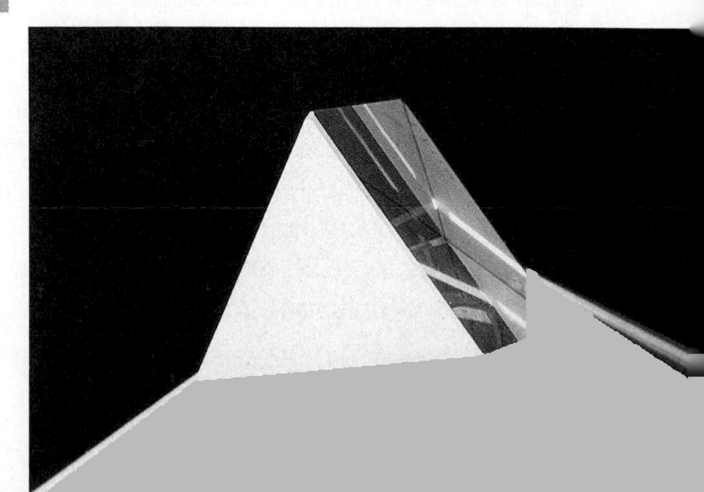

Figure 2-8

White light is a mixture of all colors of light. When white light passes through a prism, different colors are refracted different amounts. The different amounts of refraction separate the white light into a spectrum.

A Mixture of Lights

In the 1600s, Isaac Newton first observed and explained how a prism affects light in the way you've just seen. He proposed that white light is a mixture of all colors. He also showed that different colors of light bend differently—refract—as they pass through a prism, so they emerge as separate bands of color called a **spectrum**. Let's see what the spectrum tells us about the makeup of light. When Newton looked at the spectrum, he observed a pattern that had roughly seven colors, as seen in **Figure 2-9**.

Do the activity on the next page to find out what happens when colors of light combine.

Figure 2-9

When you look at the spectrum produced by passing white light through a prism, you probably see six or seven colors. The colors of the spectrum are often listed as red, orange, yellow, green, blue, indigo (violet-blue), and violet, but the actual number of colors perceived varies from person to person.

Find Out! ACTIVITY

How do lights mix?

You know that white light is made up of the colors you observed with the prism. When those colors combine, white light appears.

What To Do

1. Obtain three flashlights; three rubber bands; green, red, and blue cellophane; and white paper.
2. Fold the green cellophane into a square several layers thick and place it over the lens of one flashlight. Hold it in place with a rubber band.
3. Do the same with the other colors of cellophane and the other flashlights.
4. In a darkened room, shine all three flashlights onto the white paper to make three circles that overlap.

Conclude and Apply

1. What do you see where green and blue overlap? Green and red? Blue and red? All three?
2. Move just one flashlight closer to and farther away from the paper. How do the colors change? Move each of the other two flashlights. What happens?
3. *In your Journal,* draw and label a diagram showing one of the ways the lights mixed.

Why the Sky Is Blue and Sunsets Are Red

Rainbows are rare enough to be a new delight each time we see one. Reflection and refraction are responsible for their colorful effect. Think about the blue sky for a moment. Do you know what accounts for the blue color?

Rayleigh Scattering

The different colors we see in the sky are not caused by refraction. An effect known as Rayleigh scattering scatters sunlight to produce the colors. Gas molecules in the atmosphere scatter blue light from the sun.

Mixing Colors with Lights

Were your results similar to what is shown in **Figure 2-10**? Blue plus green made a shade of blue called cyan, blue plus red made a shade of red called magenta, and red plus green made yellow. Where all three colors of light mixed, you got white. How did you get white with only three colors?

If you could combine the three colored lights, each with just the right brightness, you would be able to produce every color of the spectrum. Red, blue, and green light are called the primary colors of light.

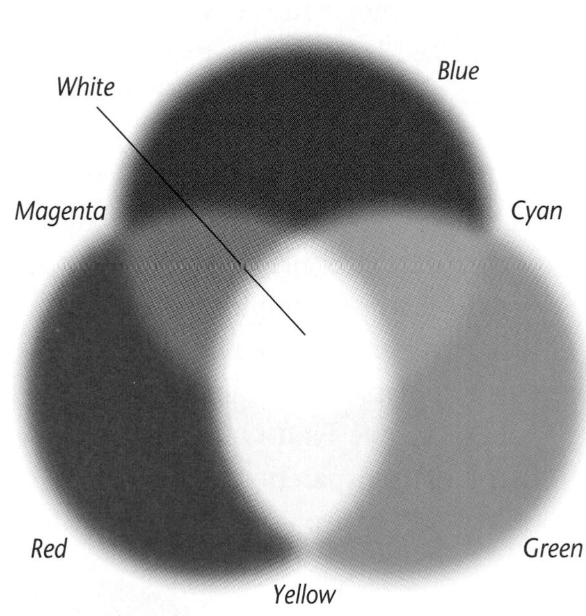

Figure 2-10

White light is produced when the three primary colors of light—red, green, and blue—are mixed.

Green and yellow scatter very little, and orange and red light scatter even less in the upper atmosphere. You can see this when the sun is high in the sky by comparing the sky nearer the sun to the sky farther away. The sky is whiter near the sun because you are looking at an area that contains all colors. The sky farther away has more scattered blue light, which is reflected to our eyes by dust particles and water droplets.

Sunrise and Sunset

At sunrise and sunset, light from the sun passes through more of the atmosphere close to Earth's surface. This layer of the lower atmosphere contains particles that scatter sunlight even more effectively. Blue and violet light and some of the green and yellow light scatter so well that only red and orange light are left to reach our eyes. If you look at the sky farther away from the sun, you can still see the scattered blue and violet light.

You Try It!

Make a simple model of the atmosphere. Fill a clear glass with water and add two to five drops of whole milk. Darken the room and shine a flashlight through the glass. What color do you see coming through the glass? Look at the light coming out of the top of the glass. It has been scattered (reflected away) by the milk particles. What color is it?

Light Filters

The color you see when light hits an object depends on which colors are reflected and which ones are absorbed. The paper on this page reflects all colors, so you see white. The ink on the page absorbs all colors, so you see it as black. Any colors you see in the photographs depend on the color of light reflected from them.

Sunglasses, like the colored cellophane in the Find Out activity, are a type of transparent material called a filter. Filters may be transparent for one or more colors of light. These colors pass through the filters, but the other colors are absorbed. The color of the filter is the color of light that passes through it.

Imagine it's a sunny day, so you put on your sunglasses. Your sunglasses absorb certain colors of light and allow other colors to pass through like the filters in **Figure 2-11**. Everything you observe through your sunglasses is seen in the colors of light that pass through your sunglasses.

Figure 2-11

These gym shoes and socks are seen under white light.

A White objects reflect all colors equally, so they appear to be the color of the light falling on them. The shoes and socks are viewed through a red filter.

B These shoes and socks are viewed through a blue filter. How do they appear now?

Mixing Colors with Pigments

A blue that you see produced from mixing paints and a blue that you see from mixing lights may appear exactly the same to your eyes. However, two very different processes produced the same blue. Paints are examples of pigments—materials that absorb some colors and reflect others. You can make any pigment color by mixing different amounts of the three primary pigments of yellow, magenta, and cyan. A primary pigment's color depends on the color it reflects.

The key to understanding why mixing colored pigments is different from mixing colored lights lies in a very simple fact. When you mix lights, you are adding different light to the mixture. When you mix pigments, in a way, you are taking different colors away from the mixture. More colors of light are actually being absorbed, and not reflected for you to see. **Figure 2-10** shows what happens when you mix colored lights. Compare it with **Figure 2-12**, which shows what happens when you mix pigments. What do you see?

Mix colored lights, and the resulting colors are lighter because they're closer to white—there are more different colors in the mix. If you mix pigments, the resulting colors are closer to black because they absorbed more colors of light—fewer different colors are reflected to your eyes. But, just as you can dim and brighten three primary colored lights to produce any color, you can mix primary pigments in unequal amounts to produce any color. The results are the same—you can create the entire spectrum. All paint colors are produced by mixing only a small number of pigments.

Figure 2-12

The three primary colors of pigment appear black when they are mixed.

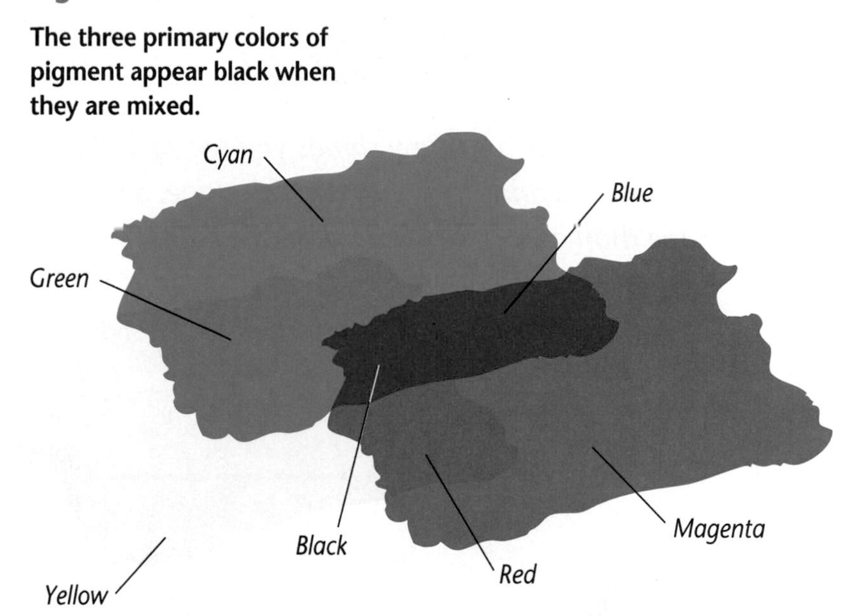

Our eyes are most sensitive to the color yellow-green. That's why the preferred color for new emergency vehicles, such as fire trucks, is yellow-green.

Figure 2-13

A variety of colors can be produced by mixing just two of the primary pigments. If you start with yellow and add magenta, a bit at a time, each addition will produce a new color.

DESIGN YOUR OWN
INVESTIGATION

Seeing Colors

Think about the many things you see each day—flowers, the sky, the words and the photos on this page. Some things are easier to see than others, depending on the light, how far away from you it is, and the color.

Preparation

Problem

Which colors are easiest for human eyes to see? If you want the letter M to stand out from a given distance, does the color of the letter and the background affect your ability to see it?

Form a Hypothesis

Look at the photos on this page, then decide on a hypothesis predicting the easiest single color and combination of colors to see from a long distance.

Objectives

- Observe what color is easiest for most people to identify from a long distance.
- Compare and contrast color combinations for ease of identifying letters at a distance.
- Demonstrate that letters are easier to read against certain color backgrounds.

Materials

scissors
glue, tape, or paper clips
posterboard and art paper of various colors including black and white

Safety Precautions

Be careful when using scissors.

DESIGN YOUR OWN

INVESTIGATION

Plan the Experiment

1. Look at the posterboard and paper. As a group decide what colors you will test for your hypothesis.
2. Discuss the best way to test your hypothesis, then write a procedure for the experiment. Make certain that colors are compared under the same conditions of distance and light.
3. Design a data table *in your Science Journal* or on a word-processing program.
4. Determining which color or colors are easiest to identify is a judgment. Most people will agree on the easiest color to see, but perhaps not everyone. To make your data more reliable, you need to test each color more than once. Ten people determining which color is easiest to identify gives stronger information than one person determining that color.

Check the Plan

1. Make certain your data table is designed to record each individual test.
2. Before you start the experiment, have your teacher approve your plan.
3. Carry out your experiment. Make observations and record your data.

Analyze and Conclude

1. **Interpret Data** Was your hypothesis supported by the data? Use your data to explain why or why not.
2. **Use Numbers** In each experiment, add up and record the number of times a specific color was chosen as the easiest to see from a long distance away. What percentage of the time was this color chosen? Percentages are figured by dividing the number of times chosen by the total number of trials. Then multiply by one hundred and add a percent sign. Use your calculator.
3. **Use Numbers** Find what percentage of the time the most easily seen combination of colors was chosen in the tests.
4. **Interpret Data** Using the percentages found in the questions above, write a conclusion about which colors and color combinations are easiest to see.

Going Further

If you were designing a sign to be seen easily at a distance, what colors would you choose? Use your data to explain your choice.

Light and Pigments Together

Figure 2-14

A An object's color can change depending on the light you see it in. The walls of this experiment box, lit here by white light, appear blue, yellow, red, and white.

B Lit by red light, the same walls appear purple, orange, red, and pink.

The Investigate you just finished shows that the color of an object is determined by the light shining on it. Objects merely absorb or reflect certain colors of light or allow certain colors to pass through. Our idea of what something looks like depends upon the light we see it by.

Remember the sweater we talked about at the beginning of this section? The color looked different depending on where you were. The color of the light source determined the color you saw. Look at **Figure 2-14** to compare the same colors in different lights.

Life Science CONNECTION

Natural Dyes

The bright colors in the fabrics that your clothes are made from are usually created by using synthetic dyes. Long before these dyes existed, however, people dyed fabrics with natural dyes.

To dye natural fabrics such as cotton, linen, silk, and wool, you can use strong solutions made by boiling vegetables such as beets or spinach, parts of plants such as tea leaves or wildflowers, and barks of various trees. The shades will vary depending on the strength of the dye solution, the soil in which the plant grew, whether fresh or dried plant parts were used, and the way the fabric was treated before it was dyed.

Beets

The colors from natural dyes are not as bright as those from chemical dyes. They are much softer—often described as "earth tones."

Here are some of the colors you can get from common plants:

reds: oregano leaves, tea leaves, beet roots, fruits of the lipstick tree

Your Eyes

Light enters your eye through an opening called the pupil, a black spot in the middle of the eye, that looks like a small hole. It is really the entrance to a fluid-filled chamber inside the eye.

The colored area around the pupil is the iris. This ring of tiny muscles usually contains some blue or brown pigment. The iris muscles control the size of the pupil according to the amount of light available.

In bright light, the iris muscles contract and make the pupil smaller. This limits the amount of light entering the eye. In dim light, the iris muscles relax. The pupil enlarges, allowing more light to enter the eye. The light that enters your eye passes through the lens, a structure that focuses the light on the retina at the back of your eye. The lens changes its shape as your eyes focus on objects near and far away. The **retina** is a tissue that is sensitive to light. Your eyes can detect all kinds of colors and shapes, lights and shadows, because of the retina. Your eyes can be compared to two cameras, always taking pictures.

Connect to...
Life Science

Cats have excellent vision in dim light but they cannot distinguish colors very well. Investigate how a cat's eye might be different from your eye.

Onions

Spinach

yellow: barberry stems and roots, goldenrod blooms, saffron crocus blooms, onion skins
violet: hibiscus flowers, oregano leaves
blue: cornflowers, hollyhock flowers, wild indigo branches
green: onion skins, sorrel leaves, spinach leaves, dyer's broom tops
brown: hibiscus flowers, juniper berries, tea leaves
gray: blackberry shoots
black: barberry leaves, yellow dock roots

Before dyeing a fabric, it must be treated with a mordant, a dye-setting compound. Without a mordant, the fabric's color would easily wash or fade away. Alum, ammonia, and vinegar are mordants.

You Try It!

Make your own dye.

1. Use from one-half to one cup of leaves or flowers of the plants listed.
2. Place the plants in a plastic bag and crush them with your fingers.
3. Place the crushed plants in one cup of water and heat the water to a gentle boil. Simmer gently until most of the color has been removed from the plants.
4. Cool the mixture, filter it, and collect the liquid.
5. Cut two pieces of worn cotton fabric. Soak one piece in vinegar, wring it out, and allow it to dry.
6. Place both pieces of fabric into the dye. Stir until the fabric absorbs the color.
7. Wring out the fabric and allow them to dry. Then try washing them. Does the color come out?

How You See Color

The retinas in your eyes contain two different kinds of light-sensitive structures. These structures, or light **receptors**, respond to changes in light and color. **Rods** are receptors that are sensitive to light and dark. You see black-and-white images when the rods in your retina are stimulated by dim light. **Cones** are receptors that are sensitive to all the colors in the visible spectrum of light. You have three types of cones, referred to as red, green, and blue cones. Different colors of light will cause different combinations of cones to respond to them. The combination of these three types of cones lets you see the entire spectrum. You see color images when the cones in your retina are stimulated by color and bright light. Because color-blind people lack one or more kinds of these cones, they see colors differently, as shown in **Figure 2-16.**

Figure 2-15

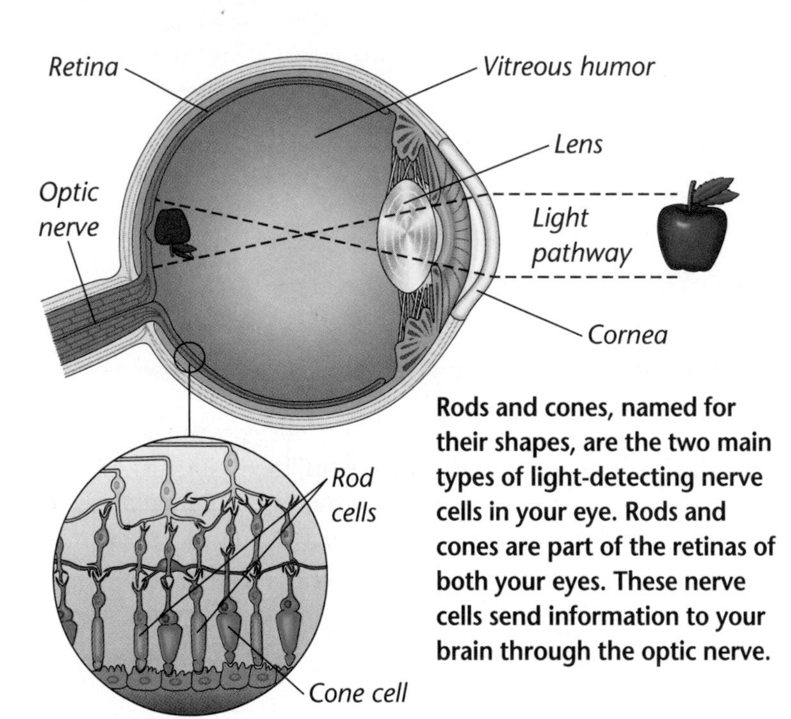

Rods and cones, named for their shapes, are the two main types of light-detecting nerve cells in your eye. Rods and cones are part of the retinas of both your eyes. These nerve cells send information to your brain through the optic nerve.

■ Night Vision

Have you noticed that you don't see colors very well at night, or any time the light is dim? This is because cones, the color receptors in your retina, are not very sensitive to dim light. The light entering your eyes must be fairly bright before you can see colors. Rods

A The rods in your retina are most sensitive to light and dark.

B Red cones respond primarily to red and yellow light.

C Green cones respond primarily to green and yellow light.

D Blue cones react primarily to blue and violet light.

E Your brain works to combine all this information into a single image made up of both black-and-white and color images.

How Do We Know?

Three kinds of cones

In the middle 1960s, scientists showed for the first time that individual cone receptors of the eye react best to different light colors. Using a device that measures the amount of light absorbed by a tiny object, they found that single cone receptors absorbed more light of one color than light of other colors. They reasoned that if a cone absorbed light of a certain color, then that color would cause a reaction in the cone. By repeating the experiment on many different cones from the eye, they found that all cones can be classified into only three groups. One group absorbs blue light best, another absorbs green light best, and the third absorbs red. We now call these the blue, green, and red cones of the eye. These three kinds of cones are all we have and all we need to see all the colors of the spectrum.

are much more sensitive to dim light.

The rods and cones in the retinas of both your eyes send information to your brain through a large nerve at the back of the retina. Your brain interprets the information as images and color.

How important is light and color to your life? Think about the different things you look at every day. Imagine what your life would be like without your vision. In the next chapter, you will learn about sound and your sense of hearing.

Figure 2-16

Color-blind people lack one or more of the three kinds of cones and cannot distinguish all colors. Color patterns like these are used to test for color blindness.

A People who cannot distinguish the difference between blue and yellow cannot see the 5 in the first pattern to the right.

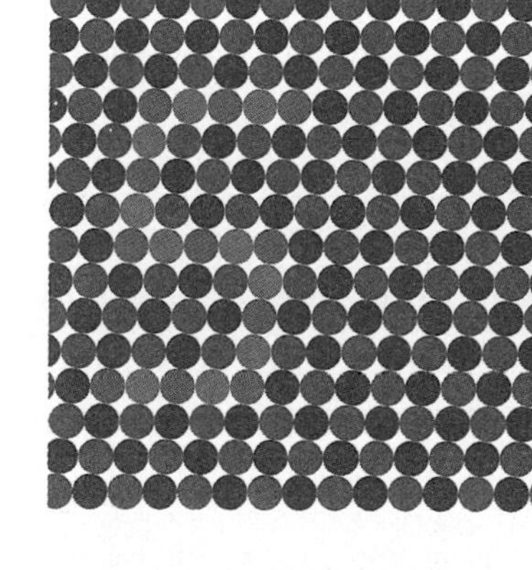

B People who cannot distinguish between red and green cannot see the 5 and 3 in the second pattern below.

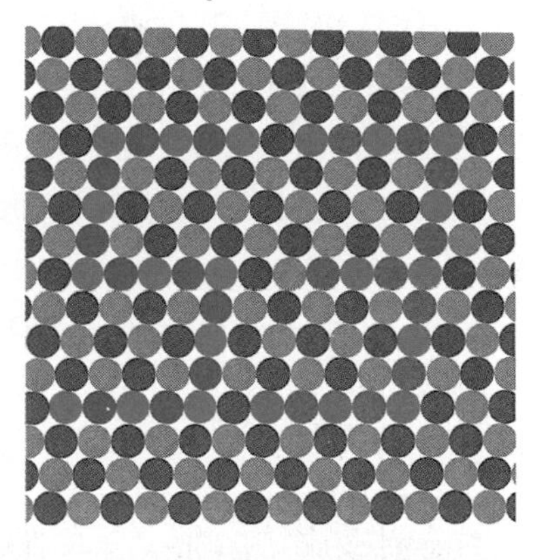

check your UNDERSTANDING

1. What colors make up white light?
2. What is the difference between red pigment and red light?
3. Name each part of the eye and describe its function in allowing you to read the words on this page.
4. What color would you see if all types of cones in your eyes were strongly stimulated?
5. **Apply** What color would you see if you mixed yellow and blue light? Why? Yellow and blue pigments? Why?

Science and Society

Light and Color in Our Lives

Most of the time, we just take light for granted. More and more, researchers are finding that light is necessary for our mental and physical well-being. Light can affect how we feel about our surroundings, how we feel about others, and how well we do our work.

Performance

While people respond differently, in general researchers have found that the brighter the room, the better the performance. Brightness generally seems to improve performance until the light reaches the point of glare. At this point, people tend to feel tired, irritable, or bored.

Sound Level

The brightness of light also affects the sound level of conversation. When people enter a brightly lit room, they tend to gather in larger groups, while dimmer rooms lend themselves to smaller groups and quieter conversations.

Health

During the dark hours of the night, the brains of animals and humans secrete a chemical, melatonin, which affects many of the body's functions, including temperature and mood. During the fall and winter, there are more hours of darkness and, therefore, more melatonin is produced. This causes some people to feel very tired and sometimes depressed. One form of this condition is known as Seasonal Affective Disorder (SAD).

Artificial Daylight

The symptoms of SAD are treated by having the patient sit under very bright light—about three times brighter than normal—for several hours early in the morning. This seems to change the body's rhythms and makes the patient feel better.

Color

Color also has important effects on the way we feel and on our actions. Colors like orange tend to make us feel more active and may affect the amount that we eat. Blue is a more calming color.

Science Journal

In your Science Journal, compare the mood created by the lighting and colors used in different stores or restaurants.

Seeing Things Differently

If you look closely at the petals of a rose, you will see that what appears from a distance to be a solid color is actually made up of many colors. The pink rose petals may have specks of red, blue, white, or yellow in them.

Impressionists

Early painters tried to copy their subjects exactly. They wanted the pink rose in the painting to look exactly like the pink rose on the bush. During the 1870s and 1880s, a group of artists decided that they were more interested in the impression of a rose than its exact look. As a result, they were called Impressionists.

These artists used color to reach their goals. They did not give objects firm outlines or fill in large areas of their canvasses with solid colors as others had done. Instead, they noticed that when they looked at a rose or a person, there were not distinct outlines, but a gradual blending of colors as one shade touched another. They showed the light as it affected colors, so that sometimes the same pink rose was pale, other times very vivid.

Monet

Claude Monet was one of the best-known Impressionist painters. He is famous for his ability to show how light played among the flowers in his garden. He painted many pictures of the same flowers in the same place, but they were all different, depending on the angle of the sun, the time of day, and the season of the year. One of Monet's paintings entitled *Water Lilies* is shown here.

The paintings of the Impressionists are very valuable today, and people consider them some of the most beautiful art ever created. Although they do not contain every detail of their subject, the paintings do give an "impression" of the subject that includes the feelings that the artist had about the subject.

You Try It!

Look out the window or go outside and look at an area of trees, grass, and flowers. Do you see every detail in the landscape? Do you see every vein in the leaves or cracks in the tree bark? Or do you get an "impression" of the scene?

Infrared Astronomy

One of the newer techniques for learning about the universe is infrared astronomy. Visible light is part of an energy spectrum that includes X rays near the high energy end and radio waves near the low energy end. Infrared radiation has less energy than visible light but more than radio waves. Most infrared radiation coming from space is absorbed by water vapor and carbon dioxide in Earth's atmosphere, but certain wavelengths pass through and can be detected.

Problems

One problem with studying infrared radiation on Earth is that Earth, and the instruments themselves, emit infrared radiation. Infrared telescopes are set up at high altitudes to avoid detecting Earth's infrared radiation and to avoid interference from Earth's atmosphere.

Using infrared detectors in space can solve problems with Earth's radiation and atmospheric interference, and cooling the instruments to extremely low temperatures ends the problem of the equipment's own radiation.

Ms. Adriana Ocampo, a scientist working at the Jet Propulsion Laboratory, works with the Near-Infrared Mapping Spectrometer (NIMS), a device that detects infrared radiation from objects in space and maps the radiation using computer technology.

Ms. Ocampo's NIMS is being used within our own solar system by the space probe *Galileo,* which was launched in 1989. *Galileo* arrived at Jupiter in December of 1995, where it will remain through 1997. NIMS is being used to study the atmosphere and surface chemistry of Jupiter and its satellites.

Ms. Ocampo is a planetary geologist. She utilizes NIMS data to study the makeup and development over time of the surfaces of Jupiter's moons.

Use the World Wide Web to find infrared images at NASA's Jet Propulsion Laboratory (JPL). How might such data on planetary atmospheres and temperatures be used?

chapter 2
REVIEWING MAIN IDEAS

Science Journal

Review the statements below about the big ideas presented in this chapter, and answer the questions. Then, reread your answers to the Did You Ever Wonder questions at the beginning of the chapter. *In your Science Journal,* write a paragraph about how your understanding of the big ideas in the chapter has changed.

1 When light hits an object, the light is reflected, absorbed, or passes through the object. The object may reflect some colors, absorb others, and still let others pass through. ***How do you know that a material is translucent?***

2 When light moves from one kind of material to another, the light changes speed, which causes it to refract. ***Explain how refraction affects what your eyes see when you observe an object that is underwater.***

3 White light (or visible light) is a combination of three main colors of light—red, blue, and green. How you see color depends on the combination of light and pigment. ***What colors of light will yellow pigment reflect when viewed in white light?***

4 Light reflected from an object enters your eye and strikes the light-sensitive retina. Here rods react to light and dark and cones react to color. Your brain combines the information into one visual image of the object. ***Why do some people see colors differently from other people?***

chapter 2

CHAPTER REVIEW

Using Key Science Terms

cone
opaque
receptor
reflection
refraction
retina
rod
spectrum
translucent
transparent

An analogy is a relationship between two pairs of words generally written in the following manner: a:b::c:d. The symbol :: is read "as." For example, cat:animal::rose:plant is read "cat is to animal as rose is to plant." In the analogies that follow, a word is missing. Complete each analogy by providing the missing word from the list above.

1. window:wall::transparent: ________
2. notes:musical scale::colors: ________
3. cellophane:transparent::waxed paper: ________
4. mirror:reflection::prism: ________

Understanding Ideas

Answer the following questions in your Journal *using complete sentences.*

1. Why does blocking a light source with an object produce a shadow?
2. What three things can happen when light hits an object?
3. Explain the difference between a regular reflection and a diffuse reflection.
4. Describe the functions of cones and rods.
5. How do the processes of producing colors by mixing paints and mixing lights differ?

Developing Skills

Use your understanding of the concepts developed in this chapter to answer each of the following questions.

1. **Concept Mapping** Using the following events, complete the sequence concept map of how you see: *Light is focused on the retinas. Light enters the pupils of your eyes. Information is sent through a nerve to your brain. Your brain uses this information to make the images you see. The light passes through the lenses of your eyes.*

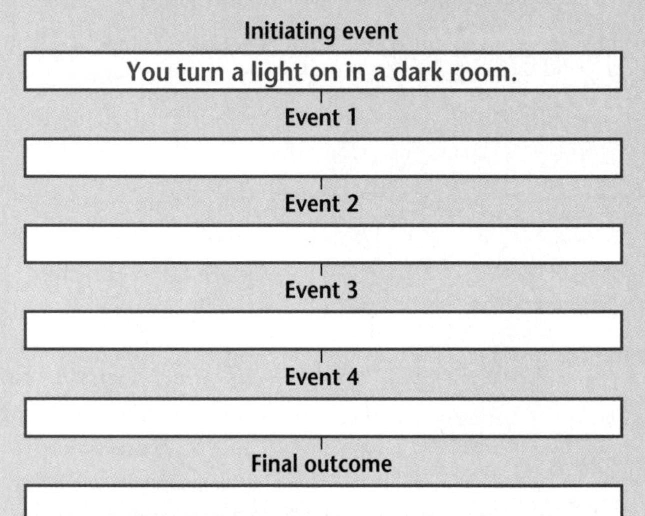

2. **Observing and Inferring** Use the index cards and flashlight from the Find Out activity on page 55 and investigate how far a flashlight will shine. Dim the lights in the classroom. Increase the distance between the flashlight and the cards and then between the cards themselves. How far did the flashlight shine? Think about how far light can travel.

chapter 2
CHAPTER REVIEW

Critical Thinking

In your Journal, *answer each of the following questions.*

1. Imagine that you have one lamp with a small, bright bulb. You'd like to avoid a harsh glare on your paper. What might you do?
2. Sylvia did an experiment in which she shone different colored lights on an object that had been placed in front of white paper. Below are her data and observations. What color was the object? What else do you know about the object?

Data and Observations

Color of light	Color of object	Cast a shadow
yellow	yellow	yes
green	green	yes
red	red	yes

3. Explain how a stained glass window can absorb light, reflect light, and/or let light pass through. Based on your answer, tell what parts of the window are opaque, translucent, or transparent.

Problem Solving

Read the following problem and discuss your answers in a brief paragraph.

The new member of the drama club lighting crew was beside himself. The director of the play wanted two more spots of light on the set. He wanted more white light on the stage and a spot of yellow light on the backdrop. But only six lights were available. Two had permanent red filters in place, two had permanent blue filters, and two had permanent green filters. The crew member asked the lighting chief. She told him an easy way to solve the problem.

1. How would you make more white light?
2. How would you make a spot of yellow light on the backdrop?

CONNECTING IDEAS

Discuss each of the following in a brief paragraph.

1. **Theme—Systems and Interactions** How does a flashlight use reflection? Look closely at the parts of a flashlight. You may want to take it apart and examine them.
2. **Theme—Scale and Structure** Name two opaque things, two transparent things, and two translucent things in the room with you now.
3. **Theme—Systems and Interactions** What would absorb more sunlight—a white piece of plastic or a black piece of plastic?
4. **A Closer Look** Recall that a prism breaks up light into the colors of the spectrum. What do you think is acting like a prism in the case of a rainbow?
5. **Science and Society** Auditoriums and theaters often dim the lights before a performance begins. Why do you think this is done?

CHAPTER 3

Sound and Hearing

Did you ever wonder...

- **If you could hear sounds on the moon?**
- **Why you make a sound when you blow into a soft drink bottle?**
- **Why the different strings on a stringed instrument produce different sounds?**

Science Journal

Before you begin to study about sound and hearing, think about these questions and answer them *in your Science Journal.* When you finish the chapter, compare your journal write-up with what you have learned.

Today is moving day. Welcome to your new home! As you unpack, you hear a dog yapping next door. Someone turns a stereo up, and you hear your favorite song. A voice calls out, "Randy, please turn that down," and suddenly you can barely hear the music. Now you hear the whine of an electric saw, the pounding of a hammer, and the roar of traffic.

You've learned a bit about your new neighborhood before you've even had a chance to look around. You know that there is a dog next door, someone named Randy likes the same music you do, carpenters are working on your block, and a busy street is close by.

How did you discover all this? Simply by listening.

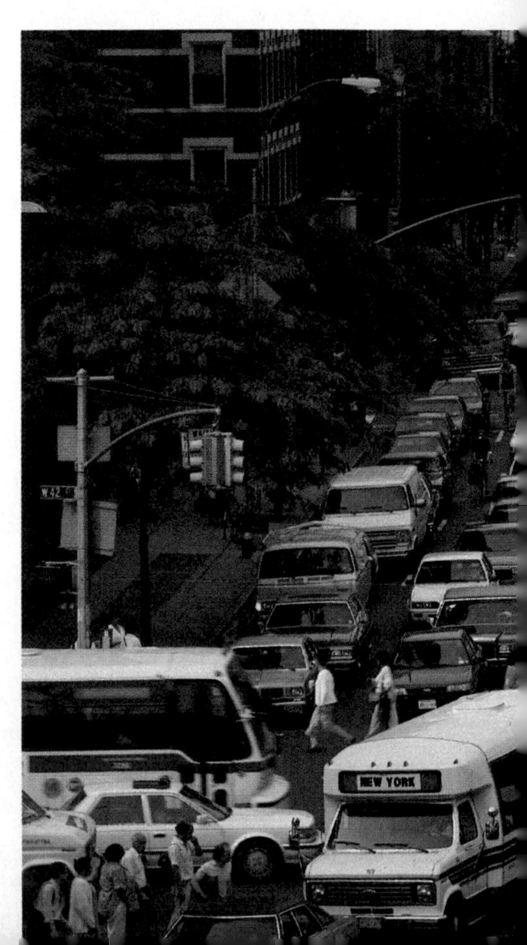

In this chapter, you'll find out what all sounds have in common, and how you are able to distinguish one sound from another.

Explore! ACTIVITY

How are sounds produced?

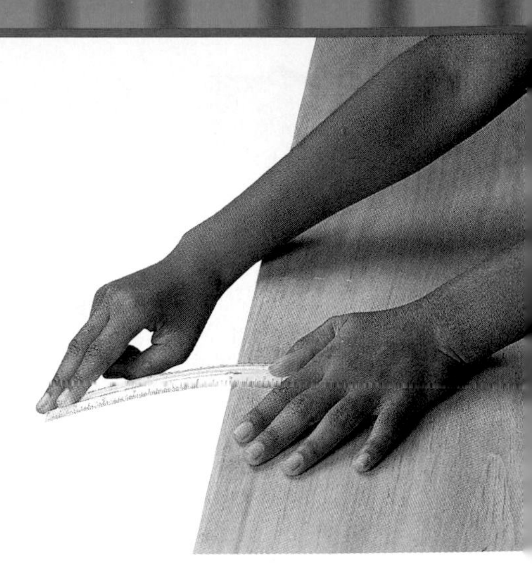

When you hear a sound, you are actually sensing the vibrations of your eardrums.

What To Do

1. Place a wooden ruler on a desk so that more than half of the ruler extends over the edge of the desk.
2. Use one hand to hold the ruler firmly against the desk. With the other hand, snap the free end of the ruler so it vibrates up and down.
3. *In your Journal*, describe what you see and hear.

Sources of Sound

Section Objectives
- Recognize that sounds are created by vibrations.
- Distinguish between compression and rarefaction.
- Describe the way sound travels through matter.

Key Terms
compression
rarefaction
medium

Vibrations Produce Sound

What sounds did you hear on your way to school this morning? The growling engine and squeaking brakes of a school bus? The roar of traffic as you walked along the street? A radio blaring from a neighbor's open window? Did you notice the sound of your own footsteps or the wind blowing past your ears? We hear so many different sounds all the time that we aren't usually aware of all of them. Sit quietly for a minute and listen to the sounds around you. What do you hear right now?

Figure 3-1

The harp, like all stringed instruments, makes sound when a player causes its taut strings to vibrate.

Sound and Matter

Your ears allow you to recognize many different sounds, but do you know what these sounds have in common? All sounds are produced by vibrating objects. When you did the Explore activity at the beginning of this chapter, you created a sound by making the ruler vibrate up and down rapidly. Vibrations are very quick, back-and-forth motions repeated over and over again. You could see the ruler vibrate, and those vibrations made a sound you could hear.

Here is an activity that will give you some clues about what sound is and how it travels through matter to your ears.

Find Out! ACTIVITY

How does sound travel through matter?

Vibrations produce sound. But what is sound and how does it travel through matter to reach your ears?

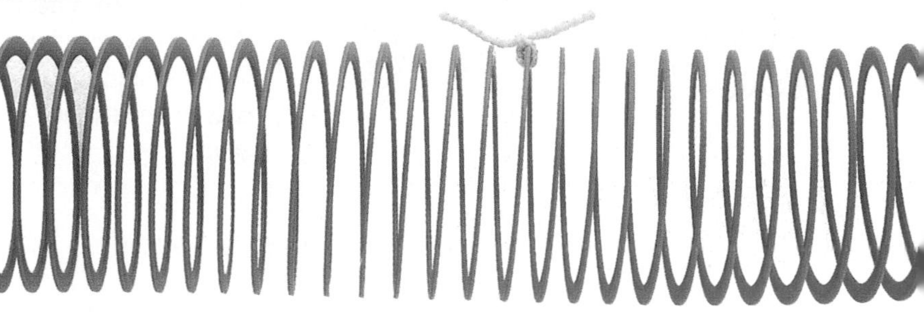

What To Do

1. Working with a partner, obtain a coiled spring and a small piece of colored string.
2. With your partner, put the coiled spring on the floor and stretch it to a length of at least 2 meters. Make sure all of the coils are about the same distance apart.
3. With one hand, squeeze together about 15 or 20 of the coils near you and observe what happens to the unsqueezed coils.
4. Release the bunched coils.
5. Quickly push your end of the coiled spring toward your partner, then pull it back to its original position.
6. Repeat the motion several times. Vary the speed.
7. Hold your end of the spring steady while your partner does the pushing.
8. Now, tie the colored string to one of the coils. Repeat the experiment and observe the string.

Conclude and Apply

1. *In your Journal*, draw what happens when you squeeze the coils.
2. Describe what happens when you push and pull the spring.
3. What happens to the string as the spring moves?

Figure 3-2

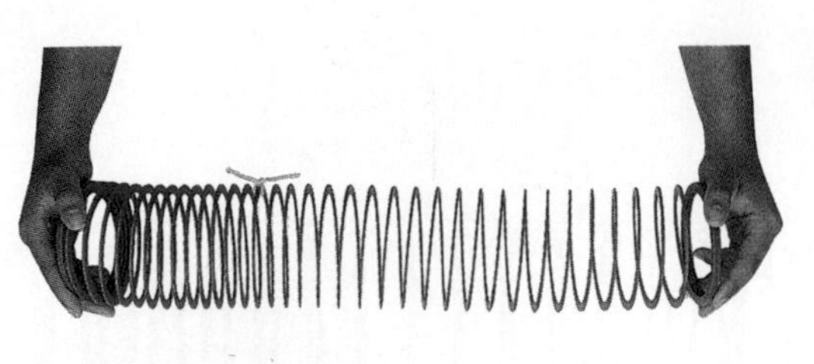

A When you pushed against the coiled spring, the coils near the string were close together and the other coils were farther apart.

B The pattern of squeezed and stretched coils was transmitted down the length of the spring.

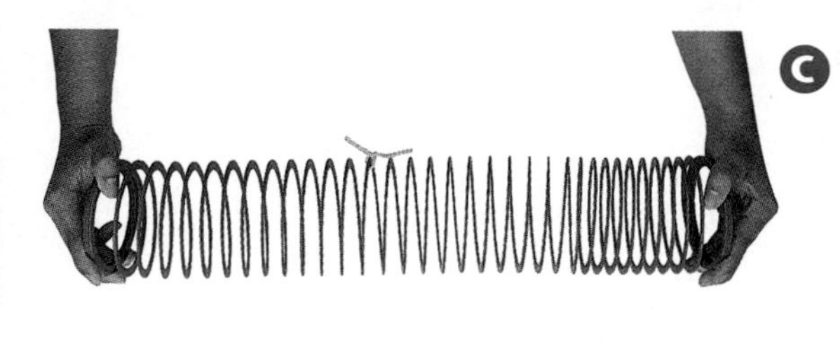

C The string did not travel with the pattern. The coils, unlike the pattern, did not travel the length of the spring. Each coil moved only slightly forward and then back to its original position.

In the Find Out activity, you created a pattern that moved down the length of the coiled spring. **Figure 3-2** shows how the pattern looks.

■ Compression and Rarefaction

Air is made up of particles so tiny you cannot see them. When everything is quiet, these air particles are about the same average distance apart, just like the coils of the stretched out spring.

A vibrating object pushes air particles just as your hand pushed the coiled spring. The vibrations create a pattern of bunched-up and spread-out particles that moves through the air. The pattern spreads out from the object in all directions. The part of the pattern with bunched-up particles is called the area of **compression**. The part with spread-out particles is called the area of **rarefaction**. **Figure 3-3** shows how a vibrating ruler affects the air particles around it.

Figure 3-3

A When the ruler vibrates upward or downward, it pushes the particles of air in front of its movement closer together—forming an area of compression.

B At the same time, the air particles on the opposite side of the ruler spread farther apart—forming an area of rarefaction.

C As the ruler vibrates up and down, it creates a pattern of compressions and rarefactions that travels through the air to your ear.

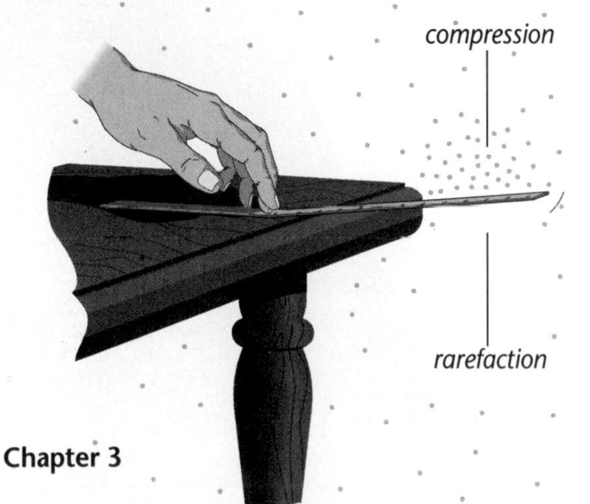

Sound Requires a Medium

Vibrations produce sound by creating patterns of compression and rarefaction. Any solid, liquid, or gas that carries the pattern of sound is called the **medium** for that sound. For sound, the medium is the matter between the vibrating object and your eardrum. The medium conducts the sound to your ears. The sounds you hear almost always come to your ears through the medium of air, which is a gas.

Have you ever listened to sounds under water or put your ear against a wall or the ground to try to hear something more clearly? In the Find Out activity you can investigate how sound travels through other materials.

Connect to... Life Science

Dolphins and porpoises make and analyze reflected sounds to communicate and locate prey. This is called echolocation. Make a diagram illustrating how dolphins produce and receive sounds.

Find Out! ACTIVITY

Can sound travel through string?

Air isn't the only kind of matter that sound can travel through.

What To Do

1. Tie about 50 cm of string to each end of a metal coat hanger.
2. Wrap the other ends of the string around each index finger.
3. Gently swing the hanger so the hook taps against a table or chair. Listen for the sound it makes.
4. Place your index fingers with the string attached in your ears and tap the hanger again.

Conclude and Apply

1. Which is a better conductor of sound, air or the string and your fingers?
2. Predict how a wire in place of the string would conduct sound.

Figure 3-4

The alarm goes off but no sound is heard. Explain what has happened.

As you saw in the Find Out activity, sound also travels through solids. Sound travels faster through liquids and solids than through gases.

One reason liquids and solids conduct sound better than air is that sound travels through them much faster than it travels through air. **Figure 3-5** shows the speed of sound through various materials.

Sound and a Vacuum

If you clapped your hands on the moon, you would make absolutely no sound. Why not? Because the moon has no atmosphere. There is no air through which sound can travel. There is no medium to carry the vibration patterns.

In a famous experiment shown in **Figure 3-4**, a clock's alarm is set to go off. The clock is placed on a piece of thick felt and covered with a glass dome. When the alarm rings, you hear it even though the sound is muffled by the felt and the glass cover. The experiment is repeated, but this time the air is pumped from the glass dome. The alarm goes off but you hear no sound. Why? There is no air inside the glass to carry the sound. Why is the piece of felt necessary in this experiment? Felt is used to muffle any sound that would be carried by the table.

Life Science CONNECTION

Sounds Are All Around You

Your ears are very sensitive instruments. They pick up many more sounds than you're aware of because your brain does such a good job of blocking out what you don't need to hear. Unless you make a conscious effort to listen to all the sounds around you, you may have no idea that many of them are there.

Take a moment just to listen. What do you hear? What about the sounds outside? Imagine how hard it would be to concentrate in noisy places like the subway station pictured here, if you always noticed every sound around you.

Because your senses are constantly bombarded with all sorts of information, your brain needs a way to tune out some of it. Otherwise you couldn't concentrate.

Figure 3-5

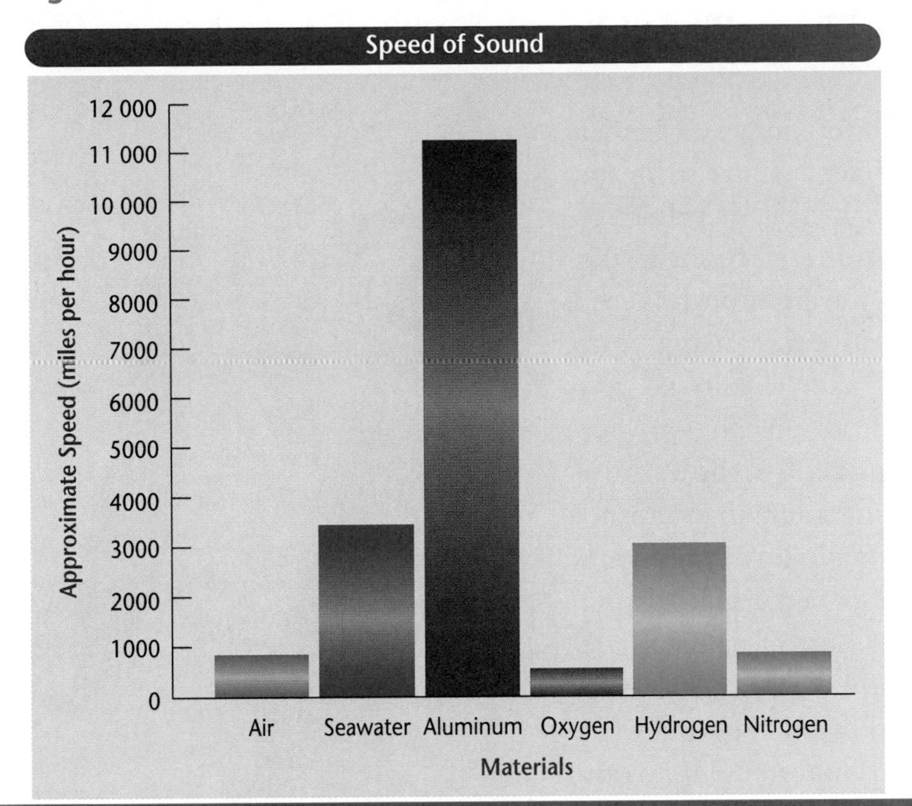

SKILLBUILDER

Making and Using Graphs

Use the information in **Figure 3-5** to answer these questions. If you need help, refer to the **Skill Handbook** on page 657.

1. Which material conducts sound fastest?
2. Which material conducts sound most slowly?
3. What is the speed of sound through aluminum?
4. Air is made up of many gases, including oxygen and nitrogen. How can you relate this information to the sizes of the bars on the graph for these materials?

RAS

An area in your brain called the reticular activating system (RAS) sorts out all the information your senses provide. The RAS is a network of nerve cells deep within your brain stem at the top of your spinal cord. It helps you focus your attention on specific sounds while tuning out all the others.

The RAS regulates your level of awareness by screening the messages from your senses and passing on only what seems important or unusual. For instance, your RAS helps you ignore the sound of lockers slamming in the hallway to concentrate on what your teacher says. And when a fire alarm goes off in that same hallway, your RAS automatically puts that message through.

Science Journal

Write a paragraph *in your Science Journal* that describes the sounds you hear in the morning when you wake up and the sounds you hear right before you fall asleep at night. What do these sounds tell you about your environment and the activities that are going on?

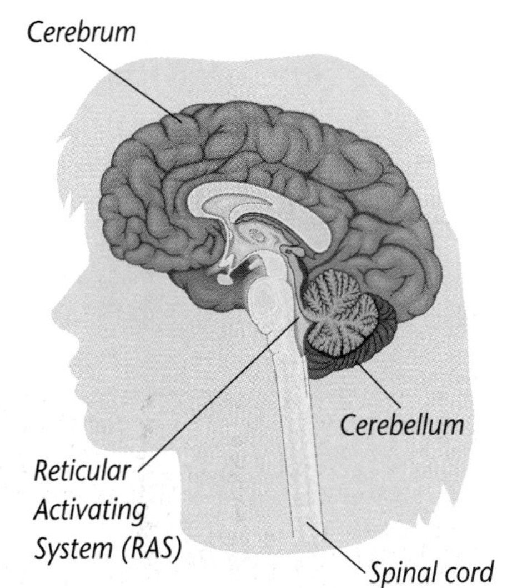

How You Hear Sound

When an object vibrates, whether it's a vibrating ruler, a guitar string, or your vocal cords, it creates a pattern of compressions and rarefactions in the air. The pattern travels through the air particles to your ear, causing your eardrum to vibrate. The sound you hear is really the air pushing on your eardrums. **Figure 3-6** shows how vibrations become sound in your ears.

When you made observations in Chapter 1, you gathered information with your eyes. Most of us are aware that we depend on our sight to observe the world around us. But what you hear is also important. Your ears give you information about things you can't see. Remember moving day and how you found out about a possible new friend named Randy?

Figure 3-6

When a friend shouts your name, how do you get the message?

Ear canal

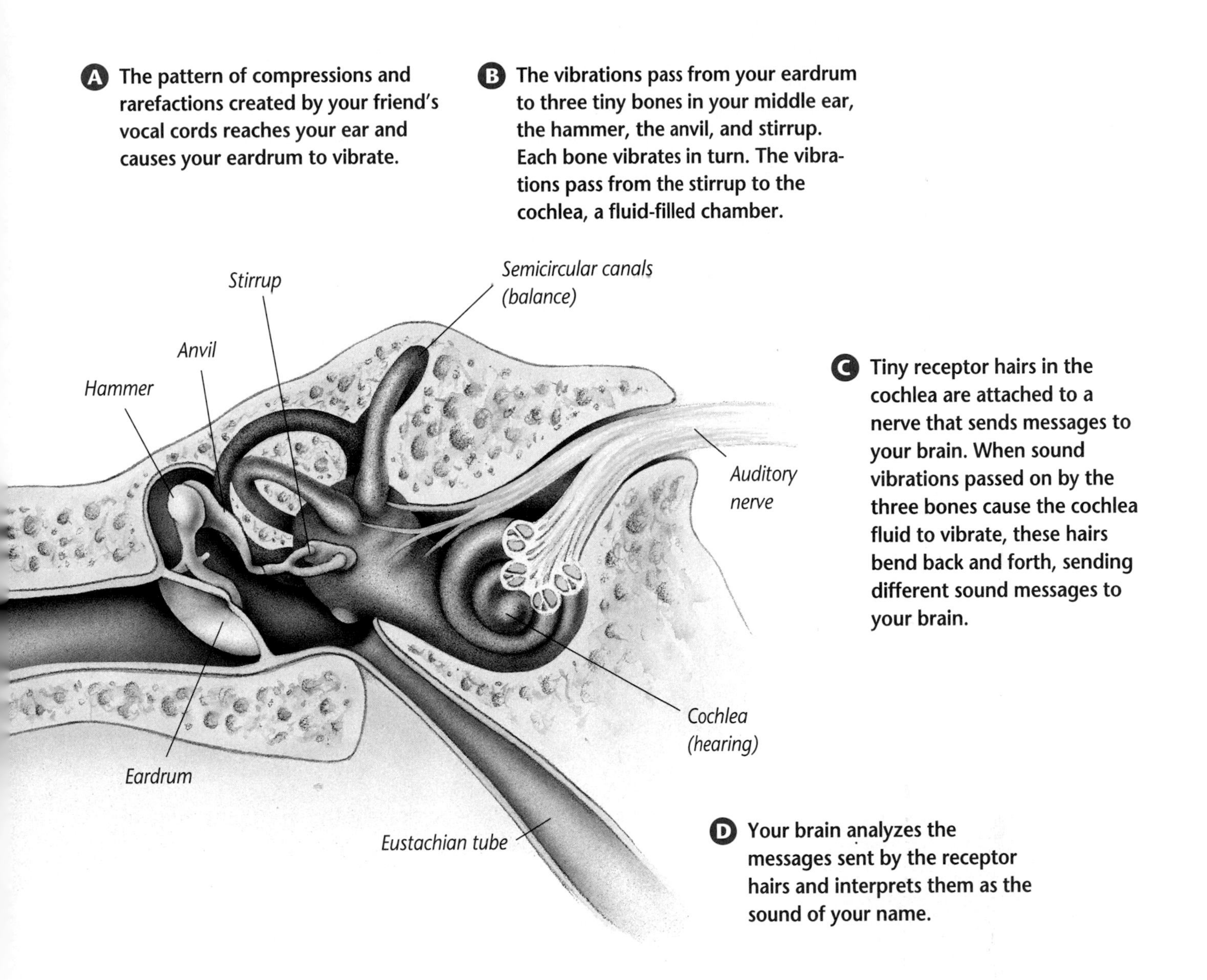

check your UNDERSTANDING

1. Why doesn't a ruler that is sitting by itself on your desk make a sound? What must happen to an object before it makes a sound?
2. Explain how to use a coiled spring to show the compressions and rarefactions that are created by a vibrating object.
3. Explain how a vibrating object that is some distance away from you causes your eardrums to vibrate.
4. **Apply** Imagine you are traveling in outer space. You see a nearby satellite explode when a large meteor crashes into it. Would you hear the boom? Why or why not?

Frequency and Pitch

Section Objectives

- Use the length or thickness of a vibrating object to predict whether its sound will be high or low.
- Describe the relationship between pitch and frequency.
- Compare the sound frequencies humans hear with the sound frequencies animals hear.

Key Terms

frequency
hertz (Hz)
pitch

The Pitch of Sound

Have you ever made a sound by blowing across the top of a soft drink bottle? Did you notice that the sound changes as you drink more and more of the liquid inside the bottle? As you drink, what replaces the liquid in the bottle? Air.

When you blow across the top of the bottle, the air inside the bottle vibrates. The amount of air inside determines whether the sound will be higher or lower. Do the next activity to find out what happens if you change the length of a vibrating solid.

Explore! ACTIVITY

Does the length of a vibrating object affect the sound it makes?

At the beginning of this chapter you learned you could create a sound with your ruler.

What To Do

1. Extend exactly half the ruler's length beyond the edge of the desk.
2. Snap the free end and listen to the sound.
3. Vary the length of the ruler that extends over the desk and observe the sound changes.
4. *In your Journal,* record how the sound changes as you change the length of the ruler.
5. When is the sound higher? Lower?
6. When does the ruler vibrate faster? More slowly?

In the Explore activity, you observed that a longer segment of ruler produces a lower sound than a shorter segment. **Figure 3-7A** and **B** shows the compressions and rarefactions your vibrating ruler makes in the air around it.

Figure 3-7C shows one cycle of the ruler. The number of times an object moves back and forth in one second is one way to keep track of an object's motion. The number of times an object vibrates in one second is called its **frequency**. We measure frequency with a unit called hertz, named after the German scientist Heinrich Hertz. One **hertz** (abbreviated Hz) is a frequency of one vibration per second or one cycle per second.

This next activity will show you another way to create high and low sounds.

Figure 3-7

A Because a long ruler vibrates slowly, it creates bands of compression and rarefaction that are farther apart. The result is a low sound.

B A shorter ruler vibrates more rapidly than a longer one. Faster vibrations create compressions and rarefactions that are closer together. The sound is higher.

C Each back-and-forth vibration of the ruler's motion is one cycle.

1 Cycle

Find Out! ACTIVITY

How do you make changes in sound on the strings of an instrument?

Take a close look at an acoustic guitar, violin, or other stringed instrument. Do the strings all look the same?

What To Do

1. Choose a stringed instrument and pluck the strings, one at a time.
2. Choose one string and pluck it. Push the string firmly against the fret board with your finger and pluck it again.
3. Loosen one string by turning the tuning peg. Pluck the string as you gradually tighten the peg.

Conclude and Apply

1. Which has a higher sound, a thick string or a thin string under the same tension? Why?
2. *In your Journal,* discuss two ways to change the sound a string makes.

■ Changing Pitch

Your ears recognize differences in sound frequencies as differences in pitch. **Pitch** refers to the highness or lowness of the sound you hear. When you hum along with your favorite music, you raise and lower the pitch of your own voice. If you listen carefully, you can hear that the pitch of your voice rises and falls even when you're just talking with friends.

As you discovered in the Find Out activity, thicker strings produce lower-pitched sounds. Changing the length of a string and changing the tension on the string will also change its pitch. **Figure 3-8** shows three ways to obtain different pitches on stringed instruments.

Figure 3-8

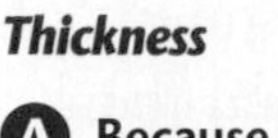

Thickness

Ⓐ Because they are heavier, thicker strings vibrate more slowly than thinner strings vibrate. The slower the vibration, the lower the pitch.

C string

D string

E string

Your Vocal Cords

What happens when you talk? How do you make those sounds? Just like other sounds, speech is produced by vibrations. When you speak or sing, the air you breathe out vibrates your vocal cords. The vocal cords are two thick folds of lip-shaped tissue that stretch across your larynx near the top of your windpipe.

Controlling Pitch

When you make a high-pitched sound, your muscles in your larynx stretch your vocal cords, which tightens them and brings them closer together. When you make a lower sound, your vocal cords relax a bit and move farther apart. You can control the pitch of your voice by tensing or relaxing your vocal cords. But changing the pitch of your voice rarely takes conscious effort because your brain adjusts your vocal cords automatically.

When you whisper, you form words with just your tongue and lips. Place your hand on your throat and say something out loud. Can you feel the vibrations? Now touch your throat and whisper. Your vocal cords should keep still.

Ventriloquists make their voices seem to come from someone else—often from a puppet or dummy.

Length

B **Holding a string down against the fretboard shortens the vibrating part of the string and raises the pitch of the note produced. The shorter the vibrating object, the faster the vibrations and the higher the pitch.**

Tension

C **Turning the tuning peg one way reduces the tension on the string. The vibrations slow down and the pitch gets lower. When you turn the peg the opposite way, the tension increases, the vibrations speed up, and the pitch gets higher.**

Ventriloquists speak by moving only the tip of the tongue.

You Try It!

Practice these steps in front of a mirror, watching carefully for movement.

1. Bring your teeth together without tightening your jaw.
2. Part your lips slightly and smile a little.
3. Move your tongue to sound the vowels.
4. Next, try the consonants. Sounds like f, v, p, b, and m are tricky. With practice, you can learn to imitate these sounds with just your tongue.

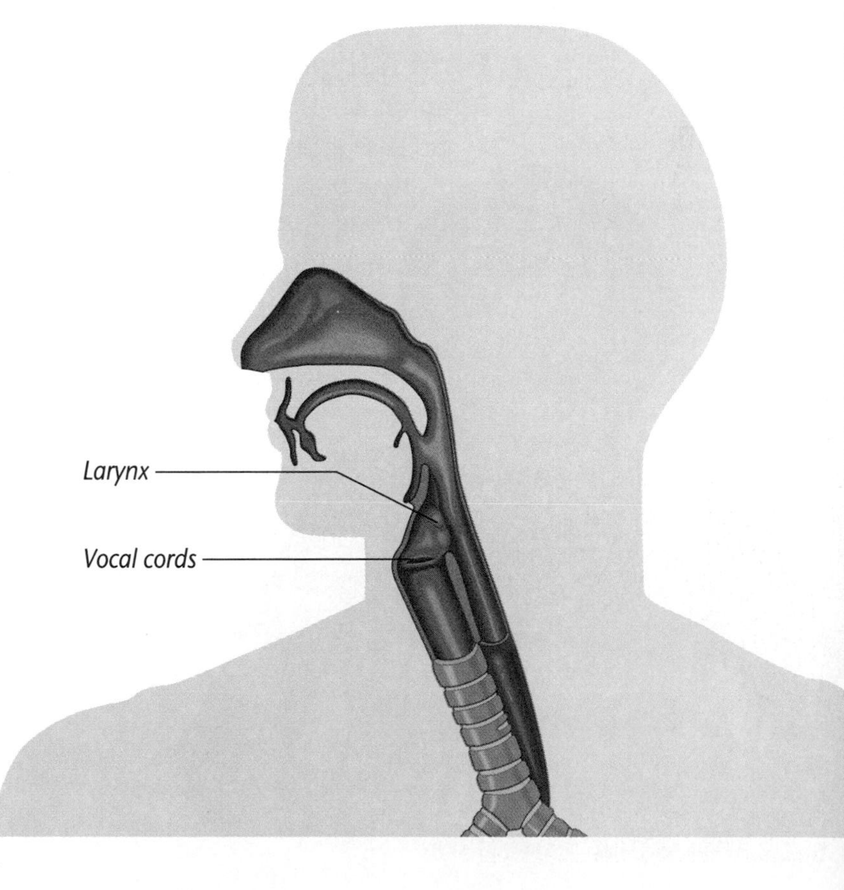

DESIGN YOUR OWN

INVESTIGATION

Length and Pitch

You have learned that shortening the length of a guitar string speeds up the vibrations and raises the pitch of the sound. If you produce a sound by blowing across a test tube full of water, what happens to the pitch of that sound when you empty the tube to half full and blow across it?

Preparation

Problem

When air is blown across the top of a test tube, the column of air inside the tube vibrates. When water is added to the tube, what happens? How does this added water affect pitch?

Form a Hypothesis

Based on what you have learned about changing pitch, decide on a hypothesis for your group. Write it down.

Objectives

- Observe how pitch changes with varying amounts of water in the test tube.
- Conclude from your investigation how the length of the vibrated column of air affects pitch.

Materials

test tubes with an approximate diameter of 2.5 cm
test-tube rack
felt-tip marker
water
small graduated cylinder
small metric ruler

Safety Precautions

Be careful handling glass test tubes.

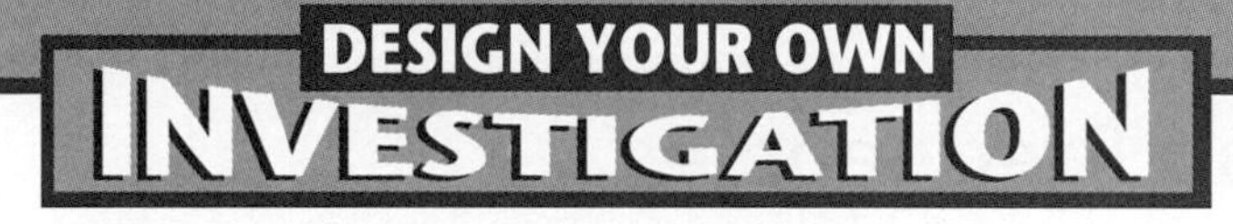

Plan the Experiment

1. Examine the materials and plan how your group will test the hypothesis. Write a step-by-step procedure.
2. *In your Science Journal,* draw diagrams of all the test tubes you use. Record your data on this diagram.
3. How will you measure the length of the column of air? Be sure to record the measurements on your diagram.

Check the Plan

1. Who will blow across the test tubes? Do the tubes need to be identical? Who will judge the sound? Do you need more than one person's opinion to judge the pitch?
2. Before you begin your experiment, make certain that your teacher approves your plan.
3. Carry out the experiment. Make observations and record your data on the diagrams *in your Science Journal.*

Analyze and Conclude

1. **Analyze Data** Which test tube produced the lowest pitch? How much water was in it?
2. Which test tube produced the highest pitch? How much water was in it?
3. **Compare and Contrast** Compare the pitches of all the bottles. How did the amount of water in the test tube affect the pitch of the vibrating column of air?
4. **Conclude** Make a statement about how the length of a vibrating column of air affects its pitch.
5. **Use Math** From your diagram, construct a bar graph relating column size to pitch.
6. What basic musical instrument does your test-tube instrument resemble?

Going Further

Can you create a musical scale by blowing across test tubes with varying amounts of water in them? How many test tubes will you need to create a musical scale of one octave?

Sound Frequencies

Have you ever seen a dog or cat perk up its ears as if it just heard something when you didn't hear anything at all? Dogs, cats, and other animals can hear sounds that humans can't hear. **Figure 3-9** shows the sound frequencies that humans and animals can hear.

As the figure shows, many animals hear a wider range of sound frequencies than humans. Hearing is important for an animal's survival. Finding food and detecting danger depends on a keen sense of hearing. Many animals have a keener sense of hearing than either sight or smell. The design of many animals' ears differs from that of humans. Bats have large outer ears that pick up more vibrations than small ears. Animals such as dogs and cats have movable outer ears which they move to locate sound without moving their heads.

There are many more sounds around us than our ears can hear. Not all the sounds we hear are pleasing to us. In the next section, you will learn how to distinguish between the sound of music and and the sound of noise.

Figure 3-9

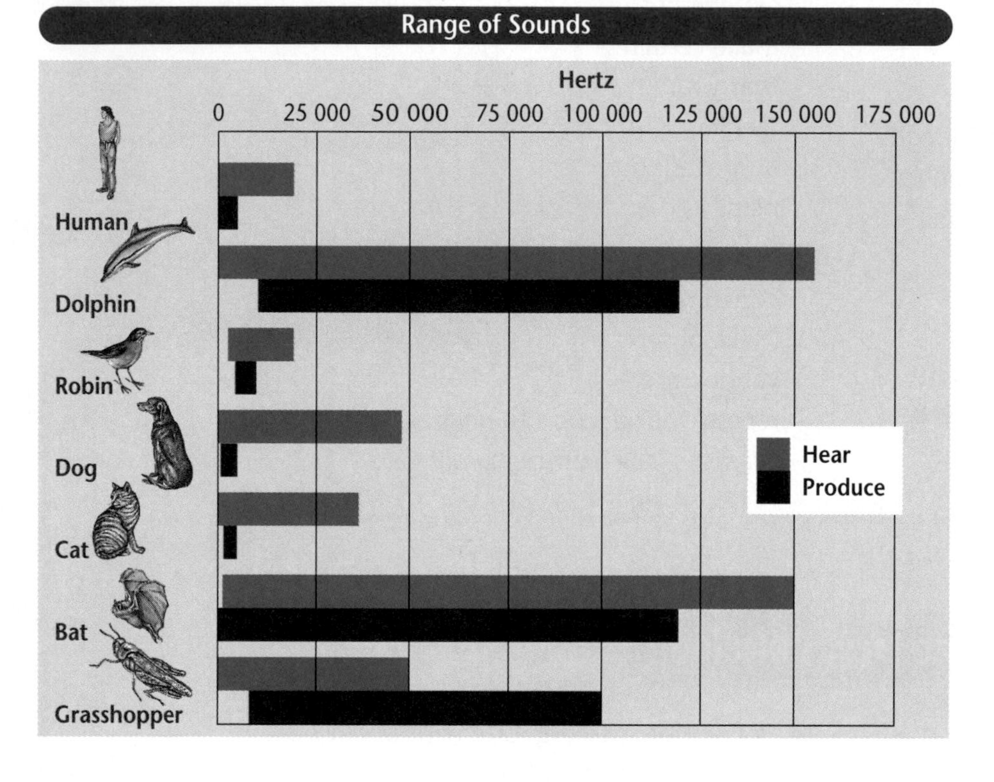

1. If you stretched out a thick rubber band and plucked it, how would the pitch of that sound compare with the pitch of a thin rubber band stretched to the same tension? Why?
2. Would a whistle with a sound frequency of 3000 Hz have a higher or lower pitch than a whistle whose frequency was 5000 Hz? Explain your answer.
3. Use **Figure 3-9** to compare the abilities of humans and dolphins to hear different frequencies.
4. **Apply** Explain how an acoustic guitarist can play all the pitches of a ballad with just six strings.

3-3 Music and Resonance

What Is Music?

You've just gotten home from school. You throw down your books, turn on some music, and dance around the room as you sing along with your favorite song. Has anyone ever called your favorite music a jumble of noise? Have you ever heard music that sounds noisy and confusing to you? What is the difference between music and noise?

Both music and noise are sounds. We sometimes think of noise as unpleasant or annoying. But some noisy sounds, like falling rain or ocean waves, can also be pleasant.

You can make noise by tapping your pencil on the desk or speaking nonsense syllables. You can also use those sounds to create music. You could tap your pencil in rhythm or make up a melody for nonsense syllables. A sound that's considered noise in one situation might be music in another. The opposite is also true. A radio left on a music station overnight is noise to the person who's trying to sleep in the next room. Audiograms show a picture of sound vibrations. Using the audiograms in **Figure 3-10**, how would you describe the difference between the vibrations made by a noise, such as an electric saw, and the vibrations made by a musical instrument, such as the violin?

Section Objectives

- Distinguish between music and noise.
- Explain how different musical instruments produce sounds of different quality.
- Describe resonance.

Key Terms

resonance

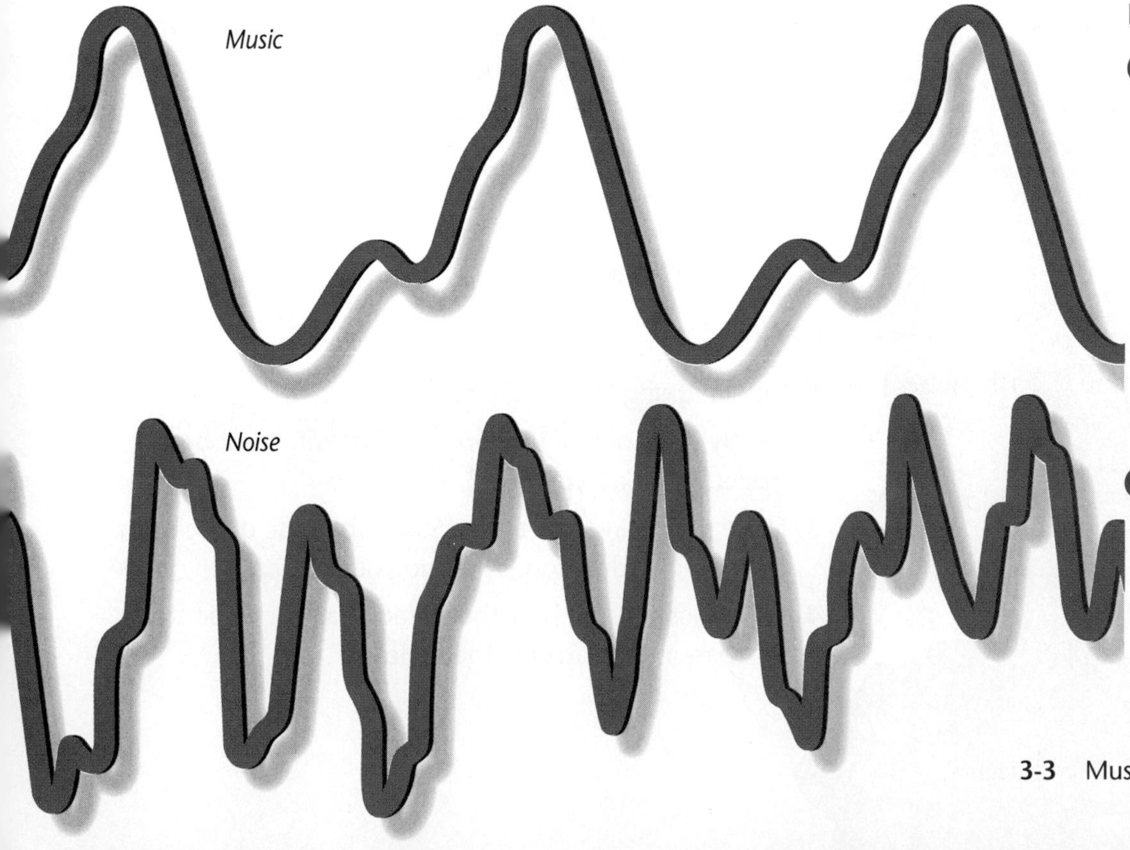

Music

Noise

Figure 3-10

A Audiograms are visual records of sound vibrations. Although each musical instrument produces its own distinctive pattern, musical instruments in general produce organized patterns.

B Objects that create noise, in contrast to music, produce unorganized patterns.

Sound Quality

Think back to the activity in which you played the guitar. The thinnest string on a guitar vibrates at about 330 Hz. You can play a note that vibrates at about 330 Hz on a clarinet, a cello, a piano, or a trumpet. You could even sing a note at this pitch with your voice. But, even though the pitch is the same, the quality of the sound will be different. An instrument's quality of sound depends on a variety of things—whether the sound is made by a vibrating string or a vibrating column of air, the material the instrument is made of (wood, metal, plastic, or a singer's vocal cords), the size of the instrument, and its shape. The way the vibrations are set into motion can also have an effect on sound quality. For example, strumming guitar strings with your fingers and plucking them with a plastic guitar pick produces sounds with different qualities.

Here is an activity that shows how the quality and the loudness of a sound can be changed. The activity uses a tuning fork, which is a metal object designed to vibrate at a particular frequency.

Figure 3-11

A Stradivarius violins produce a quality of sound unmatched by any other violin.

B Chemical analysis has shown the wood used in the violins had a higher than normal salt content. The wood also absorbed more varnish than usual.

C The varnish contained minerals that made it extremely hard. All these factors contribute to the pleasing, rich tones produced when the violins are played.

Explore! ACTIVITY

What is resonance?

What To Do

1. Hold a tuning fork by the stem.
2. Gently strike one of the fork's prongs with a rubber mallet. What do you hear?
3. Strike the tuning fork again. Stand the base of the stem on a table or desk top. What do you hear now?
4. *In your Journal,* tell how the sound changes when the fork base is held against the table.

Resonance

The tuning fork in the Explore activity doesn't make a very loud sound all by itself. But what happens when you hold the stem of the tuning fork against the table? The sound gets louder. Can you explain why? You know that vibrating objects produce sound, and that sound can travel through solids such as the table as well as through air. **Figure 3-12** shows what happens when the tuning fork is placed against the table.

An acoustic guitar's sound doesn't come just from the vibrating string making patterns of compression and rarefaction in the air. It also comes from the vibrations of the guitar body and the air inside it. When the string is attached to the guitar, the body of the instrument and the air inside it vibrate at the same frequency as the string. This tendency for an object to vibrate at the same frequency as another sound source is called **resonance**. Resonance means to resound, or to sound again. Resonance is what caused the sound of the vibrating tuning fork to get louder when you placed it against the table.

Cartoons and television commercials sometimes show a singer singing a long, loud, high note that causes a crystal glass to shatter. This can happen only if the singer produces a sound frequency the glass can resonate with. If you could sing a very loud note of the right frequency and hold the note long enough, you could make a glass vibrate so strongly that it would shatter!

Figure 3-12

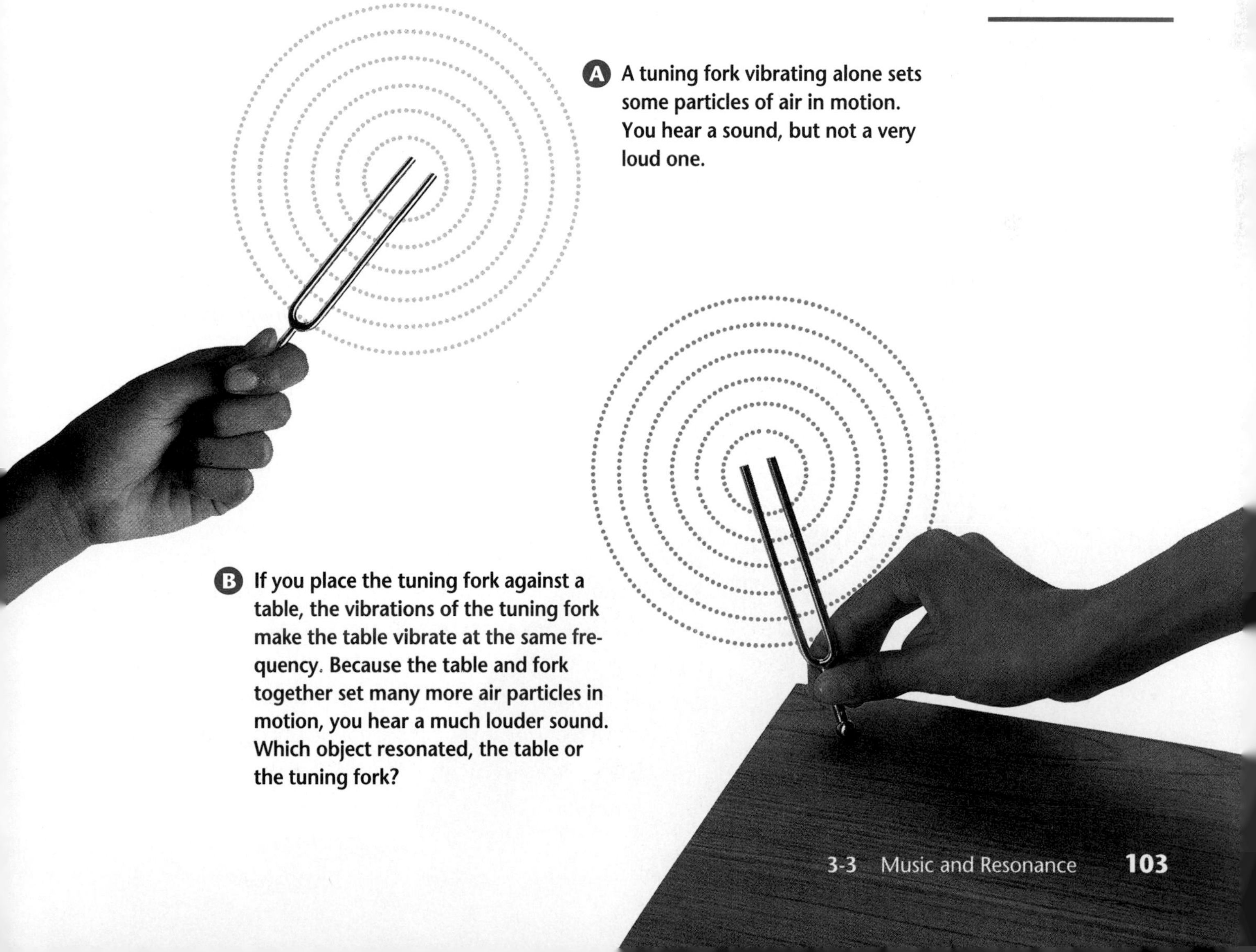

A A tuning fork vibrating alone sets some particles of air in motion. You hear a sound, but not a very loud one.

B If you place the tuning fork against a table, the vibrations of the tuning fork make the table vibrate at the same frequency. Because the table and fork together set many more air particles in motion, you hear a much louder sound. Which object resonated, the table or the tuning fork?

INVESTIGATE!

Length and Resonance

A tabletop resonates with the frequency of a vibrating tuning fork. The body of a guitar resonates with its vibrating strings. In this experiment, investigate the resonance of the air inside a glass tube.

Problem

Can you find the length of a tube of air that will resonate with a given sound frequency?

Materials

2 tuning forks of different frequencies (256 Hz or higher)
1 1000-mL graduated cylinder (or bucket or pitcher about 30 cm deep)
metric ruler
plastic or glass tube, 2.5 cm in diameter, about 45 cm long, open at both ends
rubber mallet
water

What To Do

1. Copy the data table *into your Journal.*
2. Find the number and the letters Hz on your tuning fork and record it under *Tuning Fork Frequency* in the data table.
3. Fill the graduated cylinder or bucket with water.
4. Hold one end of the tube while you place the other end partway into the cylinder or bucket of water (see photo ***A***).

A   *B*

5 Have your partner strike the tuning fork with the mallet and hold the fork over the tube.

6 Raise or lower the tube in the water until the loudest sound is produced.

7 Have your partner ***measure*** the distance from the top of the tube to the water's surface (see photo ***B***). Record the length in the table. This is the length of the column of air that resonates with the vibration of the tuning fork.

8 Repeat Steps 5–7 for the second tuning fork.

Data and Observations	
Tuning Fork Frequency	Length of the Column of Air

Analyzing

1. ***Interpret*** your table to answer these questions. For which tuning fork is the length of the column of air longer? Which column of air resonates at the lower frequency?
2. How does the length of a column of air relate to its resonant frequency?

Concluding and Applying

3. Obtain a different frequency tuning fork by trading with another group. Look at its frequency and ***predict*** how the length of the column of air that resonates with this tuning fork will compare with your earlier trials. Record your prediction in your Journal. Repeat the experiment and see how your prediction compares with what you observe.
4. **Going Further** Have you ever heard an object in a room buzz when a certain note is played loudly on the radio? Explain what causes this to happen.

Figure 3-13

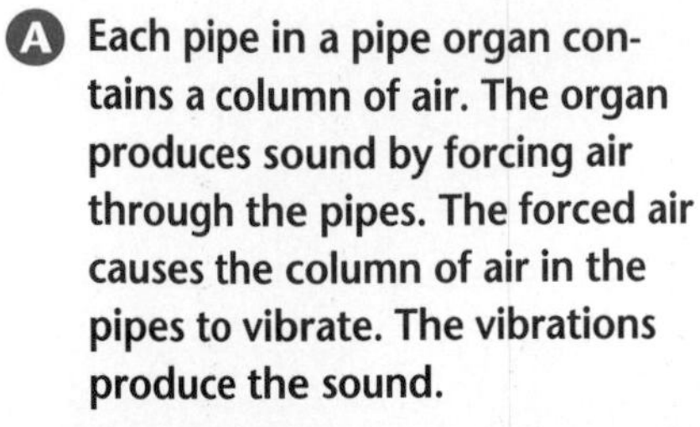

A Each pipe in a pipe organ contains a column of air. The organ produces sound by forcing air through the pipes. The forced air causes the column of air in the pipes to vibrate. The vibrations produce the sound.

B The sound a pipe makes depends on its shape and size. Longer pipes produce the lowest notes, while shorter pipes produce higher notes.

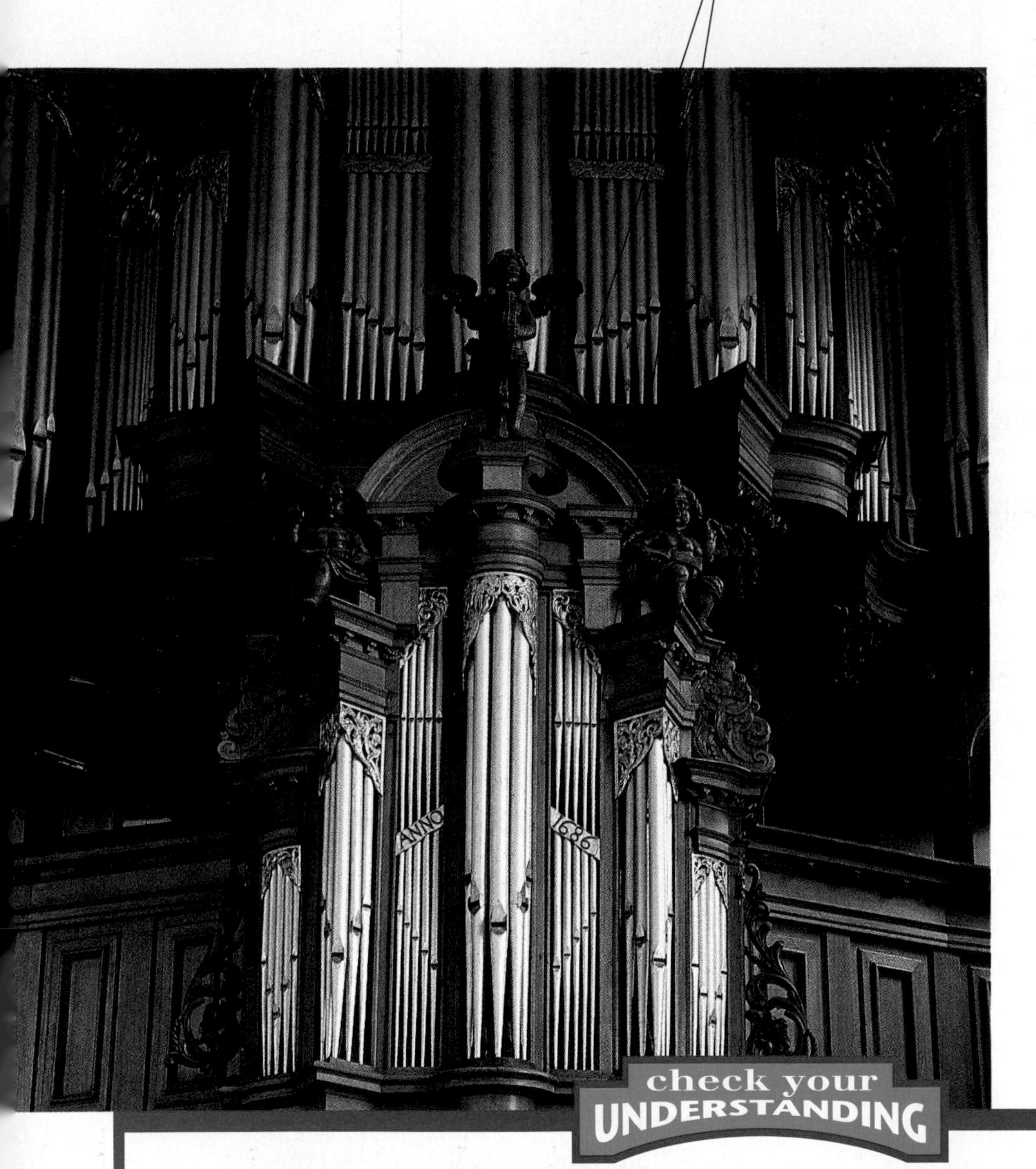

In the Investigate, you found that the resonant frequency of an air column was related to its length. The type of material from which an object is made and the object's shape also affect the frequency at which an object resonates. Thick plate glass windows will vibrate as heavy trucks rumble by on the street. A certain note played on the piano may cause a chandelier to vibrate.

There are many sounds around us, with many different qualities. Sometimes people have different ideas about what makes a sound pleasant and what makes a sound unpleasant. What kinds of sounds do you like? Rain falling or rap music? What is your least favorite sound? Traffic noise or thunder? The next time you hear a sound that you really like, try to describe its characteristics.

check your UNDERSTANDING

1. Compare and contrast music and noise.
2. Why can you identify different musical instruments just by listening, even when they are playing the same pitch?
3. Using a guitar, how would you explain resonance?
4. **Apply** The body of an acoustic guitar is hollow, with an opening just under the strings. Explain why it is constructed this way. Hint: Remember that the strings are not the only part of the guitar that vibrates.

EXPAND your view

Technology Connection

Active Noise Control

How many noisy sound sources can you name? Loud music, jackhammers, car mufflers, lawn mowers, jet engines, electric motors in fans and drills—and more. Passive methods of noise control try to reduce noise by surrounding the sound source with either foam insulation to absorb the noise or baffles to redirect it. Now there's a better idea. It's called active noise control.

How Does It Work?

Think of a noise source—say, an exhaust fan in the kitchen. Now picture its noise signature on an audiogram. There would be jagged hills and valleys in a pattern on the screen. Each noise source has its own unique noise signature.

Active noise control (ANC) devices use computer technology to produce something called anti-noise, whose noise signature is a mirror image of the noise's. Where the noise's pattern shows a hill, the anti-noise's pattern shows an identical but reversed valley. Where the noise has a valley, the anti-noise has a hill of exactly the same shape.

The ANC device analyzes the noise, predicts the signature of the anti-noise, and projects the anti-noise through speakers located near the fan. When the noise and the anti-noise reach your ear (or an oscilloscope) together, the result is a flat noise signature and no noise at all.

Factory workers, firefighters, pilots, construction workers, and many others are using ANC delivered by headphone to save their hearing and improve their efficiency on the job. Some new ANC devices have a built-in feedback loop so that if the noise changes, the anti-noise changes.

In one ANC car muffler design, a microphone near the exhaust pipe samples the engine sound. The computer chip in the ANC device produces the correct anti-noise, which is played by speakers mounted around the exhaust pipe. This design reduces engine noise 10 percent more than conventional mufflers. These ANC mufflers may be available on cars very soon.

Using Computers

Using graphics software, make a diagram using audiograms that explains how ANC technology works.

Heart and Soul

Louis Armstrong, left; Midori, above

The sounds from instruments are the result of vibrations. A trumpet player blows into a mouthpiece, causing the air in the body of the trumpet to vibrate. The pitch and sound can be changed by varying the pressure of the player's lips on the mouthpiece, and by opening or closing three valves.

A violin player draws a bow across the strings of the violin to produce vibrations. The body of the violin vibrates at the same frequency. The strings produce different sounds. The player changes the pitch by pressing the strings against the neck of the violin, changing the length of the string that is vibrating.

Playing an instrument requires more than using the science of sound. It requires the skill of the player. Trumpeter Louis Armstrong and violinist Midori are recognized as musicians with very special talents.

Louis Armstrong

Louis Armstrong was born in 1900 in New Orleans—the city where jazz was born. He moved to Chicago, then on to New York where he became a major figure in jazz. In addition to playing the trumpet, he sometimes sang nonsense syllables, called scatting. Armstrong died in 1971, but he is still remembered worldwide by his nickname Satchmo and revered for what he could do with sound.

Midori

On her third birthday, Midori was given a violin half the size of an adult's. Midori practiced endlessly with her mother, a professional violinist in Osaka, Japan. Midori was invited to play in a summer festival at Aspen, Colorado when she was only eight years old. Her power, technique, and skill amazed everyone. Midori and her mother moved to New York City in 1982 so that Midori could study at the Juilliard School of Music. Since then, Midori has performed in many countries, including her native Japan.

You Try It!

Listen to a recording of Louis Armstrong and to one of Midori. How does the music make you feel?

Making Waves—Sound Waves, That Is

West Virginian Torey Verts knows a lot about why things sound the way they do. She's a professional sound engineer. "When you listen to a record, you are hearing a lot more than your favorite band. Computers get a lot of use in the studio today. We can completely change a band's sound. For example, if the singer can't hit high notes, the engineer can turn a dial, and suddenly there's no problem. We can speed the music up or add special effects and synthesizers. Even though the sound engineer can do all these things, I don't think musicians have much to worry about. After all, who wants to see a computer in concert?"

Think Fast

Torey, like many sound engineers, is a musician herself. "If I could, I would be up on the stage playing my guitar. That's why I love to work live concerts. Engineering lets me be a part of the sound. Of course, live concerts can be tough. If something goes wrong with the sound, you've got to fix it fast. You can't ask the audience to take a break while you find a loose connection." Torey has found that a good understanding of scientific principles can really help when you need to solve a problem.

"If you want to get involved in music, you've got to learn as much as you can about the sciences," says Torey. "But you also need to know what sounds good. The best way to learn is to listen. Try to hear what it is you like about a song. What makes it sound good? What would make it sound better? And don't be afraid to listen to bad music either. Knowing what doesn't work is just as valuable as knowing what does."

You Try It!

Many radios, stereos, and CD players let you make adjustments to the sound that you hear. As you listen to a song, gently turn the treble knob as far to the right as it will go. Play the same song again and adjust the bass knob. What is the difference between these two adjustments? Reminder: When you have completed this assignment, be sure to return both knobs to their original positions.

chapter 3 REVIEWING MAIN IDEAS

Science Journal

Review the statements below about the big ideas presented in this chapter, and answer the questions. Then, re-read your answers to the Did You Ever Wonder questions at the beginning of the chapter. *In your Science Journal*, write a paragraph about how your understanding of the big ideas in the chapter has changed.

1. Sounds are created by vibrating objects. When an object vibrates, it creates a pattern of compressions and rarefactions in the particles of the air. ***How do air particles in an area around a vibrating object move?***

2. We usually hear sounds that travel to our ears through the air. But any kind of matter can conduct sound. ***Why couldn't an observer in space hear an explosion on a nearby satellite?***

3. Your ears recognize differences in sound frequencies as differences in pitch. Pitch refers to the highness or lowness of a sound. ***How does changing the tension on a guitar string affect the pitch of the note it produces?***

4. The tendency for any object to vibrate at the same frequency as another sound source is called resonance. Resonance means to resound, or to sound again. ***When a violin string is plucked, what resonates?***

CHAPTER REVIEW

Using Key Science Terms

compression
frequency
hertz (Hz)
medium
pitch
rarefaction
resonance

Give the science term with a meaning opposite to that of the following phrases.

1. a squeezed together area
2. a spread out area
3. two sound sources vibrating at different frequencies.

For each set of terms below, explain the relationship that exists.

4. compression, vibration, rarefaction
5. frequency, pitch
6. pitch, compression, resonance

Understanding Ideas

Answer the following questions in your Journal *using complete sentences.*

1. What does the frequency or pitch of a sound source describe?
2. What creates the pattern of sound that travels to your ears when an object vibrates?
3. In what unit is frequency measured?
4. How does sound travel in air compared to water?
5. How does the pitch of a 4-inch column of air compare to the pitch of a 3-inch column of air?

Developing Skills

Use your understanding of the concepts developed in this chapter to answer each of the following questions.

1. **Concept Mapping** Using the following terms, complete the concept map of sound: *compressions, gas, liquid, medium, rarefactions, solid, vibrations.*

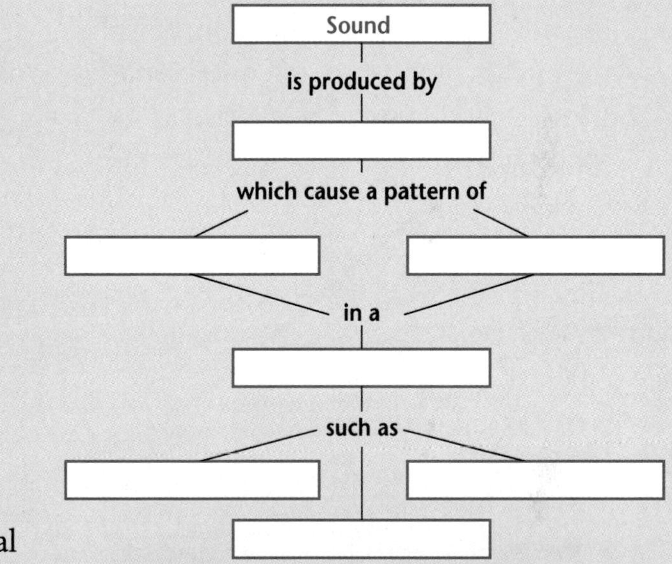

2. **Making and Using Graphs** Using **Figure 3-9** on page 100, arrange in order from narrowest range of frequencies heard to widest range of frequencies heard, the following: dog, dolphin, bat, human.
3. **Predicting** Repeat the Find Out activity on page 89 using a different material, such as thick rope or plastic string. Predict how the new material will conduct sound as compared to the string. Test your predictions.

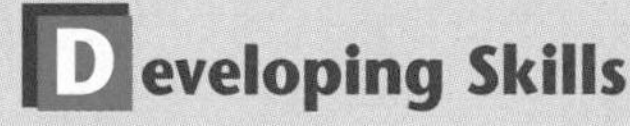

CHAPTER REVIEW

Critical Thinking

In your Journal, *answer each of the following questions.*

1. At the beginning of an outdoor band concert, Lee's trumpet was in tune. During intermission the trumpet was left out in the sun. The sun warmed up the metal, expanding it, and actually making the trumpet slightly larger. When Lee began to play after intermission, how did the pitches of the different notes sound?
2. In a science-fiction movie, when a space ship explodes in outer space, the vibrations from the sound nearly destroy a nearby spaceship. If you were technical advisor for the movie, what would your advice be about this scene?

Problem Solving

Read the following problem and discuss your answers in a brief paragraph.

Your class is putting on a variety show, and you've been assigned to put together a "kitchen" band. That is, you must come up with instruments made from ordinary household items like pots and pans, glasses, silverware, and other common articles.

1. Suggest at least five different types of instruments for your band. Remember, they must be able to produce different pitched notes and play a melody.
2. How is each of the instruments played and where does the sound come from? What vibrates to produce the sound?

CONNECTING IDEAS

Discuss each of the following in a brief paragraph.

1. **Theme—Stability and Change** How are frequency and pitch related?
2. **Theme—Systems and Interactions** Explain how a stethoscope would help a doctor listen to a patient's heart.
3. **Theme—Stability and Change** You are drinking a soft drink out of a 10-ounce bottle. Every time you take a swallow, you blow across the top of your bottle to make a sound. Describe how the sound will change as you get closer and closer to finishing your drink.
4. **Technology Connection** Identify some noises in your neighborhood that might be reduced by ANC.
5. **Science and Society** A violin, a viola, and a cello are about the same shape, but don't sound the same. What could cause this?

unit 1
UNIT REVIEW

In this unit, you investigated how your senses function and how they are used to obtain information about your world. Your senses were used to observe patterns and features on Earth and in the sky.

You used light and sound as two primary means of obtaining information about your world. The color of the light and whether it is reflected from a surface or refracted by it enabled you to identify characteristics of objects.

Try the exercises and activity that follow—they will challenge you to use and apply some of the ideas you learned in this unit.

CONNECTING IDEAS

1. You may have seen flash photographs showing several people. The flash is bright white, so why do some of the people have red eyes and other people have eyes that appear normal?
2. You and your friends are in a swimming pool. While underwater, one of your friends taps on a metal railing. Why do you have trouble locating the sound source while you are underwater? How might the interaction of your other senses help you determine where the metal railing is located?

Exploring Further ACTIVITY

What makes all the patterns of light you see inside of a kaleidoscope?

What To Do

1. Obtain three small identical mirrors.
2. Tape them together to form a triangular shape with the reflective sides turned inward.
3. Tape a triangular piece of paper to one end of your kaleidoscope, and drop pieces of colored paper into it.
4. Look inside and describe what you see. What causes the pattern of color in your kaleidoscope?

Interactions in the Physical World

Freeze it or fry it! Extremes of temperature can't hurt this substance. The ceramic dish is made of a special glass designed to withstand rapid temperature changes. In Unit 2, we'll look closely at many substances around us to discover how they can interact and change.

NATIONAL GEOGRAPHIC

try it!

Do all materials interact in the same way? Salt, a substance necessary for us to survive, is a result of sodium and chlorine combining chemically. Not all materials, however, will react with each other. Some materials will not even mix together. What do you think will happen when a sample of powdered drink mix is shaken vigorously with water, then with oil?

What To Do

1. Place some water into a jar and add some drink mix.
2. Close the jar and shake it rapidly. Stop shaking and observe what has happened to the drink mix and water.
3. Now, try the same thing using cooking oil instead of water. How did the oil and water differ?
4. Based on what you have observed, what predictions can you make about other mixtures?

CHAPTER 4

Describing the Physical World

Did you ever wonder...

- ✓ **Why cake batter pours, but cake crumbles?**
- ✓ **How you can smell someone's perfume after that person has left?**
- ✓ **Why water splashes, but chalk breaks?**
- ✓ **If you could get fresh water from the ocean?**

Science Journal

Before you begin to study about describing the physical world, think about these questions and answer them *in your Science Journal.* When you finish the chapter, compare your journal write-up with what you have learned.

How the air feels, looks, and smells are clues as to what may be in the air that day. When the air is hazy and feels damp, it might mean that smoke, fog, and other matter are in the air. In and around some cities, those clues might mean that the air contains smog—a kind of air pollution.

Clues about how the air feels, looks, and smells, however, don't tell you exactly what air is. Is air the same all over the world? Is it made of one thing or a number of things? How do you begin to identify, describe, and classify the kinds of matter in the air around you?

You do some of these things already. This chapter will give you new ways of observing and classifying not only air, but many other materials in the physical world.

▶ ***In the activity on the next page, explore a model of smog.***

Can you make a model of smog?

What To Do

1. Place two closed, heat-proof jars in front of a dark background.
2. Leave one jar alone. Open the other jar.
3. With your teacher's help, drop a burning wooden splint into the open jar. Quickly close the lid so that the flame goes out and the jar fills with smoke.
4. Shine a flashlight through both jars. *In your Journal*, describe what happens to the light.

Composition of Matter

Section Objectives

- Differentiate among substances, elements, compounds, and mixtures.
- Give examples of heterogeneous and homogeneous mixtures.

Key Terms

substance, mixture, heterogeneous mixture, homogeneous mixture, element, compound

How Can You Identify Substances?

The jars in the Explore activity were filled with air and smoke. The light that went through the jar filled with air came out in a clear beam. However, something in the smoke affected how the light came out. Air and smoke are two different kinds of matter.

Find Out! ACTIVITY

What are some characteristics of water?

What To Do

1. *In your Journal,* make some observations about a glass of plain water. What color is it? How does it smell? How does it feel?
2. Place a drop of water from the top of the glass on a microscope slide. Look at it under a microscope at low power.
3. Compare it with a drop taken from the bottom of the glass. Try taking a smaller drop from the middle of the glass. Is there any difference in how each drop looks under the microscope?
4. Compare drops of water from your glass with drops from a classmate's glass.

Conclude and Apply

1. What characteristics of water did you observe?
2. What can you conclude about the characteristics of all the drops of water in a glass of water?

One drop of water is exactly like every other drop of water. In fact, all pure water everywhere has the same characteristics. It is colorless, odorless, tasteless, feels wet, and is made of only one kind of material.

Another way to describe water is to say that water is a substance. A **substance** is anything that contains only one kind of material. Sugar is also a substance. It is made of only one kind of material and always has the same characteristics. It tastes sweet and dissolves when mixed with water. List other everyday things you see or use that are substances.

Identifying Mixtures

Is paper a substance? Do you think paper is made of only one kind of material? Look closely at the paper and slice of pita bread shown in **Figures 4-1B** and **4-1C**. Would you say bread is a substance? Why or why not?

Both paper and bread contain tiny bits of several different substances. Any material made of two or more substances in which the basic identity of each substance is not changed is called a **mixture.**

Think back to the two jars you used in the Explore activity at the beginning of this chapter. Did either of the jars contain a substance? You might think that the jar with only air in it contained a substance and the smoke-filled jar contained a mixture of air and smoke. Actually, air itself is a mixture, although you can't see the different substances that make up air.

In **Figure 4-1B**, were the different materials in pita bread mixed together evenly, or were they scattered throughout? A mixture in which the different substances are distributed unevenly is called a **heterogeneous mixture.** Both bread, chocolate milk, and the mixture of smoke and air are heterogeneous mixtures.

Suppose you make a mixture of salt and water. If you stirred the salt and water together thoroughly, would you be able to see the salt? Do you think that all parts of this mixture would taste the same? The salt is distributed evenly throughout the water. A mixture in which the different substances are distributed evenly throughout is called a **homogeneous mixture.** Salt water is a homogeneous mixture. What other homogeneous mixtures can you name?

Figure 4-1

A The separate particles of tea and water in this glass of cold tea are too small to be seen and are evenly distributed. These properties make cold tea a homogeneous mixture.

B If you look carefully at this pita bread you can see various sized particles of different substances scattered throughout. Pita bread is a heterogeneous mixture.

C Paper is a heterogeneous mixture. If you examine most paper through a magnifying glass, you can see that separate particles are scattered throughout.

D No matter how long you let powdered drink mix and water stand, the evenly distributed particles that make up this homogeneous mixture will not separate.

Separating Mixtures

When you make smoky air or salt water, you are putting substances together to make a mixture. Can you take mixtures apart to separate the substances?

Hand-separating the substances in some mixtures is one way to take them apart. What other methods can be used? Suppose you had a glass of sand and water. It would be difficult to separate the sand and water by hand. **Figure 4-2** demonstrates one method of mixture separation.

Can a filter be used to separate salt and water? Usually not. The particles that make up salt are small and are

Figure 4-2

If you stirred sand into a glass of water and poured the mixture into a filter-lined funnel, the water would slowly drip through. The sand would not. Many heterogeneous mixtures can be separated this way.

Separating Mixtures

You know that you can use properties like size, color, or shape to separate substances in a mixture. You can use the property of boiling point by heating liquid mixtures and collecting each substance as its vapor changes back to a liquid.

Property of Attraction

A more difficult property to observe is the attraction that particles in a substance have for one another and for other substances. For example, when you place a drop of water on a piece of waxed paper, the water stays in a spherical shape. But when you drop the water onto newspaper or a paper towel, the water spreads out. How can this be explained? On the waxed paper, the particles in the water have a greater attraction for one another than they do for the waxed paper. On the distributed throughout the water. They would pass through the filter with the water. Some other method of separation is needed for most homogeneous mixtures. Such a method might involve changing any liquid part of the mixture into a vapor. The solid part would remain behind, as shown in **Figure 4-3**. Evaporation and boiling are two such methods.

You've seen how substances and mixtures are related and how they are different. And you've seen that there are different kinds of mixtures. You know that there is more than one way to separate a mixture. This knowledge can help you classify materials.

Figure 4-3

Salt stirred into a glass of water cannot be separated with a filter. But if you boil the mixture, the water will vaporize and rise into the air as steam. The salt will be left behind in the beaker. Boiling is one way to separate some homogeneous mixtures. What is another method?

paper towel, though, the water particles have a greater attraction for the paper.

This property of attraction is another method that can be used to separate mixtures.

You Try It!

1. Cut newspaper, paper towel, and filter paper into strips 2 cm wide by 8 cm long.
2. Tape one end of each strip to the middle of a pencil.
3. Dip a toothpick into green food coloring and make a line across the bottom of each paper strip about 2 cm from the bottom. Allow the lines to dry.
4. Add 15 mL of water to a jar.
5. Place the pencil across the top of the jar so that just the tips of the paper strips contact the water. The strips should not touch the sides of the jar.

6. Wait 10 to 15 minutes and record your observations *in your Science Journal*. How would you use your observations to describe the attraction of the colored pigments for themselves and the paper?

Life Science

Calcium, phosphorus, iron, potassium, and sodium are some of the elements your body needs to function properly. Create a chart that includes how each element is used by your body and a food source for each element.

The Building Blocks of Matter

What would you get if you took apart your bike? The wheels are made of rubber, the seat may be covered with plastic, and the frame may be made of alloys or metals. The lights may be covered with glass. With the right equipment, you could separate the alloys into the metals from which they are made. The same is true of the rubber, plastic, and other parts. Each is some combination of simpler materials.

Elements

Eventually, though, you would reach a point where you couldn't break down the parts into any simpler materials. At that point, you would have a collection of elements. An **element** is a substance that cannot be broken down further into simpler substances by ordinary physical or chemical means.

How can you demonstrate this? Let's do the next activity to find out.

How is an element different from a mixture?

What To Do

1. Fill a small test tube about half full of iron powder. Fill another test tube with the same amount of sulfur powder. Record the physical appearance of each.
2. Take a few grains of iron, place the iron on a glass slide, and look at it under the microscope. Make another slide of sulfur particles and examine them under a microscope. Record *in your Journal* how the iron and sulfur are different.
3. Now hold a small magnet near the slide containing the iron. What do you observe? Clean the magnet and hold it near the sulfur particles. What do you observe now?
4. Empty both test tubes into a mortar. Take a pestle and carefully grind the two substances together until the contents look the same throughout. What have you just made?
5. Take a few grains of this mixture, put it on a glass slide, and look at it under a microscope. What do you observe? Remove the slide from the microscope and hold a small magnet near it. What happens?
6. Clean the magnet and repeat this step until no more particles are attracted from the slide. Examine the slide once again under the microscope.

Conclude and Apply

1. What do you see now?
2. What can you conclude from your observations?

Mixtures are made by combining two or more substances together in such a way that each keeps its own properties. Mixtures can physically be separated into simpler substances. If you mixed together the particles of iron and sulfur, you made a mixture. This mixture could be separated back into iron and sulfur by using a magnet.

Iron and sulfur particles, however, cannot be broken down any further, using either physical or chemical methods. If you were to continue grinding down samples of each into smaller and smaller particles, you would still be left with particles of iron and sulfur. Iron and sulfur are already in their simplest forms. Both iron and sulfur are examples of elements. Elements are known as the building blocks of matter.

■ Compounds

What would have happened if you had heated the iron and sulfur mixture? You would have made a new substance which would not look like the iron and sulfur mixture, nor iron or sulfur by itself. You would have made something totally new called iron sulfide. Heating can cause such chemical changes to occur.

Iron sulfide has properties different from those of either iron or sulfur. It is a new substance. A substance whose smallest unit is made up of more than one element is a **compound**. Iron sulfide is an example of a compound. What properties does a compound have that make it different from either an element or a mixture?

Figure 4-4

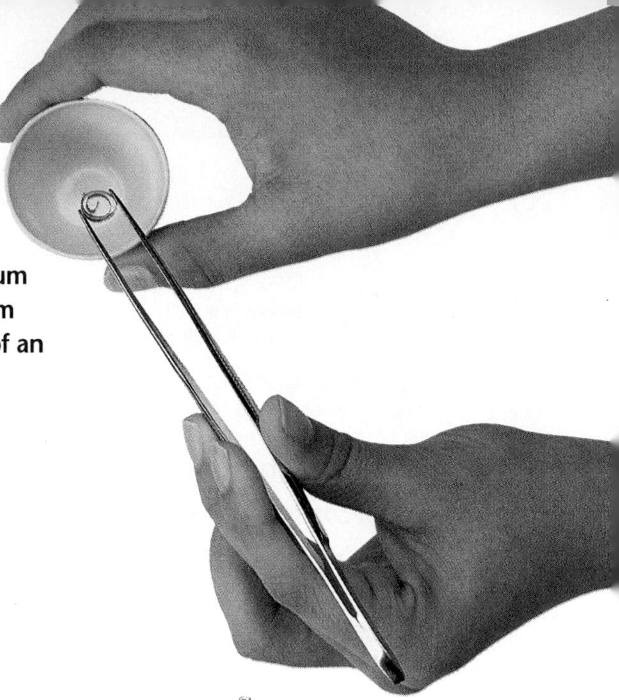

A Magnesium is a silver-white metal. Like the oxygen in air, magnesium is in its simplest form and is an example of an element.

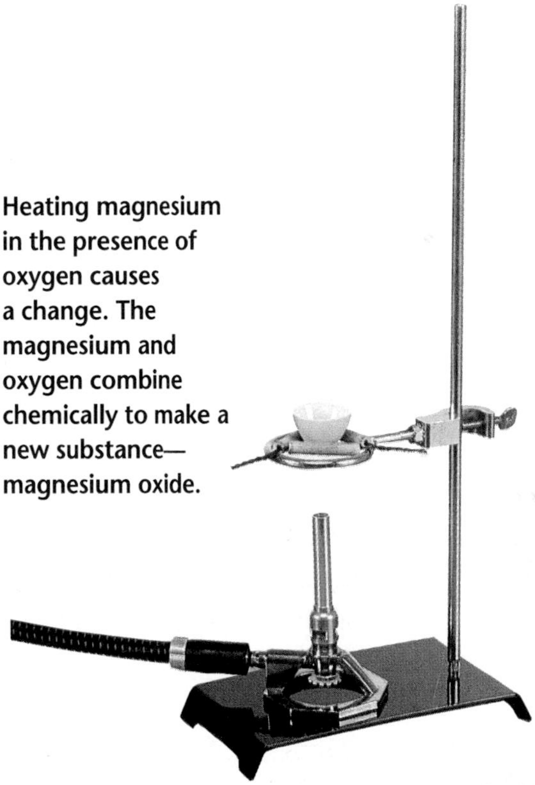

B Heating magnesium in the presence of oxygen causes a change. The magnesium and oxygen combine chemically to make a new substance—magnesium oxide.

C Magnesium oxide does not look like the original coil of magnesium nor the invisible gas oxygen. Magnesium oxide is a new substance with a look of its own.

DESIGN YOUR OWN
INVESTIGATION

Elements, Compounds, Mixtures

Developing a system of classification helps turn a definition into a tool for solving problems. For example, you can classify vehicles as a car, pick-up truck, or van based on identifying characteristics. Can a similar system can be made to distinguish among elements, compounds, and mixtures?

Preparation

Problem

How can their differences help you distinguish among elements, compounds, and mixtures?

Form a Hypothesis

Find the definitions of elements, compounds, and mixtures from your text. If you were classifying objects based on these definitions, what characteristics would you assign to an element? To a compound? To a mixture?

Objectives

- Define element, compound, heterogeneous mixture, and homogeneous mixture.
- Develop a list of identifying characteristics based on the definitions.
- Classify an object as an element, a compound, a heterogeneous mixture, or a homogeneous mixture.

Possible Materials

small amount of rock salt
glass of lemonade
aluminum foil
baking soda
small piece of granite
copper wire
piece of graphite (carbon)
vinegar and oil salad dressing

Safety Precautions

Never eat, drink, or taste anything used in a laboratory experiment.

DESIGN YOUR OWN

INVESTIGATION

Plan the Experiment

1. Work as a group to choose objects and agree on a hypothesis. Record *in your Science Journal* the identifying characteristics that you will look for as you classify the objects.
2. Design a data table *in your Science Journal* to record the names of your test objects and the classifications you assign them.

Check the Plan

1. Do your identifying characteristics correspond to the definitions of substances and mixtures?
2. How will you keep track of your observations and explanations?
3. Before you begin, have the teacher check your plan and your list of objects.
4. Carry out the experiment.

Copper Vinegar and oil Aluminum Granite Graphite Rock salt Lemonade Baking soda

Analyze and Conclude

1. **Observe and Infer** If you know the name of a substance, how can you find out if it is an element?
2. **Compare and Contrast** How do compounds differ from mixtures?
3. **Classify** What homogeneous mixtures did you identify? How did you determine the difference between homogeneous and heterogeneous mixtures?
4. **Classify** Did your list of identifying characteristics help you to correctly classify the objects? How would you change your list if you were to repeat the experiment?
5. **Make and Use Tables** Make a table that lists the four kinds of substances and mixtures, their differences, and the classifications you made. Look in the Skill Handbook under Making Tables if you need help.

Going Further

Use your list of identifying characteristics to classify the contents of your refrigerator at home. Identify whether there are more substances or mixtures.

■ Compounds vs. Mixtures

In the Investigation you just completed, different elements, compounds, and mixtures were examined and compared. Let's now summarize the differences between compounds and mixtures.

First, compounds cannot be separated by physical means. If you melted water when it was in the form of ice, the hydrogen and oxygen in it would not separate out—you would simply get liquid water.

Second, the substances that make up a compound do not keep their own properties. **Figure 4-5** demonstrates this property using sugar as an example. A mixture such as brass, on the other hand, still retains many of the physical properties of the elements that are used to make it—copper and zinc.

Third, the same compound always has the same composition. If you went from store to store buying samples of sugar and then took the time to break each down into its elements, you would always end up with the same amounts of carbon, hydrogen, and oxygen.

In the next section, you will learn how to describe different materials.

Figure 4-5

A Carbon is an element that has three natural forms: diamond, graphite, and amorphous charcoal. Carbon has a unique ability to combine with itself and with other elements in various ways to form millions of different compounds. Sugar is a compound made of carbon, hydrogen, and oxygen.

B If you mix cinnamon and sugar, you have a mixture called cinnamon-sugar. This mixture can be separated back into cinnamon and sugar by physical means. How would you go about it?

check your UNDERSTANDING

1. Differentiate between water and chocolate milk.
2. Give three examples of heterogeneous mixtures you use at school. Tell why they are heterogeneous.
3. Name three homogeneous mixtures you might eat, drink, or use at home. Explain your choices.
4. How can you distinguish between a piece of cotton and a piece of bronze?
5. State three properties of sugar that make it a compound.
6. **Apply** How might you separate a mixture of salt and fine sand?

4-2 Describing Matter

Physical Properties

Suppose you are given the task of separating the materials in some wild bird food. You would observe the color, size, and shape of each type of grain or seed. You could describe some of the grains and seeds as flat, round, small, pointed, yellow, black, white, or striped. You could also use the characteristics of shape, size, and color to help you distinguish one kind of seed in the mixture from another. Notice that you can make such descriptions without changing the grains in any way.

When you use characteristics such as color, shape, and brittleness to describe an object or a material, you are naming some of its physical properties. Any characteristic of a material that can be observed or measured is a **physical property**. When you describe physical properties, the substances that make up the material are not changed. How are the physical properties of chalk different from those of an aluminum can?

Later in your studies, you will observe the color, brittleness, and hardness of some materials. But first, familiarize yourself with some of the most common measurements related to physical properties.

Section Objectives

- Recognize examples of physical properties.
- Measure length, volume, and mass of different materials.
- Relate density to mass and volume.

Key Terms

physical property
density

Explore! ACTIVITY

Can you measure without a ruler?

What To Do

1. Walk across the front of your classroom. As you walk, line up the heel of one foot with the toe of the other foot.
2. *In your Journal,* record how many footsteps you took to walk across the classroom.
3. Compare this number with the number of steps your classmates used. You'll probably find that the number of footsteps used to measure your classroom differs from one student to another.
4. Now try to measure a pencil and a button using footsteps. How many footsteps do you think it is from your house to school?

Table 4-1

Most of the world's countries use standard units of measurement. The standard units were designed to multiply and divide easily and to make both large and small quantities convenient to measure. This table shows the International System of Units, abbreviated SI.

SI Units			
Unit	**Abbreviation**	**Size Comparison**	**Similar-sized Object**
kilometer	km	1000 meters	ten football fields
meter	m	100 centimeters	guitar, baseball bat
decimeter	dm	1/10 meter	a little more than a new crayon
centimeter	cm	1/100 meter	staple
millimeter	mm	1/1000 meter	tooth on edge of stamp
kilogram	kg	1000 grams	your science textbook
gram	g	1/1000 kilogram	large paper clip

In the Explore activity, you measured objects in "footstep" units. Maybe this type of unit works well enough for some measurements, but it has some problems. For example, the measurements are not the same from one person to the next. In addition, very large and very small measurements are not easy to make with this unit.

People around the world need to be certain that their measurements are understood by others. They also want to be sure that a bolt of cloth in Delhi, India, will be measured in the same way as a bolt of cloth in Paris, France. Therefore, most of the world's countries use standard units of measurement. This standard measuring system is called the International System of Units, abbreviated SI, and is shown in **Table 4-1**.

Length

You may use a meterstick to measure the length of an object, such as a book. Just what does it mean to measure length? Is length the number of pages between the covers of a book? Or is it the number of minutes from the beginning to the end of a movie? In scientific measurement, length is the distance between two points. That distance could be the diameter of the period at the end of this sentence or the distance from Earth to the moon.

Study **Table 4-1**. What SI units of measure might you use to measure the length of a book? Would the book be changed when its length is measured? Is length a physical property of this object? Explain.

Volume

In addition to measuring the length of your book, you may also wish to use the meterstick to measure the book's width and height. If you then multiplied these three measurements, you would find out how much space the book occupied.

You would have found the volume of the book. Volume is the amount of space an object or a material occupies. Can you measure the length, width, or height of a substance like water? Liters and milliliters are the most common units used to express the volume of water and similar substances. **Figure 4-6** demonstrates volume measurement of a sugar cube and water.

How much space do you think a small rock takes up? Can you use a ruler to help you find its volume?

Figure 4-6

A milliliter and a cubic centimeter are equivalent measures of volume—the amount of space an object or a material occupies.

A The volume of a sugar cube can be found by multiplying its length times its width times its height. The cube's volume is 1 cm x 1 cm x 1 cm or 1 cubic centimeter, written 1 cm^3. Would you say that volume is a physical property? Why?

B If you poured 1 mL of water into a 1-cm cube, the cube would be filled. 1 mL of water occupies exactly 1 cm^3 of space. Although the liter and milliliter are not SI units, they are used with that system.

Explore! ACTIVITY

How can you measure the volume of a rock?

What To Do

1. Use a rock about the size of a golf ball.
2. Add 250 mL of water to a 500-mL beaker.
3. Carefully add the rock.
4. Record *in your Journal* what happens to the level of the water in the beaker. Is the change related to the volume of the rock?

When you put the rock in the beaker, the water level went up. The two materials in the beaker took up more space than the water alone. The amount the water level went up tells you the volume of the rock. You can find the volume of the rock by subtracting the volume before the rock was added from the final volume.

DID YOU KNOW?

A newborn African elephant is about 95 cm high and has a mass of about 120 kg. By the time the elephant reaches full size (at about age 20), it is 340 cm high and has a mass of about 5400 kg.

■ Mass

Although you can now find the volume of a book, a rock, or a glass of water, can you tell how much material is in each one? Mass is the amount of matter in an object or a material. Look at the table tennis ball and golf ball in **Figures 4-7** and **4-8**. The golf ball has more mass than the table tennis ball.

If you study **Table 4-1** on page 128, you'll notice that kilogram is an SI unit of mass. Masses of small objects are measured in grams.

Like length and volume, mass is a physical property that is used to describe materials. Knowing the mass of an object could be useful in gathering more information about the object. How might knowing the mass and the volume of an object be useful?

Figure 4-7

The golf ball contains more material than the table tennis ball. You might say the golf ball has more matter. Mass is the amount of matter in an object or in a material. The golf ball has more mass than the table tennis ball.

Inside a golf ball

Inside a table tennis ball

Figure 4-8

This double pan balance clearly shows that although the table tennis ball and the golf ball appear to have about the same volume, their masses are quite different. Which would feel heavier if you picked them up? Why?

Density

Which of the grocery bags shown in **Figure 4-9** would you rather carry? Density is another physical property used to describe materials. **Density** is the amount of mass an object or a material has compared to its volume. Density can be expressed as the mass of an object divided by its volume. Recall that grams (g) are units of mass, and cubic centimeters (cm^3) are units of volume. So one way density can be measured is in grams per cubic centimeter, written g/cm^3.

Suppose two identical bags were tightly closed, and you couldn't see inside them. Would you be able to tell which bag contained sand and which contained sugar? Surely you could determine the mass of the material in each bag. Perhaps you could guess the volume of each material. But suppose you knew the density of the material in each bag. Would you then be able to tell whether a particular bag contained sand or sugar?

Because sand and sugar have different densities, you could use this property to tell which material was in each bag. In the activity that follows, you will use density to identify a material.

Figure 4-9

A These grocery bags are the same size and have equal volume. Both are filled to capacity. The bag of paper towels has much less mass than the bag of cans.

B The amount of mass an object or a material has compared to its volume is a measure of its density. Which has the greater density—the bag of cans or the bag of towels?

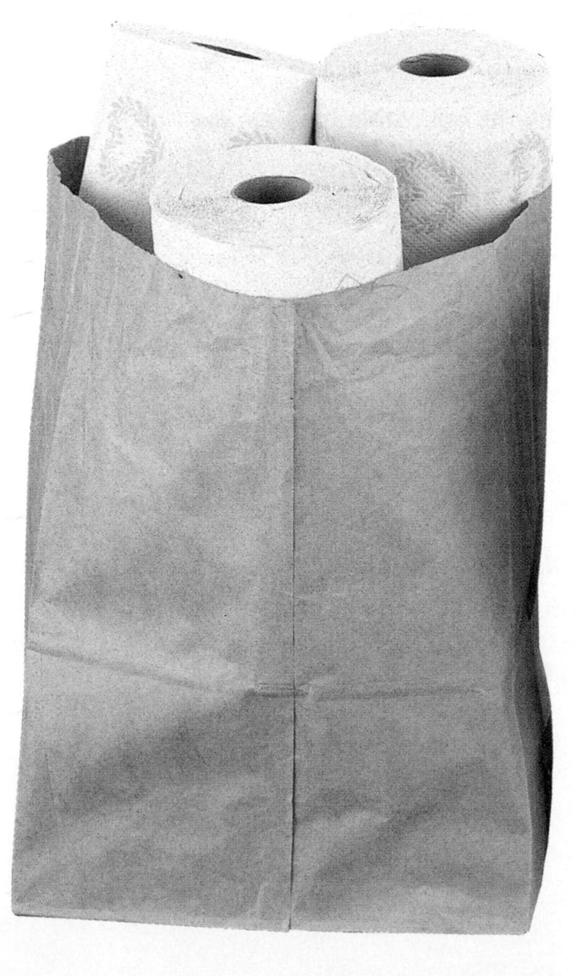

INVESTIGATE!

Using Density

In this activity, you will find the density of three materials. You will use this information to help you identify an unknown material.

Problem

How can density be used to identify an unknown material?

Safety Precautions

Avoid open flames.

Materials

- water
- rubbing alcohol
- unknown (liquid) substance
- 100-mL graduated cylinder
- saturated saltwater mixture
- pan balance and set of masses
- goggles

What To Do

1. Copy the data table *into your Journal.*
2. Use the balance to measure the mass, in grams, of a clean, dry graduated cylinder (see photo ***A***). Record the mass in your table.
3. Fill the cylinder with water to the 50-mL mark (see photo ***B***).
4. ***Measure*** the mass of the filled cylinder and record it in your table under the heading *Total Mass* (see photo **C**). Then discard the water as directed by your teacher.
5. ***Calculate*** the mass of the water by subtracting the mass of the empty cylinder from the total mass. Record the result under the heading *Actual Mass.*

Data and Observations					
Material	Mass of Cylinder	Total Mass	Actual Mass	Volume	Density (g/cm³)
Water				50 mL	
Salt water				50 mL	
Alcohol				50 mL	
Unknown				50 mL	

6 Repeat Steps 3-5, first using the salt water, then the rubbing alcohol, and finally the unknown material. **CAUTION:** *Alcohol burns readily, and its fumes can be irritating. Wear goggles. Be sure that the room is well-ventilated, and there are no open flames.*

7 Record the data for each material.

Analyzing

1. ***Calculate*** the density for each material by dividing its actual mass by its volume. Round to two decimal places.
2. Which known material had the highest density?

Concluding and Applying

3. What was the unknown material?
4. How did finding the density of the unknown material help you identify it?
5. **Going Further** What other physical properties might you also look for and measure in identifying materials?

Figure 4-10

A **The densities of milk and seawater are both 1.03 g per cm³. What tools of identification other than density could you use to identify these substances?**

B **This bolt and piece of chalk are nearly the same length and volume. What tools of identification could you use to identify these substances?**

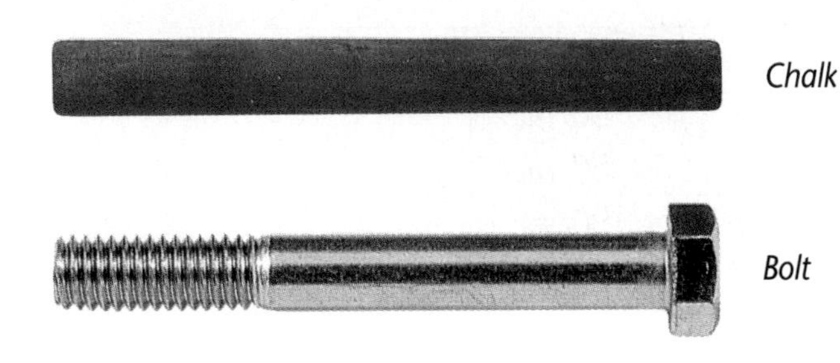

C **This 1/2 kilogram of sugar and 1/2 kilogram of salt have the same mass and are the same color. What tools of identification could you use to identify these substances?**

Salt

Sugar

Like sand and sugar, the water, salt water, and alcohol you used in the Investigate have different densities. These differences helped you to identify an unknown substance.

■ Tools of Identification

You already have many tools in your material identification kit. The physical properties of color, shape, length, volume, mass, and density are some of these tools or clues. Look at the objects pictured in **Figure 4-10**. Is knowing just the density enough to identify these objects? Is knowing only the length and volume enough information? What about mass and color? When you are trying to identify materials, remember to use every clue or tool you have available. Using only one or two tools alone may not be completely reliable. As you continue with this chapter, you will be adding more tools to your identification kit.

check your UNDERSTANDING

1. Choose an object or a substance that you use at home or at school. Describe it using at least three of the physical properties you learned about in this section.
2. How do length, volume, and mass differ from one another? What units are used to measure each?
3. What physical properties of a wooden block is its density related to? How could density be used to identify another sample of wood?
4. **Apply** How might you use physical properties to identify and separate broken glass and water?

4-3 Physical and Chemical Changes

Physical Changes

Think about the different properties of chalk. Length, color, and brittleness are some of those properties. Do substances change when you change their physical properties? Does chalk still remain chalk?

Section Objectives
- Distinguish between physical and chemical changes.
- Differentiate between chemical and physical properties.

Key Terms
physical change
chemical change
chemical property

Figure 4-11

A When you break sticks of chalk in pieces, length and mass change. But the substance is still chalk.

B Even if you ground the pieces to powder, you would still have chalk. Breaking and grinding are called physical changes.

Find Out! ACTIVITY

Do changes in physical properties affect substances?

What To Do

1. Put an empty can with no label on it into the freezer for use in a little while.
2. Remove one ice cube from the freezer and place it on a small dish. Watch what happens. Is the substance that forms the same as the substance that made up the ice cube?
3. Put the dish with this substance in it back in the freezer. Observe the dish after an hour. What changed? How does this new substance compare with an ice cube?
4. With your teacher's help, boil some water. Is the steam that goes into the air the same substance as the water you started with?
5. Remove the can from the freezer. Using tongs, carefully hold the cold can near the steam. Record what happens *in your Journal.*

Conclude and Apply

1. How are ice and steam the same as the water you drink?
2. How are they different?

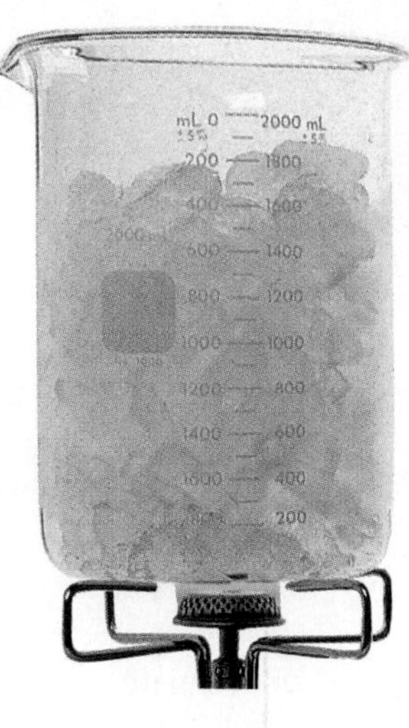

Figure 4-12

A When ice cubes melt, their shape changes.

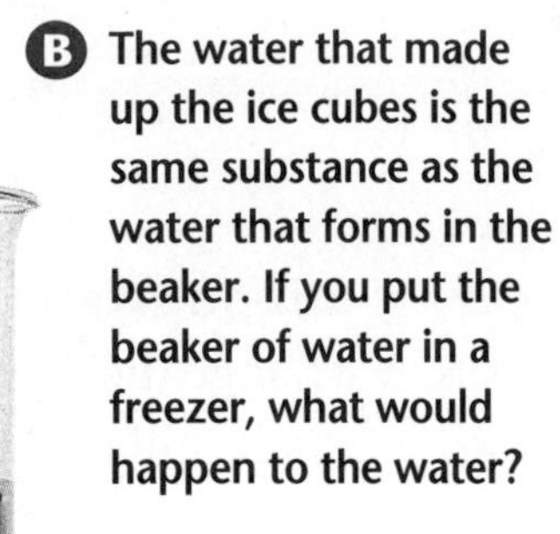

B The water that made up the ice cubes is the same substance as the water that forms in the beaker. If you put the beaker of water in a freezer, what would happen to the water?

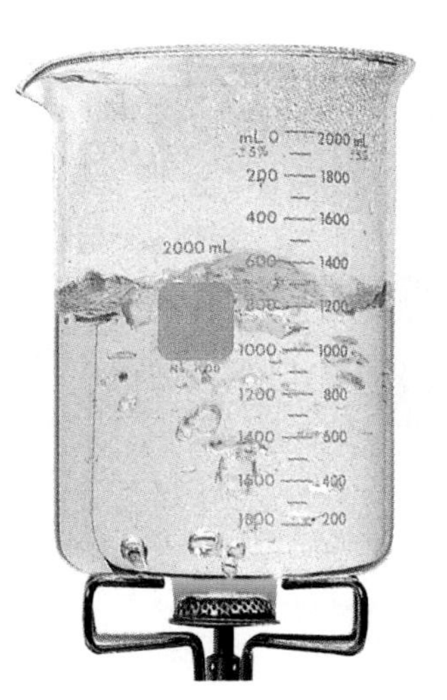

C If you boil the water, its shape and volume would again change, but the substance remains water. Boiling, melting, and freezing are physical changes.

In the Find Out activity, some of the physical properties of the substance water changed, but the water itself was not changed. Changes in physical properties caused by melting, freezing, boiling, and breaking, for example, are physical changes. In a **physical change**, the physical properties of a substance may change, but the kind of substance does not change. You can change the physical properties of many substances. All of the changes will be physical changes and will not change the identity of the substance. But when a chemical change occurs, such as wood being burned, is the identity of the substance changed? Let's find out.

Can the identity of a substance be changed?

Wear safety goggles while you or others are doing this activity.

What To Do

1. Observe the physical properties of an old, discolored copper penny.
2. Place the penny in a small glass jar with a lid.
3. Add about 2 tablespoons of household ammonia and close the jar quickly. Observe the contents of the jar after one-half hour.
4. With forceps, carefully remove the penny and rinse it off with water. Dry it with a paper towel and examine it. Do you think the penny will be old-looking again if you let it sit for awhile?

Conclude and Apply

1. *In your Journal,* record what ways the properties of the penny and the ammonia changed.
2. Do you think the substances changed?

Chemical Changes

In the Find Out activity, you saw that some of the copper in the penny was changed into a different substance. A change during which one of the substances in a material changes into a different substance is a **chemical change**. During a chemical change, the identity of a substance changes.

What clues did you have that a chemical change took place in the penny? Certainly, the change to the shiny copper color was one indication. What other clues can tell you that a chemical change has taken place? The smell of burnt toast or an automobile's exhaust fumes can be evidence that new substances have been formed. The smell is different from the smell of bread or gasoline. The foaming of fizzy tablets in a glass of water and the smell of ozone in the air after a thunderstorm are also signs that chemical changes have occurred. When a rocket blasts off, the light, sound, and smoke that accompany it are all clues that chemical changes are taking place.

Figure 4-13

A Wood chips are made of certain substances.

B When wood chips are set afire, a chemical change takes place.

C Are the ashes and smoke that result still wood? Why?

How Do We Know?

Tests for Chemical Change

Sometimes the usual clues for identifying a chemical change do not work. Perhaps there is no smell or maybe you missed the flash of light. There is one way you can be sure a chemical change has taken place. If the substances after the change are different from the substances before the change, you can be certain the change was chemical.

There are several tests that tell you what substances are present in a material. One such test is a little like looking at the colors of a rainbow formed when the sun shines through drops of rain. This test involves using an instrument called a spectroscope to look at the colors produced by glowing substances.

When viewed through a spectroscope, each glowing substance produces its own personal rainbow. Sodium, for instance, produces a particular yellow light. No other substance produces the same color light as sodium.

If the light produced by a glowing substance has the same colors in it before and after a change, then the substances have not been changed. You could conclude that the change was physical. What would you conclude if the colors of light produced before and after a change are different?

Chemical Properties

Wood burns because there is something about it that makes it able to burn. This characteristic, called flammability, is a chemical property of wood. A **chemical property** is any characteristic that gives a substance the ability to undergo a chemical change. Why are fire doors not made out of wood?

SKILLBUILDER

Observing and Inferring

Observe a burning candle and record your observations. For example, you might note how the candle changes over time. What evidence do you observe that physical and chemical changes are taking place as the candle burns? If you need help, refer to the **Skill Handbook** on page 659.

Some substances undergo chemical change when they are exposed to light. The next time you visit a drugstore, look around. Notice that some vitamins, drugs, and other products that are sensitive to light are stored in containers that light can't get through. These substances are changed into other substances when light comes in contact with them. Hydrogen peroxide, when exposed to light, changes chemically into water and oxygen gas and is no longer useful for cleaning wounds.

Figure 4-14

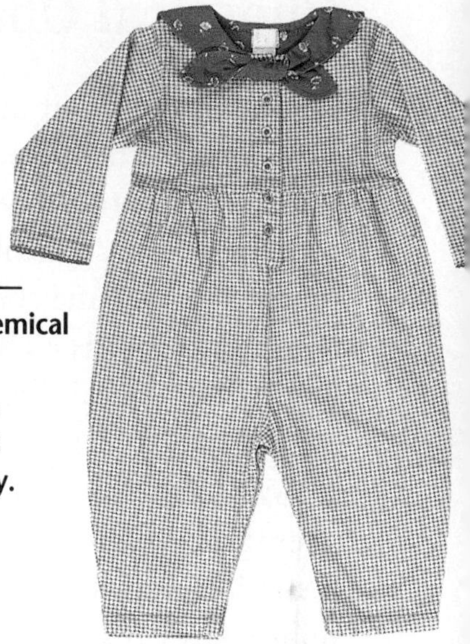

A Most untreated cloth is flammable—it has the chemical property of flammability, which means it burns easily.

B This playsuit has been badly burned in a test for flammability. Since 1953, The Flammable Fabrics Act has made it illegal to sell children's sleepwear in the United States that burns easily. To comply with this law and keep people safe, manufacturers chemically treat clothing to reduce its flammability.

check your UNDERSTANDING

1. When you mix sugar in water, the sugar disappears. Explain why this is an example of a physical change rather than a chemical change.
2. How is flammability different from burning?
3. Why is light sensitivity considered a chemical property rather than a physical property?
4. **Apply** Give one example of a physical change and one example of a chemical change that might occur when a meal is prepared.

4-4 States of Matter

Solids, Liquids, and Gases

Section Objectives

- Distinguish among solids, liquids, and gases.
- Describe physical changes relating to solids, liquids, and gases.

Can you see a way to group some objects together in the photo below? Perhaps you'd put the water, alcohol, and seawater in one group. What properties do sand, sugar, a penny, a nail, and a rock have in common? In which group would you put the air inside the jar? Practically everything you are likely to see or use can be classified as a solid, a liquid, or a gas. These terms refer to the three basic states of matter. Clearly solids, liquids, and gases have different properties. What properties can you use to identify solids, liquids, and gases? You will group objects in the following activity.

Explore! ACTIVITY

How can objects be grouped?

What To Do

1. Look at the objects and materials pictured in the photograph below.
2. Can you see a way to group some objects together?
3. *In your Journal,* write down your suggested classifications and place each object under the appropriate heading.
4. Can you think of a different method of grouping these objects together?

Identifying Solids

You probably have a pretty clear idea of what a solid is. Certainly a rock is solid. But how would you describe a solid so that anyone would know what you mean? You might say that a solid is hard. Cotton balls and pillows are solids, too, yet they don't seem very hard, do they? The following activity explores the common properties of solids.

Explore! ACTIVITY

What do all solids have in common?

What To Do

1. Examine a small rock, a fork, a penny, a paper clip, a cotton ball, a feather, a grain of sand, and any other solid you can find.
2. List *in your Journal* as many physical properties of solids as you can. Do they seem to have any physical properties in common?
3. Imagine placing these objects in different containers such as a tray or a bowl. Do you think the shape or size of any solid will change during such activities?

Figure 4-15

Every substance has its own melting point.

Paraffin melts between 50° C and 57° C.

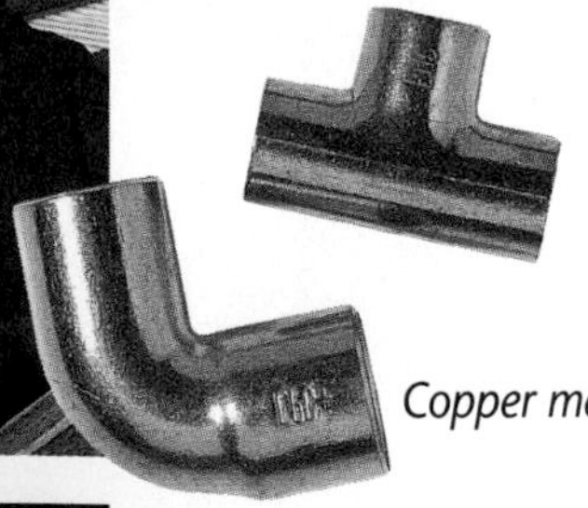

Copper melts at 1083° C.

Silver melts at 961° C.

None of the solids changed in size or shape when you held it or put it in different containers. Any material that has a definite volume and a definite shape is a solid.

Melting is a physical change in which a solid becomes a liquid. An ice cube would melt in your hand but a penny wouldn't. Why do these two solids act so differently?

Room temperature is about 23°C. Ice melts at 0°C, which is lower than room temperature, while copper doesn't melt until its temperature reaches a little more than 1083°C. So, copper has a much higher melting point than ice. Each solid substance has its own melting point. Melting point is a physical property of solid substances.

Identifying Liquids

You know that when a solid melts it forms a liquid. Yet the properties of liquids are clearly different from the properties of solids. What properties do all liquids share that could help you identify them?

Solid carbon dioxide changes to carbon dioxide gas without first changing to a liquid. Because of this property, solid carbon dioxide, often called dry ice, is used to make smoke rise up from the stage in plays and concerts. The smoke is actually water vapor condensing as it comes into contact with cold carbon dioxide gas.

Find Out! ACTIVITY

What do all liquids have in common?

What To Do

1. Find several see-through containers having different shapes. The more unusual the shape the better.
2. Add some food coloring to a pitcher of water.
3. Use a measuring cup or graduated cylinder to pour the same amount of colored water into each container. Observe what happens to the shape of the water in each container.
4. Pour the water from one container back into the graduated cylinder. Did the volume change?

Conclude and Apply

1. *In your Journal*, record whether the shape of the colored water changed. When?
2. Do liquids have a definite volume? How do you know?

As you observed in the Find Out activity, liquids can be poured, and can change shape to fit the container they are in. Any matter that has a definite volume, but takes the shape of its container is a liquid.

Freezing is a physical change in which a liquid becomes a solid. Each liquid has its own freezing point. Water, for example, freezes at 0°C. Mercury, which is a liquid at room temperature, won't freeze until the temperature is -38.87°C. Like the melting point of a solid, the freezing point of a liquid is a physical property.

Figure 4-16

When grape juice is in a container, it takes the shape of the container. Liquids do not have a definite shape the way solids do. This physical property can help you identify liquids. Any matter that has a definite volume, but takes the shape of its container, is a liquid.

Identifying Gases

Air is a mixture of gases that is all around you, but you can't see it. How can you tell when a substance is a gas?

Explore! ACTIVITY

What are some properties of gases?

What To Do

1. Blow up two differently shaped balloons. Record what happens *in your Journal.*
2. Cover a clear, glass jar with a cap. Cover a rectangular container with a piece of cardboard. What is the shape of the air occupying each container?
3. Put a drop or two of rubbing alcohol into a small, flat dish. What happens after a few minutes? Hold a mirror close to your mouth and gently breathe out onto the mirror. What do you observe?

Earth Science CONNECTION

Are Tin and Oxygen Liquids?

The state of a substance depends upon its temperature. We classify a substance as solid, liquid, or gas according to which state it is in at "room temperature" on Earth—23°C.

Water

You know that water freezes at 0°C and boils at 100°C. Water can exist naturally in the solid, liquid, and gaseous states on Earth. But what about other planets? What is "room temperature" on them? The surface temperature of a planet would determine in what state a substance would be.

If you lived on Mercury or Neptune, would substances exist in the same states as they do on Earth? On Mercury, surface temperatures may range from -193°C to 427°C just from nighttime to daytime. If water existed on Mercury, it would constantly be changing states.

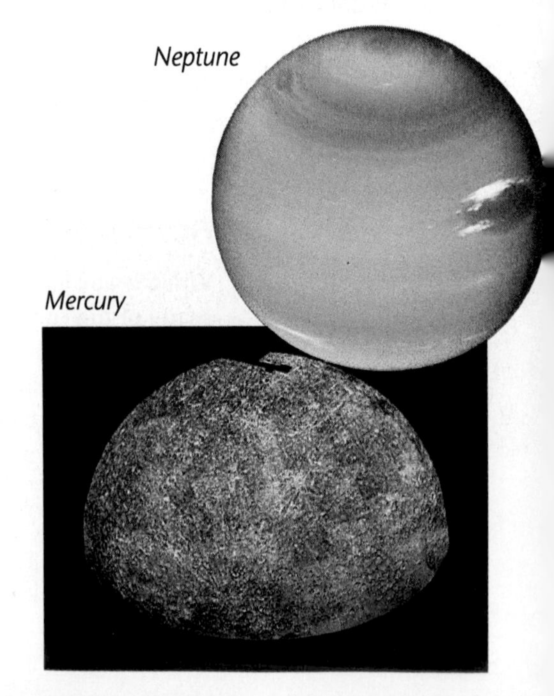

When you blow into a balloon, the gases you breathe out go into the balloon. These gases take up space inside the balloon, so they have volume. Could you measure the volume using a graduated cylinder? What did you conclude from the Explore activity about the shape of gases? Matter that has no definite shape and no definite volume is a gas.

A gas spreads out to fill a container it's in, no matter how large the container. Remember what happened to the alcohol in the dish in the Explore activity? After a few minutes, it disappeared into the air. The liquid alcohol quickly turned into a gas. The alcohol evaporated. When you open a bottle

Figure 4-17

A If you drop an antacid tablet into a glass of water, the sodium hydrogen carbonate in the tablet releases carbon dioxide gas bubbles.

B The bubbles rise to the surface, break, and become part of the air in the room. Carbon dioxide, like all gases, has no definite shape and no definite volume. What is the main difference between a liquid and a gas?

Iron, Lead, and Gases

What about iron and lead? Look at the table. Is there anywhere on Earth where these substances would exist as liquids? How about on Mercury? As you can see, lead would sometimes be in the liquid state if it were found on Mercury.

Substance	Melting Point, °C	Boiling Point, °C
Hydrogen	-259	-253
Iron	1536	2860
Lead	327	1740
Oxygen	-218	-183
Tin	232	2270

What about gases? We just assume that oxygen and carbon dioxide are gases. That's because average temperatures on Earth are above the boiling points of these substances. Remember that during the process of boiling, a liquid is changing to a gas. It doesn't have to be considered hot by humans living on Earth.

Planet	Temperature
Mercury	–193 to 427°C
Earth	–88 to 58°C
Mars	–124 to -31°C
Saturn	–176°C
Neptune	–218°C

Saturn

Earth

You Try It!

Look at the boiling points of the substances in the table above. Then look at the temperatures of the planets on the table to the left. On which planet(s) would tin be a liquid? On which planet(s) would oxygen be a liquid?

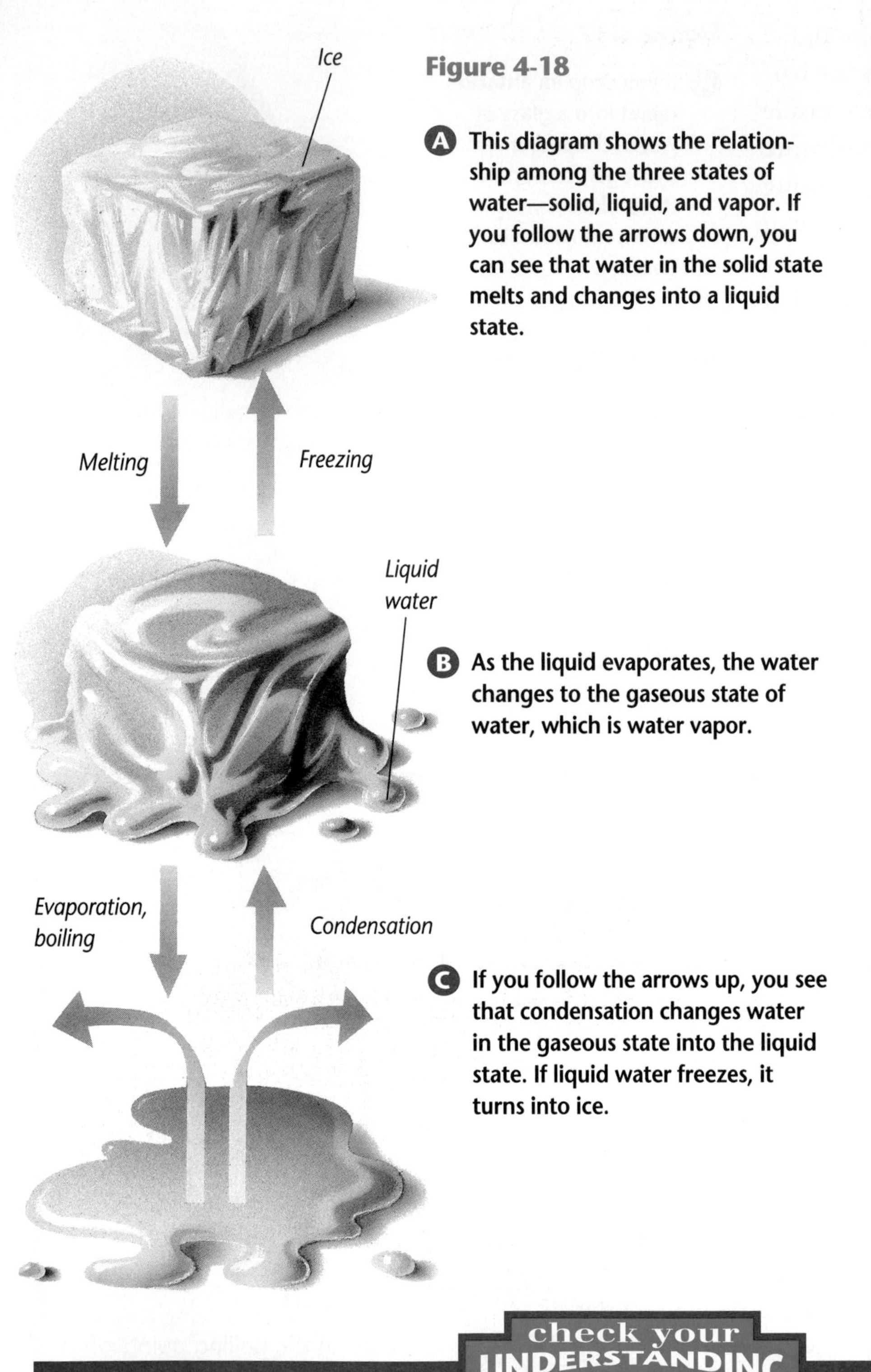

Figure 4-18

A This diagram shows the relationship among the three states of water—solid, liquid, and vapor. If you follow the arrows down, you can see that water in the solid state melts and changes into a liquid state.

B As the liquid evaporates, the water changes to the gaseous state of water, which is water vapor.

C If you follow the arrows up, you see that condensation changes water in the gaseous state into the liquid state. If liquid water freezes, it turns into ice.

of perfume, which contains alcohol, the odor soon becomes noticeable. The gas given off does not stay in the opened container. It spreads out to occupy the entire space available to it.

Can a gas become a liquid? What happens when you bring a cold can near steam? Some of the boiling water goes into the air as water vapor. The water forms liquid water when it touches the cold can. The water vapor condenses to form liquid water. Cooling speeds up condensation. Now think about what condensed on the mirror in the Explore activity. How do you know there is water vapor in the air you breathe out?

Figure 4-18 shows the relationship among solids, liquids, and gases. How can what you've learned in this chapter help explain how smoke, fog, and other mixtures in the air can reach areas thousands of meters from their source?

check your UNDERSTANDING

1. How are a brick, milk, and helium, which is sometimes used to fill balloons, different?
2. Is chocolate syrup a solid, a liquid, or a gas? Why do you say so?
3. What physical change occurs when you leave ice cream in a dish on the counter for a few minutes?
4. **Apply** Describe a place or a situation where you could find water as a solid, as a liquid, and a gas all at the same time.

Taking a Spin

Did you ever go into an amusement park ride that looked like a large, round room? You and the other riders stand with your back against the wall. Then the room begins to rotate, and you are pressed against the wall. When the room is spinning fast enough, the floor drops, and you are held against the wall.

What Is a Centrifuge?

In scientific and technical work, machines that work very much like this amusement park ride are often used to separate materials from mixtures. These machines are called centrifuges, and they work by separating materials in mixtures according to the density of the material. A centrifuge is pictured on this page.

How Are Centrifuges Used?

A good example of the use of a centrifuge is for the separation of the materials in blood. Blood is a heterogeneous mixture containing plasma, blood cells, and other materials. Since plasma and blood cells are used for different purposes, it is necessary to separate them. Blood is placed in small tubes that hang down from the part of the machine that spins. The tubes are mounted so that, as the machine begins to spin, the tubes pivot upward into a horizontal position. As the machine spins around, sometimes at thousands of spins per minute, the denser materials move to the bottom of the tube, and the less dense materials stay toward the top of the tube. Because red and white corpuscles, plasma, platelets, and other materials in the blood have different densities, they will separate.

You Try It!

Other liquids can be separated by using the action of a centrifuge. For example, cream can be separated from milk. Which do you think has the greater density—cream or milk? Design an experiment to find out. You might be surprised.

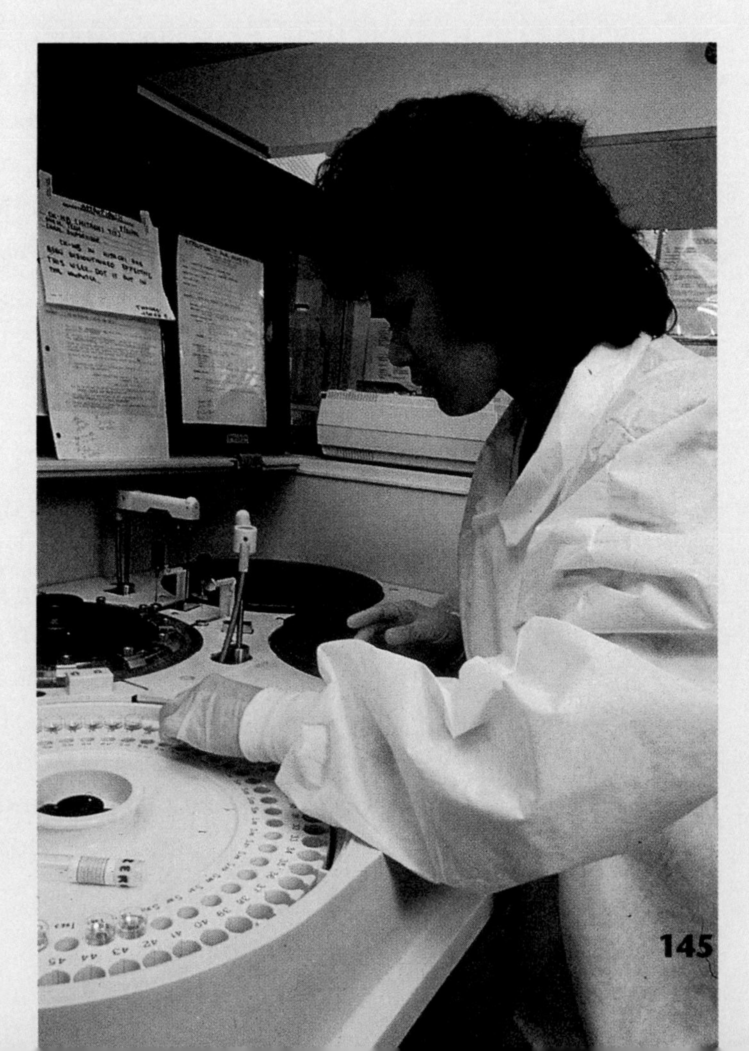

Metrics for All?

In the United States, athletes compete on courses that are measured in meters, medicine is sold in milligrams and milliliters, and many automobile parts are measured in metric units. However, carpenters still buy lumber in feet and inches, and farmers measure their land in acres and their crops in bushels. Fabric is sold by the yard, and milk by the quart. Most highway signs give distances in miles and speed limits in miles per hour.

The Metric Conversion Act

In 1975, the Metric Conversion Act became law. The law states that the federal government will coordinate and plan the increasing use of the metric system on a voluntary basis. So, for the time being, we are living with two different systems.

The Metric System Controversy

For nearly 100 years, those favoring the metric system have argued for its widespread use in the United States, but opponents have argued just as vigorously against it. People from industry say that such a change would require them to replace or convert their machinery—a costly process. Those in favor say that machinery is often replaced anyway, and the cost would be a one-time expense that would produce lasting benefits. Trade would be easier with other countries, most of which use metrics.

Since the metric system is based on multiples of 10, calculations are much easier. Using metrics might reduce calculation errors and save time. Some people have estimated that up to two years could be cut out of traditional math courses in school because fractions and conversions would not be taught.

EXPAND your view

The System

The metric system, called SI from the French "Le Systeme Internationale d'Unités," is the standard system of measurement used worldwide. All SI units and their symbols are accepted and understood by the scientific community. In SI, each type of measurement has a base unit—meter (m) for length, kilogram (kg) for mass, etc. Look at the table on the following page to see these base units.

In the English system, you have to remember that there are 12 inches in one foot, 3 feet in one yard, and 5280 feet in one mile. In SI units, there are prefixes that indicate which multiple of 10 should be used. You would say that there are 10 millimeters in a centimeter, 100 centimeters in a meter, and 1000 meters in a kilometer—all multiples of 10.

Comparing English and SI Units

1 mile

1 kilometer

(Mile is 1.6 times longer than kilometer)

1 yard

1 meter

(1.09 x longer than yard)

1 qt

1 liter

(1.06 x larger than quart)

1 pound

1 kilogram

(weighs 2.2 pounds)

Metric Conversion

Many people resist the switch to metrics because they are not very familiar with metric units. They have grown up using feet, pounds, and gallons and feel more comfortable continuing to use them. Most people, however, do not really know very much about these units, especially about how they relate to each other. Do you know how many cubic inches are in a fluid ounce? How many ounces are in a pound, or inches in a mile? For that matter, did you know that there are two kinds of miles—the nautical mile and the statute mile? How many feet are in each? How many square feet make one acre?

SI Base Units

Measurement	Unit	Symbol
Length	Meter	m
Mass	Kilogram	kg
Time	Second	s
Electric current	Ampere	A
Temperature	Kelvin	K
Amount of substance	Mole	mol
Light intensity	Candela	cd

Should We Convert?

Do you think the government should pass a law requiring that the United States convert completely to SI units by a given time? Would the advantages of adopting the metric system outweigh the possible disadvantages?

Look at the diagram comparing SI and English units. Which SI unit would you use to measure each of the following?

a. a large carton of milk
b. your height
c. your mass
d. the length of your arm
e. distance across a state

Alma Woodsey Thomas—Color Field Painter

Alma Thomas was an artist who achieved prominence in the mainstream art community. She worked in the modern tradition of Color Field painting.

Education

She was born in 1891 in Columbus, Georgia. Because her aunts were teachers, she decided at an early age that teaching could be her way to a better life, too. Her family moved to Washington, D.C., in 1907. In 1924, she was the first graduate of the new art department at Howard University.

Thomas taught art in the Washington schools for 35 years. During that time, she earned an M.A. at Teachers College of Columbia University. During her teaching career, she exhibited realistic paintings in shows of African American artists. In the 1950s, she took painting classes at American University and became interested in color and abstract art.

Color and Abstract Art

By 1959, Thomas's paintings had become abstract. By 1964, she had discovered a way to create an image through small dabs of paint laid edge to edge across the painting's surface. In *Iris, Tulips, Jonquils, and Crocuses,* the color bands move vertically and horizontally across the canvas to represent a breeze moving over a sunlit spring garden. In

Autumn Leaves Fluttering in the Wind (shown at right), rust-colored patches move in patterns like those of swirling autumn leaves. The glimpses of blue, yellow, and green between the patches represent the sky and land.

Thomas's paintings are mosaic patches of color that she said, "represent my communion with nature." She wrote, "Color is life. Light reveals to us the spirit and living soul of the world through colors."

What Do You Think?

Alma Thomas wrote that she was "intrigued with the changing colors of nature as the seasons progress." Describe how you would paint a natural scene using the Color Field painting style.

chapter 4 REVIEWING MAIN IDEAS

Science Journal

Review the statements below about the big ideas presented in this chapter, and think about each question. Then, reread your answers to the Did You Ever Wonder questions at the beginning of the chapter. *In your Science Journal*, write a paragraph about how your understanding of the big ideas in the chapter has changed or expanded.

1 A substance is made of only one kind of material. A mixture consists of two or more substances, each with its own identity. ***Are the materials shown substances or mixtures?***

2 An element is a substance that cannot be broken down further into simpler substances by ordinary physical or chemical means. A compound is made of two or more elements that are chemically combined, and always has the same chemical composition. ***Does a chemical compound have the same physical properties as the elements that make it up?***

3 Physical properties, such as color, shape, hardness, length, mass, volume, and density, are used to describe and identify materials. ***Are chemical properties, such as flammability, also used to describe and identify materials?***

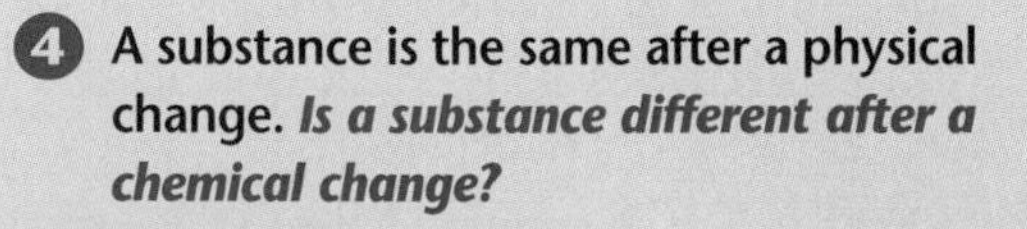

4 A substance is the same after a physical change. ***Is a substance different after a chemical change?***

chapter 4 CHAPTER REVIEW

Using Key Science Terms

Give two examples of each of the following:

chemical change
chemical property
compound
density
element
homogeneous mixture
heterogeneous mixture
mixture
physical change
physical property
substance

Understanding Ideas

Answer the following questions in your Journal *using complete sentences.*

1. Name two ways of separating mixtures.
2. What do you need to know about a material to determine its density?
3. a. How do a chemical change and a physical change differ?
   b. How do a heterogeneous mixture and a homogeneous mixture differ?
   c. How do a physical property and a chemical property differ?
   d. How do a mixture and a substance differ?
4. How do the properties of solids, liquids, and gases differ?

Developing Skills

Use your understanding of the concepts developed in this chapter to answer each of the following questions.

1. **Concept Mapping** Using the following terms, complete the concept map of classification below: *compounds, elements, heterogeneous, mixtures*

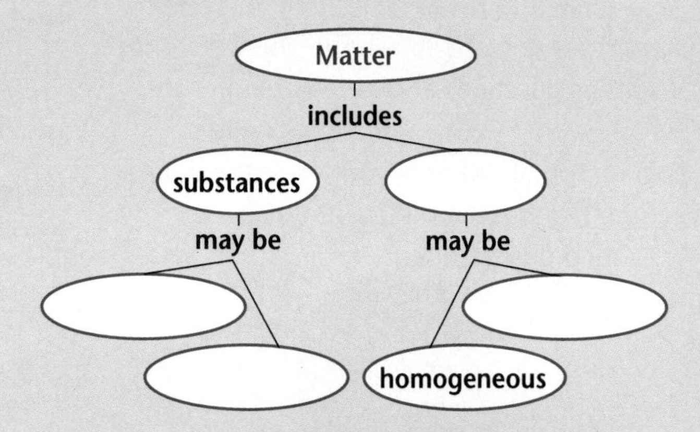

2. **Making and Using Graphs** The following graph shows the mass of a given number of pebbles. Use the graph to: a) estimate the number of pebbles in a sample that has a mass of 20 g; b) estimate the mass of 110 pebbles.

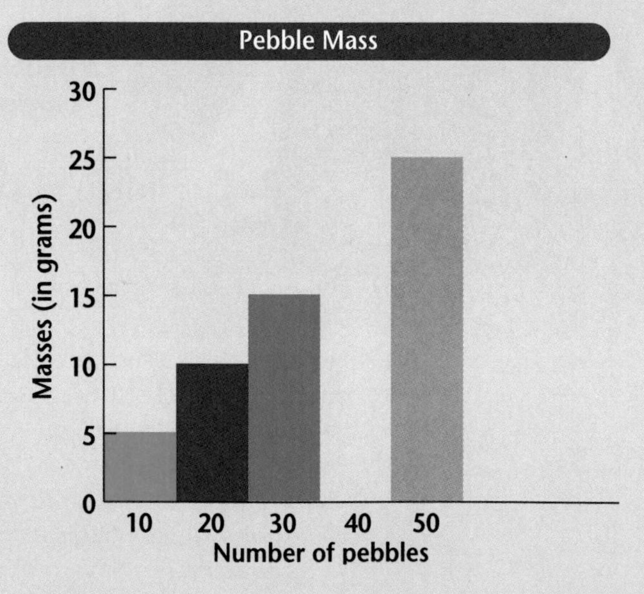

3. **Observing and Inferring** You fill a pan up to the top with cold water, which you plan to heat to make tea. Before the water comes to a boil, you notice that a small amount of water has spilled over the top of the pan. How did this happen?

CHAPTER REVIEW

4. **Measuring in SI** An object has a density of 1700 kg/m^3. What is its density in units of g/m^3?

Critical Thinking

In your Journal, *answer each of the following questions.*

1. How might you determine whether a sample of matter is a substance or a mixture?
2. The density of steel is greater than the density of water, so a solid bar of steel sinks when it is placed in water. What can you infer about a steel ocean liner, knowing that it floats on water?
3. You have a 200 cm^3 glass of milk. What is the mass of the milk?

Problem Solving

Read the following paragraph and discuss your answers in a brief paragraph.

You are walking along the beach, when you find a small, shiny chunk that looks like silver. You would like to determine whether the chunk is actually pure silver or just some other silvery-colored material.

1. Assume that you have available a sample of silver having the same mass as your chunk. Using only materials you can find in your kitchen, how can you use density to see if the material might be silver?
2. Assume your density test shows that your chunk might be silver. With the help of a chemist, how might you use chemical properties to further test your chunk to see if it is silver?

CONNECTING IDEAS

Discuss each of the following in a brief paragraph.

1. **Theme—Systems and Interactions** List at least two physical properties that can be observed using each of your five senses.
2. **Theme—Stability and Change** You know that milk is stored in the refrigerator rather than in the cupboard. Explain why this is so.
3. **Science and Society** Give three arguments in favor of the United States converting completely to the SI system, and three arguments against it. Which arguments do you feel are stronger?
4. **Earth Science Connection** Imagine that a new planet has been discovered farther from the sun than Pluto. Would you expect the new planet to have an atmosphere in which you could breathe? Explain.
5. **How It Works** Explain how centrifuges can be used to separate heterogeneous mixtures, such as blood.

CHAPTER 5

MATTER in SOLUTION

Did you ever wonder...

- Where the sugar goes when it dissolves in a glass of lemonade?
- Why you can add more sugar to a cup of hot tea than to a glass of iced tea?
- Why you don't have to shake milk before you drink it?

Science Journal

Before you begin to study about matter in solution, think about these questions and answer them *in your Science Journal.*

It's a cold morning, and you've just gone into the kitchen for breakfast.

As you eat, changes are going on. Your instant oatmeal is getting soggier in your bowl. Bits of powdered hot chocolate settle out in your cup, but they vanish again when you stir them with your spoon. Your apple juice, however, remains unchanged.

From a scientist's view, you are eating three mixtures made with water. Yet as you have probably guessed by now, not all mixtures look or act the same. Why is your apple juice clear, while your hot chocolate is cloudy? Why doesn't your oatmeal disappear in water like your hot chocolate? This chapter will help you answer questions such as these.

In the activity on the next page, explore materials that seem to disappear in water.

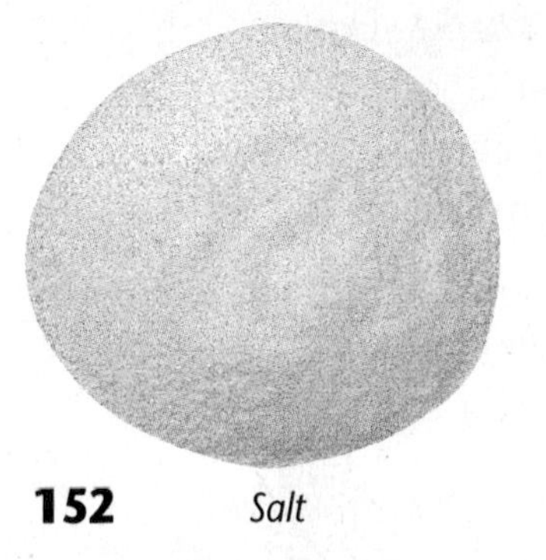

Salt

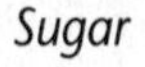

Sugar

Corn meal

Flour

Explore! ACTIVITY

What materials seem to disappear in water?

What To Do

1. Add a teaspoon of sugar, salt, flour, corn meal, and rice to separate glasses of water.
2. Observe and record what happens *in your Journal*.
3. Stir the contents of each glass and wait for a few minutes more.
4. What happens now? Which of the solids seems to disappear? Which can you still see?

Rice

Types of Solutions

Section Objectives
- Classify solutions.
- Define and identify solutes and solvents.
- Describe three factors that affect the rates at which solids and gases dissolve in liquids.

Key Terms

solution
solute
solvent

What Is a Solution?

Think back to the cold-weather breakfast at the beginning of this chapter. The hot chocolate, the oatmeal, and the apple juice were all examples of mixtures, which you read about in Chapter 4. Each was a mixture with water. In the Explore activity, you saw how sugar and salt seem to disappear in water, while flour, corn meal, and rice do not.

Shampoo, toothpaste, and detergent all depend on water to make them work, too. When you clean your hair, teeth, or clothes, you are trying to remove bits of dirt. One way to do this is to mix the dirt with something that will remove it, such as a mixture of soap and water. How can you demonstrate this? The following Find Out activity should help.

How can you make a homemade cleanser?

What To Do

1. Place 8 g of powdered sugar in a mortar.
2. Add two drops of peppermint oil and 3 g of castile soap.
3. Mix these together with a pestle.
4. Add 22 g of calcium carbonate, and mix thoroughly.
5. Finally, add corn syrup until a paste is produced. This is now a homemade cleanser.
6. Carefully stain a small section of material, such as a dishcloth, with dirt.
7. Apply some of your homemade cleanser to an old toothbrush, along with a few drops of water. Try scrubbing the stain. Record what happens *in your Journal.*

Conclude and Apply

1. Wash away the cleanser with a little water. What happens now?
2. Explain *in your Journal* why you think this is happening.

■ Separation of Solutions

If you could separate the ingredients from your cleanser, you would find that their physical appearance has been changed upon mixing, but not their individual properties. Such a material is a mixture, as is shown in **Figure 5-1**. Mixtures may be separated by mechanical means. Can all mixtures be separated as easily as this?

Figure 5-1

Everyday cleansers such as shampoo and bar soap are mixtures. They work in much the same way as the cleanser you made in the Find Out activity.

Find Out! ACTIVITY

Can all mixtures be separated by mechanical means?

What To Do

1. Fill two 400-mL beakers about halfway with water.
2. Add 10 g of sand to the first beaker and 10 g of table salt to the second beaker. Stir both mixtures well.
3. Clamp a funnel to each of two ring stands and fold a piece of filter paper to fit in each.
4. Place an empty beaker underneath each funnel.
5. Slowly pour some of your mixture of sand and water into one funnel.
6. Now, pour some of your mixture of salt and water into the other funnel. Record your observations *in your Journal.*

Conclude and Apply

1. Which mixture leaves something behind on the filter paper?
2. Which mixture does not?
3. Which mixture can be separated by filtering, a mechanical means?

■ Properties of Solutions

Sand and salt form mixtures with water, yet they cannot be separated in the same way. While sand can be separated from water by filtering, salt cannot. Why do you think this is? Certain mixtures, such as salt and water, are called solutions and cannot be separated by filtration. Have you ever made instant soft drink on a hot day and watched the crystals disappear in water as you stirred them? Clear soft drink is an example of a solution. What properties does a solution have that make it different from other kinds of mixtures?

Explore! ACTIVITY

What are the properties of a solution?

What To Do

1. Add 1 teaspoon of soft drink crystals to a quart of water in a clear pitcher. Stir until all the crystals have disappeared.
2. Look carefully at the soft drink. Do you see any crystals floating in the pitcher? Record your observations *in your Journal*.
3. Darken the lights in the room and shine a flashlight through the pitcher. What do you observe?
4. Use a straw to remove a small amount of soft drink from the top of the pitcher. Taste it. Now carefully use the straw to remove a small amount of soft drink from the bottom of the pitcher. Taste it. How do the two samples compare?
5. Cover the pitcher and let it sit undisturbed overnight. Look at the soft drink again the next day. Does it look the same?

When you make a soft drink, you mix together two kinds of materials, soft drink crystal and water. Because they are so small and are mixed evenly throughout the water, you don't see the single particles of soft drink. Also, a sample from the top will have the same number of dissolved particles as one drawn from the bottom and so will taste as sweet. After waiting, neither material will settle out. Any mixture made up of tiny particles that are evenly mixed and do not settle out is called a **solution**.

A solution is made up of two types of materials, one of which may seem to disappear in the other. Remember the soft drink crystal disappearing in the water? Any substance that seems to disappear, or dissolve, is called a **solute**. The substance in which the solute dissolves is called a **solvent**. Generally, the substance present in the largest amount is the solvent. In your soft drink, what is the solute? What is the solvent? Because water can dissolve so many different solutes to form solutions, chemists often call it a universal solvent.

Figure 5-2

The sea is one of the world's largest solutions. Sodium chloride is the major solute and water is the solvent.

Types of Solutions

Solutions are important to all living things, as shown in **Figure 5-3**. Water carries dissolved nutrients to all parts of a plant. The ocean is a vast water solution of minerals and dissolved gases from Earth's crust. Medicines are often solutions of different chemicals. Some of your body fluids, such as urine and saliva, are water solutions.

Solutions may be mixtures of two or more solids, liquids, or gases, or any one of these in another. Some types of solutions are shown in **Figure 5-3**. Typically, the solute is named first, followed by the solvent. For example, if the solute is a gas and the solvent is a liquid, they form a gas-liquid solution. What type of solution is lemonade that is made with powdered drink mix? **Figure 5-3** shows examples of different solutions.

You've separated sand and water by filtering, so you know this mixture is not a solution. Solutions cannot be separated by filtering because the dissolved particles are too small. How can solutions be separated? In the following Investigate, we will examine solutions and evaporation.

Figure 5-3

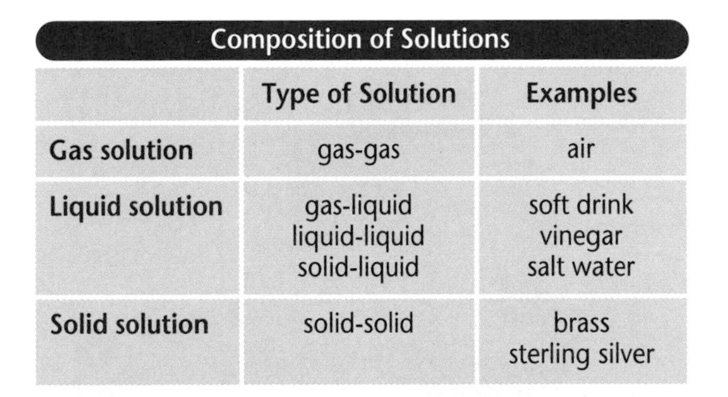

Composition of Solutions

	Type of Solution	Examples
Gas solution	gas-gas	air
Liquid solution	gas-liquid liquid-liquid solid-liquid	soft drink vinegar salt water
Solid solution	solid-solid	brass sterling silver

A The air you breathe is a gas-gas solution of oxygen and other gases dissolved in nitrogen.

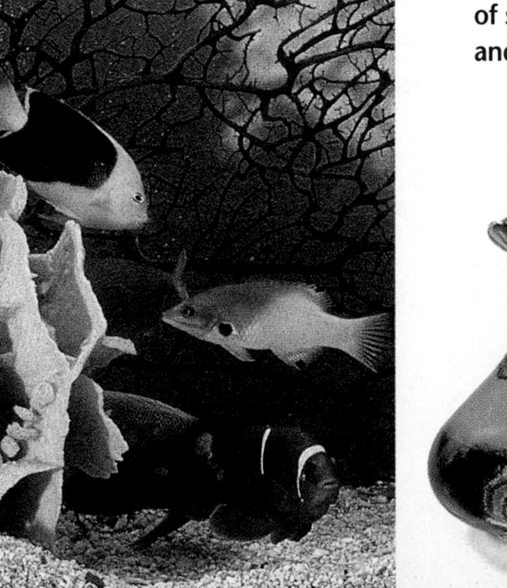

B This salt water aquarium holds a solid-liquid solution of sodium chloride and water.

C Sterling silver is a solid-solid solution of 7.5 percent copper and 92.5 percent silver.

D Vinegar is a liquid-liquid solution, made up of 5 percent acetic acid and 95 percent water.

E What can you observe about this soft drink that indicates that it is a gas-liquid solution?

INVESTIGATE!

Evaporation and Solutions

You've seen that solutions cannot be separated by letting them stand or by filtering. In this activity, you'll try to separate a solution using evaporation.

Problem

Can solutions be separated by evaporation?

Materials

- safety goggles
- Epsom salt (magnesium sulfate)
- large beaker (400 mL)
- thick, water-absorbent string
- water
- graduated cylinder (100 mL)
- 2 small beakers (250 mL)
- spoon or stirring rod

Safety Precautions

What To Do

1. Copy the data table *into your Journal.*
2. Put on your safety goggles. ***Measure*** 200 mL of water into a graduated cylinder and then pour this into the large beaker.
3. Dissolve as much Epsom salt as you can in the water. To do this, slowly add the solute to the water until some of the solute stays undissolved after stirring.

Data and Observations

Date	Observations	
	Beakers	String

A

4 Fill the two small beakers with the Epsom-salt solution. Place them side by side about 10 cm apart. Drape the string between the beakers with the ends of the string submerged in the solutions. It should be set up as in the illustration (see photo ***A***). The string should sag slightly between the beakers. Let the setup stand undisturbed for several days.

5 ***Observe*** the setup every few days and record your observations in your data table.

Analyzing

1. What happened to the water level in the beakers? Where did the water go?

2. What happened on the string between the beakers?

Concluding and Applying

3. ***Predict*** the effect of the following changes in the outcome of this Investigation.

a. You dissolved only half as much Epsom salt in the water.

b. No string was placed between the beakers.

4. Which part of a solid-liquid solution evaporated in the activity, the solute or the solvent? Which part was left behind?

5. **Going Further** ***Infer*** why evaporation can't be used to separate gas-gas solutions?

Epsom salt and hot water make up a solution that has long been a home remedy for reducing inflammation and easing aching muscles.

Dissolving

Figure 5-4

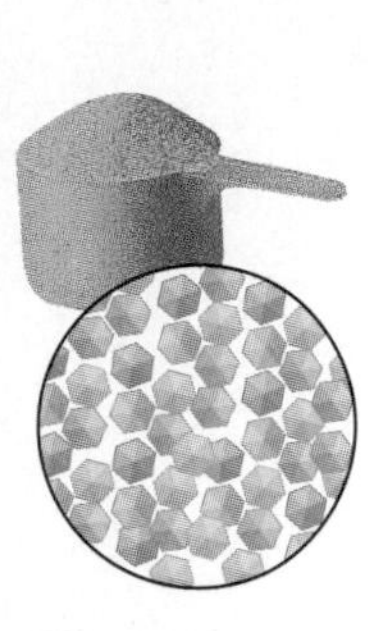

A If you take a scoop of soft drink crystals ...

B and add them to water, the crystals break down.

C The crystal particles become evenly mixed with the water particles.

Remember the last Explore activity? When you added the soft drink crystals to water, the crystals seemed to disappear. You can taste the soft drink, so you know the materials from the crystals are still there. Where did they go? Just how do the particles of solid and liquid mix together in the first place? How does the process of dissolving work?

Figure 5-4 shows how dissolving occurs. How do you think this happens? Earlier you learned that a solution is made up of tiny particles. Does the particle size of a solid affect how fast it can dissolve in a liquid?

Find Out! ACTIVITY

How does particle size affect dissolving?

What To Do

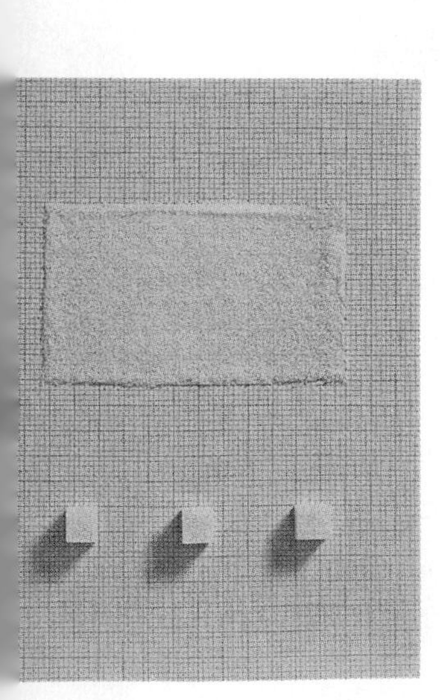

1. Pour 100 mL of distilled water into each of two containers.
2. Grind three sugar cubes into a fine powder. Place this powder on a sheet of folded paper for easy pouring.
3. Have a partner place three whole sugar cubes into one container of water at the exact same time that you add the three powdered cubes to the other container. Immediately start timing. Stir both solutions.
4. *In your Journal,* record the times when the powdered sugar has dissolved and when the three cubes have dissolved. Which took longer to dissolve, the powder or the cubes?
5. Grind up three more sugar cubes. Spread the powder as thinly and as evenly as possible onto a sheet of centimeter graph paper (see photo).
6. Count and record how many squares the powder covers. This number is the surface area, in cm^2, of the part of the paper that is covered.
7. The surface area of the powder is six times that of the area covered. What is the surface area of the three whole sugar cubes? How do these two numbers compare?

Conclude and Apply

1. Which particles seem to dissolve faster—smaller or larger ones?
2. Which particles have a greater total surface area—smaller or larger ones?

A larger surface area lets more solid solute come in contact with more solvent. Grinding or breaking up a solid solute increases the surface area of the solute, as you can see in **Figure 5-5**. Thus, dissolving happens more quickly when a solid solute is broken into smaller pieces. What other factors affect the rate of dissolving?

Figure 5-5

A Each side of a 10-cm cube has a surface area of 100 cm^2. The total surface area for the cube is 600 cm^2.

B When the cube is broken down into eight 5-cm cubes, the total surface area increases to 1200 cm^2. Unbroken, the cube had 6 surfaces. How many surfaces are there now?

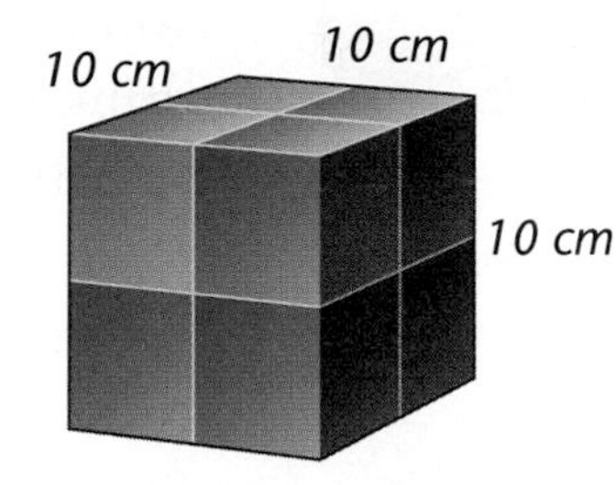

Total surface area = (10 cm × 10 cm) × 6 sides = 600 cm^2

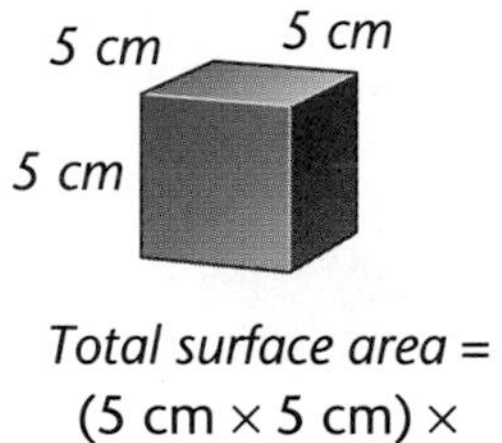

Total surface area = (5 cm × 5 cm) × 6 sides = 150 cm^2

Total surface area = 8 blocks × 150 cm^2 = 1200 cm^2

Find Out! ACTIVITY

How do stirring (or shaking) and temperature affect dissolving?

What To Do

1. Fill two glasses with water.
2. Add 3 teaspoons of sugar to the first glass and let it sit.
3. Add 3 teaspoons of sugar to a second glass and stir the contents rapidly.
4. Stop stirring and let the second glass sit. Record your observations *in your Journal.*
5. Fill a third glass with hot water and a fourth one with ice water. Add 3 teaspoons of sugar to each. Do not stir.
6. In which glass does the sugar seem to dissolve more quickly?
7. Now, stir the contents of each glass. What do you observe?

Conclude and Apply

1. How does shaking or stirring affect dissolving?
2. How does temperature affect dissolving?

Figure 5-6

Ⓐ If a solute, such as dye, is added to a solvent, such as water, the dye will slowly dissolve and mix with the water particles.

Ⓑ Stirring speeds up the dissolving process.

You have now found out that sugar dissolves faster in hot, rather than cold water. **Figure 5-6** shows how the solute and solvent mix together faster when stirred or shaken. Solids are not the only substances that can be dissolved in liquids. As you already know, a carbonated soft drink is an example of a gas dissolved in a liquid. Shaking or stirring an opened bottle of soft drink causes it to spurt out as more gas particles, exposed to the surface, freely escape. Shaking or stirring slows down dissolving for a gas in a liquid, but speeds up dissolving for a solid in a liquid. How does temperature affect the dissolving of a gas in a liquid?

a CLOSER LOOK

Can We Change the Freezing Point?

Water freezes at 32°F (0°C). However, this doesn't always suit our needs. Ice may be great for hockey, but it can be disaster for someone walking on a frozen sidewalk. So, we alter our environment to suit ourselves.

Antifreeze

We use antifreeze to melt ice on car windshields, and to prevent ice from forming in the water used to cool automobile engines. Water takes up more volume when it freezes. If water freezes in a car engine, it can expand enough to crack the engine!

Lowering the Freezing Point

Experiments show that by adding certain substances to water, we may lower the solution's freezing point. The freezing point depends upon the number of particles dissolved in a liquid. When you add

Find Out! ACTIVITY

How does temperature affect dissolving of a gas in a liquid?

What To Do

1. Carefully open a chilled bottle of carbonated soft drink.
2. Cover the opening with a balloon and secure it with tape.
3. Shake the drink. **CAUTION:** *Don't point the bottle at anyone.* Record what happens *in your Journal.*
4. Repeat the procedure with an unchilled bottle of soft drink of the same size, brand, and flavor. Contrast the results from the cold and warm drinks.

Conclude and Apply

Assuming both bottles had an equal amount of gas before they were opened, which bottle had the greater amount of dissolved gas in it after shaking?

antifreeze to the water in the radiator of your car, the freezing point of the water in your radiator goes down to a lower temperature.

Salt

Salt is a substance that lowers water's freezing point and is used to melt snow on roads and sidewalks. Like commercial antifreeze, the more salt that is added, the lower the freezing point of the substance.

You Try It!

1. Fill three small unbreakable containers with equal amounts of cool tap water.
2. Dissolve one tablespoon of salt in one container and two tablespoons of salt in another. Add nothing to the third container of water.
3. Put the three containers of water in your freezer and leave them there. Check them every hour. Which of the contents froze first? Second? Last? Explain your observations *in your Journal.*

SKILLBUILDER

Using Observations to Form a Hypothesis

You are helping set up one fish bowl in your warm, sunny classroom and another in the air-conditioned media center. Both tanks are the same size and contain the same amount of water. Based on the amount of oxygen that can dissolve in the water, to which tank would you be able to add more fish? Explain why. If you need help, refer to the **Skill Handbook** on page 663.

In the last activity, you found that the warm soft drink inflated the balloon more. This happened because when the bottles were opened and the pressure inside them was released, more gas escaped from the warm soft drink than from the cold soft drink. More carbon dioxide gas can dissolve in cold water than in warm water. The same is true for all gases. More gas can dissolve in cooler solvents.

The amount of a gas in a solvent has a very important consequence to fish and other aquatic animals. As Earth's atmosphere warms, the ocean's surfaces warm as well. What happens to the amount of oxygen dissolved in the water as the water is warmed? What effect might this have on fish, which require oxygen in order to live?

All solutions are mixtures, but not all mixtures are solutions. A solution is made up of tiny particles that are evenly mixed and do not settle out on standing. Unlike other types of mixtures, solutions cannot be separated by mechanical means. The rate of dissolving solute in a solvent is influenced by particle size, stirring or shaking, and temperature. As you have seen, however, gas solutes are affected by these actions differently than solid solutes in the same liquid solvents.

Figure 5-7

A The amount of a gas that can be dissolved in a liquid decreases as the temperature of the liquid increases.

B Fish take the oxygen they need to live from the water. What might happen if the temperature of the water in this fish tank increases?

1. Air, vinegar, and sterling silver are three solutions. Identify which kind of solution each is. Name the solute and solvent in each.
2. You sprinkle some powdered sugar on a warm, moist, freshly baked cake. A while later you notice that the powdered sugar has disappeared. What happened to it?
3. A soup recipe calls for bouillon powder or bouillon cubes. Use of which ingredient would speed up the making of the soup? Why does this occur?
4. **Apply** A laboratory receives a bottle of red liquid for analysis. After it sits overnight, bits of red powder are found on the bottom of the bottle. When the lab technicians shine a light through it, the top of the beam appears pink, while the bottom half looks dark red. Small particles are floating throughout the bottle. Does the bottle contain a solution? Explain your answer.

5-2 Solubility and Concentration

Reaching the Limit

Most of the solutions you know about have water as the solvent. Water is the best solvent known because more substances can dissolve in water than in any other liquid. Do you think that two different solutes can dissolve in water in the same amounts? Let's find out.

Section Objectives

- Describe how solubility varies for different solutes and for the same solute at different temperatures.
- Interpret solubility graphs.
- Compare and contrast saturated and unsaturated solutions.
- Infer solution concentrations.

Key Terms

solubility, saturated, unsaturated, concentrated, dilute

Explore! ACTIVITY

Do sugar and salt dissolve in water in the same amounts?

What To Do

1. Put 100 mL of water in each of two 400-mL beakers.
2. Add 50 g of table salt to one beaker and 50 g of sugar to the other beaker.
3. Stir both at the same rate. Compare and contrast the results in your Journal. How much of each solute dissolved?

Not all solutes can dissolve in water in the same amounts. You have just seen that more sugar than salt can dissolve in the same amount of water. Look at **Figure 5-8.** Only 16.3 g of the chemical calcium chromate can be dissolved in 100 g of water at room temperature before no more will go in, while the same amount of water can dissolve 120 g of chromium (III) sulfate!

Figure 5-8

A You can dissolve up to 16.3 g calcium chromate in 100 g of water at room temperature before the solute stops dissolving.

Calcium chromate

B In the same amount of water at the same temperature, you can dissolve up to 120 g chromium (III) sulfate.

Chromium (III) sulfate

Solubility

The amount of a substance that can dissolve in 100 g of solvent at a given temperature is called **solubility**. **Figure 5-9** records the solubility of various solutes in water at room temperature.

What is the solubility of potassium chloride at room temperature? Thirty-four grams of potassium chloride will dissolve in 100 g of water at room temperature before no more will go in. Its solubility in water at room temperature is 34.0 g/100 g water.

Substances that seem to dissolve in a liquid at a certain temperature to form a solution are said to be soluble. Those that do not seem to dissolve are called insoluble. Solubility tables help you learn how much of a solid will dissolve in a solvent at a given temperature.

In the salt solution that you just made, you started out with 50 g of salt, but not all of it dissolved. According to **Figure 5-9**, only 36.0 g of the salt dissolved in 100 g of water. What do you think would happen if you poured even more salt into the solution? In solid-liquid solutions, when no more solid solute will dissolve, the extra solute settles out. The solution becomes saturated because no more solute will dissolve in the solvent. A **saturated** solution is one that has dissolved all the solute it can hold at a given temperature.

Figure 5-9

This table shows the amount of various substances that will dissolve in 100 g of water at room temperature.

Solubility of Various Substances

Substances	Uses	Solubility
Barium sulfate	X rays	0.00025 g/100 g water
Calcium carbonate	chalk	0.0015 g/100 g water
Lithium carbonate	ceramics	1.3 g/100 g water
Potassium chloride	light salt	34.0 g/100 g water
Sodium chloride	table salt	36.0 g/100 g water
Sucrose	sugar	204.0 g/100 g water

Potassium chloride is used as a bleaching agent in some photograph processing procedures.

Lithium carbonate is a component of glazes for ceramics. Glazing prevents the item from absorbing liquids.

Sucrose is the most common of sugars and the least expensive. Its role as a sweetening agent in cookies is only one of its many uses.

Solubility Graphs

Solubility graphs can help you compare solubilities of the same substance at different temperatures. For example, look at **Figure 5-10**. The solubilities of four substances are drawn in this graph. Temperature is plotted on the horizontal axis, and solubility is plotted along the vertical axis.

Look again at the graph in **Figure 5-10**. Of the substances shown on the graph, which is the least soluble at 60°C? What happens to the solubility of a given solute as the temperature rises?

If you raise the temperature of the water, you can add more potassium chloride to the solution. What do you think would happen to a sugar solution if you heated it? Would more or less sugar solute be able to be dissolved at a higher temperature? The next activity will show you.

Making and Using Graphs

Copy the following data table. Using Figure 5-10, estimate the solubility (in grams per 100 g of water) of salt (sodium chloride) and sugar (sucrose) at 50°C and 100°C. Copy your answers in your data table. If you need help, refer to the **Skill Handbook** on page 657.

g per 100 g H_2O	50°C	100°C
Table Salt (sodium chloride)		
Sugar (Sucrose)		

Figure 5-10

This solubility graph tells how much of a substance can dissolve in 100 grams of water at a given temperature.

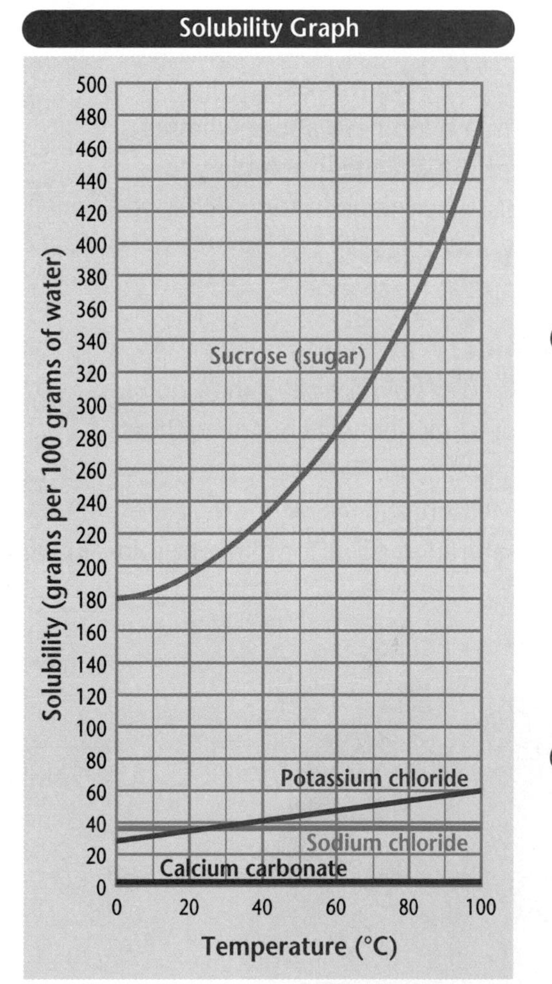

A **Find the sucrose line and follow it up. The graph shows that more and more sucrose can be dissolved in the same amount of water as the water temperature increases.**

B **The chart shows that calcium carbonate is practically insoluble at any temperature.**

C **Using the chart, you can predict how much of a substance can be dissolved in 100 g of water at a specific temperature. For example, at 60°C about 285 g of sucrose can be dissolved.**

D **How much sodium chloride can be dissolved at 80°C? How much potassium chloride can be dissolved at this temperature?**

DESIGN YOUR OWN
INVESTIGATION

Saturating a Solution at Different Temperatures

A solvent can dissolve only a certain amount of solute before it is saturated. However, changing the temperature changes the situation. The point of saturation is different for different temperatures.

Preparation

Problem

How does the solubility of table sugar in water change at different temperatures?

Form a Hypothesis

Form a hypothesis about whether there is a change in solubility for sugar when temperature is changed. How will solubility change when temperature changes?

Objectives

- Predict how the saturation point of a solution will change with differing temperatures.
- Measure the temperature at the saturation point for different solutions.

Materials

a two-hole stopper containing a thermometer and a copper wire stirrer
large test tube
test-tube holder
distilled water
table sugar
graduated cylinder
laboratory balance
hot plate
beaker of water
safely goggles
oven mitt

Safety Precautions

Be careful when using the hot plate and when inserting the stopper into the test tube.

Data and Observations

Grams of Sugar	mL of Water	Saturation Temperature (°C)	Grams of Sugar Per 10(of Water
28.7	10	60°C	287

DESIGN YOUR OWN
INVESTIGATION

Plan the Experiment

1 You will need to find the temperature at the saturation point for different solutions. The saturation point is reached when the solution cools enough that crystals of solute begin to form in the solution. If you begin with 28.7 g of sugar and 10 mL of water and run one test, how would you change the solution for another test? Would you add 2 mL of water? Would you add 2 g of sugar? In your group, decide how you will change the solution for each of three trials.

2 Copy the data table into your Science Journal and record the second and third solutions your group has agreed to test.

3 Set up the equipment as shown in the photo. How will you dissolve the sugar? You should not need to heat the solution to more than 80°C. How will you find the saturation point? Watch the temperature closely as the solution cools and you look for crystals.

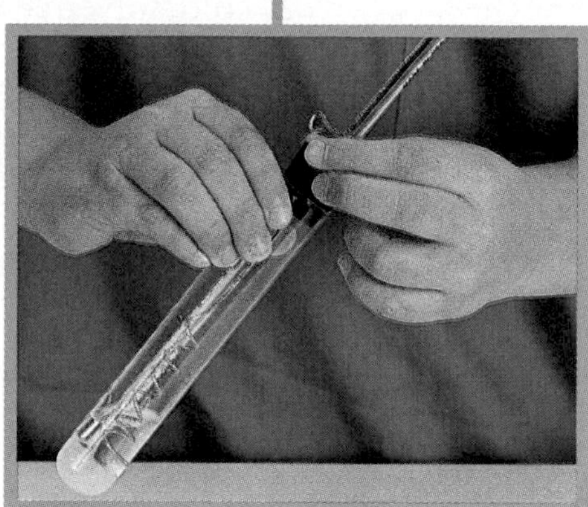

Check the Plan

1 What will stay constant in the three trials? What will change?

2 Will you stir the contents of the tube while it heats? While it cools?

3 Before you start the experiment, have your teacher approve your plan.

4 Carry out your experiment. Make observations and complete your data table *in your Science Journal.*

Analyze and Conclude

1. **Use Math** Calculate the grams of sugar per 100 g of water at each saturation temperature. Use the following formula and insert the appropriate numbers for grams of sugar and milliliters of water from your data table.

$$\text{Mass of sugar} = \frac{\text{? g sugar}}{\text{? mL water}} \times 100 \text{ mL of water}$$

2. **Measure in SI** What were the three saturation temperatures?
3. **Compare and Contrast** How did the mass of sugar that dissolved in 100 g of water change as the temperature changed?
4. **Hypothesize** Explain how your hypothesis was supported or disproved.
5. **Use Graphs** Graph the solubility versus temperature for the sugar-water solution.

Going Further

Predict the solubility of sugar at 0°C, the freezing point of water, and 100°C, the boiling point of water.

Connect to...

Earth Science

In a limestone cave, calcium carbonate is being dissolved and deposited. Give a presentation about two different speleothems. Include a drawing and a description of how each one is formed.

You have just seen that the solubility of sugar increases with an increase in temperature. That is, the amount of sugar that dissolves in water increases as the temperature increases. A cold solvent will usually hold less solute than a hot solvent will hold. As the temperature of the solvent rises, more solute will dissolve in it.

Unsaturated vs. Saturated Solutions

When you added 50 g of sugar to water in the Explore activity, all the sugar dissolved in the water. A solution that can hold more solute at a given temperature is an **unsaturated** solution. An unsaturated solution has room for more solute particles. Each time a saturated solution is heated to a higher temperature, it may become unsaturated. The term unsaturated is qualitative. It doesn't give you an exact amount. In an unsaturated solution, more solute can be dissolved in the solvent. As soon as the solution becomes saturated at a given temperature, no more solute can be dissolved at that temperature.

Suppose you make a saturated sugar solution at 60°C and then let it cool to room temperature. Part of the solute will become solid again. Why do you think this happens? Most saturated solutions behave in a similar way when cooled.

Life Science CONNECTION

Keeping the Balance

When the human body is working properly, the concentration of fluids inside its cells is the same as the concentration of fluids that surround them. For example, sodium chloride makes up slightly less than one percent of blood cells and the fluid around them. If the concentration of sodium chloride is higher outside the cells than inside, fluids ooze out

Sodium chloride around cells

Fluid around cells

Sodium chloride in cells

Flow of water

Concentration

You've already discovered that solubility is the number of grams of solute that will dissolve in 100 grams of solvent. Sometimes you do not need to know exactly how much solute is dissolved. All you may need to know is that one solution contains more solute than another solution contains.

A **concentrated** solution has a large amount of solute in a solvent. A **dilute** solution has a small amount of solute in a solvent. The terms, concentrated solution and dilute solution, can be used daily to describe such

Figure 5-11

You add two tablespoons of chocolate to your milk; your friend adds six tablespoons. Which drink is more dilute? Which is more concentrated? Why?

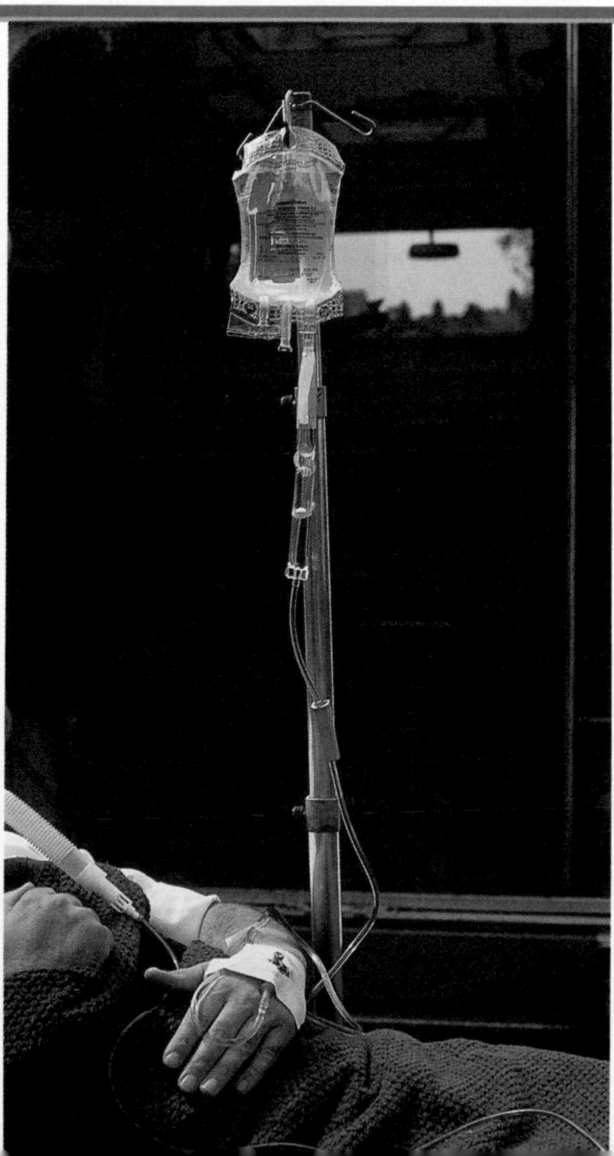

of the cells and into the surrounding fluid and reduce the sodium chloride concentration there. This change could cause the cells to become short of water, or dehydrated.

On the other hand, if the sodium chloride concentration outside the cells is lower than the concentration inside the cells, the cells can become flooded with fluids. This problem can become severe enough to cause cells to burst.

Intravenous Fluids

Doctors attempt to balance fluid concentrations by giving patients fluids intravenously, as shown in the photograph. In this procedure, a bag containing the proper fluids is hung above the patient and allowed to drain through a tube into the patient's vein and through the bloodstream. In this way, cells are surrounded by fluids containing the proper concentrations of substances.

What Do You Think?

How would a patient's body react if it received too much sodium chloride intravenously?

common items as medications, cleaning products, tea, coffee, lemonade, soup, and even chocolate milk.

Concentrated and dilute are relative terms, like large and small. But there are ways you can describe solution concentrations precisely. Have you ever read the label on a juice box to see how much actual juice is in there? Look at **Figure 5-12**. How much juice are you actually drinking when you purchase such products?

What have you discovered about solubility in this section? Solubility of a solution is the amount of solute that can dissolve in 100 g of solvent at a given temperature. The solubility of a solid solute in a solvent generally increases with temperature. Solubility tables and graphs help you predict how much of a solute will dissolve in a solvent at a given temperature. Solvents that hold as much solute as they can contain are saturated, while those that hold less solute than they can are unsaturated. Concentrated solutions contain more solute in a solvent than equal amounts of dilute solutions.

Are there any other kinds of mixtures that are not solutions? Yes, and in the next section you will read about two.

Figure 5-12

One way to describe solution concentrations precisely is to state the percentage of solute by volume of solution.

A One drink label states that the percentage of juice by volume is 100 percent.

B The other drink contains 10 percent juice and 90 percent water. Which of the two drinks is more concentrated?

1. Suppose you want to make super-sweet lemonade. You stir 2, 3, 4, or more teaspoons of sugar into a cup of lemonade, and it all disappears. But eventually you add another teaspoon of sugar, and it no longer dissolves. Why?
2. Look back at **Figure 5-10**. How much sugar would have to be dissolved in 100 g of water at 30°C to form a saturated solution? How much sugar would have to be added to form an unsaturated solution at the same temperature?
3. **Apply** You add 1 teaspoon of lemon juice to a cup of water, and a friend adds 4 teaspoons of lemon juice to another cup of water. Into whose cup would more spoons of sugar need to be added to make the lemonade sweet? Explain.

5-3 Colloids and Suspensions

Nonsolutions

No matter what the concentration of a solution, the particles are always too small to be seen. Because of this, gas solutions and liquid solutions are always transparent. They may be colored, like coffee, tea, or apple juice, but they are always transparent.

Think about things in a kitchen that seem to be transparent. Water, maple syrup, glass, and gelatin desserts come to mind. They are all mixtures, and they all look transparent. Are they all solutions? Let's find out.

Section Objectives
- Distinguish between a colloid and a suspension.
- Recognize at least two mixtures that are colloids.

Key Terms
colloid
suspension

Explore! ACTIVITY

Are all transparent mixtures solutions?

What To Do

1. Make a gelatin dessert by following the package directions. Use a transparent bowl.
2. When the gelatin has set, look at it from the side. Record *in your Journal* whether it is transparent.
3. Shine a beam of light from a flashlight through the dessert. Is the gelatin still transparent? Is gelatin a solution?

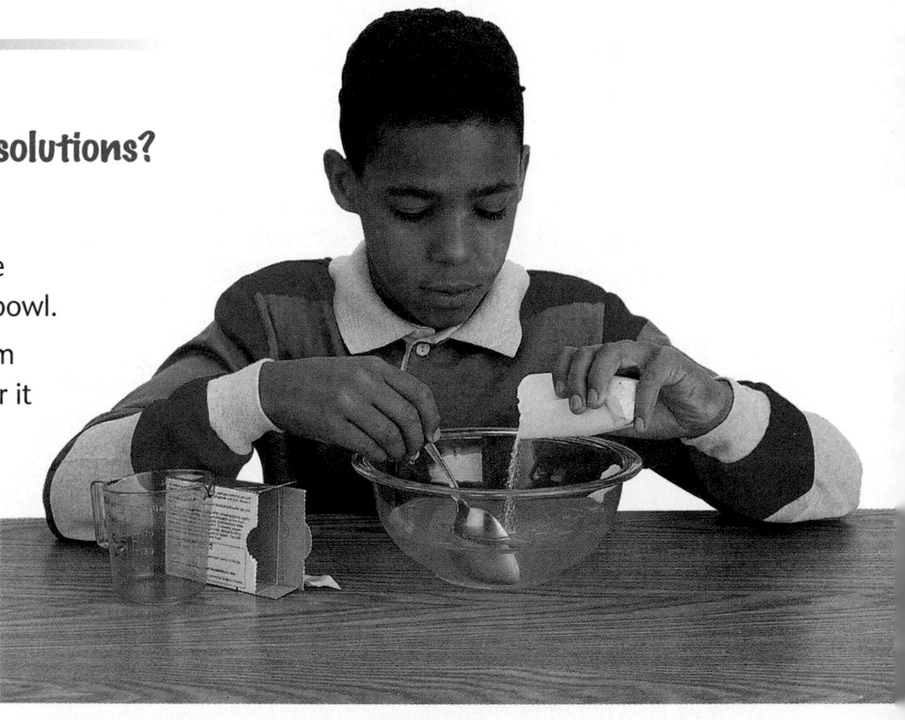

When you mix water with another material, the combination meets part of the definition of a solution. It is a mixture. You can tell by looking at it whether it also satisfies a second part of the definition. Its particles are too small to see. If you're not sure, shine a light through the mixture, as you did when you made gelatin. True liquid solutions will be clear. Nonsolutions will not. A solution will not show the path of the beam of light. Think back to when you made a soft drink in the first section and shined a flashlight through the transparent pitcher. Did you see any particles? Solution particles are too small to block the light from going straight through.

A nonsolution, however, will show a clearly defined beam of light. Look at **Figure 5-13**.

Figure 5-13

A The particles in a solution are too small to scatter light. If you shine a light through a mixture and the light shines straight through, the mixture is a solution.

B The container directly in front of the light is filled with salt water and the other with gelatin dessert.

C The gelatin dessert particles scatter the light, but the salt water does not. Which is a solution?

Colloids

Not all liquid mixtures are solutions. Milk is a mixture of water, fats, proteins, and other substances. It is a mixture but not a solution. Milk is a colloid. A **colloid** is a mixture that, like a solution, does not settle out. Unlike the small particles in a solution, however, the particles in a colloid are large enough to scatter light. That is why milk looks white.

Dirty air may be a colloid, too. Its particles scatter light. You have seen the scattering of light by dust particles when a beam of sunlight shines into a dark room through a slit in the curtain. The dust particles, many of them too small to be seen, look like bright speckles as the light is scattered by them.

Some mixtures, such as muddy water, are neither solutions nor colloids. What are they called?

How Do We Know?

The Ultramicroscope

Richard Zsigmondy, an Austrian chemist, worked at a glass factory making both clear and colored glass. Colored glass is made when different substances are mixed in melted clear glass. Zsigmondy wanted to study how particles behaved in his glass. In 1902, he developed a device that he called an ultramicroscope, shown in the figure. An ultramicroscope focuses on a colloid at right angles to the light source. The background is dark. Only the light scattered from colloid particles enters the microscope. The colloid particles can be seen not as particles with definite outlines, but as small sparkles. The device enabled Zsigmondy to see that particles in colloids are constantly moving in random, zigzag paths. This is one reason they do not settle out. In 1925, Zsigmondy received a Nobel Prize in Chemistry for his work on colloids.

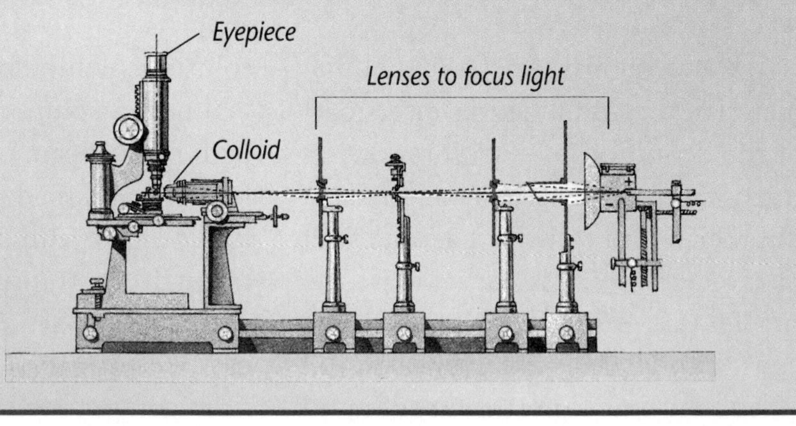

Explore! ACTIVITY

When is a mixture not a solution or a colloid?

What To Do

1. Fill a glass with muddy water.
2. Let the glass sit for 30 minutes. Record your observations *in your Journal.*
3. Stir the contents carefully. What do you see now?
4. Wait a few minutes and then examine the glass again. Is the color the same throughout the glass?
5. Now, let the glass sit overnight. What do you observe the next day? Is muddy water a solution?

Suspensions

Muddy water is a suspension. A **suspension** is a mixture containing a liquid in which visible settling occurs. The particles of solute are larger than the particles of solvent. The force of gravity causes these particles to settle out.

As in a colloid, the particles in a suspension are not homogeneous. In the last activity, you noticed that the muddy water turned different shades of brown, even after stirring. A suspension is different from a solution because its particles are not evenly mixed and are large enough to settle out.

Figure 5-14 classifies mixtures according to four basic properties.

Figure 5-14

You can classify most mixtures by testing for the four properties listed in the chart.

Solutions, Colloids, and Suspensions

Description	Solutions	Colloids	Suspensions
Scatter light	No	Yes	Yes
Settle upon standing	No	No	Yes
Can be separated using filter paper	No	No	Yes
Sizes of particles	Small	Medium	Large

A **How would you classify a mixture that scattered light but did not settle upon standing and could not be separated using filter paper?**

B **If you could see the particles in a mixture without using a microscope, how would you classify it?**

Figure 5-15

A Bronze—made from copper and tin—is a solid-solid solution commonly used to make ornamental objects, such as this ceremonial vessel from China.

B Fog is an example of a colloid that contains liquid particles mixed in a gas. Its states of matter are described as liquid in gas.

C Dust in the air is a type of colloid.

D Paint is a colloid made of solid pigment particles in solvents. How would you describe its states of matter?

E Italian salad dressing contains spices, oil, and vinegar. How would you classify this mixture?

Particles in some mixtures are large enough to interfere with the movement of light through the liquid. These mixtures are not classified as solutions, but they may be suspensions or colloids. If the particles in a mixture settle out of the system, the system is a suspension. If particles of a cloudy or light-scattering system do not settle out, the system is a colloid.

Homogeneous mixtures make up a large percentage of the materials in your life. The air you breathe, the water you drink, and even the steel that was used to build your school—each is a homogeneous mixture. Suspensions and colloids are not homogeneous mixtures. Although materials may seem very different, many of them have a great deal in common.

1. List two examples of colloids.
2. Identify mayonnaise as a colloid or a suspension. Explain your answer.
3. **Apply** A glass of orange juice sits on the kitchen counter. After an hour, bits of pulp settle out on the bottom of the glass. What type of mixture does this represent?

Down to the Sea Again

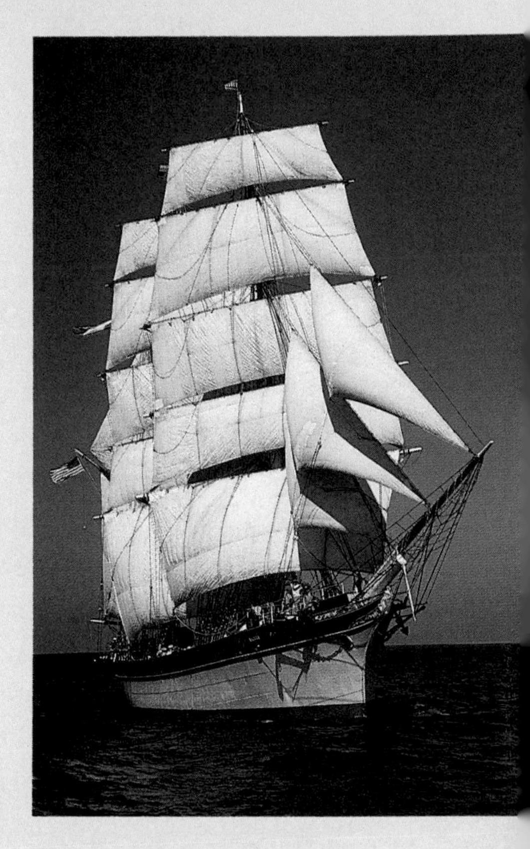

One of the world's largest solutions—the ocean—has inspired exploration throughout recorded history. Scientists and explorers have written volumes filled with ocean facts, and they continue to examine the vast solution that makes up almost three-fourths of Earth's surface.

The sea fascinates creative writers and storytellers as well. They have passed along their sea legends from generation to generation. To storytellers, the ocean may be a setting for adventure or a symbol with spiritual meaning, not a scientific problem to be solved.

Herman Melville's *Moby Dick* is a famous example of a story dealing with the seafarer's way of life. Other writers who have used the sea to express themselves include Walt Whitman, Stephen Crane, and William Shakespeare.

The poem "Sea Fever" is yet another example of sea-inspired writing. The poem was written by John Masefield, England's poet laureate from 1930 to 1967, who became a sailor when he was 13 years old. When you read the poem, you'll realize that the poet draws mainly from the visual and emotional parts of his experience.

As you read the poem, think of ways a scientist might talk about the things the poet describes. Do you think of the sea as Earth's vast solution? Or do you see it as a place of romance?

I must go down to the seas again, To the lonely sea and the sky.
And all I ask is a tall ship and a star to steer her by.
And the wheel's kick and the wind's song and the white sail's shaking.
And a gray mist on the sea's face, and a gray dawn breaking.

I must go down to the seas again, for the call of the running tide
Is a wild call and a clear call that may not be denied;
And all I ask is a windy day with the white clouds flying,
And the flung spray and the blown spume, and the sea-gulls crying.

I must go down to the seas again to the vagrant gypsy life,
To the gull's way and the whale's say where the wind's like a whetted knife;
And all I ask is a merry yarn from a laughing fellow-rover,
And quiet sleep and a sweet dream when the long trick's over.

Science Journal

In your Science Journal, write a short poem about a special place. Describe the sights, sounds, smells, tastes, and emotions you experienced there.

Science and Society

Cleaning Up the Oceans

You already know that the oceans are loaded with salt. But have you ever thought about other substances that are in seawater? Oceanographers and other scientists are very interested in knowing more about the contents of the oceans. Some of these experts are simply curious while others want to know more about the vast amounts of chemicals dumped or washed into the oceans from industrial and hospital waste.

Chemical Waste

For example, some people have dumped radioactive hospital wastes—materials from testing procedures and cobalt treatments—into the oceans. Now, concerned citizens want to know if these wastes will leak from their containers and mix in the seawater. Will they harm sea plants and animals? Will contaminated seawater affect humans? Is there some way to prevent such pollution? Mercury is another dangerous industrial waste that has been dumped into seawater. In the past, shipbuilders used paint that contained mercury because the mercury prevented the growth of marine plants and animals on the hulls of ships.

Years ago, some people thought mercury could be dumped on the ocean floor without harming anyone. They figured that because the mercury would not dissolve easily in the seawater, it could be safely deposited there.

However, scientists eventually learned that chemical processes in the ocean changed the mercury so that it could get into fish. People eating the fish could get mercury poisoning, which can cause very serious health problems. The United States government now prohibits the dumping of wastes that contain mercury, and the use of mercury compounds in paint.

EXPAND your view

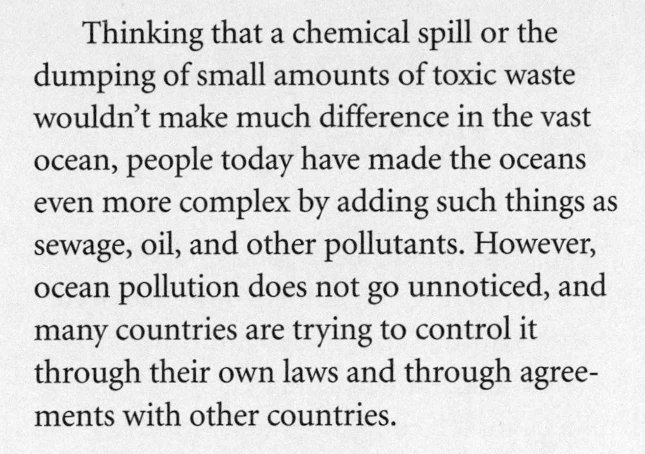

Thinking that a chemical spill or the dumping of small amounts of toxic waste wouldn't make much difference in the vast ocean, people today have made the oceans even more complex by adding such things as sewage, oil, and other pollutants. However, ocean pollution does not go unnoticed, and many countries are trying to control it through their own laws and through agreements with other countries.

Solid Waste

In addition to chemicals, tons of solid materials are deposited into the oceans. Plastics thrown into oceans pose problems because they do not easily decompose or dissolve in seawater. That means they may clutter the oceans for years, sometimes harming wildlife and frequently destroying the natural beauty of the sea.

One biologist walked 1.5 miles along the beach of a Pacific island to see how much trash he could find. He found hundreds of pieces of garbage, including 74 bottle tops, 25 shoes, 6 light bulbs, toys, cigarette lighters, and a football. The amazing thing about his discoveries was that the island was at least 3000 miles from any continent.

He knew there must be an enormous amount of trash floating in the ocean if he was able to find so much on an uninhabited island. He was so concerned about what he had found there that he wrote to a scientific journal to tell his story.

Cleaning Up the Problem

What can we do about this severe problem? The United States Congress has passed laws to control some dumping of industrial wastes into the oceans. Scientists are trying to develop ways to control environmental damage caused by accidental chemical spills, such as oil spills. In fact, some researchers have released oil-eating organisms into the ocean to break up oil spills. Others have attempted to contain oil spills by surrounding them with barriers.

Who Is Involved?

Individuals and organizations everywhere worry that pollution has gotten out of control. They're working to repair the environment by talking to their congressional representatives and even by picking up trash on beaches.

What Do You Think?

You and a partner are in charge of a campaign to clean up the oceans. Think of ways that individuals and organizations can help and explain how you will promote your ideas.

So You Think the Ocean Is Salty?

What do you think happens when rivers flow into a sea that doesn't drain, but instead loses a lot of its water through evaporation?

You may have guessed that the concentration of salt in the sea increases with time.

The Great Salt Lake

The Great Salt Lake of Utah is a well-known salt sea that has grown so salty that it has become a tourist attraction and a source of various natural resources.

Gathering Salt

Businesspeople once sold salt taken from the lake. At first, dried salt was found on the shore and hauled away. The problem with that method, however, was removing the mud gathered along with the salt.

Later, some ambitious folks boiled the salty water in large containers until they were left with salt they could sell. Unfortunately, they were also left with other chemicals that had been dissolved in the water. However, salt was not always easy to come by in those days, so slightly contaminated salt was more acceptable then than it would be today.

In some cases, salt is all too easy to collect at the Great Salt Lake. Swimmers, for example, are attracted to the Great Salt Lake because they can float on its surface with little effort. But when they return to shore, the water evaporates from their skin, leaving them covered with salt crystals.

What Do You Think?

Why is the concentration of salt water increasing in the Great Salt Lake?

chapter 5
REVIEWING MAIN IDEAS

Science Journal

Review the statements below about the big ideas presented in this chapter, and answer the questions. Then, re-read your answers to the Did You Ever Wonder questions at the beginning of the chapter. *In your Science Journal*, write a paragraph about how your understanding of the big ideas in the chapter has changed.

1 Solutes dissolve in solvents to form solutions. Solutions may be made up of solids, liquids, and gases. ***What properties do solute particles demonstrate?***

2 Solutes dissolve in solvents at different rates. ***What factors affect the rate of dissolving?***

3 Solubility is the amount of solute that can dissolve in 100 g of solvent at a given temperature. ***How is a concentrated solution different from a dilute solution?***

4 Colloids and suspensions are two other types of mixtures. ***How do colloids and suspensions differ from solutions?***

CHAPTER REVIEW

Using Key Science Terms

colloid
concentrated
dilute
saturated
solubility
solute
solution
solvent
suspension
unsaturated

For each set of terms below, choose the one term that does not belong and explain why it does not belong.

1. solute, solvent, solution, suspension
2. unsaturated, saturated, concentrated, solution
3. colloid, dilute, solubility, concentrated
4. solution, suspension, solvent, colloid

Understanding Ideas

Answer the following questions in your Journal *using complete sentences.*

1. How does an increase in temperature usually affect the solubility of:
   a) a solid in a liquid?
   b) a gas in a liquid?
2. What are some methods that you might use to increase the rate of dissolving of a solid?
3. Five grams of sucrose are dissolved in 100 g of water. Which of the Key Science Terms can be used to describe the resulting solution?
4. A solution of 30 g of sodium chloride in 100 g of water is cooled from 90°C to 10°C. What visible change would you notice in the solution?
5. Compare the size of particles in a solution, suspension, and colloid.

Developing Skills

Use your understanding of the concepts developed in this chapter to answer each of the following questions.

1. **Concept Mapping** Fill in the concept map using the following terms: *gelatin, muddy water, salt water, solution, suspension.*

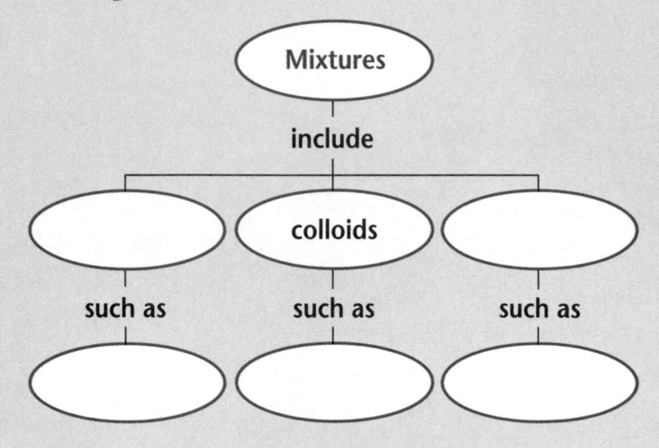

2. **Measuring in SI** Two salt solutions are prepared. In the first solution, 1.2 kg of salt are dissolved in 5 liters of water. In the second solution, 56 g of salt are dissolved in 200 mL of water. Which solution is more concentrated?
3. **Observing and Inferring** Gas trapped in ice can make it look cloudy. Which of these ice cubes was probably made with cold water? Which was probably made with hot water? Explain.

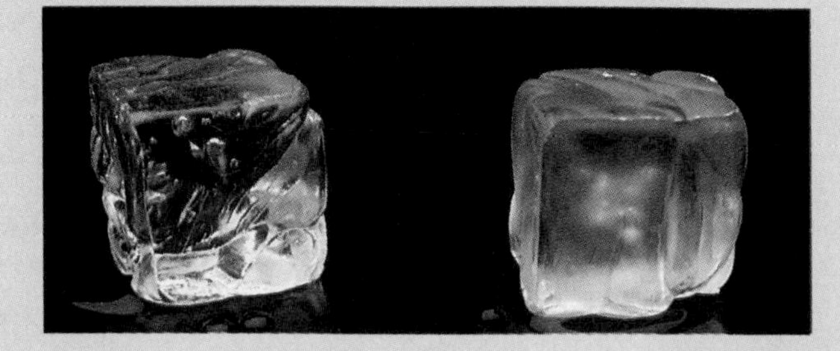

CHAPTER REVIEW

4. **Sequencing** Use **Figure 5-10** to list the four substances in order from least soluble in water to most soluble, at 5°C and at 75°C.

Critical Thinking

In your Journal, answer each of the following questions.

1. White light shining through a prism separates into a spectrum of colors. Can a colloid act as a prism? Explain.
2. Oil and vinegar do not mix. Yet, when you pour a small amount of each in a bottle and then shake the bottle vigorously, you can make a mixture of salad dressing that will stay together for some time. Explain why you think this is possible, using the concepts learned in this chapter.
3. A large bottle of fabric softener states it contains enough softener to soften 100 loads of laundry. A different brand in a smaller bottle also states it contains enough to soften 100 loads of laundry. Explain how this can be.

Problem Solving

Read the following paragraph and discuss your answers in a brief paragraph.

On a rafting trip, your friend asks you if you want a cracker. Your mouth is dry, but you eat it anyway. The cracker has absolutely no taste, and you struggle to swallow it. Then you take a long, gulping drink of water. Now you eat another cracker, and it tastes delicious!

At home later that afternoon your mother gives you a couple of crispy cookies for a snack. They taste okay, but with a glass of cold juice, they taste even better.

Oh, no! Broccoli for dinner! You'll eat it because you know it's good for your body, but you also know that if you eat it quickly, you can hardly taste the broccoli. The longer you chew it, the more you can taste it.

Think about the three sets of facts just presented. Try to draw a conclusion from them. Hint: Remember what this chapter is about.

CONNECTING IDEAS

Discuss each of the following in a brief paragraph.

1. **Theme—Stability and Change** Powdered drink mix forms a solution in water. Is this a physical change or a chemical change? Explain.
2. **Theme—Interactions and Systems** The moon has no water on it. Could there be solutions on the moon? Explain your answer.
3. **A Closer Look** Salt is cheaper than antifreeze. Why do you suppose we don't put salt in the car radiator, instead of antifreeze?
4. **Economics Connection** Why is the concentration of salt in the Great Salt Lake so high?

CHAPTER 6

Acids, Bases, & Salts

Did you ever wonder...

- ✓ Why lemons taste sour?
- ✓ Why a skull-and-crossbones symbol is on a can of drain cleaner?
- ✓ How an antacid can settle your upset stomach?

Science Journal

Before you begin to study about acids, bases, and salts, think about these questions and answer them *in your Science Journal.* When you finish the chapter, compare your journal write-up with what you have learned.

You might think that what is made from stone will last forever. If you were to examine the stone used in structures, it would give you clues about what has happened in the environment since the stone was placed there. You might notice that many famous buildings and landmarks are gradually being worn away. How does this happen?

In this chapter, you will find out about the substances—acids, bases, and salts—that control many chemical changes around us. Understanding the properties of these substances can help you understand some problems of our environment and what some possible solutions are.

▶ ***In the activity on the next page, explore some structures that may have been damaged by these chemical changes.***

Quebec City, Quebec, Canada

Is stone deteriorating in your neighborhood?

What things in your neighborhood are made of stone? Can you see the effects that certain chemicals in the environment have on stone?

What To Do

On the next nice day, explore the area around your home or school.

1. Examine structures such as buildings, sidewalks, and streets. Examine the gravestones in a cemetery if one is nearby.
2. Look for examples of deteriorating rock. What is evidence of deterioration of rock?
3. *In your Journal,* explain what you think could be causing the deterioration.

Worn stone columns at the Acropolis in Athens, Greece

6-1 Properties and Uses of Acids

Section Objectives

- Describe the properties of acids.
- Name and compare some common acids and their uses.

Key Terms

acids

Acids in the Environment

In the chapter opener, you saw how the rock of sidewalks, streets, gravestones, and perhaps even structures in your neighborhood can deteriorate. Do this simple activity to discover one reason why rocks wear away.

Find Out! ACTIVITY

What effect does a substance known as an acid have on rock?

The effects of acid on certain types of rock can be easily observed.

What To Do

1. Mass about 5.0 g of marble chips and place them in a 250-mL beaker.
2. Next, add 50 mL of a very dilute solution of sulfuric acid. **CAUTION:** *Sulfuric acid is poisonous and can burn the skin. You may also use vinegar or club soda, but the reaction time will be much slower.*
3. Observe the mixture for several minutes.
4. Stir the mixture vigorously. Then let it sit until it stops bubbling.
5. Pour the mixture through a filter paper placed in a funnel.
6. Rinse and dry the marble chips and mass them again.

Conclude and Apply

1. Did the mass of the rocks change?
2. *In your Journal*, explain your answer to Question 1.

You've just discovered that acid can have a harmful effect on marble. Marble is a rock commonly used in buildings and sculptures. When acids are present in the air, they react with stone and certain other materials and can damage the environment. How do acids get into the air?

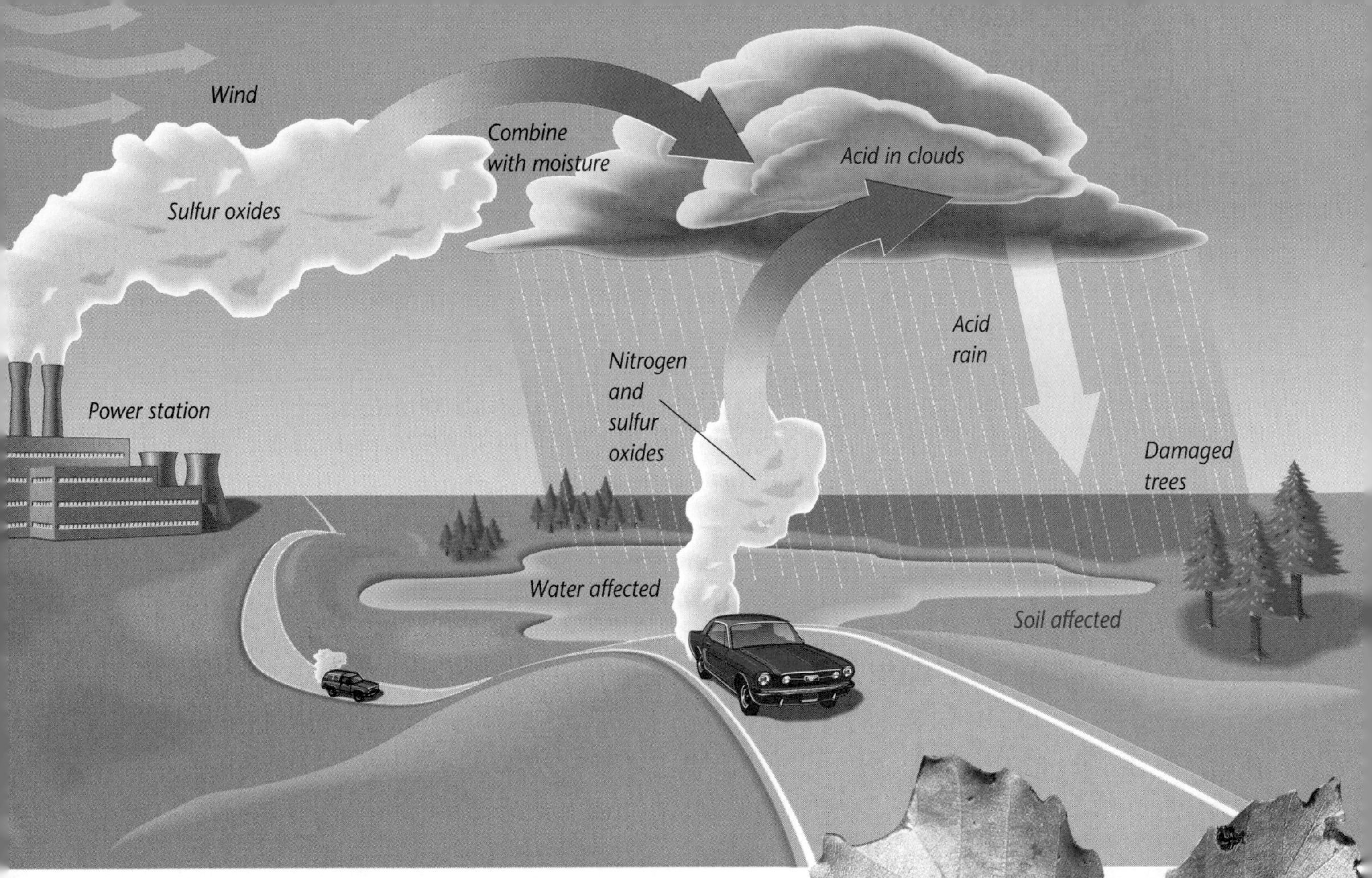

Figure 6-1

A Nitrogen oxides and sulfur oxides released as waste from traffic, factories, and power stations rise into the air. When these compounds combine with water in the air, they dissolve into nitric acid and sulfuric acid. These acids become part of raindrops, which fall to Earth as acid rain.

B Acid rain damages plants, kills fish, and erodes building materials. The destruction is not always local. Clouds of acid-rain drops can be carried by the wind and fall as acid rain hundreds of kilometers from their source.

Acid Pollution

Volcanic eruption and other natural phenomena add pollutants to our atmosphere, causing rain to be acidic. However, since humans started affecting the environment, the natural balance of this pollution cycle has been changed by compounds added to the atmosphere by human activities.

Examine **Figure 6-1**. You can see how compounds produced by the burning of fossil fuels, such as coal or petroleum products, combine with moisture in the air. The result of this is acid rain, which can fall great distances from its source.

Acid rain may make the water in lakes unfit for fish to live. It can harm and kill plants, as can be seen by the leaf in **Figure 6-1**. Even hard building materials, such as marble, can be seriously damaged.

Surface water is usually slightly acidic. It will dissolve exposed limestone that is at or near the surface. Make a poster that shows the location of limestone caves in your state.

Properties of Acids

If you had a glass of orange juice this morning, you remember the tart taste in your mouth. A sour or tart taste is one property of an acid. The sour taste of foods such as citrus fruits and tomatoes is due to the presence of weak acids.

Many acids are extremely reactive. Most acids contain the element hydrogen. By reacting with some metals, these acids seem to destroy or corrode the metal and release hydrogen as a gas. Have you seen a car battery that is corroded where cables are attached? Corrosion is a chemical change that may occur when acid and metal come in contact with each other. Some acids react more strongly with metals than do others. You could rank acids on the basis of their strength of reaction.

You know that most acids in food are safe to eat. Some other acids, however, are strong and can damage body tissues. That's why taste should never be used as a way to test for the presence of an acid. Acids are part of your everyday life. Most common **acids** are compounds that contain hydrogen, taste sour, and are corrosive.

Earth Science CONNECTION

Turning Rocks to Soil

Do you remember seeing something gray, green, or brownish covering bare rocks or the limbs of trees? This scaly-looking substance is really a group of organisms called lichens.

What Are Lichens?

Lichens are made up of fungi and algae that have formed a relationship helpful to both of them—the algae provide food through photosynthesis, and the fungi provide protection. There are three basic groups of lichen: crusty or flaky, papery or leafy, and stalked or branching.

Some lichens appear to grow out of solid rock. If you look with a microscope, however, you can see that tiny threadlike growths anchor the lichen to the rock surface.

Rocks into Soil

Rock-growing lichens play an important role in converting rocks into soil. Lichens produce a dilute, acidic solution that slowly dissolves the minerals. Soon cracks appear in the rock and the threads of the lichens dig deeper into the rock. The cracks fill with water that freezes and melts, making the cracks bigger.

After a long time, the rocks break apart into smaller pieces, and eventually become soil.

Acids Around You

The acids in acid rain, in car batteries, and in citrus fruits are just three examples of the acids around you. There are others that affect your life every day. Some are probably quite familiar to you.

Explore! ACTIVITY

What are some common acids?

If you look around your home, you will discover that many familiar items contain acids.

What To Do

1. With an adult's help, check ingredients on labels to see if acids are listed.
2. Make a list of the acids that are in your home and how they are used.
3. Bring your list to school and compare it with your classmates' lists.
4. Make a class list of all the products containing acid that are used in the home.

Once this process begins, plants can also grow in the cracks and speed up the breakup of the rocks.

When the rocks break apart, new soil with new minerals forms and more plants begin to grow. Soil that is worn out from over-use or eroded by wind or water is made healthier with the addition of new soil from broken rocks.

Other Uses

In addition to breaking up rocks, lichen acids are also useful ingredients in perfume making. They are used to make all the different ingredients in perfume mingle together to make a pleasant smell. Lichen extracts are also used to manufacture antibiotics, medicines, puddings, and fabric stiffeners.

You Try It!

You can use lichens to test whether a solution is acidic or basic.

Gather some lichens from rocks and trees. Then dip one into an acidic solution, such as white vinegar, and another into a basic solution, such as household ammonia. What do you observe?

Industrial Acids

You may have been surprised to learn how many acids you use every day. You probably found that vinegar contains acetic acid and soft drinks contain carbonic acid and phosphoric acid. Besides aspirin, how many acids did you find that are important to your health? Ascorbic acid is often added to packaged foods to help them stay fresh longer. There are some acids that you may depend on that you never directly use. These industrial acids are used in the manufacture of several important products.

How Do We Know?

Hydrogen in Acids

One of the key properties of acids is that most of them contain hydrogen. But no one has ever seen a single acid particle. How do we know acids contain hydrogen? Thousands of reactions of acids have been studied, and in almost every case hydrogen has either been produced or was a key element in the reaction.

■ Hydrochloric Acid

Because some acids react with certain metals, acids play an important role in industry. One acid that is both commonly and industrially used is hydrochloric acid. Industrial-strength hydrochloric acid is a colorless liquid that gives off strong fumes. The fumes not only can burn your skin but can also harm your lungs and eyes. The fumes react with water on the surfaces of these organs, causing severe burns. Crude hydrochloric acid, or muriatic acid as it is commonly called, is used in industry in a process known as *pickling*. In this process, impurities are removed from metal surfaces by dipping the metals in hydrochloric acid. Muriatic acid is also used to clean concrete and excess mortar from brick.

You might be surprised to learn that hydrochloric acid also helps you digest the hamburger you may have eaten for lunch. Hydrochloric acid in the stomach helps break down food so that it can be further digested. The stomach is protected from this stomach acid by a coating of mucus that keeps the acid away from the stomach lining. Hydrochloric acid can make a hole in metal or a cotton cloth, yet it does not necessarily harm the lining of your stomach.

Figure 6-2

Hydrochloric acid is both a common acid and an industrial acid. Crude hydrochloric acid, or muriatic acid as it is commonly called, is used in industry to clean the surfaces of materials such as concrete or steel.

Figure 6-3

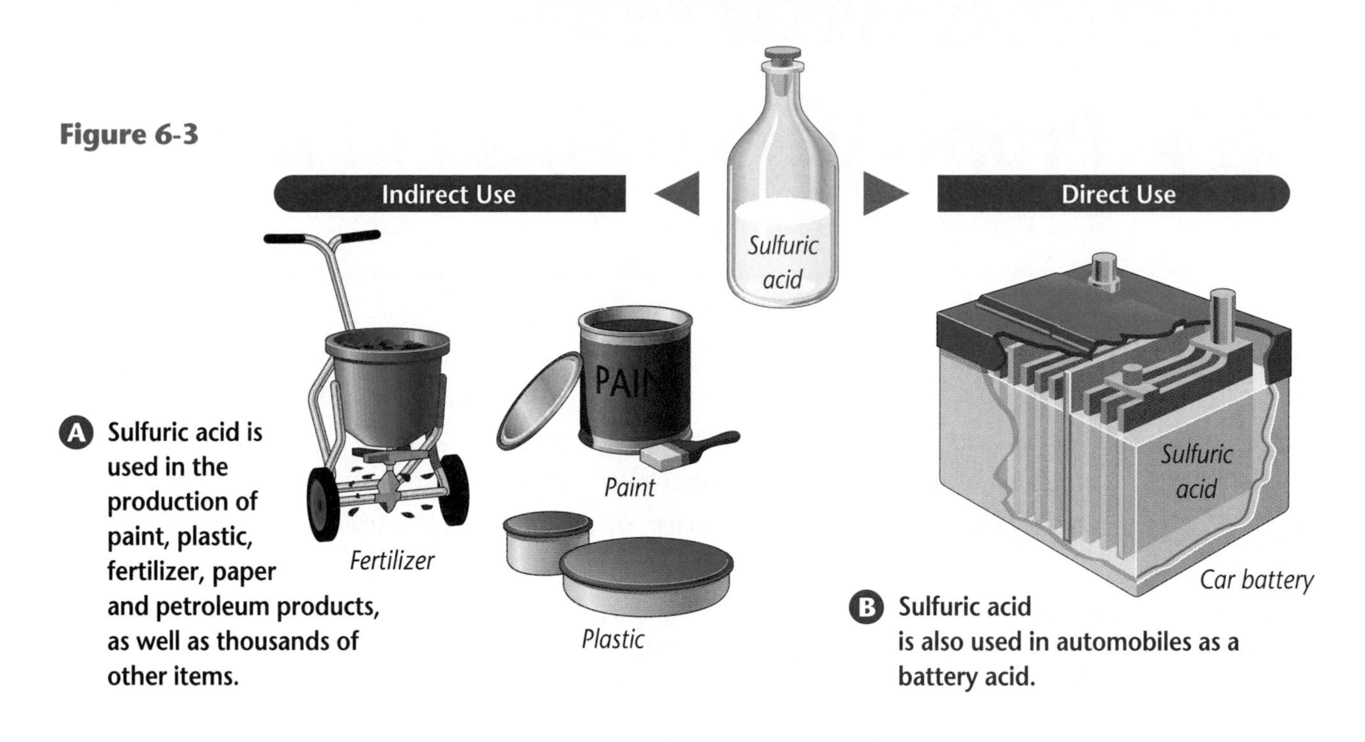

A Sulfuric acid is used in the production of paint, plastic, fertilizer, paper and petroleum products, as well as thousands of other items.

B Sulfuric acid is also used in automobiles as a battery acid.

Sulfuric Acid

You learned about the effect of dilute sulfuric acid on marble at the beginning of this chapter. Sulfuric acid is another industrial acid commonly used in automobile batteries and is often called battery acid. Concentrated sulfuric acid is a thick, syrupy liquid that can also cause severe burns. Sulfuric acid is one of the most widely used chemicals in the world. Examples of its uses are shown in **Figure 6-3**. It is used in the production of metals, fertilizers, plastics, paper, and petroleum products, as well as thousands of other items. The amount of sulfuric acid a country uses is a measure of how economically advanced the country is. Over 30 billion kilograms of sulfuric acid are produced every year in the United States. Half of it is used by industries in this country, and the rest is exported.

You have seen what a useful group of chemicals acids can be. They can help or threaten your health. Weak acids in food keep you healthy, but acid rain threatens the environment. In the next section, you will learn about another group of chemicals that can also affect your environment.

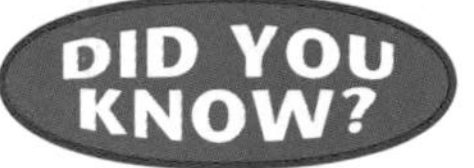

In the late 1800s, gold was discovered in western North America. Mistaken for gold in many areas was a mineral called fool's gold. An acid would dissolve most of the fool's gold but leave the real gold unchanged. Thus, *acid test* came to stand for a test that reveals the genuine article.

1. How are all acids alike? How do acids differ from one another?
2. From the list of acids developed by your class, name the two you use most often and tell how you use them.
3. **Apply** You want to store lemon slices in the refrigerator. Will you store them in a plastic bag or in aluminum foil? Explain your answer.

Properties and Uses of Bases

Section Objectives

- Describe the properties of a base.
- Name and compare some common bases and their uses.

Key Terms

bases

Properties of Bases

You probably think of the word *base* as part of the game played on a baseball diamond. But bases, like acids, are an important group of chemical compounds that you use every day.

You can find out more about bases by doing the following activity.

Which materials are bases?

Bases have properties that you can observe.

What To Do

1. Measure 1 tablespoon each of baking soda, laundry detergent, cornstarch, sugar, and salt.
2. Place each material on a piece of paper.
3. Using a magnifying glass, examine each sample and describe it.
4. Rub each material between your fingers. **CAUTION:** *These materials are safe to touch. Do not test any unknown material by touching it.*
5. Label each cup with the name of a material.
6. In each cup, add each material to 300 mL of water and stir.
7. Now, touch each liquid with your fingertips. Rub your fingers together. Be sure to wash your fingers after touching each liquid.

Conclude and Apply

1. Can you identify each material by looking at it?
2. Can you identify, when dry, these materials by the way they feel?
3. Do all the liquids feel the same?

Most undissolved bases are solids. Although there are materials, such as oil, that are not bases but are slippery, when a base is dissolved in water, it feels slippery because it reacts with the oil on your skin. Which of the powders in the Find Out activity may have been bases? Bases also have a bitter taste, but strong bases, just like strong acids, can burn the skin. Never use taste or touch as a way to test for the presence of an *unknown* base.

Bases Around You

When you washed your face this morning, you probably used a product that has a base in it. Laundry detergents and shampoos may also contain bases. Bases help clean because of a very interesting property that is explained in **Figure 6-4**. Therefore, the soap can remove the grease or dirt from your skin, clothes, or hair and then be rinsed away by water. **Bases**, then, are compounds that taste bitter, are usually solids, and feel slippery when dissolved in water. Like acids, bases can be weak and not very reactive, or they can be strong and violently reactive.

You have seen that many products in your home contain acids. Explore how bases can also be found in many household products, including soaps, detergents, and shampoos.

Figure 6-4

Bases help clean because of a very interesting property.

A One end of a soap, detergent, or shampoo particle is soluble in grease, while the other end is soluble in water.

B The soap can pull the grease or dirt away from your skin, clothes, or hair and then be rinsed away by water.

Explore! ACTIVITY

What bases can you find around you?

To identify a base, one clue to look for is the word hydroxide in the name of any chemical.

What To Do

1. Look at the common bases and the ways they are used that are listed in the table.
2. Many items in your home contain bases. With the help of an adult, find out what these items are and how they are used.

Some Common Bases and Their Uses

Name	Where Found
Aluminum hydroxide	Deodorants, antacids
Ammonium hydroxide	Household cleaner (ammonia water)
Calcium hydroxide	Manufacture of mortar and plaster
Magnesium hydroxide	Laxatives, antacids
Sodium hydroxide	Drain cleaner

Acids and bases have several characteristics, such as reactivity, in common. How can you identify which substances are acids and which substances are bases? This Investigate will show you.

DESIGN YOUR OWN

INVESTIGATION

Identifying Acids and Bases

Acids and bases are used for different purposes. Their uses often correspond to the way they react to various substances. Litmus paper, which is red in the presence of an acid and blue in the presence of a base, can be used to identify acids and bases.

Preparation

Problem

How can acids and bases be identified?

Form a Hypothesis

As a group, form a hypothesis that will help you determine which substances are acids and which are bases.

Objective

- Identify acids and bases based on their reactions with litmus paper.

Possible Materials

test-tube rack
six test tubes
household ammonia
cola
table salt
lemon juice
vinegar
baking soda
orange slices
deodorant
piece of antacid tablet
red and blue litmus paper
stirring rods
distilled water

Safety Precautions

Goggles and apron should be worn at all times when using these weak acids and bases. Do not allow the substances to contact your skin.

DESIGN YOUR OWN INVESTIGATION

Plan the Experiment

1 Within your group, choose six of the available substances to test.

2 What procedure will you follow to test each substance? Will you use both kinds of litmus paper? Is it important to use clean stirring rods?

3 Water is a neutral liquid; it is neither acidic nor basic. How will you use it as you test the solids?

4 How will you keep track of your findings? In your Science Journal, design a table or chart to use during your experiment.

Check the Plan

1 Have another group read your plan after they have finished writing their own. Do they understand what you plan to do?

2 Before you begin, have your teacher approve your plan.

3 Carry out the experiment.

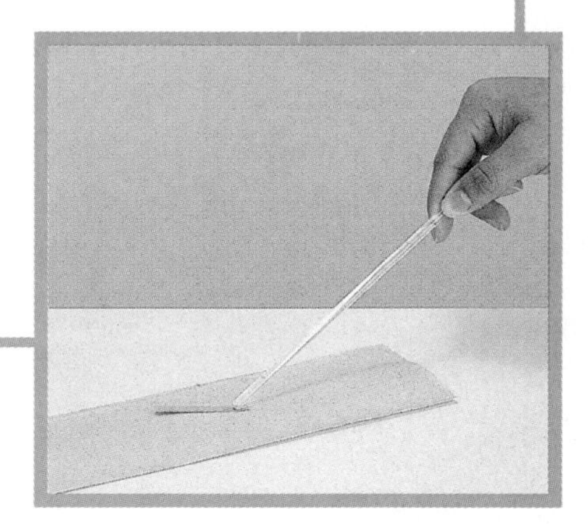

Analyze and Conclude

1. **Observe** What changes did you observe for acids? For bases?
2. **Infer** Which substances did you infer were acids? Bases?
3. **Analyze** How effective was your procedure? Are there things you would change if you were to do it again?
4. **Conclude** List any substances that showed no change with the litmus test. What can you determine about them?

Going Further

Predict how the bases you identified in the Explore activity on page 193 would affect litmus paper.

Bases and Your Health

You have learned that several acids, such as ascorbic acid, vitamin C, are important to your health. As with acids, bases are important to your health and well-being. Blood and many other body fluids are mildly basic; that is, they contain a base. Your body would not function properly without the correct balance of acids and bases. For example, antacid tablets, which are a mild base, will reduce excess stomach acid and also help maintain the acid-base balance. The Find Out activity that follows shows you how to make a common antacid.

How can you make an antacid with a base?

Household ammonia contains ammonium hydroxide. The chemical name for Epsom salt is magnesium sulfate. When these two compounds react, they produce magnesium hydroxide. Magnesium hydroxide is a base found in a product called milk of magnesia.

What To Do

1. Fill a glass jar half full of water.
2. Stir in 1 teaspoon of Epsom salt into the water.
3. Pour 2 teaspoons of household ammonia into the jar. Do not stir! Let this solution stand for five minutes. **CAUTION:** *DO NOT taste this solution. DO NOT let anyone else taste this solution.*

Conclude and Apply

1. What do you observe happening?
2. What do you think the white milky substance is?
3. Why do you think it is called *milk* of magnesia?

You have read how a base can react with an acid in your stomach and how other bases are needed for your health. Bases are also useful in industry to make many products that we use daily.

Industrial Bases

The most widely used base is ammonia gas dissolved in water. Pure ammonia gas has a distinctive and very irritating odor. You may know this base as household ammonia, a cleaner. It is especially good for cleaning windows. It is also used to manufacture fertilizers, medicines, plastics, refrigerants, and dyes.

Calcium hydroxide, commonly called lime, is often used on lawns and gardens where the soil is too acidic. One effect of the amount of acid in soil is shown in **Figure 6-5**. Different plants need different amounts of acid in the soil. Calcium hydroxide reduces the acidity of the soil.

Sodium hydroxide, or lye, is a very strong base. Because a great amount of thermal energy is released when sodium hydroxide dissolves in water, it is used as a drain cleaner and an oven cleaner. Sodium hydroxide is very dangerous. Anyone using it must wear gloves and eye protection and must avoid inhaling the fumes.

The next time you use any of the products mentioned in this section, stop and think about what properties the product has and why it has them.

Comparing and Contrasting

List ways that acids and bases are similar. Then list the ways in which they are different. If you need help, refer to the **Skill Handbook** on page 659.

Figure 6-5

Hydrangeas produce blue flowers in acidic soil and pink flowers in basic soil. How are hydrangeas like the litmus paper you used in the Investigation?

1. Dishwater feels slippery. What can you infer about the detergent used to wash dishes?
2. How is the structure of a base related to its cleaning properties?
3. **Apply** State three different uses for common bases and identify the specific base used.

6-3 An Acid or a Base?

Section Objectives

- Analyze a pH reading and tell what it means.
- Explain what an indicator shows about acids and bases.

Key Terms

pH
indicator

The Acid-Base Balance

You have learned that acids and bases are important in keeping your body functioning properly.

In Your Body

You could never digest your food without the hydrochloric acid in your stomach. During digestion, the food moves from the stomach to the small intestine. Bile, which is made by the liver to help digest food, is then added to the acidic food mixture, adjusting the acidity of the mixture. If the mixture is too acidic, disorders such as ulcers can result.

On the other hand, blood is basic (that is, it contains a base), and in order for food nutrients to be safely absorbed by the blood, they, too, must be basic. If the acid-base balance in your body becomes unbalanced, you could become seriously ill.

Figure 6-6

The pH of a solution indicates how acidic it is. The pH scale is a series of numbers used to measure pH. The scale starts with 0 to indicate the most acidic solution and ends with 14, which indicates the most basic solution. The number 7 on the scale identifies neutral solutions that are neither acidic nor basic.

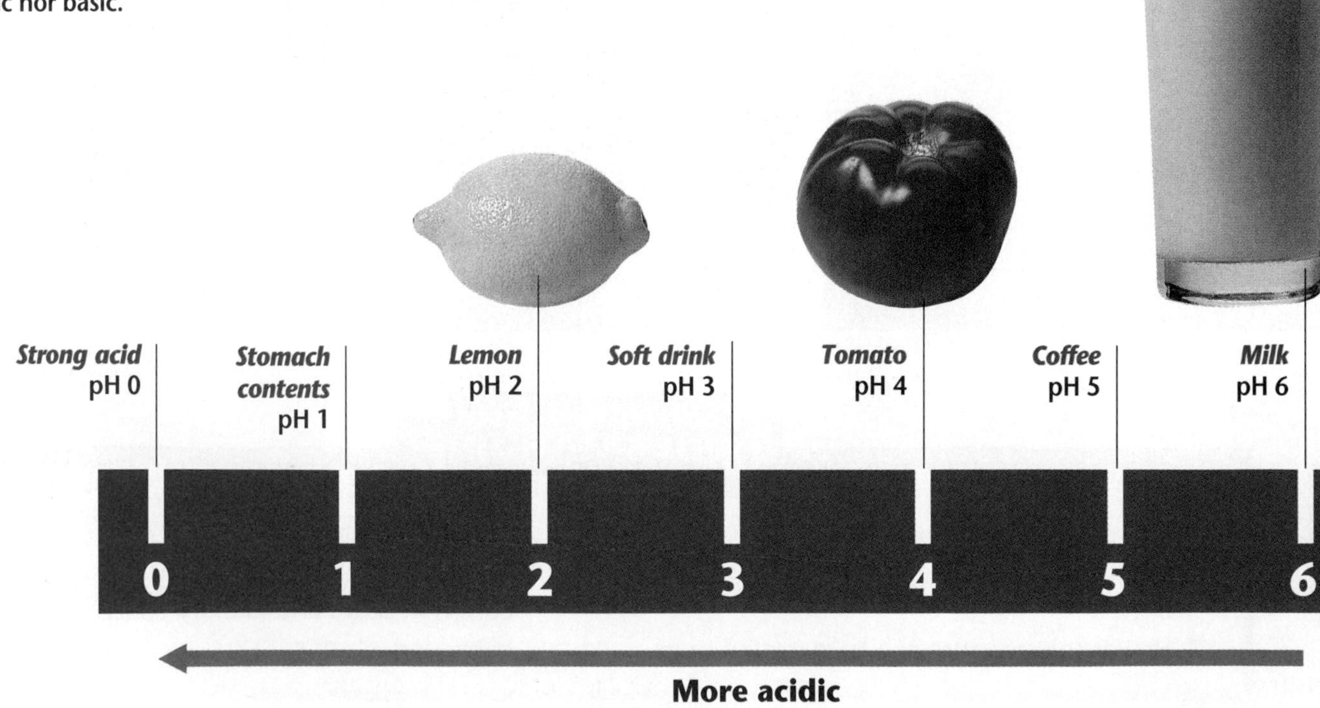

■ The pH Scale

It is important to maintain the balance between acids and bases in swimming pools and in tanks for tropical fish. You need to control the acidity of the water. To control the acidity, you need to adjust the pH by adding either acids or bases.

What is pH? **pH** is a measure that shows the acidity of a solution. The pH scale shown in **Figure 6-6** is used to measure pH. Its values range from 0 to 14.

Looking at **Figure 6-6**, you can see that solutions with a pH value less than 7 are acidic. The lower the value, the more acidic the solution. This means that a solution with a pH value of 1 is very acidic. Solutions with a pH value greater than 7 are basic. The higher the pH number, the more basic the solution. The number 7 on the pH scale represents a neutral solution that is neither acidic nor basic. Pure water has a pH value of 7.

Any material that can be put into solution can be tested to find its pH. You can see that a variety of common items, from foods to batteries, are acidic, and a variety of items, from cleaners to baking soda, are basic.

How can we find the pH of an acid or a base? The following Investigate will show you one way.

Making and Using Graphs

Find the pH of the following materials: rainwater, apples, club soda, seawater, drain cleaner, distilled water, and milk of magnesia. Now use a bar graph to plot the pH of the materials against the pH scale in **Figure 6-6**. If you need help, refer to the **Skill Handbook** on page 657.

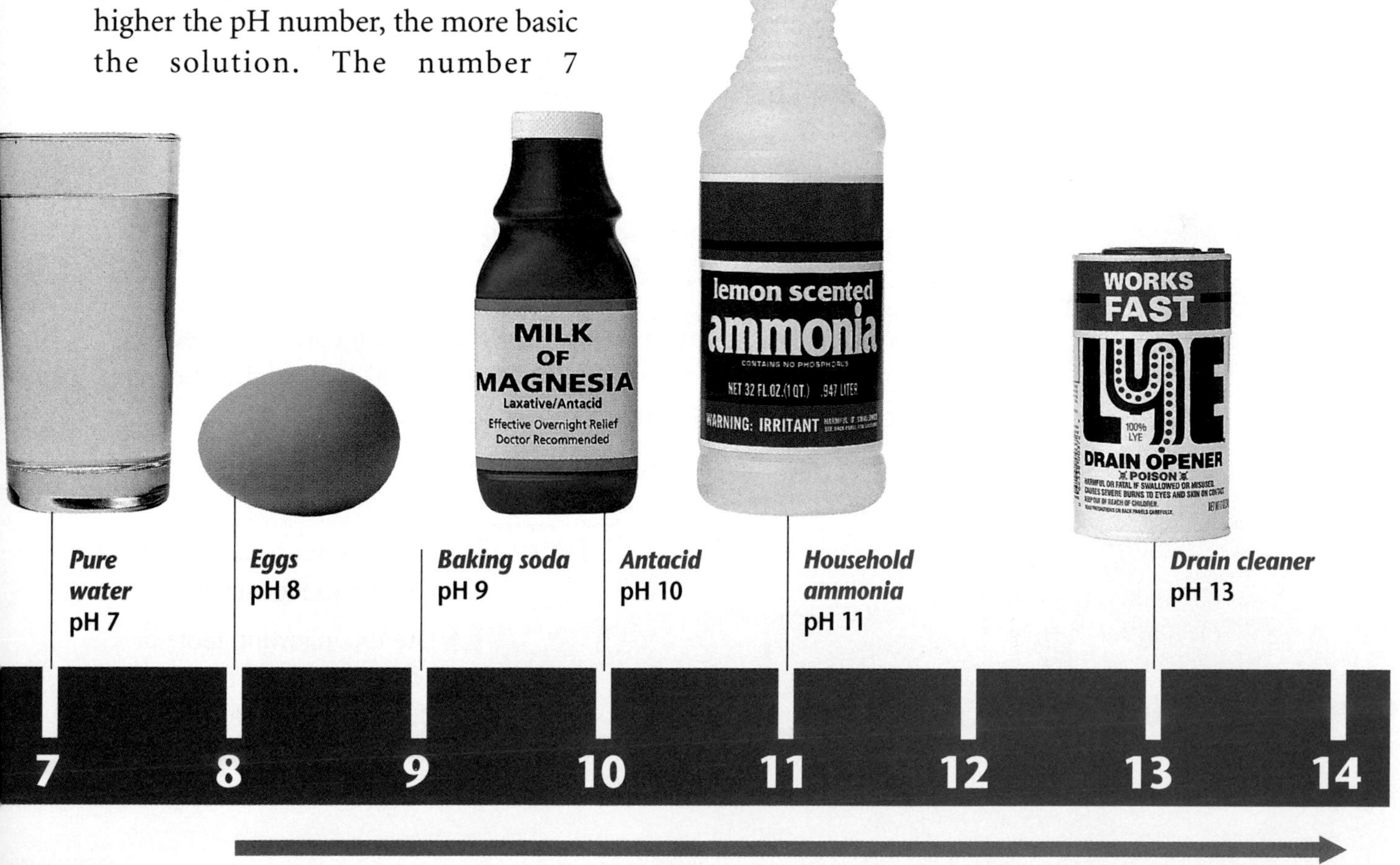

INVESTIGATE!

Finding pH

Certain substances change color when pH changes. A common substance of this type found in nature is red cabbage juice. In this Investigate, you will test the pH of household liquids using red cabbage juice.

Problem

How can cabbage juice indicate the relative pH of acids and bases?

Safety Precautions

Use caution when working with acids and bases. Wear lab aprons and goggles.

Materials

safety goggles
apron
7 test tubes
test-tube rack
100-mL graduated cylinder
red cabbage juice
grease pencil
7 dropping bottles with:
- household ammonia
- baking soda solution
- hydrochloric acid solution
- white vinegar
- colorless carbonated soft drink
- sodium hydroxide solution
- distilled water

What To Do

1. *In your Journal*, make a data table in which you can record your prediction of pH, the color of the cabbage juice, and the relative pH of the acid or base for each of the seven solutions to be tested.
2. Wear an apron and goggles. Mark each test tube with the substance name (see photo ***A***).
3. Fill each test tube with 15 mL of the cabbage juice.
4. Use the following table of colors to predict the relative pH of the test solutions. Record these predictions in your table.

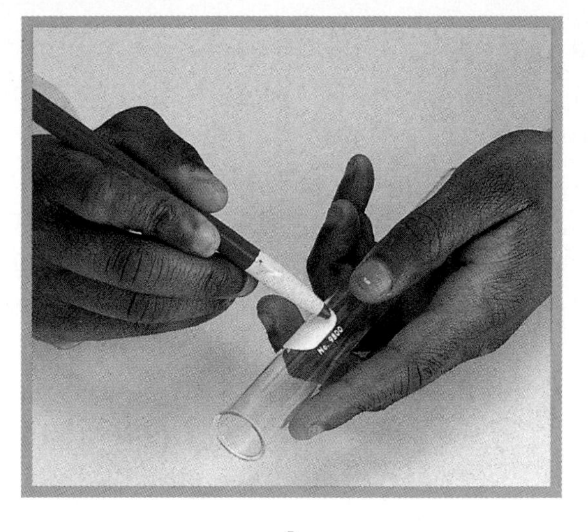

B

5 Add 5 drops of each test solution to the test tube labeled with its name (see photo ***B***). **CAUTION:** *If you spill any liquids on your skin, rinse the area immediately with water. Alert your teacher if any liquid is spilled in the work area.*

6 ***Observe*** any color changes of the cabbage juice. In your data table, record the color and relative pH of each solution.

Cabbage Juice Color	Relative pH
bright red	strong acid
red	medium acid
reddish purple	weak acid
purple	neutral
blue green	weak base
green	medium base
yellow	strong base

Analyzing

1. ***Classify*** which test solutions were acids and which were bases.
2. Which base was weakest?
3. Which acid was strongest?
4. ***Infer*** why distilled water didn't change the color of the cabbage juice.

Concluding and Applying

5. How do your predictions ***compare*** with the results?
6. How does cabbage juice indicate the relative strength of acids and bases?
7. **Going Further** ***Predict*** how other substances at home would react with the cabbage juice. Ask an adult to help you test your predictions.

Indicators and pH

One way to identify acids and bases is to use a pH meter. This meter uses electrical measurements to read out precise pH values.

As you saw in the Investigate, another way of determining pH is by using an indicator. An **indicator** is a substance that is one color in one pH range and another color in another range. To determine pH, you match the color to that of a known color.

Acid-base indicators come in two varieties—a solution or indicator paper. You already know about one of the most common indicators—litmus paper. Remember that litmus turns blue in the presence of a base and red in the presence of an acid. Would it change color in pure water? Why or why not?

Another common acid-base indicator is called phenolphthalein. Phenolphthalein is colorless in an acid, but it turns bright pink in the presence of a base. Phenolphthalein is also used to treat paper strips.

Another indicator that involves several color changes is universal indicator, shown in **Figure 6-7**.

For living things to grow and be healthy, there must be a balance in acids and bases. In the next section, you'll discover a way in which acid rain damage might be temporarily repaired.

Figure 6-7

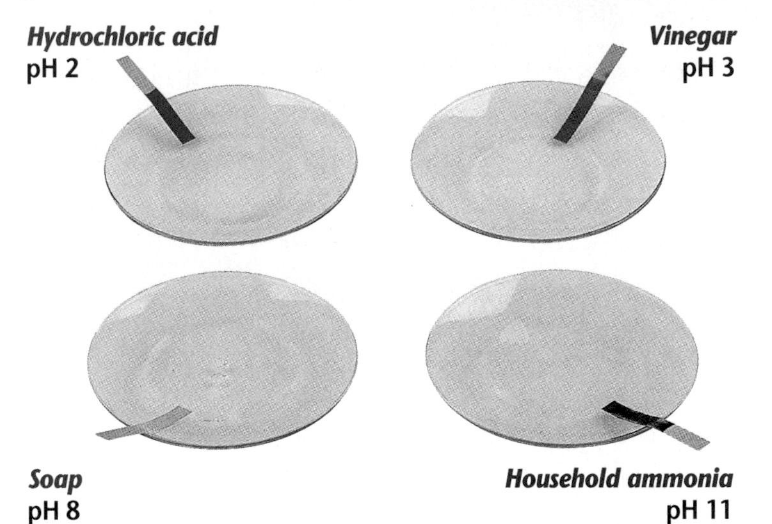

A The acidity of a solution can affect the color of certain dyes found in nature. Various dyes react at different pHs. A combination of indicators is used to make a universal indicator paper.

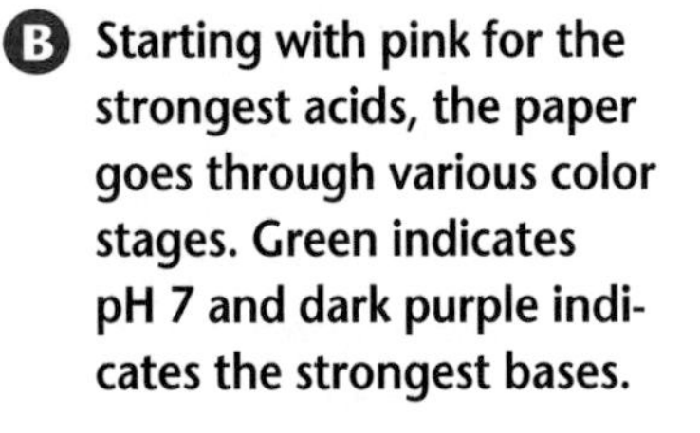
B Starting with pink for the strongest acids, the paper goes through various color stages. Green indicates pH 7 and dark purple indicates the strongest bases.

1. Describe two common acid-base indicators. Which colors will you observe in an acidic solution? In a basic solution?
2. Arrange the following list of solutions in order from most acidic to most basic.
   rainwater, pH 5.8
   club soda, pH 3.0
   seawater, pH 8.0
   drain cleaner, pH 13.0
   distilled water, pH 7.0
3. **Apply** Which of the substances mentioned in Question 2 should have a poison symbol on its label? Explain why.

6-4 Salts

Neutralization

You've probably heard commercials on television that say, "Are you bothered by an upset stomach? Try our product to neutralize excess stomach acid. You'll feel better fast!"

Would the pH of such a product be less than or greater than 7? For you to feel better, the pH would have to be greater than 7 because only a base can neutralize an acid.

Neutralization is the chemical reaction that occurs between an acid and a base. During neutralization, acidic and basic properties are canceled, or neutralized. For example, you've read how lime is used to neutralize acidic soil and how you can use an antacid to neutralize excess acid in your stomach.

Products of Neutralization

A **salt**, another type of compound, is formed as part of neutralization. Water is also formed. This reaction can be written as follows:

acid plus base produces a salt plus water

The same reaction can also be expressed using the names of specific chemicals:

hydrochloric acid plus sodium hydroxide produces sodium chloride plus water

To see how neutralization occurs, do the following Find Out activity.

Section Objectives

- Observe a neutralization reaction.
- Explain how salts form.

Key Terms

neutralization
salt

Find Out! ACTIVITY

How does neutralization take place?

What To Do

1. Put 10 mL of household ammonia in one test tube and 10 mL of white vinegar in another.
2. Test each with litmus paper. What do you observe? Which liquid is the acid? Which liquid is the base?
3. Add ammonia, drop by drop, to the test tube of vinegar, stirring with a stirring rod after each drop.
4. After adding 5 drops, test your solution with litmus paper.
5. Then, test with litmus for each additional drop.

Conclude and Apply

1. *In your Journal*, describe what change you observe in the litmus.
2. Record how many drops of ammonia it took to get a neutral solution.
3. Explain how you know the solution is neutral.

Salts

We usually think of salt as just table salt, sodium chloride. Many different salts, however, are formed in neutralization reactions. You come in contact with some of these salts every day but may not have realized that these compounds are salts. One example is calcium carbonate, or chalk. This salt is also used in the manufacturing of paint and rubber tires. Another salt, potassium nitrate, is also known as saltpeter and is used to make fertilizer and explosives.

Like acids and bases, salts are important in industry. **Figure 6-8** shows some salts and gives examples of how they are used. For example, table salt is important in food preparation. It's used in the curing of hams and bacon and in the production of lunch meats such as bologna, sausage, and wieners.

Many salts are also useful as raw materials. Chlorine, a chemical used to purify water, is obtained from sodium chloride. Other salts are used in the production of rubber, water softeners, chemicals, paints, fertilizers, and many other products you use every day.

Food Pioneer

You have learned in this chapter that salts are used in the preparation of foods. Pioneering food chemist Dr. Lloyd A. Hall developed new methods of using salts in preparing and preserving foods.

Hall was born in Elgin, Illinois in 1894, and he developed an interest in chemistry during high school. In 1925, Hall became director of research at Griffith Laboratories, where he studied the use of salts in meat curing.

Preserving Foods

Hall developed a method of combining sodium with nitrate and nitrite so that the sodium could preserve the meat before the nitrogen-containing salts could penetrate the meat and cause disintegration. The new technique was called flash-drying, and the resulting crystals

Dr. Lloyd A. Hall

Figure 6-8

A **Sodium chloride, which you know as table salt, is used in food preparation and in the manufacture of chemicals.**

B **Baking soda, sometimes called sodium bicarbonate, is the salt sodium hydrogen carbonate. This salt is part of the extinguishing material in one type of fire extinguisher, and is also commonly used in food preparation.**

C **This iron chromate salt is a yellow pigment used to color ceramics, glass, and enamels.**

D **Potassium permanganate is used in tanning leather. This salt is also used to purify water.**

were more effective than any meat-curing salts used before. Hall's work had a major impact on the meat industry.

Spices had been used for many years to preserve food. Hall found that many spices were actually contaminating the foods they were supposed to preserve. The spices were often infested with molds, yeasts, and bacteria. Hall developed a method to sterilize these spices without ruining their appearance, quality, and flavor. His method was also used for preparing medicines, medical supplies, and cosmetics.

Fats and oils often spoiled, or became rancid, when components of the fat interacted with the oxygen in the air. Many antioxidants, agents that prevent spoiling, would not dissolve in fat, so they could not effectively mix with the product. Hall developed a fat-soluble antioxidant mixture that was 99.64 percent sodium chloride. The remaining ingredients were the key to preserving the fats and oils.

Hall served as a science adviser in two wars. He helped solve the problem of keeping food for the military fresh and healthful. He was the first African American to be on the board of directors of the American Institute of Chemists.

What Do You Think?

If you've ever gone on a camping or hiking trip, you may have wished you could take along some of your favorite foods. What might a food chemist invent to keep those foods from spoiling along the way?

When the plankton are killed, the fish that depend upon them for food soon die.

Soil and land plants can also suffer from the effects of acid rain. Acid rain can dissolve important mineral nutrients and make the soil highly acidic. Some plants are adapted to normally acidic soil, but others are not. These are the ones that suffer from acid rain.

Possible Solutions

Science and industry are constantly searching for cleaner, more efficient fuels. Harnessing the energy in the sun, the wind, and the atom as an alternative to coal and oil is a major goal. Industry is also hard at work to find ways to use coal and oil without causing harmful by-products.

Science Journal

Acid rain is a controversial subject. Some people who earn money from coal and gas production and from the industries that use them claim that acid rain is not a problem. Find more information about acid rain and decide whether it is a serious threat to our environment. Summarize your decision *in your Science Journal.*

"In Times of Silver Rain"

In this chapter, you've read about acid rain and the unfavorable effects it has on the environment. To get a different view of rain, read the poem, "In Times of Silver Rain" by Langston Hughes (Bontemps, Arna Wendell, ed. *Golden Slippers: An Anthology of Negro Poetry for Young Readers*).

To Langston Hughes, rain is filled with beautiful images that inspire poetry. His image of "silver rain" evokes the idea of a shimmering cascade of raindrops—each like a silvered mirror reflecting the effect of rain on the plants growing on the plain.

What Do You Think?

What images does rain evoke for you?

How bad is battery pollution?

Electronic-gadget-loving Americans buy approximately 2.5 billion batteries a year and throw away more than 90 percent of them. Disposable batteries contain toxic materials such as mercury. These harmful materials can leak from landfills or fall to the ground from incinerator stacks.

Can this problem be remedied easily? Most new single-use disposable batteries are designed to work with little or no mercury. Smaller button-size batteries, which power watches and cameras, are made with silver oxide or lithium. But most rechargeable batteries contain nickel and cadmium. These batteries, which can be recharged between 300 and 1000 times, have reduced landfill waste; however, they put more than a million kg of highly toxic cadmium into the environment each year once they are discarded.

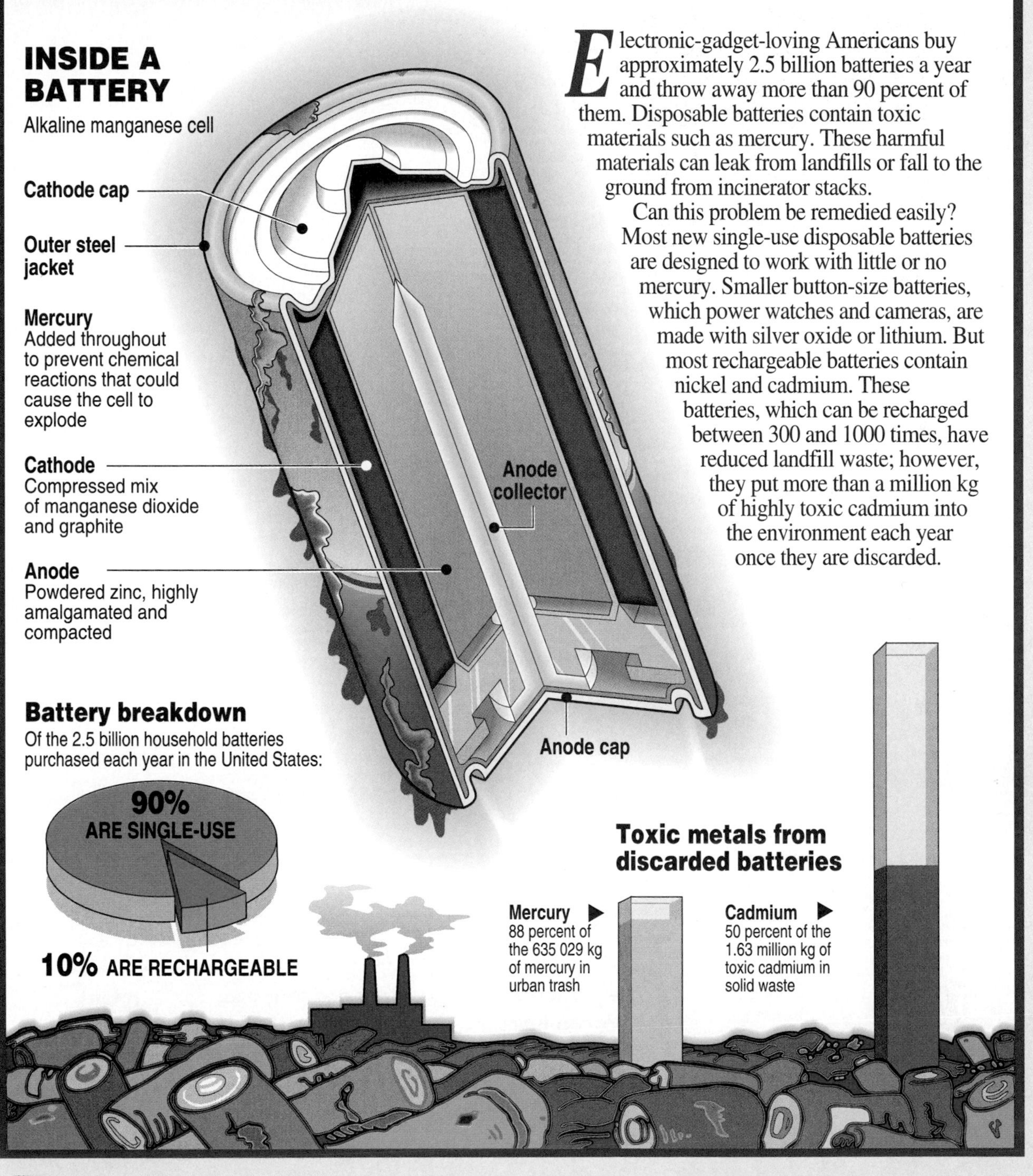

Science Journal

In your Science Journal, plan a public service brochure aimed at encouraging consumers to make use of rechargeable batteries and write a rough draft.

REVIEWING MAIN IDEAS

Science Journal

Review the statements below about the big ideas presented in this chapter, and answer the questions. Then, re-read your answers to the Did You Ever Wonder questions at the beginning of the chapter. *In your Science Journal*, write a paragraph about how your understanding of the big ideas in the chapter has changed.

1. **Acids are compounds that taste sour, may release hydrogen gas in reactions with active metals, and turn blue litmus paper red.** ***What common foods contain acids?***

2. **Bases taste bitter, feel slippery, and turn red litmus paper blue.** ***What common cleaning products contain bases?***

3. **Acids and bases can be very reactive.** ***What can happen to skin and lung tissues if they are in contact with strong acids or strong bases?***

4. **In a neutralization reaction, an acid reacts with a base to produce a salt and water.** ***Name some common salts and their uses.***

chapter 6
CHAPTER REVIEW

Using Key Science Terms

acid
base
indicator
neutralization
pH
salt

Each of the statements below contains a word or words that makes it wrong. Rewrite the sentence, replacing the incorrect word or words with a term that uses the correct science word from above.

1. An acid turns litmus paper blue.
2. A base has a sour taste and reacts with aluminum.
3. An acid and a base react, forming an indicator.
4. A measure of acidity is called neutralization.
5. A substance used to test for an acid is called an acid test.
6. A salt is always produced in a decomposition reaction.

Understanding Ideas

Answer the following questions in your Journal *using complete sentences.*

1. Explain how hydrochloric acid in your body is important to your life and health.
2. How might the burning of coal in one area of the country affect the environment in another area?
3. What would be a good indication that a grapefruit contains an acid?
4. Name five common acids found in your home and/or school.
5. What is the most commonly used base and what is it used for?

Developing Skills

Use your understanding of the concepts developed in this chapter to answer each of the following questions.

1. **Concept Mapping** Complete the concept map of acids and bases.

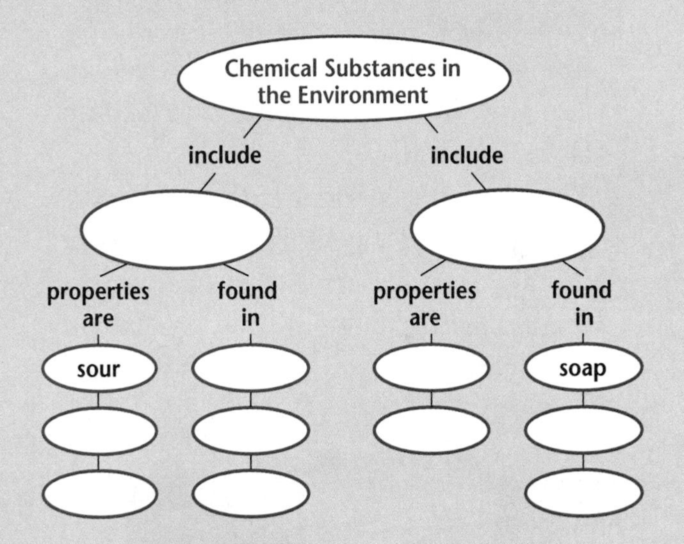

2. **Comparing and Contrasting** Repeat the Find Out activity on page 186. Use pieces of limestone or concrete rather than using pieces of marble. Compare the results with those made in the original activity.
3. **Separating and Controlling Variables** In the Find Out activity on page 203 why is it necessary to stir after each drop of ammonia is added to the vinegar?
4. **Observing and Inferring** After doing the Find Out activity on page 192, use litmus paper to identify each substance as an acid or a base. How do these results compare with those from the original activity? Which of the substances were neither acidic nor basic?

chapter 6
CHAPTER REVIEW

Critical Thinking

In your Journal, *answer each of the following questions.*

1. The leaves on the red cabbage in your garden are blue-green in color. What does this indicate about the soil?
2. The inside of a paper carton that your orange juice came in has a silvery color. Explain why it is probably plastic and not aluminum foil.
3. The chlorine generator at the pool has gone wild, and the pool's pH is as shown on the meter. Describe what effect this might have on the pool. How would you get the water back to where it is safe to swim?

Problem Solving

Read the following problem and discuss your answers in a brief paragraph.

Sheila Jones grows beautiful blue hydrangeas. Her neighbor, Manuel Ortiz, wants to grow some just like them. Sheila gives several roots to Manuel.

When Manuel's flowers bloom, they aren't blue, but pink! The person at the nursery tells Manuel to check his soil.

What do you think is the reason that Manuel's blue hydrangeas are pink? Why are Sheila's hydrangeas blue? What should Manuel do to get blue hydrangeas?

CONNECTING IDEAS

Discuss each of the following in a brief paragraph.

1. **Theme—Systems and Interactions** A recipe for spaghetti sauce states that it must be cooked in a nonaluminum pot. What is the reason for this instruction?
2. **Theme—Stability and Change** Predict the effect of acid rain on various types of landforms.
3. **Theme—Systems and Interactions** You dissolve sodium hydroxide in water. Is this mixture heterogeneous or homogeneous? Is the mixture a solution?
4. **Science and Society** What steps can be taken to reduce the amount of acid-producing substances in the air?

In this unit, you investigated how substances on Earth differ. You observed how some materials dissolve in others, forming solutions, while others do not.

You can describe an iron nail using physical properties, such as its size and mass, and chemical properties, such as its ability to react with oxygen to form rust.

Physical and chemical properties can also be used to identify substances as acids, bases, and salts.

Try the exercises and activity that follow—they will challenge you to use and apply some of the ideas you learned in this unit.

CONNECTING IDEAS

1. Ocean water is very salty. You may have accidentally tasted some while swimming, or noticed that salt crystals formed on your body as you sat in the sun to dry after swimming. How does the salt appear on your skin?
2. Suppose you are trying to decide which vinegar to buy. One brand is much cheaper than the other brand. You wonder if the cheaper brand has been diluted with water. If this is true, the acidity of the cheaper, diluted vinegar should be lower than the more expensive brand. How could you design an experiment to see if the acidity was the same for both brands?

Exploring Further ACTIVITY

What hazardous materials can be found around your home?

What To Do

1. Make a card file of dangerous materials around your home.
2. Identify acids, bases, and other toxic solutions and materials.
3. Include the danger posed by each substance and the steps to be taken if the material is accidentally spilled or taken into your body.
4. Use this activity to compile a first aid file for the home.

Interactions in the Living World

Taking the dogfish out for a walk ... er, swim? No, but like puppies underfoot, these fish follow the steps of a human visitor. The fish seek pieces of food amid sand stirred up by passing feet. In Unit 3, discover how life interacts on Earth and how living things are related.

NATIONAL GEOGRAPHIC

try it!

What do we really know about the living things around us? What do they look like? How do they move? Do they all eat the same way? Do they all make sounds? Take time to observe a living animal closely, very closely.

What To Do

1. With a partner, spend 15 minutes watching a pet gerbil or other organism available in your classroom. Describe the organism's surroundings. What does the gerbil do while you watch it? Record each observation that you make *in your Science Journal.*
2. *In your Science Journal,* write a definition for the word *life* based on your observations. Is *life* easy to define? Compare your observations with those of your classmates.
3. Try to find somethng nonliving that fits a classmate's definition. Try to find a living thing that is excluded by the definition. Is your own definition complete and accurate?

CHAPTER 7

Describing the Living WORLD

Did you ever wonder...

- What makes something alive?
- Why names are so important?
- How or if you and your cat or dog are related?

Science Journal

Before you begin to study about the features of living things and how they are classified, think about these questions and answer them *in your Science Journal.* When you finish the chapter, compare your journal write-up with what you have learned.

As you look at the zebras across the bottom of the page, you can imagine the thundering sound that they make. Can you imagine the vibration that you would feel if they were real? There is no doubt that you are looking at a picture of life in action here. Is everything around you alive? What are some things that you look for when you decide something is alive or not?

In the following activity, observe some objects and begin to think more about what life is like.

ACTIVITY

What are some signs of life?

What To Do

1. Carefully observe a lighted, dripping candle for up to five minutes. Do not touch the flame or move the candle. *In your Journal*, list some adjectives that you would use to describe any lifelike characteristics of the candle.
2. Now observe a flowering plant. *In your Journal*, list adjectives for lifelike characteristics of the plant. Then do the same for the zebras or an animal you might have in the classroom.
3. With a partner, discuss which of these objects is alive. Write a conclusion statement that both of you agree on. Be prepared to defend your statement.

7-1 What Is the Living World?

Section Objectives

- Determine the characteristics of living things.
- Apply the characteristics of living things to determine if something is alive or not.

Key Terms

organism, reproduction, stimulus, adaptation

Is It Alive?

If you visit an aquarium, or if you ever stop to watch tropical fish in a pet store, you might see some fish like the ones in the photograph that opens this unit. Look again at the photograph of the coral reef on page 214. If you were face-to-face with a fish, you'd know you were looking at a living thing. But what about the water and the sand? Or the coral? Are any of these things living?

What do living things do that nonliving things don't do? This next activity will help you identify some characteristics or traits you can use to distinguish living and nonliving things.

Find Out! ACTIVITY

What are some differences between living and nonliving things?

What To Do

1. From your teacher, obtain some mustard seeds and some gravel pieces about the same size as the seeds.
2. Describe the seeds. Can you tell if they are alive? Describe the gravel. Do you really know that the gravel isn't alive?
3. Mark 2 separate jars as A and B. Put the seeds in jar A and the gravel in jar B.
4. Soak both the seeds and the gravel for 24 hours in small, but equal amounts of water.
5. What do you predict will happen?
6. Observe the soaked seeds and the gravel for the next two days.

Conclude and Apply

1. What can you conclude about whether the seeds or gravel are alive? What signs of life do either show?
2. Based on your observations, what would you say are some differences between living and nonliving things?

Organisms

As you look around your classroom, you'll see people talking to one another, reading, or scratching an itch. Maybe it's lunchtime and your class eats lunch in the classroom, so people are drinking and eating. A plant in the window is drooped over from lack of water. A guppy in the aquarium has just laid more eggs. You and your classmates, the plant, and the guppies are all organisms. An **organism** is a living thing. In this chapter, you will learn about different organisms. Does every organism seem alive all the time? As you saw with the seeds in the Find Out activity, sometimes, it isn't so easy to tell. Seeds don't appear alive until they start to grow. Neither do the barnacles, such as those in **Figure 7-1**. Read about these organisms, then turn the page to learn about the characteristics shared by all organisms.

Figure 7-1

As adults, barnacles resemble rocks. They stay in one place and go for long periods showing no outward signs of being alive.

A An adult barnacle attaches itself to some object under water and stays there for the rest of its life. The object can be a rock, another organism, a pier, or the bottom of a ship.

B Once attached to something, a hard shell forms around the adult barnacle. An attached barnacle opens part of its shell periodically for feeding. Only then does it appear alive because it extends its legs from its shell and sweeps food into its mouth.

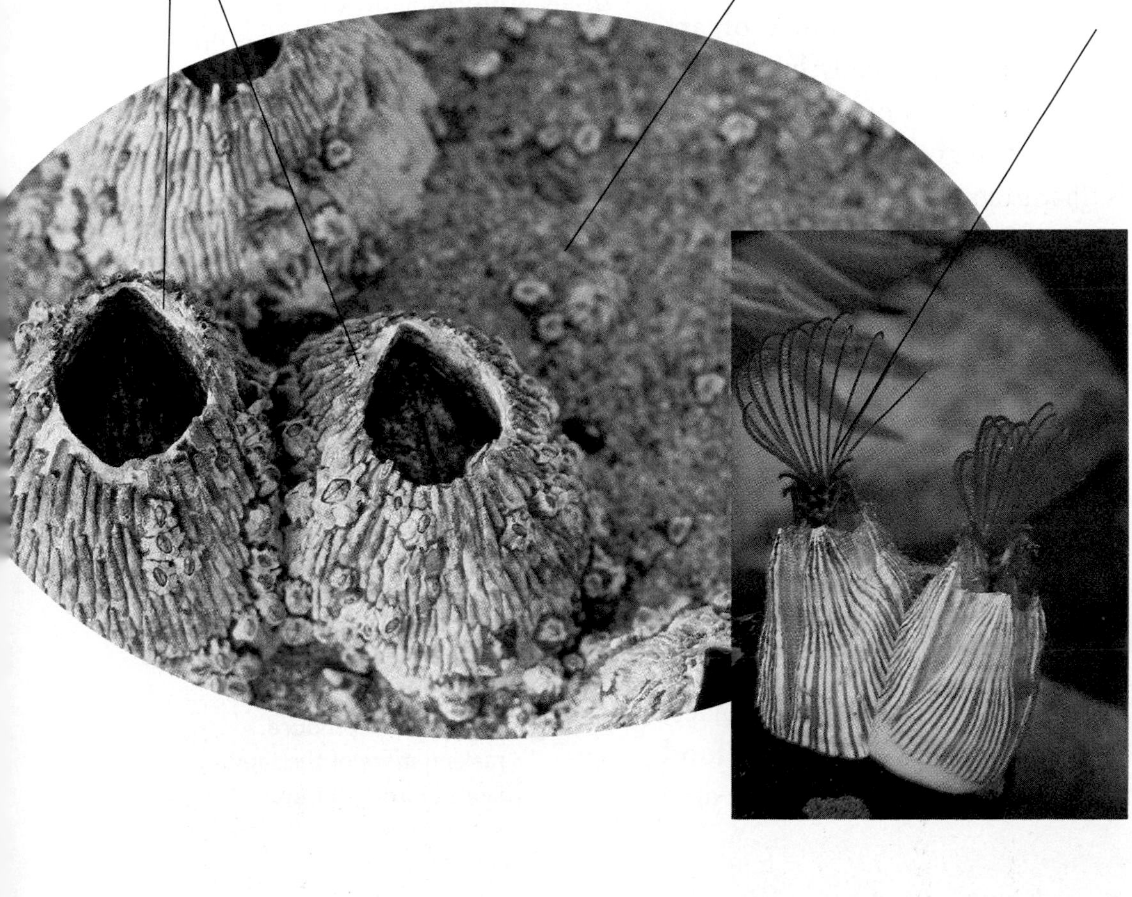

Traits of Living Things

Organisms, from mustard seeds to elephants, have traits that set them apart from nonliving things. Think about each trait described here. Think about how you yourself fit the definition of organism as you study each of these.

Organisms Are Made Up of Cells

Figure 7-2

Cells are the basic units of all organisms in which life functions take place. Some organisms, such as bacteria, are made up of just one cell. Larger organisms, such as cats, birds, bees, and trees, are made up of billions of cells. Large animal organisms also usually have many different kinds of cells. You have bone cells, nerve cells, and muscle cells. Plants contain a variety of different types of cells as well.

Most cells are very small. You'll find that you can't see most cells without the help of a microscope.

A Organisms are made up of cells. In many-celled organisms, cells may be highly specialized, like these blood cells.

Organisms Use Water and Food and Produce Wastes

Every organism is made up of a great deal of water. For example, your body is about two-thirds water. Most of this water is found inside cells where chemical reactions take place. There, energy is released from food compounds. As a result, you are able to move, think, grow, and produce new cells. Water also carries away most waste products that are made in cells.

B Organisms need water and food to develop and live.

Organisms Reproduce

If organisms did not reproduce, how would all the forms of life on Earth continue to exist? **Reproduction** is the process by which organisms make more organisms of the same kind. As you can see in **Figure 7-2C**, a single sunflower produces many seeds. Each seed is capable of producing a flower that produces more seeds. Reproduction ensures that a particular type of organism survives.

C Organisms reproduce, making more of the same kinds of living things.

D Organisms grow and develop.

Organisms Grow and Develop

So long as they are supplied with food for energy, organisms grow. Small elephants develop into large elephants. Skinny saplings grow up to become large trees. Some organisms grow in terms of the number of individuals rather than becoming larger in size. One-celled organisms usually grow to a certain size and then reproduce, resulting in an increased number of organisms.

Organisms Respond

When a cat hears the sound of a can opener, it comes running into the kitchen expecting to be fed. When you hear an unexpected loud noise, do you jump? When it gets cold, do you shiver?

E Organisms respond to their environment.

When you do any of these things, you are responding to changes in your environment. Anything an organism responds to is a **stimulus.** A stimulus produces a response—a change in behavior on the part of an organism.

Stimuli are received through the senses. Stimuli can be in the form of changes in light, temperature, sound, touch, or taste. Chemicals also act as stimuli.

Organisms Are Adapted to Their Environment

What is there about a fish that enables it to survive in water but not on land? Why does a cactus survive in the desert? Any trait of an organism that helps it survive in its environment is an **adaptation.** Fish have adaptations called gills that enable them to remove oxygen from water. Fish can't remove oxygen from air as you do. A cactus has special tissues that are adapted to hold water. The better an organism is adapted, the better its chances for surviving long enough to reproduce. Adaptations are inherited. They are not temporary adjustments that an organism makes to changes going on around it.

F Organisms such as cacti are adapted for retaining water.

In the Investigate that follows, think about whether common yeast shows any or all of the characteristics of life you've learned about here.

DESIGN YOUR OWN

INVESTIGATION

Living or Nonliving?

In this section, you have learned about the traits of living things. During this investigation, you will observe how substances react to food. Use your knowledge about living things to help you prove which substances are living.

Preparation

Problem
How can you prove that something is living or nonliving?

Form a Hypothesis
As a group, decide on a statement or prediction about whether yeast, baking soda, and salt are living or not.
Record your hypothesis.

Objectives
- Observe the changes over time when something is fed.
- Compare the reactions of test items to the traits of living organisms.

Possible Materials
microscope
coverslips
4 test tubes each with 20 drops of sugar water
1 package dry yeast
salt (NaCl)
baking soda ($NaHCO_3$)
measuring spoons
labels

Safety Precautions
Dispose of the yeast as directed by your teacher.

DESIGN YOUR OWN
INVESTIGATION

Plan the Experiment

1 As a group, decide how you will test your hypothesis. Design the experiment to prove if any of the three test items are alive. Write down the steps of your experiment.

2 What are the variables? What is the control? Before you begin, label the tubes for your experiment and record what each one will contain. Make certain that you use the same amount of each substance in the test. In this experiment, sugar water is the food.

3 Make a data table. In the table, list the traits of living things that you will observe.

4 Immediately after you put each test item into the sugar water, observe a sample of each under the microscope. At the end of the experiment, observe the samples again and compare.

Check the Plan

1 Investigations like this one take time. Plan to take observations every 10 minutes for 40 minutes. After every observation, record what you saw.

2 Before you start your experiment, make certain your teacher approves your plan.

3 Carry out the experiment.

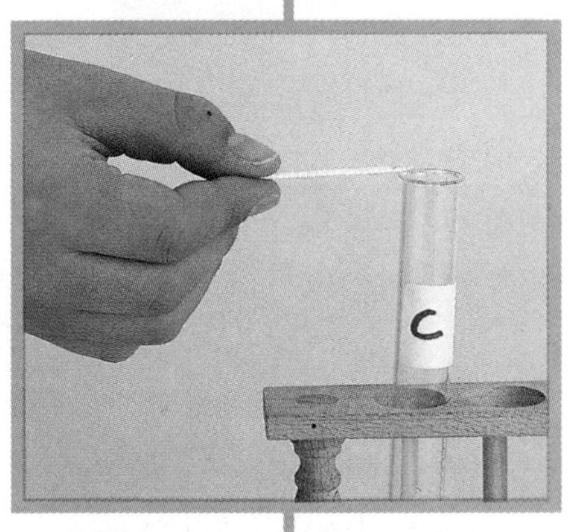

Analyze and Conclude

1. **Observe** How did test tubes A, B, C, and D change over the time you observed them?
2. **Infer** What was in the test tubes that changed? Was the change an indication of a life process occurring?
3. **Conclude** What waste product was produced in the experiment? What do you think it is? Why did it occur?
4. **Scientific Illustration** Make drawings of what you see under the microscope at the beginning and at the end of the experiment for each tube.
5. **Collect Data** In your data table, check off each trait that applies to each item tested.
6. **Conclude** Use your data to conclude whether each test item is living or nonliving.

Going Further

Design an experiment in which you test for each of the characteristics of life as described on pages 220 and 221.

Needs of Living Things

■ Food

Living things change the substances they take in as food. In the Investigate, you may have observed that the test tube that contained yeast, sugar, and water, produced bubbles. To stay alive, most organisms break down sugar and energy is released. In breaking down sugar, carbon dioxide and water are produced in a process called cellular respiration. The bubbles that you saw are bubbles of carbon dioxide.

Figure 7-3

A Like every organism, this barn swallow needs water to live. Water in food, the bird's cells, or from a pond or stream satisfies this need.

■ Water

"I'm dying of thirst!" How often have you heard that statement? What do you suppose would have happened if you had not supplied water for the yeast in the Investigate? No matter how much food is available, unless the food contains water or other water is available, an organism will not survive long.

Living organisms come in many sizes, shapes, and colors. In the next sections, you will learn why and how traits are used to classify living things.

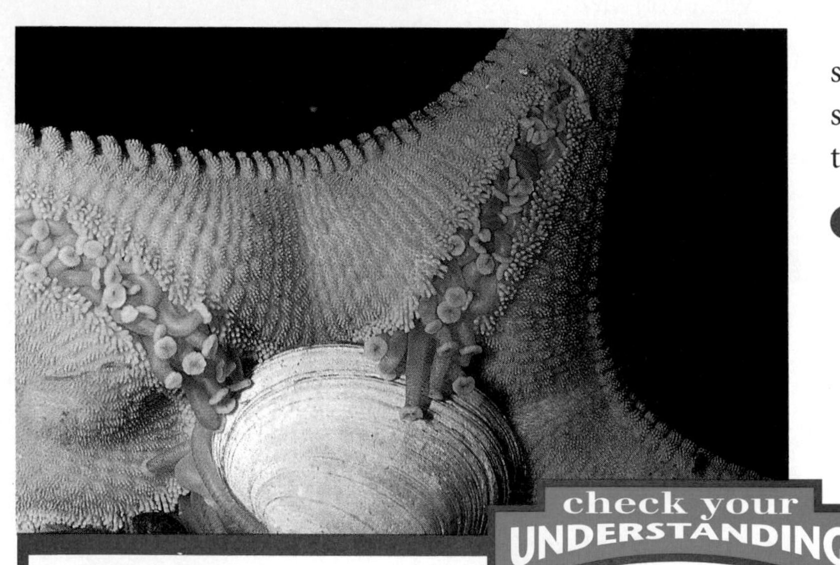

B Growth and development take energy. The fuel that supplies that energy is food. All organisms need food. This starfish eats mussels and clams. This food supplies the starfish with energy.

check your UNDERSTANDING

1. Name a trait of living things that each of the following nonliving objects appears to possess. Then explain why they are, nonetheless, not alive.
   a. a gasoline engine
   b. a crystal of salt
   c. a robot
2. Give two examples of organisms responding to a stimulus in their environment.
3. How is an adaptation different from a response to a stimulus?
4. **Apply** A pigeon pecks at bread crumbs in a park. How does the pigeon show the characteristics of living things? Does the pigeon show all the characteristics? If it does not, can you still say it is alive?

7-2 Classification

Order Out of Confusion

You rush into the record store, eager to buy the latest recording by your favorite group. You head for the first table and begin looking for it. Something must be wrong! CDs are mixed with audiotapes. Rock is mixed with reggae; country with classical; rap is right next to opera. Nothing about this place is in order! How can you find anything?

Section Objectives

- Recognize how a classification system allows scientists to communicate information.
- Describe the levels of the system used to classify organisms.
- Explain the characteristics that make up the five kingdoms of organisms.

Key Terms

classification
kingdom
phylum
genus
species

Explore! ACTIVITY

How do categories help you find what you want?

What To Do

1. Obtain a stack of blank 3 × 5 pieces of paper for category labels from your teacher.
2. Obtain several types of audiotapes or CDs.
3. With a partner, sort the tapes or CDs and develop categories for them.
4. Write each category on a separate piece of paper. Stack each matching audiotape or CD by its label.
5. Did you and your partner always agree on the categories?
6. How many ways did you find to classify the audiotapes or CDs?

Stores make it easy to find what you want by organizing recordings according to whether they are CDs or audiotapes, by musical style, and by artist. This organization is a form of classification. **Classification** is any system used to group ideas, information, or objects based on their similarities. Your method of classifying in the Explore activity may have differed from your partner's. Of course, nature isn't as easy to organize as a store. But classifying living things helps scientists organize their knowledge so that they can communicate about specific organisms.

A Scientific Way to Classify

What kind of bird do you picture when you hear the name *robin*? If you live in the United States, you may think first of the bird shown in **Figure 7-4**. But the name *robin* means something different to people living in England. They call the bird in **Figure 7-5**, robin. And the name means something else again to people in China, who call the bird in **Figure 7-6** robin. You can see that these robins aren't the same bird at all!

Figure 7-4

Scientists have a way to classify and name the huge numbers of organisms found on Earth to help keep order. Try this method yourself in the following activity.

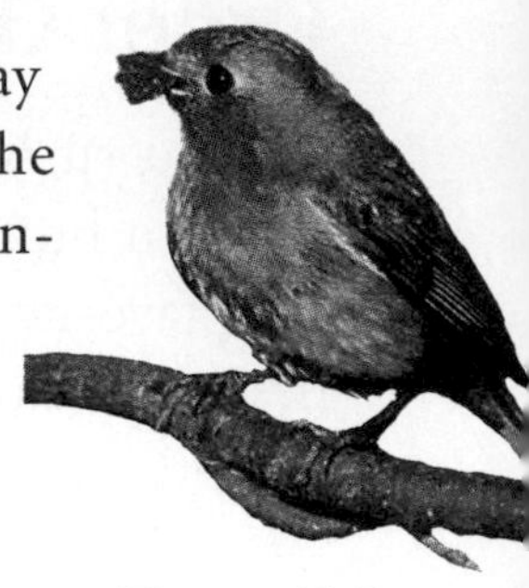

Figure 7-5

Explore! ACTIVITY

How would you name things?

What To Do

1. Obtain an assortment of tree leaves from your teacher.
2. Work with a partner to determine traits of the leaves that enable you to classify them into two or more groups.
3. After you have classified them, write a name on an index card that describes each group's most noticeable traits.
4. Tell another pair of classmates the names you've given your groups of leaves. Ask them to match each name with a group.
5. Have them explain why if they have had another opinion of what to call the leaf groups.

Common Names

People use common names, such as *robin*, for organisms that they are familiar with. Usually, that's all right because people from the same region know what organism everyone is referring to. But scientists around the world would run into trouble if they relied on common names. As in the case of the robin, they have to be able to communicate accurately with each other even if they don't speak each other's language.

A Good Reason for Classification

Organisms are classified according to their traits and given names that distinguish them from other kinds of organisms. Such a system enables scientists around the world to know they are communicating about the same organism. This is important, especially when there is a need to identify a disease-causing organism where use of a wrong scientific name could result in misdiagnosis or death.

The classification system that scientists rely on gives a unique name to each kind of known organism. The name identifies the organism and enables scientists to know how it is related to other organisms that are similar to it. Although all three birds in **Figure 7-4** through **7-6** each has the common name robin, each one has a different scientific name. A scientific name distinguishes each robin from all other kinds of robins and all other kinds of birds.

In the 1700s, a classification and naming system was developed by a Swedish scientist named Carolus Linnaeus. Linnaeus originally began by grouping all organisms into two large categories: animals and plants. These categories are called kingdoms. A **kingdom** is the most general and the largest group of organisms in the classification system. Today, scientists recognize three other kingdoms in addition to plants and animals: monerans, protists, and fungi. Turn the page to learn about each of these kingdoms.

Figure 7-6

Connect to... Earth Science

Organisms aren't the only things with a classification system. Find out what the Mohs' mineral scale is used for.

How Do We Know?

Linnaeus and the Early History of Classification

Carolus Linnaeus established the modern system of classification in the 1700s. At an early age, Linnaeus's friends and relatives noted his love for the natural world, especially botany (the study of plants).

In 1728, Linnaeus attended medical school for a short time. There, he met a botanist who persuaded him to continue his interest in plants. Later, Linnaeus became a professor of botany, and directed a major scientific expedition to study plant life in the Arctic.

It was from these early studies that Linnaeus got the idea to establish a system of classification. The 1700s were important for the field of botany. Many of the world's plants were being described and studied by scientists at this time. Linnaeus established his system to help students of botany quickly put these newly described plants into categories.

Life's Five Kingdoms

Linnaeus's system consisted of only two kingdoms into which he grouped all organisms. As scientists studied the characteristics of more and more different kinds of organisms, they realized that more kingdoms were needed to classify accurately. Since the 1950s, living things have been grouped into five kingdoms.

On these two pages are but a few examples of the members of each kingdom. The characteristics of each kingdom are also given.

■ Life's Diversity

You can see from the examples that each kingdom contains much variety. During your lifetime, you may see only a few of these organisms, but each is important in the living world. Each organism plays a role which you will learn more about in Chapters 12 and 16, which both discuss relationships in the living world.

Figure 7-7

Paramecia

Euglena

Bacteria

Moneran Kingdom

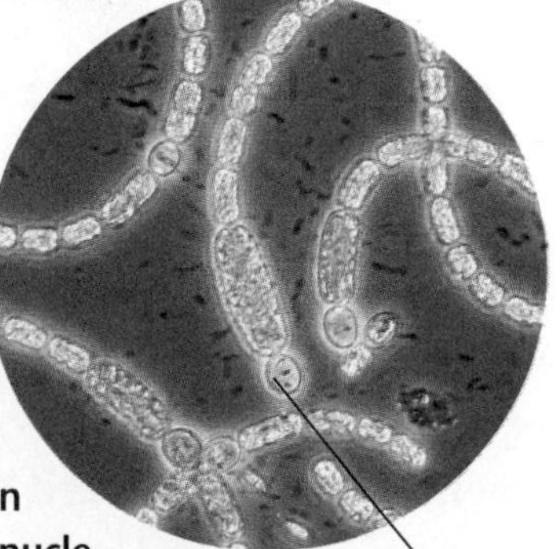

Representatives of the group of one-celled organisms known as monerans have been present on Earth for about 3.5 billion years. The single cell of the moneran has a very simple organization and does not include a nucleus. About 1800 species of monerans have been named. Monerans are grouped into bacteria and cyanobacteria.

Protist Kingdom

A The cells of protists, such as paramecium and Euglena, are more complex and organized than monerans. Protists have a nucleus that controls the cell's activities. Protists have lived on Earth for about one billion years. About 38 000 species have been identified.

B Protists are a varied group. Most protists are one-celled, but some are many-celled. Some protists, like the paramecia, swim by moving surface hairs; others whip around with a single hair-like structure. Some protists are animal-like, some others are plant-like and can make their own food, while some are parasites. You will learn about monerans and protists in Chapter 8.

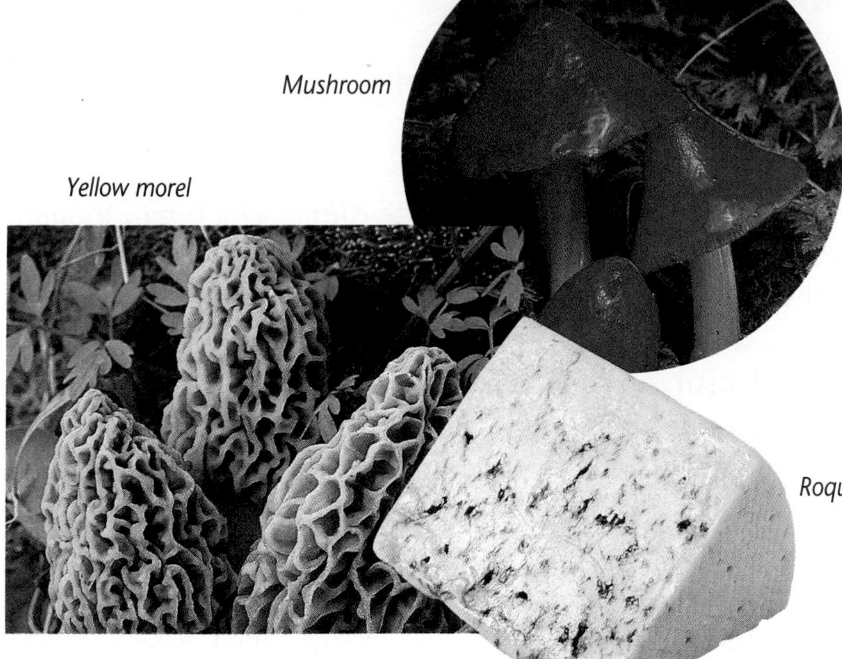

Mushroom

Yellow morel

Roquefort cheese

Fungus Kingdom

A Fungi are either one-celled or many-celled. In Chapter 8, you'll learn how fungi obtain food by decomposing other organisms.

B Various types of mushrooms and yeast are examples of fungi. Even the blue part of Roquefort cheese is the result of a fungus.

Plant Kingdom

A There are at least a quarter of a million known plant species. Scientists suspect that many more species will be discovered, especially in tropical rain forests. Plants are many-celled organisms, yet their ancestors were probably one-celled green algae—members of the protist kingdom.

B The oldest land plant fossils are about 400 million years old. In Chapter 10, you'll learn how plants make their own food by using light from the sun.

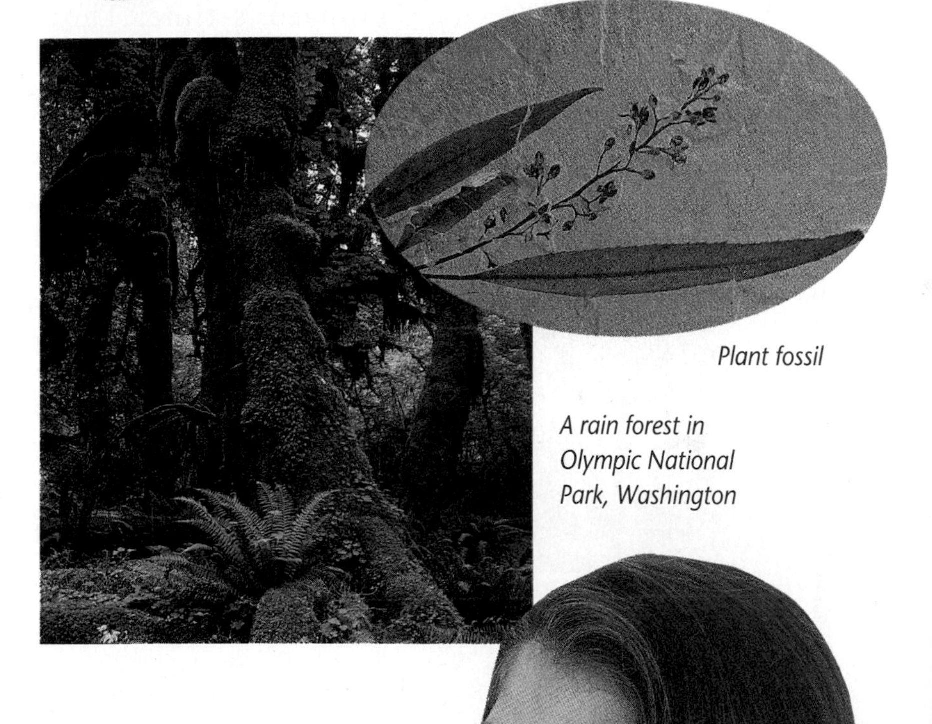

Plant fossil

A rain forest in Olympic National Park, Washington

Animal Kingdom

A Humans and butterflies are just a few of the groups of organisms classified as animals. Animals are many-celled organisms with complex body structures. In Chapter 9, you'll learn how animals must consume other organisms to survive.

B There is evidence that animals first appeared on Earth about 700 million years ago. Today, there are about one million known animal species. Some animals, such as certain worms, are so small they can be seen only with the help of a microscope. Others, such as the blue whale are the largest organisms on Earth.

Human and butterfly

Beyond the Five Kingdoms

SKILLBUILDER

Making and Using Graphs

Make a pie graph to show the number of species in each kingdom. If you need help, refer to the **Skill Handbook** on page 657.

Kingdom	Number of Species
Monera	1800
Protist	38 000
Fungi	100 000
Plant	285 000
Animal	1 million

Classification doesn't stop with five kingdoms however. Organisms within kingdoms are grouped into smaller and smaller categories.

The Subgroups

The kingdom is still the largest category into which living things are grouped, just as it was in Linnaeus's time. The plant kingdom is separated into subgroups called divisions. The fungi, monera, protist, and animal kingdoms are separated into subgroups called phyla. (The singular is phylum.) If you compare your search for a song in the record store to the animal kingdom, the store itself would be the kingdom and it would have two phyla—the audiotape section and the CD section.

Each **phylum** is separated into still smaller groups called classes. A class can be compared to the category of music you look under for your song—for example, rock music. Each class is further separated into groups

A History of Plant Classification

Plant classification is a system that is used to group and identify plants found worldwide. When did humans first start classifying plants?

The art on both this page and the next are examples of uses and classification of plants by people of different cultures. The image to the immediate right is a page from an Islamic botany book. The image on the next page is a detail from a mural, painted by Diego Rivera, depicting the preparation of herbal medicines.

A Long History

Plant classification has been practiced for thousands of years in one form or another. People have classified plants based on their uses. For example, some plants were used for food, others for making cloth and dyes. Still others, called herbs, were used for medicine.

Herbals

Around 300 B.C.E., Theophrastus, a Greek, devised a system to classify plants. Theophrastus wrote a book called an *herbal* in which he identified and described plants. To assist him, he hired a number of traveling students to called orders. An order can be likened to the alphabetical sections you find under rock music. Each order is separated into families. A family can be compared to all the audiotapes of a particular rock group.

Each family is further separated into subgroups called genera. (The singular is genus.) A genus can be compared to the particular cassette that has the song you want. Finally, each **genus** is made up of the smallest categories of all—**species**. A species might be compared to the song itself.

Figure 7-8

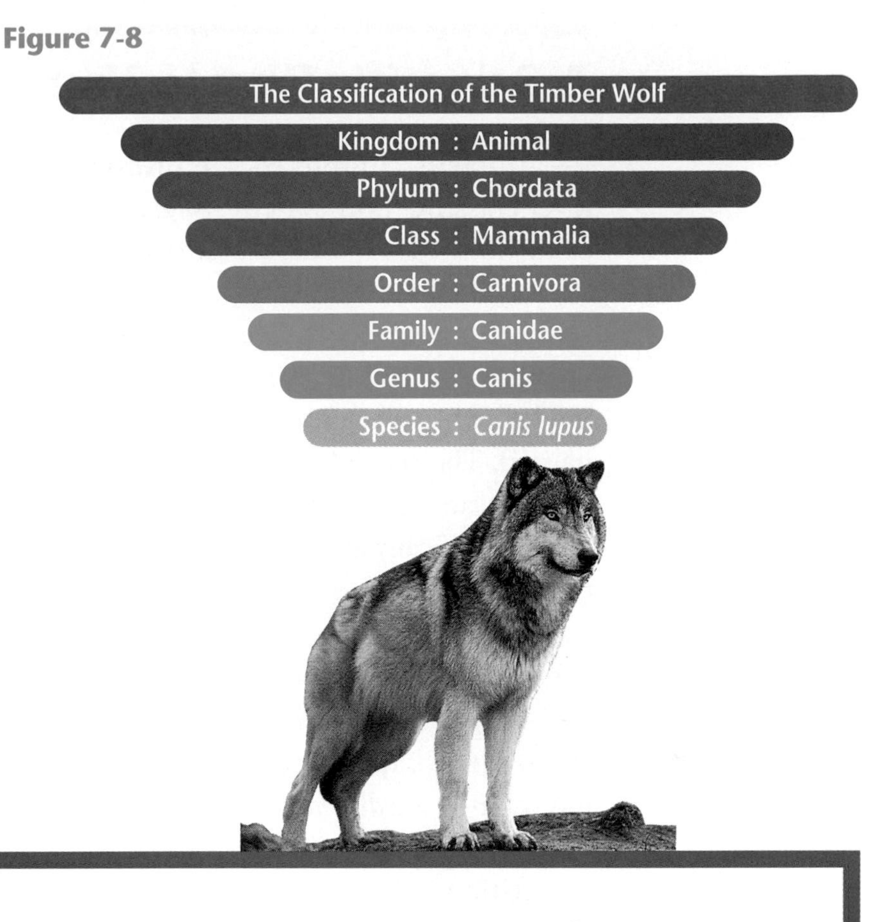

collect and observe plants in other places. As a result, he was able to include descriptions of over 500 species of plants.

After Theophrastus, there was little change in plant classification for nearly 2000 years. Classification remained mostly based on how plants could be used, instead of how they looked.

Finally, in 1735, Linnaeus published *System of Nature*, in which he described hundreds of plants and gave each a scientific name. Many of these names are still in use today.

You Try It!

Working with a partner, make an herbal identifying plants found in your area. Describe and draw each type of plant. Make up common names for each of your plants and label them. Find out how some of these plants may have been used.

A Scientific Way to Name

Linnaeus completed the multilevel classification system by giving each kind of organism a two-part scientific name. The first part of the scientific name is the genus of the organism, such as *Turdus* for the robin in **Figure 7-4**. The genus is always capitalized. The second part of the scientific name describes the organism more specifically and often tells something specific about the organism. For example, what might *migratorius* tell you about a bird? It tells you that the bird migrates, or moves from place to place. The complete specific name for the robin is *Turdus migratorius.* Other examples are given in **Figure 7-9**. A scientific name identifies a specific organism and only that organism.

Linnaeus used Latin words to name organisms because it was learned and understood by most scientists at that time. Scientists continue to use Latin names today and use Linnaeus's system to name any new organisms they discover. Some organisms have latinized names of the person who identified them, or for the location in which they were found.

In the next section, you will learn that classification continues to change and now involves more than how an organism appears.

Figure 7-9

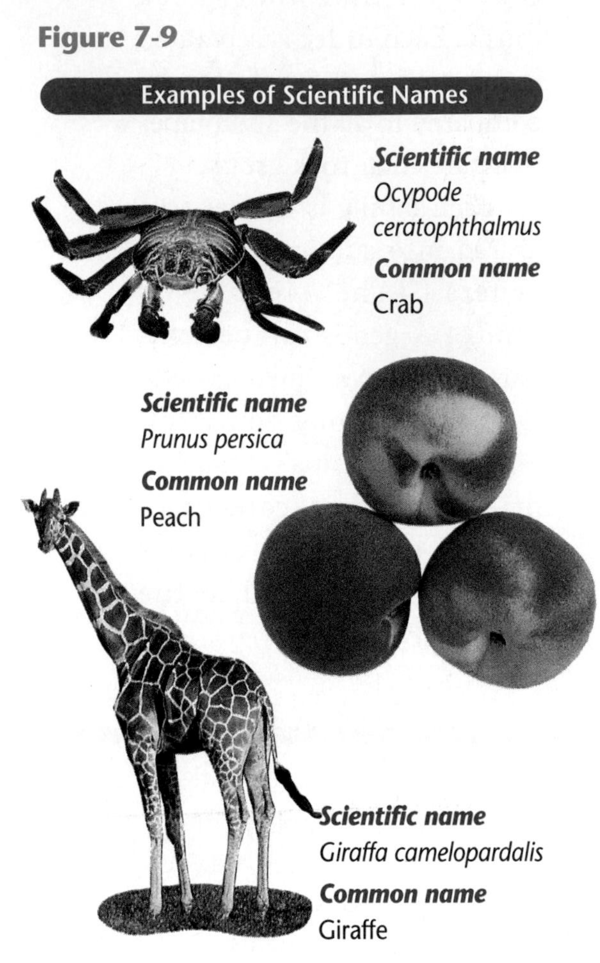

check your UNDERSTANDING

1. The scientific name for a particular large cat is *Panthera leo.* Why would a scientist want to use this name when communicating about the organism rather than just "large cat"?
2. Which level of classification would hold the largest number of organisms? Which would hold the fewest?
3. **Apply** Suppose a scientist discovered a new organism and named it *Panthera migratorius.* List everything that the name tells you about the organism.

7-3 Modern Classification

Organisms Are Related

Section Objectives
- Demonstrate that a classification system can show how organisms are related.
- Identify the traits scientists use to classify organisms.

You've seen how classifying can help scientists distinguish different species of organisms, but classifying is also important for showing how organisms are related. For example, if there is a new kind of disease-causing bacterium, it is important to know what it has in common with known bacteria. A treatment or medicine that controls or kills a known kind of disease-causing bacteria might also work on a closely related bacterium.

In the Find Out activity that follows, find out how classifications can show where relationships exist between organisms.

Find Out! ACTIVITY

How closely related are three common animals?

What To Do

1. Look at the table below, beginning with the kingdom level, and compare the cat, leopard, and deer at each level.
2. *In your Journal*, note where the animals become different from each other. Then answer the questions that follow.

Group	Domestic Cat	Leopard	Deer
Kingdom	Animalia	Animalia	Animalia
Phylum	Chordata	Chordata	Chordata
Class	Mammalia	Mammalia	Mammalia
Order	Carnivora	Carnivora	Artiodactyla
Family	Felidae	Felidae	Cervidae
Genus	Felis	Panthera	Odocoileus
Species	*Felis cattus*	*Panthera pardus*	*Odocoileus virginianus*

Conclude and Apply

1. At what level are domestic cats and deer different?
2. At what level are domestic cats and leopards different?
3. Animals closely related to the deer might be found at what levels?
4. Comment on the sentence: "The more levels two organisms both belong to, the more closely they are related."

What Traits Show Relationships?

You expect a media store to have audiotapes and CDs organized into understandable categories. In the same way, scientists need a classification system based on useful traits—traits that will help scientists see how organisms are related. What characteristics do you think would be useful?

Explore! ACTIVITY

Do obvious traits always show relationships?

What To Do

1. Collect a set of animal pictures. First, classify the animals according to color. What animals have ended up in the same group? How much do these animals have in common?
2. Now group the animals according to where they live: for example, in water, on land, underground, and so on.
3. *In your Journal,* explain if color or location are useful ways to classify.

Chemistry CONNECTION

Modern Tools for Classification

Sometimes the relationship between two different organisms is so close that it is hard to classify them based on body traits you can see or on fossil evidence alone. In such cases, scientists may look inside organisms and examine the life processes that go on.

Chemical Clues

The giant panda is an example of how an organism may be reclassified because of

Brown bear *Giant panda* *Raccoon*

How useful were color and location as classifying traits? If scientists classified organisms just by color or location, what do you think they would say about black bears, black widow spiders, and black birds?

As you've seen, this classification system also groups very different organisms together so it isn't a very useful approach.

Information from the Past

Scientists also study the traits of fossils, the ancestors of today's organisms. Fossils show how organisms that lived millions of years ago are related to organisms that live today. Fossil evidence has demonstrated that horses and donkeys are more closely related than horses and goats because horses and donkeys have more ancestors in common than do horses and goats.

Using a Key

A variety of methods are used to identify related organisms. As you have learned, many are based on appearance. One tool, called a *dichotomous key* is used to identify organisms. There are keys for plants, mushrooms, fish, butterflies, and every other kind of organism. In the Investigate on the next page, learn how to identify two kinds of birds by using a key.

new evidence. Giant pandas were thought to be bears. In the 1980s, pandas were reclassified as raccoons, animals that share some of the panda's physical traits. But later studies of their body structures and especially of the chemical composition of their cells, showed that giant pandas were more closely related to bears. Modern chemistry techniques can separate the DNA, the genetic or inherited code, of one organism from another. Similar DNA codes indicate that two organisms are related.

As you can see, classification is not written in stone, so to speak. Scientists continue to develop finer tools for determining the shared and the unique characteristics of organisms. As more is learned, new ways to classify living things are accepted.

Birds of a Feather

To refine classifications of some organisms, scientists also use tools that help them look at the microscopic details of organisms. Dr. Roxie Laybourne of the National Museum of Natural History in Washington, D.C. uses an electron microscope for bird classifications. For over 30 years, Dr. Laybourne has been studying the structure, shape, and coloring of bird feathers to find out clues that show how birds are related. The electron microscope allows Dr. Laybourne to see the small details of bird feathers. "I'm studying what it's like on the inside of the barbules, the smallest 'hairs' on the feathers," says Dr. Laybourne. "With the electron microscope, I can see lots of spots inside the barbules. This is another good way to tell one kind of feather from another, and one species of bird from another."

What Do You Think?

What benefits are there to using a combination of classification tools rather than just one?

INVESTIGATE!

Using a Key

In this activity, you will learn to use a key to identify jay birds. A key is a step-by-step guide for identifying organisms that requires that you make a choice between two statements at each step until a name is reached for an organism.

Problem

How is a key used to identify jays?

Materials

paper and pencil

What To Do

1. Look at the two jays pictured on the next page.
2. Begin with Step 1 of the Key to Jays of North America. Select one statement that is true about that bird and follow the direction it takes you in. Follow each succeeding step until you identify the bird by its common and scientific names. Use the key to classify the bird labeled ***A***.
3. *In your Journal,* make a data table like the one shown. Write the common name and scientific name for the jay.
4. Now use the same procedure to classify the species of jay labeled ***B***.

Data and Observations

Jay	Scientific Name	Common Name
A		
B		

A

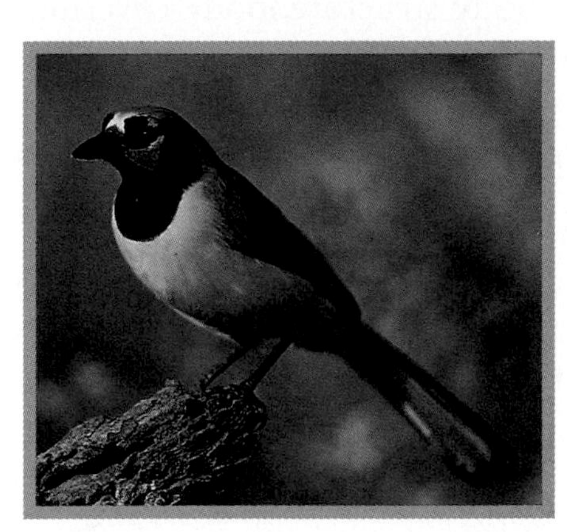

B

Key to Jays of North America

1a If the jay has a crest on the head, go to Step 2.

1b If the jay has no crest, go to Step 3.

2a If the jay's crest and upper body are mostly blue, it is a blue jay, *Cyanocitta cristata.*

2b If the jay's crest and upper body are brown or gray, it is a stellar's jay, *Cyanocitta stelleri.*

3a If the jay is mostly blue, go to Step 4.

3b If the jay has little or no blue, go to Step 6.

4a If the jay has a white throat, outlined in blue, it is a scrub jay, *Aphelocoma coerulescens.*

4b If the throat is not white, go to step 5.

5a If the jay has a dark eye mask and gray breast, it is a gray-breasted jay, *Aphelocoma ultramarinus.*

5b If the jay has no eye mask and has a gray breast, it is a pinyon jay, *Gymnorhinus cyanocephalus.*

6a If the jay is mostly gray and has black and white head markings, it is a gray jay. *Perisoreus canadensis.*

6b If the jay is not gray, go to Step 7.

7a If the jay has a brilliant green body with some blue on the head, it is a green jay, *Cyanocorax yncas.*

7b If the jay has a plain brown body, it is a brown jay, *Cyanocorax moria.*

Analyzing

1. Using the key, how many species of jay can you ***infer*** are in North America?
2. How many genera can be identified with this key?

Concluding and Applying

3. How do you know that this key doesn't contain all the species of jays in the world?
4. Why wouldn't you be successful in identifying a robin using this key?
5. **Going Further** Why wouldn't it be a good idea to begin in the middle of a key, instead of with the first step?

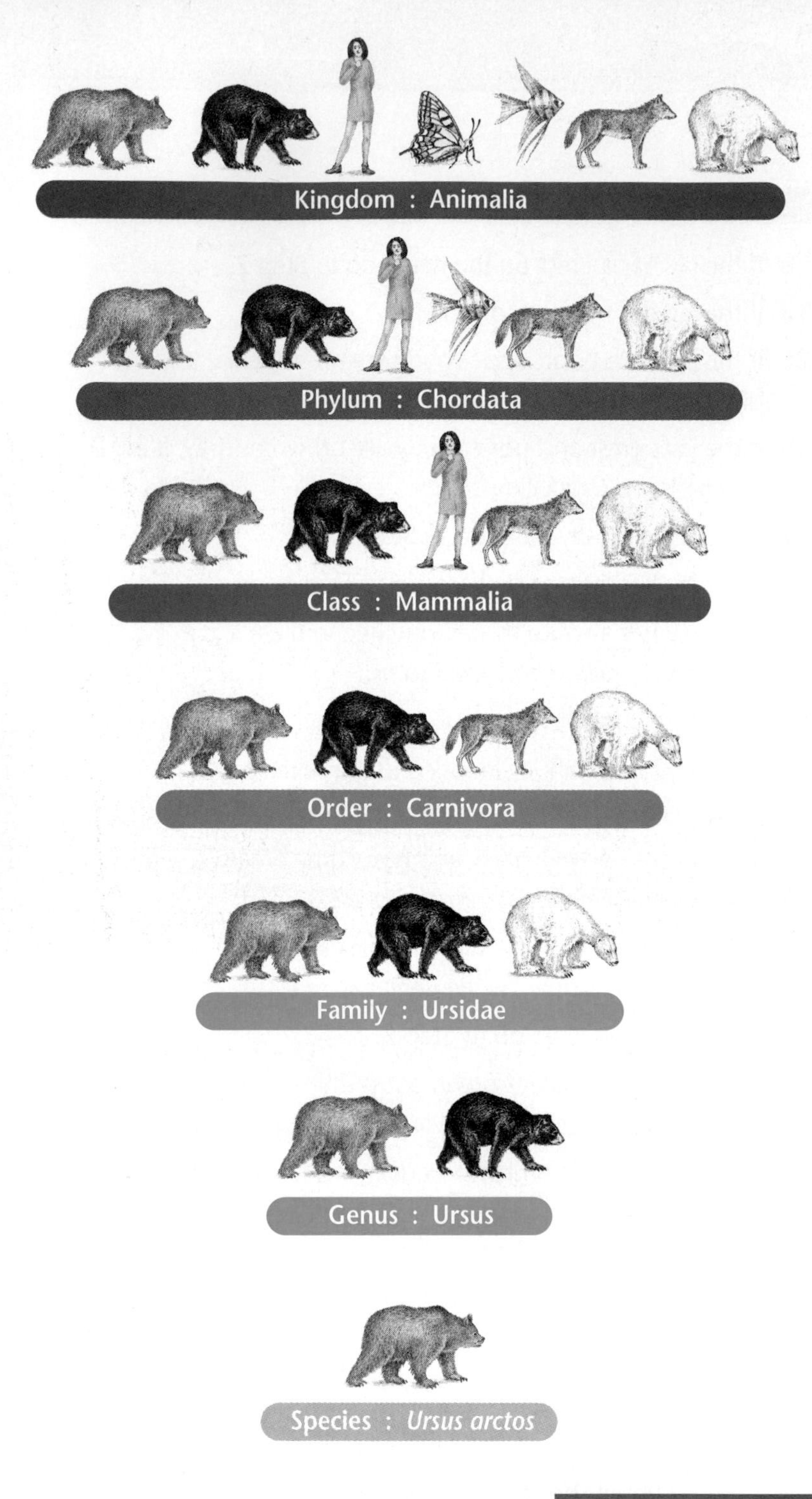

■ In Summary

With numerous levels in the classification system in use, how do scientists know which group an organism belongs to? You have seen that an organism's traits are useful in determining this. However, your idea of a trait should now be larger than it was when you started this chapter.

Now you know that scientists may look at all the organism's traits. These include cell structure, methods of reproduction, methods of obtaining food, body structure, body coverings (hair, fur, feathers), color, size, and so on. By examining the traits an organism has in common with others and the traits that make it unique, scientists can place the organism into the appropriate kingdom, phylum, class, order, family, genus, and species.

Figure 7-9

As you have learned, the classification of an organism, such as the brown bear shown here, is based on more than merely looking at its coat color. In identifying and naming an organism, its relationships to other members of its kingdoms are revealed.

check your UNDERSTANDING

1. The scientific name for the leopard is *Panthera pardus*. The scientific name for the tiger is *Panthera tigris*. Explain how their names indicate that leopards and tigers are related.
2. Why is height not a good trait to use in classifying trees?
3. **Apply** You are given an unknown organism to classify. How will you go about identifying and naming it?

Hydrothermal Vents

Can you imagine strange places at the bottom of the ocean where water comes out of Earth at temperatures of more than 300° F and where many unusual organisms thrive? Such places are called hydrothermal vents.

Hydrothermal Vents

There are many cracks in the ocean floor. So, what causes hydrothermal vents? Cold water (34°–37° F) sinks down into the cracks, where it comes into contact with hot rocks in Earth that heat the water to great temperatures. The hot water dissolves chemicals found in the rocks and flows back into the ocean floor. The vents are most common in the deepest parts of the ocean, as deep as 20 000 feet.

Who Lives There?

Groups of unusual animals such as those in the photograph on this page seem to thrive near these vents. Usually, at such depths, lone animals survive on debris or on any prey with which they come in contact. Therefore, scientists were indeed surprised when, in 1977, off the coast of South America, they found a large community of animals living near a hydrothermal vent.

Scientists were even more surprised that such communities could exist when the chemicals flowing from the vents usually would be deadly to most organisms. It since has been discovered that in the bodies of the organisms that live near the vents, bacteria are present that convert the harmful chemicals into food and energy for the larger organisms.

The organisms found in vent communities are numerous and unique. They include giant clusters of tube worms that grow to lengths of ten feet, huge white clams, and jellyfish-like animals called siphonophores.

You Try It!

Find out more about one of the organisms discussed in this article or choose another organism found in the deep sea to research. What special adaptations does the organism have for its life in the deep?

Science and Society Endangered Species

What do the giant panda, the brown pelican, and the pincushion cactus have in common? Each of these organisms is an endangered species. Endangered species are those organisms that are in danger of becoming extinct. When a species becomes extinct, no members of that species are any longer found on Earth.

Illegal Hunting

Many more organisms have become extinct during the time of Earth's existence than are found today. Usually, extinction is a natural process that may or may not occur over a long period of time. Dinosaurs are probably the best known extinct animals.

Today, however, many species become endangered as the result of the activities of human beings. Humans kill animals for their fur, tusks, and other body parts, as well as for food and sport. Many endangered animals are now protected by laws, but poachers, people who hunt illegally, disobey the laws and kill and trap thousands of endangered species yearly.

The African elephant and the black rhino are examples of animals that are endangered because of poaching. Poachers illegally kill the elephants for their ivory tusks. Black rhino horns are collected for questionable medical reasons.

Habitat Destruction

Besides the demand for products like ivory, another cause for the increasing number of endangered and extinct species is the destruction of the places where organisms live. As the human population increases, so does the need for places for humans to live. The areas where plants and animals live are cleared to make room for housing, industry, roads, and farming for this increased population. When land is cleared, most of the plants are killed. With habitats destroyed, both food sources and territories are disrupted for

Pincushion cactus

organisms such as the giant panda and pincushion cactus.

As a result of the destruction of land, some species of organisms are becoming extinct before they are identified. This is especially true as the largely unexplored rain forests throughout the world are cleared to make room for ranching and other development.

Giant panda

Pollution

Pollution also plays an increasing role in destroying organisms, such as the brown pelican. As water becomes polluted, oxygen and nutrients that are necessary to keep fish on which shore birds depend, plants, and other inhabitants alive disappear. It isn't long before all wildlife are affected.

It is too late to save species that are already extinct, but what is being done to save those that currently are endangered?

National and international laws have been passed to protect endangered species and stop the sale of products from the species. More than 100 nations have signed the Convention on International Trade in Endangered Species (CITES) agreement. Among other things, the agreement makes it illegal to trade furs and skins of endangered species and bans the trading of ivory from elephant tusks. It also regulates the trading of live animals and birds for pets.

To protect endangered species in the United States, the first Endangered Species Act was passed in 1973. The act makes it illegal to harm an organism on the Endangered Species list. Also, the law lets the government label certain areas as critical for wildlife. These are areas that species need in order to survive. The government is not allowed to disturb any lands that are identified as critical for wildlife.

Zoos and wildlife preserves are helping to increase the population of many endangered species. Through breeding programs, many of these efforts have been successful. However, in some cases, as with the giant panda, breeding in places other than the animal's natural surroundings is not always easy or successful.

Even with these efforts and more, the fight to save endangered species is far from over. You are likely to see many more species become extinct in your lifetime.

Science Journal

Choose an endangered animal and find out what has caused it to become endangered. Propose a strategy stating what could be done to save the animal from extinction.

Brown pelican

Maintaining Diversity

Many species of organisms are rapidly becoming extinct. But how many? And how rapidly?

U.S. Biological Survey

The government is mounting a survey the goal of which is to inventory each plant and animal species in the United States. About 1700 biologists from seven federal agencies (including the Fish and Wildlife Service, the National Park Service, and the Bureau of Land Management) will search wetlands, forests, deserts, bayous, shorelines and mountains.

The result will be a complete picture of the nation's ecosystems. When the survey is complete, it can be used as a biological base for deciding which land can be developed for human uses and which land needs to be set aside for wildlife preserves. After the National Biological Survey is complete, decisions about developing land will be based on reliable information.

Saving Seed

You already know of projects meant to save endangered species of animals, such as the bald eagle. But do you know about seed savings banks? Seed Savers Exchange is a network of people who swap seeds that are becoming more and more difficult to find. Their goal is to make sure that these species such as the the Scarlet Runner bean do not become extinct. The bean's seeds are pictured on this page.

Most gardeners today buy seeds from seed companies. Seed companies find it profitable to sell mostly hybrid seeds, which come from plants created by crossing two parent varieties. Hybrids tend to be healthy (because of hybrid vigor), and they can be designed to have just the qualities we want.

Before commercial seed companies, gardeners saved seeds from their best plants each year to plant the next spring. They also traded seeds among themselves. The exchange is carrying on that tradition.

Seed Savers Exchange and other seed savings banks know that their mission needs to be carried out now, before it's too late. In 1900, over 7000 varieties of apple trees could be found in the United States. Today there are fewer than 1000 varieties left.

Information on biodiversity and habitat preservation projects is available from the National Biological Service on the World Wide Web. Locate a project based near you and find out how your class can contribute.

chapter 7

REVIEWING MAIN IDEAS

Science Journal

Review the statements below about the big ideas presented in this chapter, and answer the questions. Then, re-read your answers to the Did You Ever Wonder questions at the beginning of the chapter. *In your Science Journal*, write a paragraph about how your understanding of the big ideas in the chapter has changed.

1 **Organisms are made of cells, need water and food, grow, reproduce, respond to stimuli, and adapt to their environments.** ***Do all organisms always show all of these features all the time? Explain your answer.***

Kingdom : Animal
Phylum : Chordata
Class : Mammalia
Order : Carnivora
Family : Canidae
Genus : Canis
Species : *Canis lupus*

2 **Animals are classified scientifically by kingdom, phylum, class, order, family, genus, and species. Plants are grouped into divisions instead of phyla.** ***Suggest reasons why someday scientists might devise other kingdoms in the classification system.***

3 **Classifying organisms helps scientists understand how they are related.** ***How can things like fossils and DNA show relationships among organisms?***

CHAPTER REVIEW

Using Key Science Terms

adaptation
classification
genus
kingdom
organism
phylum
reproduction
species
stimulus

For each set of terms below, choose the one term that does not belong and explain how the two remaining terms are related.

1. genus, species, stimulus
2. kingdom, organism, phylum

Give an example of each of the following.

3. stimulus
4. organism
5. kingdom
6. species

Understanding Ideas

Answer the following questions in your Journal *using complete sentences.*

1. List the characteristics that make living and nonliving things different from one another.
2. Why is a classification system helpful?
3. How is a phylum different from a kingdom?
4. The more levels two organisms both belong to in the classification system, the more closely they are related. Why?
5. Why is identifying an organism different from classifying the same organism?

Developing Skills

Use your understanding of the concepts developed in this chapter to answer each of the following questions.

1. **Concept Mapping** Complete the concept map on kingdoms shown here.

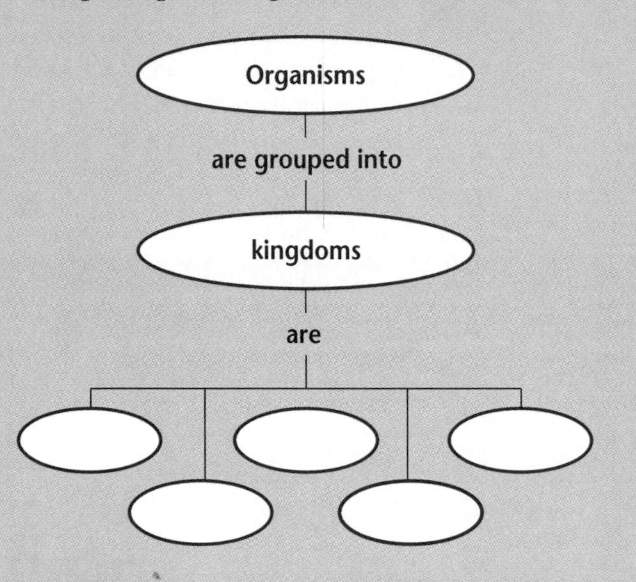

2. **Comparing and Contrasting** After doing the Find Out activity on page 233 use the classification scheme of the domestic cat and a leopard to construct a Venn diagram. Draw two overlapping circles. Label one circle for each animal named in the table. In the overlapping area, write the scientific names of the groups to which both animals belong. Write the scientific names that are not shared by both animals within each animal's circle, outside of the overlapping section. Make another Venn diagram using the classification scheme of the domestic cat and a deer. Now use the Venn diagram to help you answer the Conclude and Apply questions at the end of the activity.

3. **Classifying** After doing the Investigate activity on page 236, look at a field guide and see how these guides are used to identify organisms.

Critical Thinking

In your Journal, *answer each of the following questions.*

1. How is a yellow pages phone book similar to scientific classification?
2. Study the pie graph below. Then use information from the chapter to write a paragraph comparing the five kingdoms in terms of size.

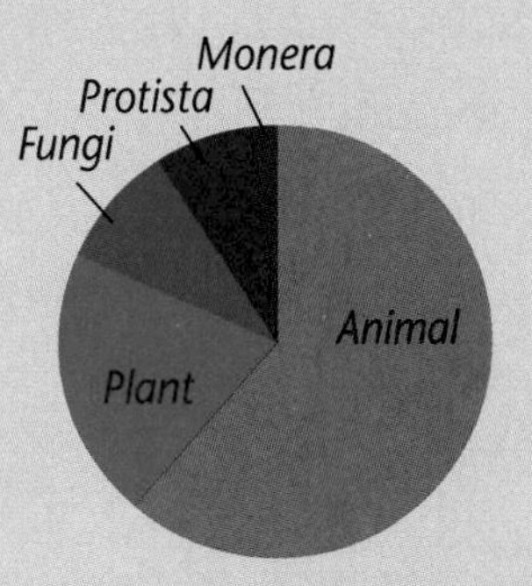

3. The scientific name for present-day humans is *Homo sapiens.* At what level are today's humans related to their ancestors, *Homo habilis?* At what level are we different from *Homo habilis?*

Problem Solving

Read the following problem and discuss your answers in a brief paragraph.

You are traveling through a rain forest. You see a plant that you think has never been described and classified.

1. What could you do to determine if you have discovered a new species?
2. Why would it be important to know if a plant that is used for making a medicine is or is not a new species?
3. What traits would you look for in order to classify and identify the plant?

CONNECTING IDEAS

Discuss each of the following in a brief paragraph.

1. **Theme—Systems and Interactions** Explain how senses transmit information about the physical world in which we live.
2. **Theme—Scale and Structure** Refer to Chapter 1 and create a classification system for different landforms.
3. **Theme—Systems and Interactions** In what ways does a person's two-part name compare with an organism's scientific name? Would it be possible to name individuals in the same way we name organisms? Why or why not? How would this show relationships?
4. **Science and Society** If there are laws protecting endangered species, why are species still becoming extinct?

CHAPTER 8

Viruses and Simple Organisms

Did you ever wonder...

- What a virus looks like?
- Why milk in a refrigerator doesn't usually sour, but milk left out does?
- Whether all bacteria and fungi are harmful?

Science Journal

Before you begin to study about viruses and simple organisms, think about these questions and answer them *in your Science Journal.* When you have finished the chapter, compare your journal write-up with what you have learned.

Helping to clean out the refrigerator on a Saturday morning is probably not your idea of fun. There are all those "mystery" containers. On top of that, when you open them, the mystery continues. Was it cottage cheese, or was it spaghetti sauce? What was once food is now fuzzy and may be pink or green, and definitely smelly. You share your world with many microscopic organisms. Some cause disease and some protect you from disease. Others decompose food and piles of leaves. Some live on your skin and others live in oceans and lakes and produce the oxygen you breathe. You can't live with many of them, and you stay alive because of others.

▶ ***In the activity that follows, take a look at yeast, one member of this very important group.***

Explore! ACTIVITY

What does yeast look like?

What To Do

1. Examine dry yeast with a hand lens.
2. Mix a small amount of yeast with cold tap water in a small dish.
3. In a second dish, mix very warm, but not steaming hot, tap water with a small amount of yeast. Add a small amount of sugar to the mixture.
4. Place a very small drop of the first mixture on a microscope slide. Add a cover slip.
5. Examine it first under low power, then under high power. *In your Journal*, describe and draw some yeast cells. Then examine a drop of the second mixture.
6. Wait 5 minutes and look at the yeast in both dishes again.
7. What changes do you see? Describe them *in your Journal*.

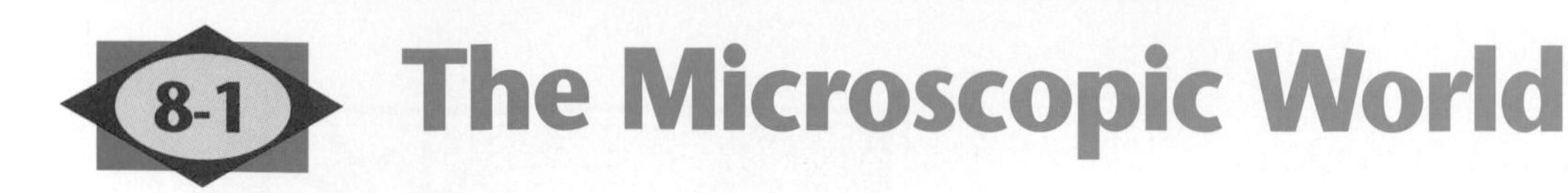

8-1 The Microscopic World

Section Objectives

- Classify organisms as being one-celled or many-celled.
- Recognize the difficulty of determining whether or not viruses are living.
- Conclude that a one-celled organism is capable of carrying out as many life functions as a many-celled organism.

Key Terms

microorganisms
producer
consumer
viruses

Simple and Complex Organisms

Many of the foods you eat, such as hamburgers and salads, come from large, complex organisms such as cattle and plants. But you might be surprised to know that many of the foods you eat are produced with the help of simple organisms such as bacteria and fungi. "Simple" does not mean that these organisms are unimportant or are capable of doing only one or two things. The yeast you looked at in the Explore activity on page 247 use sugar to obtain energy for themselves in a process that is anything but simple. Many organisms are called *simple* only because they are small. Yet their life processes are as complex as those in larger organisms such as a dog, a flatworm, and you. In the following Find Out activity, observe how some so-called simple and complex organisms compare.

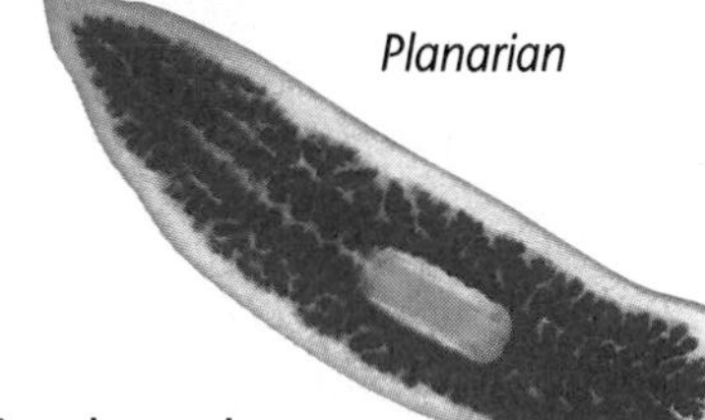

Planarian

Find Out! ACTIVITY

How do two organisms compare?

Euglena

In spite of differences in size, simple and complex organisms share many things in common.

What To Do

1. From your teacher, obtain a slide of a living one-celled organism called *Euglena* and another slide of a many-celled organism called a planarian.
2. Compare the sizes of the two organisms.
3. In what ways do the organisms resemble each other?
4. Carefully observe the activities of each organism separately. Aim the beam of a penlight flashlight at the slide. Do the organisms respond in any way to the light?

Conclude and Apply

1. Is *Euglena* limited in what it can do because it is only one cell?
2. Does having many cells enable the planarian to do more than *Euglena*?
3. *In your Journal,* write a statement comparing the terms *simple* and *complex* based on your observations.

One-Celled Organisms

If you were fortunate enough to be able to look at live *Euglena* in the Find Out activity, you probably noticed that it is a very lively organism. Just because an organism is one-celled doesn't mean that it is dull and uninteresting. The living world contains an enormous variety of one-celled organisms. Like many other living things, one-celled organisms respond to stimuli such as changes in light, heat, or chemicals in their environment. They may move toward or away from a stimulus. One-celled organisms, like the ones in **Figure 8-1**, carry out all life functions. They move, grow, consume food, release energy from food, produce waste products, and reproduce.

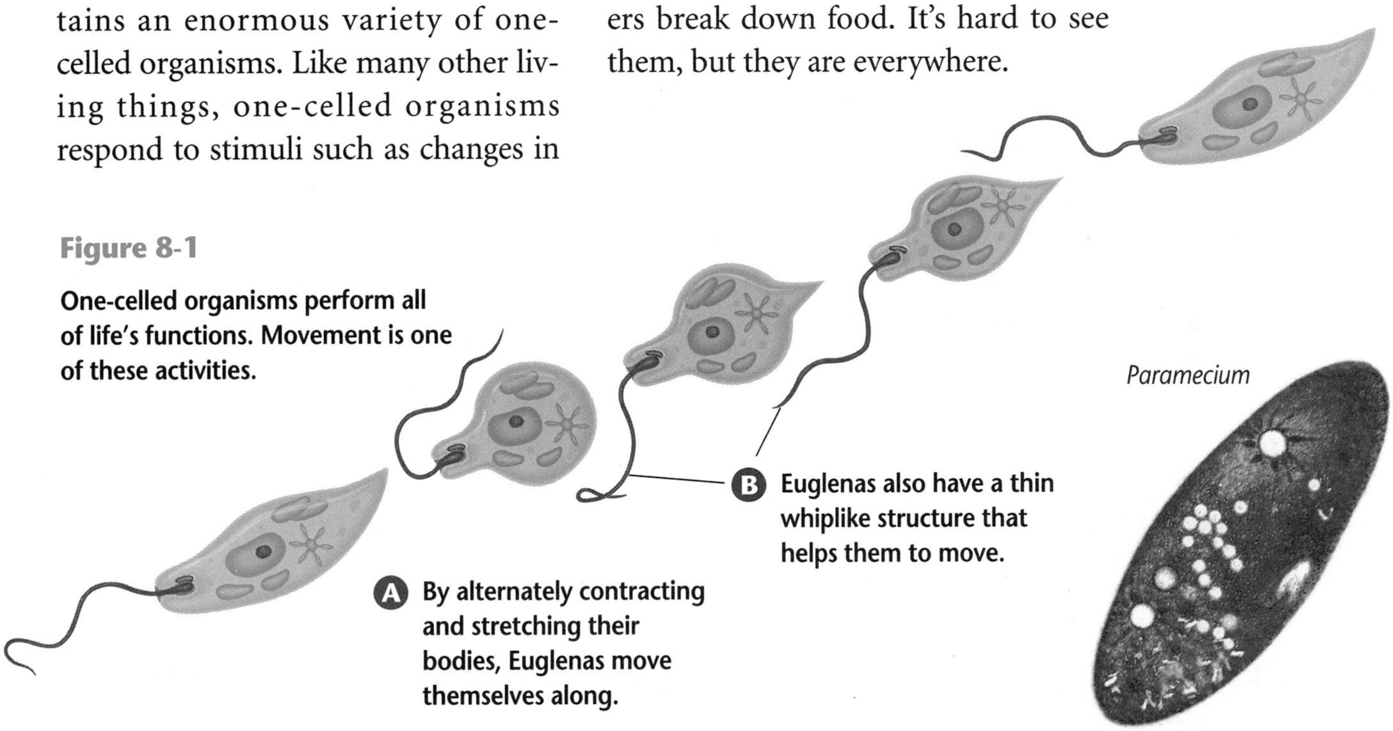

Figure 8-1

One-celled organisms perform all of life's functions. Movement is one of these activities.

A By alternately contracting and stretching their bodies, Euglenas move themselves along.

B Euglenas also have a thin whiplike structure that helps them to move.

Paramecium

C ***Paramecium*** **rolls rapidly through water, sweeping food into its mouth with the help of numerous hairlike projections that cover its body.**

Where are they found?

As hard as you might try, it is difficult to find a place where one-celled organisms do not live. You only have to check the air you breathe, a handful of soil, your skin, other animals, or food left too long in the refrigerator to find them. They live in fresh and salt water. They live in you and on you. Many keep you healthy. A few of them make you ill, but most are beneficial. Some are used to make food and others break down food. It's hard to see them, but they are everywhere.

How can you see them?

Organisms such as bacteria, protists, and fungi that are too small to be seen with the unaided eye are called **microorganisms**. You already know that living things are called organisms. *Micro-* means *small*, so *micro*organisms are very small organisms.

To see the thousands of one-celled and the small, many-celled organisms that will be studied in this chapter, you will have to look through a microscope, as you did to see the yeast and the *Euglena*.

Many-Celled Organisms

How do one-celled and many-celled organisms compare? Does a many-celled organism have an advantage over a one-celled organism? Many-celled organisms are usually larger than one-celled organisms and of course, have more cells.

The cells in larger organisms also are more specialized. That means that certain cells perform only one type of job. For instance, your bone cells form bone tissue. Bone cells are not like the cells that line your digestive tract that absorb food.

In addition, if one part of a many-celled organism is injured, the organism may be able to repair itself and will probably be able to survive. If you break a leg, your leg heals and you go on living. On the other hand, if the membrane of a one-celled organism is punctured, the organism dies. It would seem that being many-celled might have some advantages.

Classifying Simple Organisms

As you learned in Chapter 7, there are five kingdoms of living organisms. In this chapter, you will look more closely at characteristics and examples of three of those kingdoms—Monera, Protista, and Fungi. **Table 8-1** below compares these three kingdoms and illustrates a member of each kingdom. Besides structures, you'll also notice that the organisms are compared in terms of how they either produce or obtain energy. A **producer**, such as a green plant, uses light energy to make food from carbon dioxide and water. A **consumer**, such as an animal or a fungus, is unable to make its own food.

Table 8-1

Characteristics of the Monera, Protista, and Fungi Kingdoms

Characteristic	Monera	Protista	Fungi
One-celled?	all	most	some
Many-celled?	no	some	most
Has a nucleus?	no	yes	yes
Producer/Consumer?	both	both	consumer
Examples	bacteria cyanobacteria	amoeba *Euglena* algae	mushroom bread mold yeast

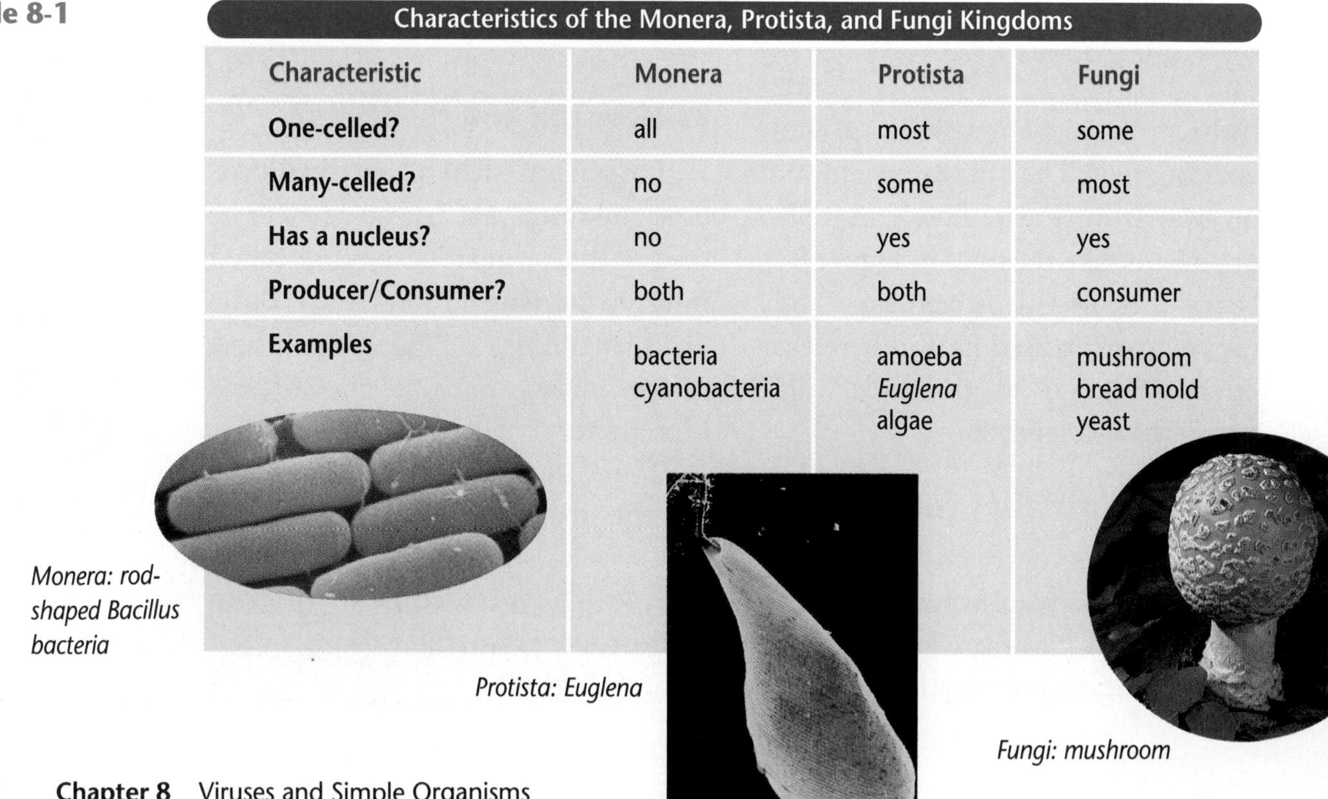

Monera: rod-shaped Bacillus bacteria

Protista: Euglena

Fungi: mushroom

Viruses

You may have noticed that none of the kingdoms includes viruses. **Viruses** are submicroscopic particles made up of a DNA or an RNA center, which is surrounded by a protein coat. DNA is the substance found in cells that determines the characteristics of organisms. RNA is a substance that cells use to make proteins.

Viruses come in a variety of shapes and sizes. You will note that scientists classify viruses by shape as described in **Figure 8-2**.

Why do you think viruses are not included in any kingdom? It has been observed that viruses cannot grow, respond to a stimulus, or break down food to release energy. However, when a virus enters a living cell, it does use materials in the cell to reproduce. The ability to reproduce is one of the few things viruses share in common with living organisms. What do some viruses look like? Work with a model in the Investigate on the next page to find out.

Figure 8-2

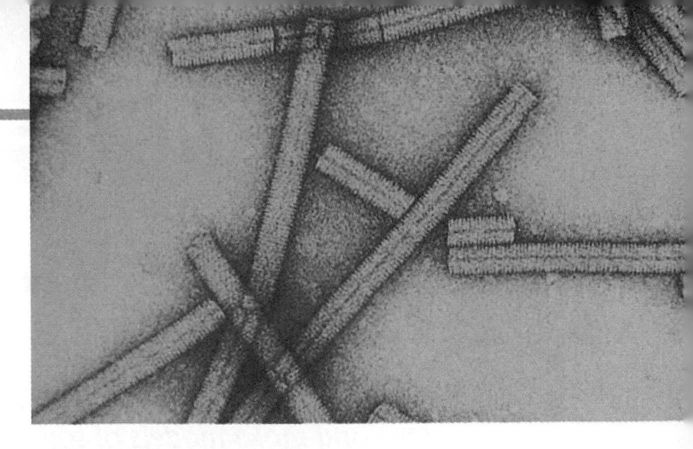

Tobacco mosaic virus

A The existence of viruses has been known since the late 1890s when the the tobacco mosaic virus was discovered. Although scientists had proof of the existence of viruses, they had no way to see them until 1939, when the first electron microscopes were available.

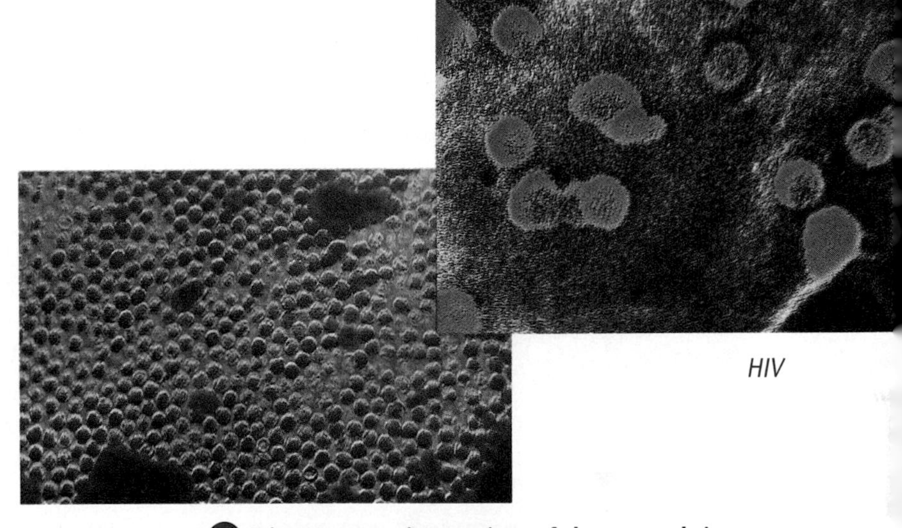

HIV

Polio virus

B Viruses come in a variety of shapes and sizes. Along with the thin, rod shape of the tobacco mosaic virus, there are viruses that are round or shaped like spiked balls, or thin threads. HIV, which causes AIDS, is round.

How Do We Know?

How do new viruses form?

How new viruses form was a mystery until 1969, when Nobel Prize winner Max Delbrük experimented by injecting two different types of viruses into one type of bacterial cell. The viruses responded rapidly and new viruses erupted, destroying the bacterial cells. Delbrük examined the new viruses and found that they were similar to the two he first injected. He also found a third type of virus that had traits that were a combination of the original two. Delbrük concluded that when two types of viruses enter a cell, DNA is exchanged, and new viruses form.

INVESTIGATE!

Shapes of Viruses

Viruses all contain similar structures and materials, yet they differ greatly in shape. In this activity, you can observe and make models of some viruses.

Problem

How can you make a model of a virus?

Materials

- 3.7 cm × 0.7 cm bolt
- 2 pieces #22-gauge wire, 14-cm long
- pipe cleaners, cut in 2-cm lengths
- 2 nuts to fit bolt
- polystyrene ball, 4.5 cm in diameter

Safety Precautions

Be careful when working with wire.

What To Do

1. Look at the photographs of the viruses taken with an electron microscope on page 251. Then, study the drawings of the viruses in Figures ***A*** and ***B*** on the next page. The drawing in Figure ***A*** represents a virus enlarged 260 000 times. The drawing in Figure ***B*** represents a flu virus enlarged 300 000 times.
2. Notice the parts in Figure ***A*** that are labeled. To make a model of the virus, attach two nuts onto a bolt and screw them on as far as you can.

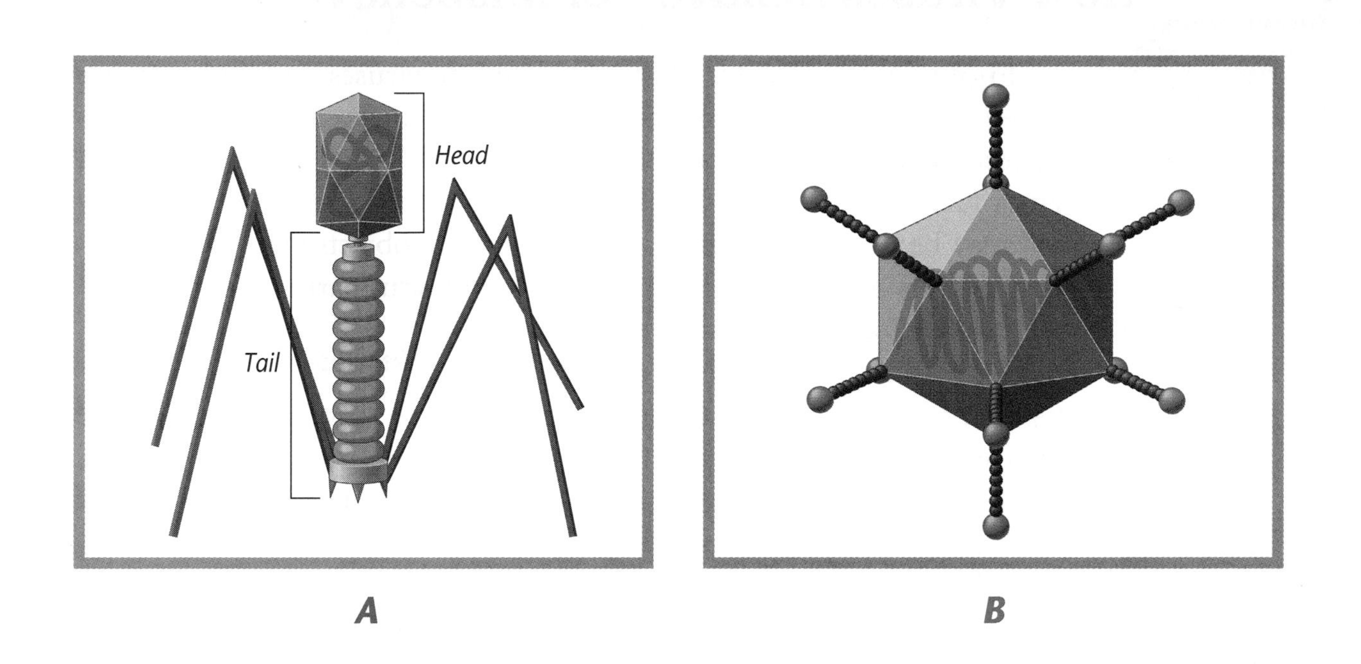

3 Twist the wires around the bolt near the bottom. Make the wire as tight as you can. Fold the wire ends and bend them so that they look similar to the drawing.

4 Use the polystyrene ball and pipe cleaners to make a model of the flu virus in Figure ***B***.

Analyzing

1. ***Compare*** your models with Figures ***A*** and ***B***. How are they alike?
2. ***Contrast*** the two viruses. How are they different from each other?
3. What is there about the structure of a virus that seems to help it get inside your cells?

Concluding and Applying

4. How does a virus differ from a cell?
5. **Going Further** What kinds of illnesses have you heard of that are caused by viruses? ***Make a table*** of at least three diseases caused by viruses that you have researched in library references. In the table, list the disease, what it affects, and where it is found. You may want to use a computer to make your table.

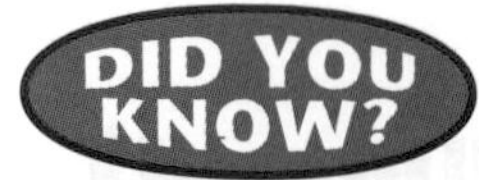

Diatoms contain oil from which they derive their energy. Vast petroleum reserves found under the oceans are the result of billions of diatoms that died and collected at the bottom of the ocean millions of years ago.

Plantlike Protists

Plantlike protists are known as algae. All algae can make their own food because they contain chlorophyll. However, not all algae are green because some have other pigments that cover up the green color of their chlorophyll. **Figure 8-9** shows examples of brown algae, also known as brown seaweed, and red algae.

There are six main groups of algae. Each group has its own characteristics. You can observe the characteristics of one group—diatoms—in the following Explore activity. Diatomite is a sandy soil made up of shells left by one type of protist, diatoms, that died about 20 million years ago.

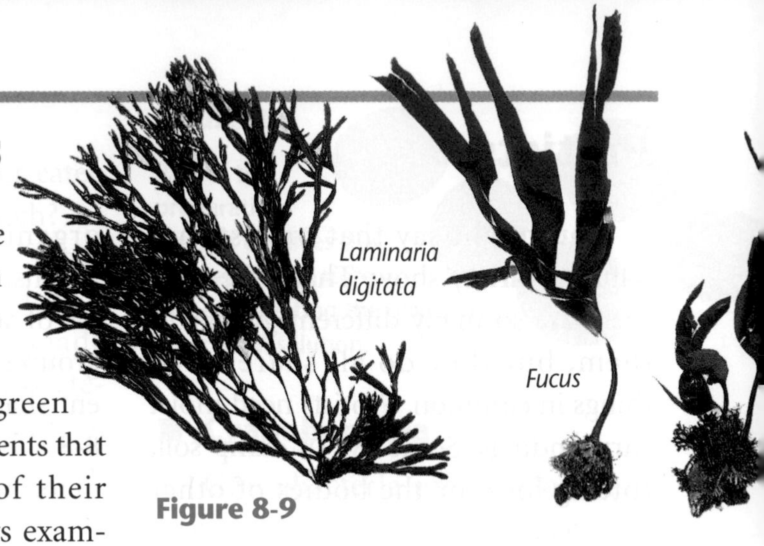

Laminaria digitata

Fucus

Rhodymenia

Chondrus crispus

Figure 8-9

Each type of algae carries pigments in its cells. The various pigments absorb and reflect different wavelengths of light, which makes each type of algae appear to be a distinctive color. Nongreen algae include red, brown, and golden-brown algae.

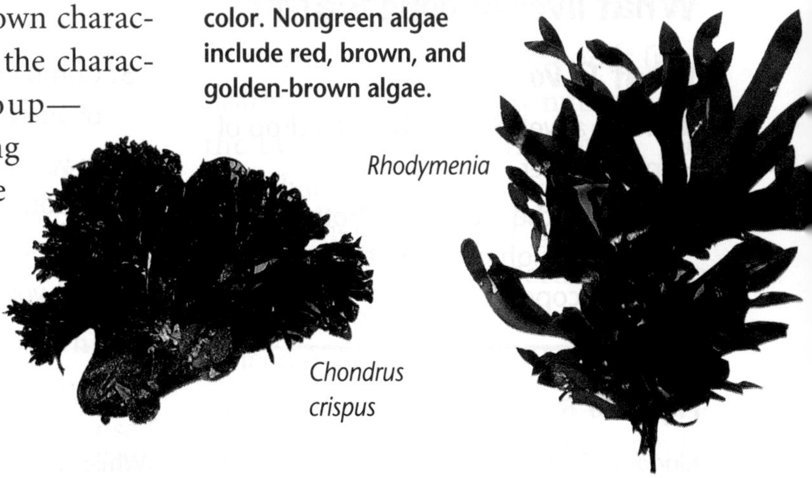

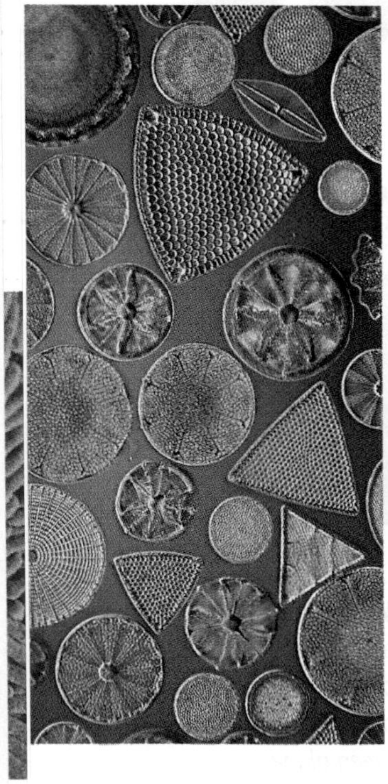

Explore! ACTIVITY

What is a diatom?

What To Do

1. Look at a sample of diatomite on a slide under low and then high power using a microscope.
2. Then, scrape the inside wall of a fish tank and make a slide. You should be able to see diatom shells in the diatomite and living diatoms in the fish tank scrapings.
3. How many different shapes of shells can you find?
4. Why do you think diatom shells survive?

The diatoms and shells you looked at in the Explore activity were from two different places—salt water and fresh water. In salt water, diatoms form an important part of plankton—the organisms on which whales and many types of fish feed. Diatom shells contain silica.

Animal-like Protists

Some protists are animal-like in that they are consumers. They do not contain chlorophyll. Animal-like protists are called protozoans. They are classified into groups according to the way they move. In the following activity, compare two different groups of protozoans.

Find Out! ACTIVITY

What characteristics do different protozoans have?

What To Do

1. Make two wet-mount slides, one of a live amoeba and the other of live paramecia.
2. Observe each organism under low power, then under high power.

Conclude and Apply

1. *In your Journal*, describe how each protozoan moves. Describe how it feeds or avoids obstacles.
2. What characteristics of the protozoans that you looked at would you use to classify them into separate groups?

Types of Movement

The amoeba that you observed moves about by forming false feet. Look at **Figure 8-10** to learn more about false feet.

The paramecium belongs to the group of protozoans that have short, hairlike structures called **cilia** all over their bodies. They use the cilia like oars to move and to sweep food into their mouths. Other protozoans have whiplike structures called **flagella** for moving through their watery surroundings.A fourth group of protozoans, such as those that cause malaria, have no structures for movement. They are parasites, living on other organisms and feeding on their tissues.

Figure 8-10

A To feed, the amoeba extends its false feet on either side of food, such as a bacterium.

B The false feet flow over and around the food, until it is completely enclosed.

C The food vacuole floats within the cytoplasm. Strong enzymes are used to digest the food.

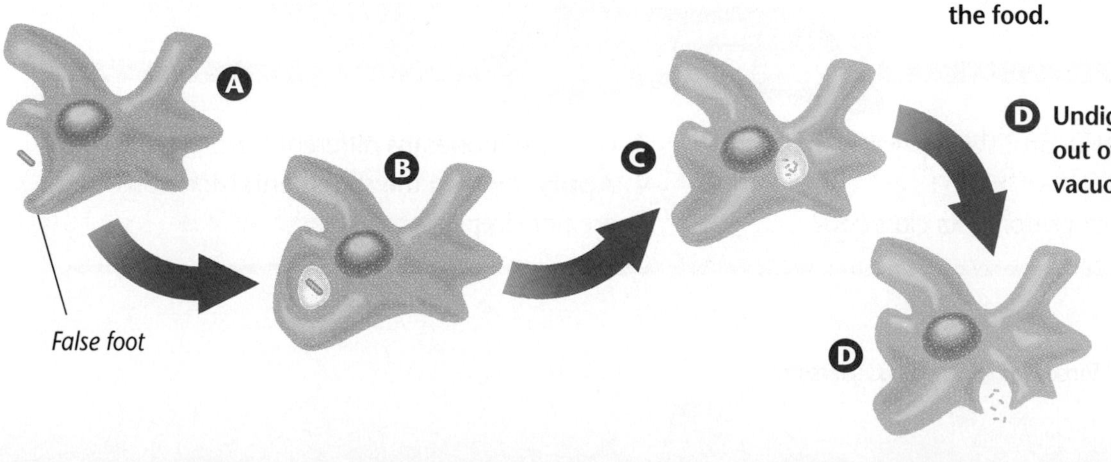

D Undigested food is forced out of the cell as the vacuole explodes outward.

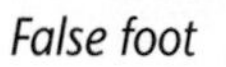

How Do Protists Affect Other Living Things?

Many protists are useful to other organisms. For example, algae, the protists that contain chlorophyll, are helpful to just about everyone, including you. Not only do they produce food in the presence of sunlight, but at the same time, they also produce most of the oxygen that Earth's organisms depend upon.

Funguslike protists, such as the slime mold in **Figure 8-11** are probably little noticed by most people. However, slime molds are recyclers that help break down leaves and fallen trees.

Disease-Causing Protists

Not all protists are helpful to other organisms. One type, *Plasmodium*, causes malaria, which kills more people on Earth each year than any other disease. **Figure 8-12** shows the protist *Trypanosoma*, another disease-causing protist.

Figure 8-11

Slime molds, which appear much like fungi at some point in their life cycles, also have protist-like features. At one point a slime mold may be made up of thousands of amoeba-like cells. Slime molds are decomposers that help break down leaves and fallen trees.

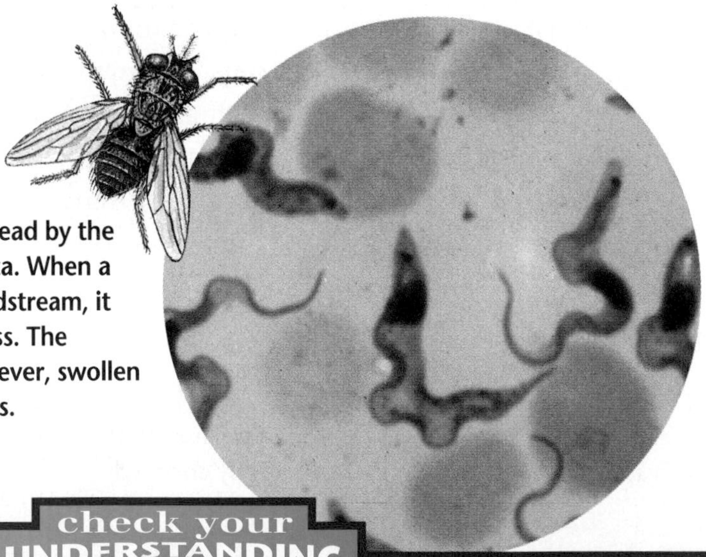

Figure 8-12

The protist *Trypanosoma* is spread by the bloodsucking tsetse fly in Africa. When a trypanosome enters the bloodstream, it causes African sleeping sickness. The symptoms of this disease are fever, swollen glands, and extreme sleepiness.

check your UNDERSTANDING

1. Why are plantlike protists important in the world?
2. How are animal-like protists classified?
3. How are monerans different from protists?
4. **Apply** Defend the statement: Monerans are not simple organisms.

8-3 Fungus Kingdom

Fungi

Have you seen any fungi lately? None? You may be surprised to learn that one-fifth of all the different kinds of organisms on Earth are fungi. Hundreds of these fungi—most of them molds—live in the soil under your feet, and in your home!

Become acquainted with one common member of Kingdom Fungi through a trip to the grocery store.

Section Objectives

- Describe the major characteristics and activities of fungi.
- Describe the way fungi affect other living things.

Key Terms

parasite

Explore! ACTIVITY

What can you learn about fungi by observation?

What To Do

1. Look at a mushroom that you might buy in a grocery store.
2. Describe its size.
3. Carefully pull the cap off the stalk and lay it aside.
4. Use your fingers to pull the stalk apart lengthwise. Continue gently pulling the stalk apart.
5. Now, look at the underside of the cap. Look at all the thin membranes. Using a hand lens, look at one of the membranes. What can you see?
6. *In your Journal,* describe how the mushroom is constructed.

Figure 8-13

A Fungi do not have the specialized tissues and organs of plants that you will learn about in Chapter 10. The body of a fungus is usually a mass of many-celled, threadlike tubes. None of the cells contains chlorophyll.

B Fungi were once classified as plants. Based on your observations, would you accept this classification? In what ways do fungi differ from plants? In what ways do they remind you of plants?

How Do Fungi Affect Other Living Things?

Figure 8-14

Fungi live in moist shady areas. Bracket fungi often grow on trees in the woods.

People find fungi useful in many ways. The fungi called yeast make bread and pizza crust rise by producing gases. Other fungi give some cheeses, such as blue cheese, very different flavors that people like. Many people enjoy mushrooms on pizza and in salads and other dishes. One kind of fungus, called *Penicillium*, produces penicillin that doctors prescribe for patients with diseases caused by certain kinds of bacteria. If you've ever seen the green, powdery fungus growing on rotting oranges and old bread, then you're already familiar with what *Penicillium* looks like.

Figure 8-15

The green growth in this photograph is *Penicillium*, from which the antibiotic penicillin is derived.

Chemistry CONNECTION

Secrets in the Soil

Being a soil scientist may not seem exciting, but in what other field can a person take frequent trips to scoop up a pocketful of soil?

Soil scientists travel all over the globe, from the arctic to equatorial jungles, collecting samples of the local soil fungi. Most of the soil fungi in the world are as yet undiscovered, scientists judge, so it's vital to collect samples from environments that are rapidly disappearing, such as tropical rain forests.

Why Collect Soil Fungi?

Soil fungi have many uses. One fungus native to Japan is being added to forest soil in the eastern United States because the fungus kills gypsy-moth caterpillars, which are serious leaf-eating pests.

Another soil fungus, found originally in the Canary Islands, contains a drug that suppresses the immune response in humans. Patients who receive transplanted organs may be given this drug to prevent transplant rejection.

Nature's Control

A new kind of cockroach trap, marketed as the country's first "biopesticide," contains a fungus that eats through the hardened, outer shell of the cockroach, eventually killing the insects.

Fungi as Recyclers

You may have seen fungi growing on an old tree lying on a forest floor. If so, you've seen an example of fungi in their most important job. Fungi are able to break down, or decompose, organic material. Food scraps, clothing, dead plants, and animals are all made of carbon-containing organic material. Fungi cannot make their own food. They do not contain chlorophyll. They are consumers. Along with many bacteria, fungi decompose organic materials and recycle these materials back to the soil. These materials are then used by plants to grow. Like many bacteria, fungi help rid Earth of mountains of waste.

Some fungi, such as the ones that cause athlete's foot and ringworm, are parasites. **Parasites** are organisms that live on or in other living things and feed on them. Fungi that are parasites cause some of the most damaging diseases in plants. Wheat rust and corn smut are two fungi that can destroy food crops.

How do fungi grow best? The Investigate on the following pages will help you find an answer.

Figure 8-16

Corn smut is a damaging fungus that attacks corn plants.

Fungi are also a big part of a field called bioremediation. Bioremediation uses living organisms to clean up wastes. Other methods, such as incineration and disposal in landfills, don't provide permanent solutions to hazardous wastes. But when you feed certain hazardous wastes to the right soil fungi, the end result is just carbon dioxide (and a bigger population of fungi). The hazardous wastes—such as PCBs, pesticides, dioxins, coal tars, and heavy fuels—are neutralized with no unwanted byproducts.

Fungi to the Rescue!

Four kinds of native fungi are presently being used to remove a pollutant from a reservoir in California's San Joaquin Valley. The pollutant, selenium, has accumulated in the reservoir because of intensive irrigation of farmland. Selenium is present in levels high enough to kill birds nesting around the reservoir. Since the Kesterton National Wildlife Refuge is nearby, a nontoxic solution is critical. The fungi ingest the selenium, convert it from a water-soluble form to a gaseous form, then "burp" the selenium into the atmosphere. The gaseous form attaches to airborne particulates and drifts away. Tests have shown the fungi can reduce selenium levels by 60 to 70 percent within three years.

You Try It!

Ask five people these two questions: What is the best-known antibiotic in the world? (penicillin) What was penicillin developed from? (fungus) How many of your subjects knew both answers?

DESIGN YOUR OWN
INVESTIGATION

The Work of Fungi

Have you ever seen mold grow on fruit? When conditions are right, mold can cover and penetrate a fruit with hundreds of thousands of tiny threadlike branches called hyphae. The cells of hyphae release substances that break down organic materials in the fruit. Then bacteria move in, causing spoilage.

Preparation

Problem

Under what conditions does a mold grow best on fruit?

Form a Hypothesis

Has anyone in your group ever seen mold on fruit? As a group, discuss the conditions under which the mold grew. Then form a hypothesis that can be tested in your experiment.

Objectives

- Design an experiment using several variables to promote mold formation on fruit.
- Compare and contrast conditions that promote mold formation.
- Infer how certain conditions interact to promote or prevent the growth of mold.

Possible Materials

peaches, apples, or oranges
paper towels
plastic bags
kitchen knife or fork
paper plate
water

Safety Precautions

Be careful with knives if you decide to cut any fruit. Dispose of all moldy products as directed by your teacher.

DESIGN YOUR OWN INVESTIGATION

Plan the Experiment

1 Examine the materials provided. Decide how you will use them in your experiment.

2 Design a procedure to test your hypothesis. Write down what you will do at each step.

3 How will you record your data? If you need a table, design one now in your Science Journal.

Check the Plan

1 List the conditions that you think will promote mold formation on fruit. Which condition will you test?

2 If you are testing more than one condition, have you allowed for a control in your experiment? What is the control?

3 Make sure your teacher approves your experiment before you proceed.

4 Carry out your experiment. Record your observations.

How is the fungus growing on this bread different from the mold you observed growing on fruit?

Analyze and Conclude

1. **Compare and Contrast** Which conditions promoted mold formation? Which conditions prevented mold formation?
2. **Recognize Cause and Effect** Was your hypothesis supported? If not, explain why it might still be right.
3. **Observe and Infer** On which fruits did mold grow the easiest? Suggest reasons for this.
4. **Infer** Suggest a good use for the moldy fruit at the end of this experiment instead of throwing it into the trash. Give a reason for your suggestion.
5. **Interpret Data** Based on the outcome of your experiment, what steps would you take to prevent oranges from molding quickly at home?

Going Further

You may have formed several hypotheses while designing this experiment. Test one of these hypotheses or design a new experiment based on an observation made while conducting this one.

How Do Fungi Meet Their Life Needs?

As you saw in the Investigate, moisture is an important factor in the growth of fungi. Under the right conditions, fungal threads can penetrate fabric, leather, fur, wood, paint, and even some plastics, to obtain the nutrients and energy they require. They do not make their own food. Can you think of a way to prevent fungal growth?

You can take a look at the reproductive parts of a fungus in the following Explore activity.

Explore! ACTIVITY

How do fungi reproduce?

What To Do

1. Examine some black or green mold on bread using a hand lens.
2. *In your Journal,* describe what you see.
3. Remove a small bit of mold and make a wet mount of the fungus.
4. Observe the mold under low power with a microscope.
5. What do you see all over the slide? What do you think these are?

A fungus begins life as a spore. In the Explore activity, you observed spore cases containing millions of these powdery reproductive cells.

You may now be thinking that even the simplest organism is very complex. The organisms you have studied so far are very different from one another in some ways. And yet they are all alike in the kinds of activities they carry out to stay alive!

check your UNDERSTANDING

1. How do fungi differ from cyanobacteria in how they obtain energy?
2. Explain why fungi are capable of reproducing in large numbers.
3. How do the moisture requirements of fungi compare with those of bacteria for life?
4. **Apply** Why doesn't a mushroom farmer have to worry about how much sunlight his or her crop gets?

Science and Society

Using Viruses To Fight Disease

One of the most amazing processes in the human body is the immune response system. Immunity is our body's built-in defense against disease.

When a disease-causing bacterium or virus enters your body through breaks in your skin or through moist membranes, your immune system mobilizes a series of defenses against these foreign particles. White blood cells traveling through the circulatory system surround and engulf most intruding microorganisms.

Antibodies and Antigens

In other instances, white blood cells produce substances called antibodies. Antibodies are proteins that deactivate and destroy particular microorganisms. Antibodies are produced in response to proteins called antigens that are located on the surfaces of bacteria and viruses. When your body produces antibodies to particular antigens, you are said to be immune to those microorganisms.

Immune for How Long?

Immunity can last a few months or years, as with the flu virus, or it can last an entire lifetime, as with the polio virus. Unfortunately, immunity against one type of antigen or virus does not protect you against all others, even though they may be similar. This is one reason why you catch a cold more than once. Your colds may seem like the same disease, but each is caused by a different virus.

Active Immunity

When your body produces antibodies in response to a particular antigen, it is called active immunity.

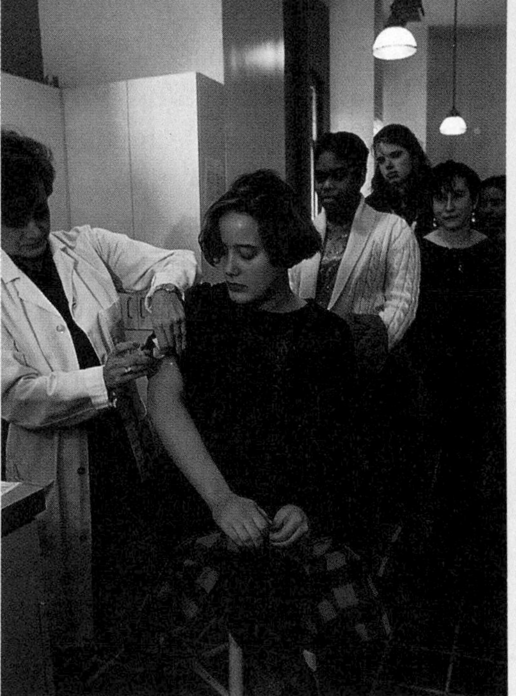

Active immunity can either be natural or artificial. When your body produces antibodies as a result of contact with a disease-causing microorganism, this is a natural process. But your body can also produce antibodies after injection with a vaccine. A vaccine is a solution of dead or weakened bacteria or viruses which, when injected into the body, causes an immune response. Vaccination is an artificial process.

Bacteria to the Rescue

In 1989, the Exxon Valdez spilled millions of gallons of oil on the Alaskan coastline. The oil soaked as much as two feet deep into the beaches. When nothing else cleaned up the spill, scientists enlisted the help of bacteria. These microorganisms, living in the soil and water, feed on hydrocarbons, a principal ingredient of oil. The scientists sprayed fertilizer on the beaches to stimulate the bacteria to grow. Within two weeks, the oily beaches that had been sprayed were much cleaner than those that had not. The number of bacteria had tripled, and they were "gobbling up" the oil. Now a similar process has been implemented to get bacteria to feed on and break up clogs in household drains.

Other Useful Bacteria

Many types of bacteria help solve our pollution problems. For example, some species of bacteria can metabolize sulfur, which occurs in large amounts in some kinds of coal. When this high-sulfur coal burns, it releases sulfur into the atmosphere, causing acid rain. However, when sulfur-eating bacteria are mixed into piles of high-sulfur coal, they change it into a much cleaner fuel.

Ongoing Problems

Medical wastes with radioactive ingredients are usually buried in toxic dumps. When these wastes decay, they produce radioactive methane gas. This gas can seep out and pollute the air. Research scientists have begun studying bacteria that change methane into water. When fertilized with nitrogen and phosphorous, these bacteria work two or three times faster to digest the dangerous methane gas.

What Do You Think?

If scientists can develop bacteria to metabolize pollution and waste, chemical companies might be able to eliminate waste treatment plants. Dump sites might be able to speed up the degradation of nontoxic waste, so that it converts to soil more quickly. Toxic waste might be changed into less harmful compounds.

Solutions to problems sometimes can cause new problems. Can you think of any new problems that might result from using bacteria to fight pollution?

chapter 8
REVIEWING MAIN IDEAS

Science Journal

Review the statements below about the big ideas presented in this chapter, and answer the questions. Then, re-read your answers to the Did You Ever Wonder questions at the beginning of the chapter. *In your Science Journal*, write a paragraph about how your understanding of the big ideas in the chapter has changed.

1 **Monera, Protista, and Fungi are the kingdoms of microscopic and simple organisms.** ***Why can you say that these organisms are anything but simple?***

2 **Monerans—the bacteria and blue-green bacteria—are the simplest and tiniest organisms on Earth. They are found almost everywhere.** ***How do monerans that are producers differ from those that are consumers?***

3 **Protists are organisms with complex cells that are either plantlike or animal-like.** ***How do protists differ from monerans?***

4 **Fungi help decompose dead organisms and recycle the materials of which these organisms were made.** ***Explain why fungi are important.***

5 **Most scientists consider that viruses are nonliving, noncellular structures.** ***What do they lack that living organisms have?***

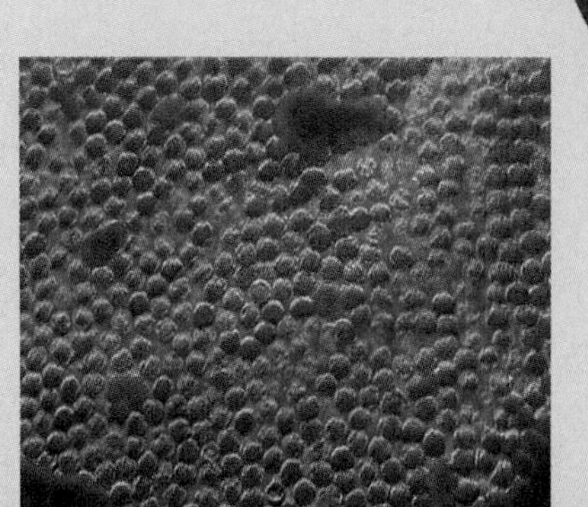

CHAPTER REVIEW

Using Key Science Terms

cilia
consumer
flagella
microorganism
parasite
producer
virus

For each set of terms below, explain a relationship that exists.

1. cilia—flagella
2. bacteria—cyanobacteria
3. parasite—virus
4. producer—consumer
5. microorganism—virus
6. parasite—producer

Understanding Ideas

Answer the following questions in your Journal *using complete sentences.*

1. How do many-celled organisms differ from one-celled organisms?
2. What is the main difference in cell structure between a moneran and a protist?
3. What would you look for in order to classify protists in a sample of pond water?
4. How are fungi similar to plants? How are they similar to animals?
5. Why do you suppose fungi are more often successful in wet or humid environments?
6. Why are algae described as being plantlike?
7. Which protist group would be described as parasites? Explain your choice.

Developing Skills

Use your understanding of the concepts developed in this chapter to answer each of the following questions.

1. **Concept Mapping** Complete the concept map for simple organisms.

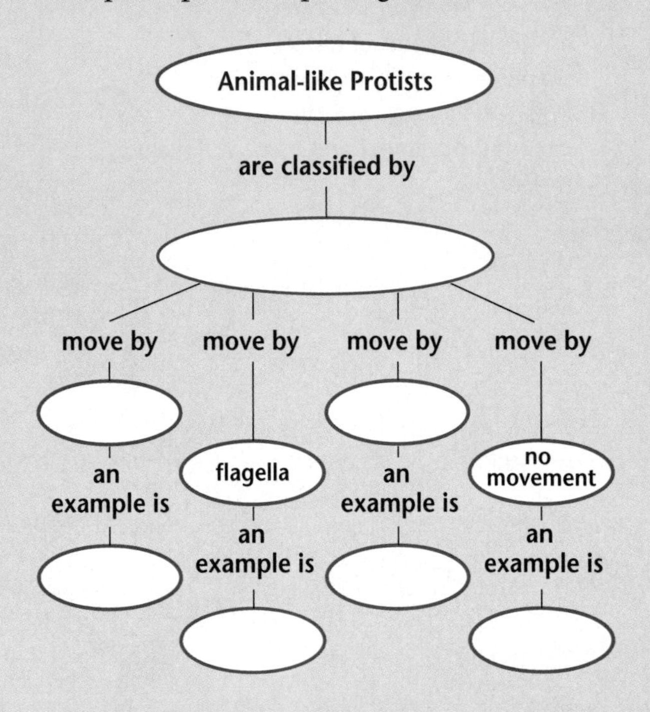

2. **Recognizing Cause and Effect** Most fossils are formed by organisms that have some sort of hard covering or contain hard substances. Which protists probably have left fossils? Explain your choice.
3. **Comparing and Contrasting** Think about places where you have seen mold growing other than on food. After doing the Investigation on page 266, design an experiment to find out what conditions are necessary for mold to grow on a piece of untreated wood and in a jar of paint. Were the conditions the same as those for growing mold on food?

chapter 8
CHAPTER REVIEW

Critical Thinking

In your Journal, *answer each of the following questions.*

1. Study the volvox in **Figure 8-8.** Why are these organisms considered to be complex? What do they contribute to the environment?
2. How is it an advantage to monerans, protists, and fungi, to be able to respond to changes in their environment?
3. How can cyanobacteria be both beneficial and harmful to a lake?
4. A scientist discovered a new kind of organism growing on a rotting log. The organism was using the log as a food source and, at the same time, helping to decompose it. How would the scientist determine in which kingdom the new organism should be placed?
5. Use your knowledge of virus reproduction to explain why it is difficult to get rid of viruses.

Problem Solving

Read the following problem and discuss your answers in a brief paragraph.

Imagine that a new kind of virus wipes out all bacteria on Earth.

1. What disadvantages for humans would there be in a world without bacteria? What advantages?
2. Would there be any way humans could live in a world without bacteria? Explain your reasons. What other organisms might adapt to fill the role of missing bacteria?

CONNECTING IDEAS

Discuss each of the following in a brief paragraph.

1. **Theme—Stability and Change** Large chalk beds of forminiferans, as much as much as 1000 feet thick, exist in Mississippi and Georgia. Why can you conclude that these areas were covered by ocean at one time?
2. **Theme—Systems and Interactions** How do bacteria and fungi contribute to the needs of all living things?
3. **Theme—Systems and Interactions** How does a one-celled organism differ from a single cell that is part of a many-celled organism?
4. **Science and Society** How is the action of healthy white blood cells similar to that of the amoeba in Figure 8-10?
5. **Chemistry Connection** Explain reasons why control of insect pests might be better accomplished with organisms such as fungi than with strong, laboratory-made pesticides.

CHAPTER 9

Animal Life

Did you ever wonder...

- ✓ How snakes and earthworms differ?
- ✓ Whether frogs and butterflies have anything in common?
- ✓ How you locate food?

Science Journal

Before you begin to study about animals, think about these questions and answer them *in your Science Journal.* When you finish the chapter, compare your journal write-up with what you have learned.

If you were given two minutes to list all of the animals that share your life, what examples would you give? Rats and rabbits? Snakes and squirrels? Cats and crickets? Bees, birds, and bats? Animals are found in big cities, small towns, and out in the country. You may think raccoons and deer are found only in the woods, yet an amazing number of them show up in suburban backyards and city parks. Countless other animals may share your home with you. You might say that you are surrounded by animals! And don't forget that people are animals, too. How long is your list now?

▶ ***In the activity on the next page, explore some traits that are unique to an animal that lives near you or with you.***

Explore! ACTIVITY

What do animals around you do?

Both cats and dogs are domesticated or tame animals that live together with humans. Other animals, such as squirrels, ants, and snakes, are not domesticated. How does living with or apart from humans affect the behaviors of animals?

What To Do

1. Choose an animal that you see every day. It may be domesticated or not. Without interfering with its activities, observe the animal closely.
2. *In your Journal,* describe what the animal looks like, and where and how it lives.
3. How does the animal behave when it doesn't seem to be aware of you? Describe how it responds to you.
4. List what it eats and how it obtains its food.
5. If possible, record any sounds your animal makes.
6. *In your Journal,* use your observations to suggest why you think this organism is classified as an animal.

What Is an Animal?

Section Objectives
- Describe the characteristics all animals have in common.
- Classify different animals by some of their characteristics.

Key Terms
invertebrate
vertebrate
endoskeleton
exoskeleton

Kingdom of Animals

Have you ever thought about all the groups that you are a part of? You are part of a family, a class in school, and a neighborhood. Maybe you belong to the school band or basketball team. As a member of each group, you have things in common with other members of each group. For example, you are probably about the same age as the other students in your class and you live in the same city or town.

■ You Are an Animal

While doing the Explore activity on page 277, you may have noticed that you and the animal you observed share some characteristics. You may both move around on legs. You may

Figure 9-1

Ⓐ Animals can't make their own food but depend on other living things to provide energy.

Ⓑ Some animals such as raccoons eat plants, some animals eat other animals, and some animals eat both plants and animals.

Ⓒ Animals have evolved adaptations that help them survive. The hard shells that protect the soft body parts of turtles and snails are examples of these adaptations.

both have eyes to see with, ears to hear with, and teeth for chewing. Look at the variety of organisms in **Figure 9-1** and ask if you have some of the same adaptations described there. Then, observe some other live organisms in the Explore activity that follows.

Explore! ACTIVITY

What are the characteristics of animals?

What To Do

1. Obtain a beaker with a fish and a snail in it.
2. Compare how the two animals move. Does movement give an animal an advantage?
3. *In your Journal,* propose a definition for "animal" based on your observations. Why do you and a snail or fish share the animal kingdom?

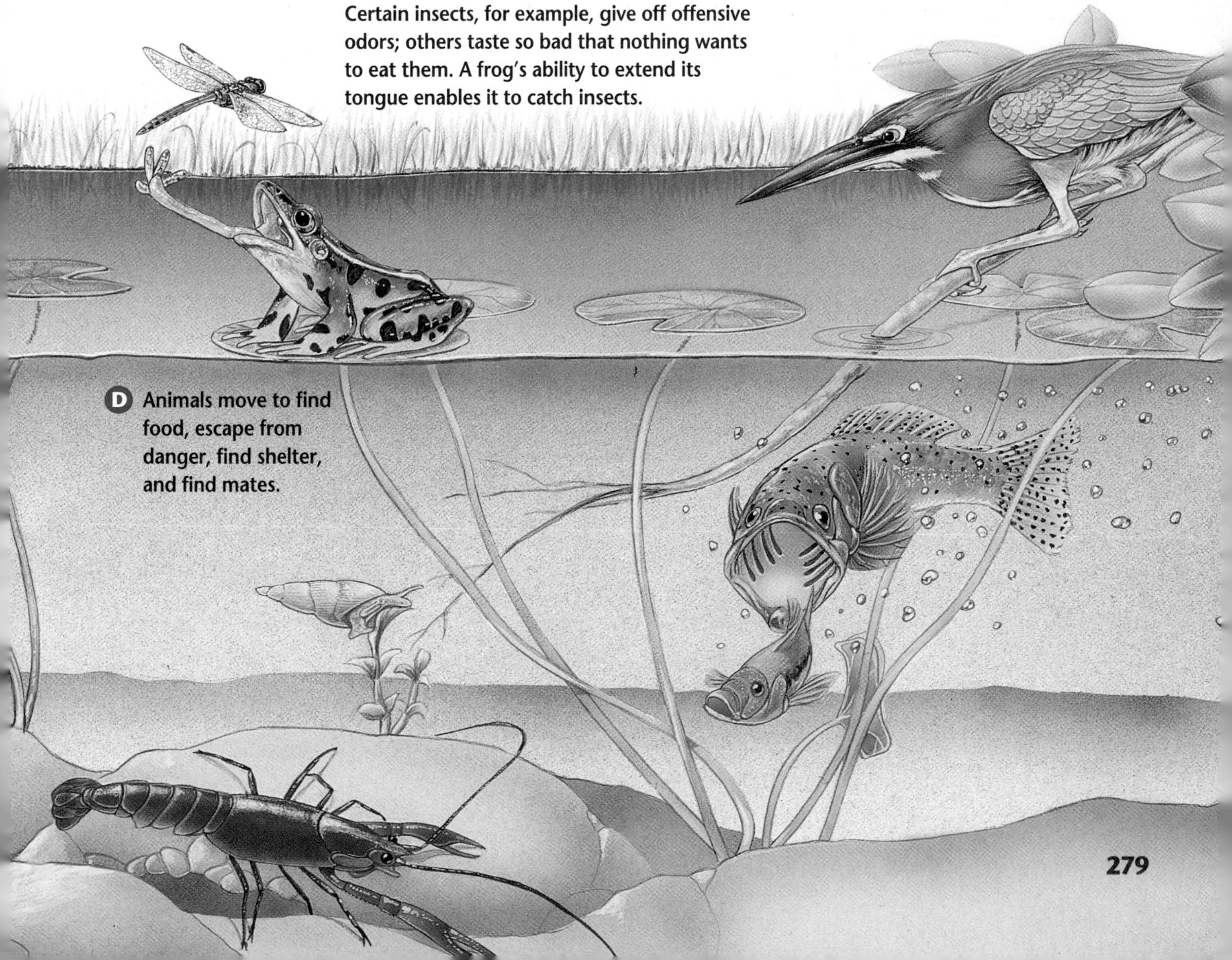

E Adaptations for survival are extremely varied. Certain insects, for example, give off offensive odors; others taste so bad that nothing wants to eat them. A frog's ability to extend its tongue enables it to catch insects.

D Animals move to find food, escape from danger, find shelter, and find mates.

Consumers and Producers

Food in some form provides the energy all organisms need to carry out their life processes. But, recall from Chapter 8 that animals can't make their own food. Green plants, on the other hand are producers. Producers make their own food. You will learn more in Chapter 10 about the process whereby plants use water, carbon dioxide, and energy from the sun to produce food.

In contrast to plants, animals are consumers. Consumers are organisms that are unable to make their own food. They must consume other organisms in order to obtain energy. Consumers are adapted in specific ways for getting the energy and nutrients they need. In the following Find Out activity, see how one feature, the beak, affects the survival of one type of consumer, namely birds.

The desert rat, a consumer native to many of the driest parts of the world meets its water needs by feeding on seeds and dry grasses from which it extracts water. In addition it is adapted with very few sweat glands, all only on its feet.

Find Out! ACTIVITY

How useful is a bird's beak?

Each species of bird is uniquely adapted for obtaining the food it requires.

What To Do

Observing the beaks to the right, and using the description below, match the bird to the type of food it eats.

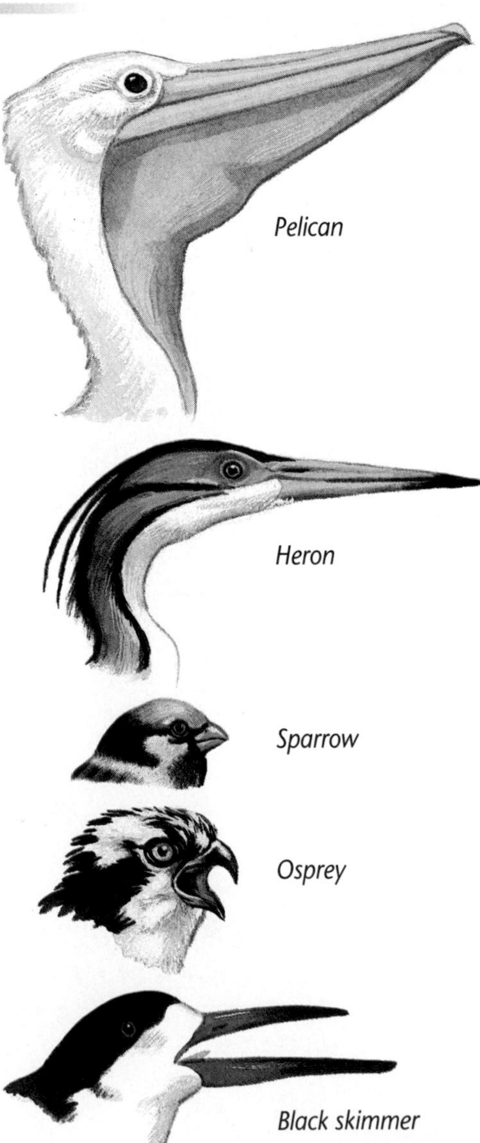

Conclude and Apply

1. Which bird has a long, sharply pointed bill to spear fish?
2. Which bird's bill is short and thick, enabling it to crush seeds?
3. Which bird's lower bill enables it to skim food from the water's surface?
4. The powerful, sharp, hooked beak on this bird enables it to tear flesh.
5. This bird has a pouch under its lower jaw in which it collects fish.
6. *In your Journal,* write a statement explaining how an adaptation such as a beak affects survival in birds.

Finding Food

As you learned in the Find Out activity, birds have unique body parts adapted for obtaining food. You are probably more familiar than you realize with adaptations that enable animals to feed.

Many animals depend heavily on their senses to locate food. How do you find food at a mall? What senses do you use? Is it possible that you smell food first and then see the restaurant? Maybe you hear the clatter of dishes? The important words here are *smell*, *see*, and *hear*.

Sight and Smell

Humans have fairly well-developed senses of sight, smell, and hearing, but other members of the animal kingdom are even more dependent on these senses for survival than you are. Hunting animals, such as the coyote or wolf, will often pick up the scent of prey. They will follow the scent until they find the animal they are tracking.

The expression "eagle-eyed" gives a clue to an animal that depends on a very sharp sense of sight. For birds of prey that hunt, such as eagles, owls, and hawks, excellent vision is a necessary adaptation for the survival of their species.

Hearing

Not all organisms rely on sight or smell for survival however. In Chapter 3, you learned that sound travels through solids, liquids, and gases. That means that you might be able to hear under almost any condition. Scientists have found that hearing is particularly well-developed in many marine animals. Dolphins and whales use echolocation to determine where an object is located.

In the following Investigate, find out what attracts a mealworm to food.

Figure 9-2

A The mountain bluebird's large eyes allow the bird to keep a look-out for danger and for insects to eat.

B A mountain bluebird searches for food by hovering in the air and watching for insects on the ground. When it sees an insect, the bird swoops down and uses its strong beak to catch and hold its prey.

DESIGN YOUR OWN
INVESTIGATION

Picky Eaters

Are there certain foods that you do not like to eat? Maybe you don't like spinach because of its taste or texture. Other members of your family may not like corn. Do animals, like people, have food preferences? In the following activity, you will observe how mealworms respond to different kinds of food.

Preparation

Problem

How can you determine food preferences of mealworms?

Form a Hypothesis

As a group, discuss the factors that might influence the mealworms' preference for one food over another, such as moistness or odor. Agree upon these factors, then form a hypothesis about the food that mealworms prefer.

Objectives

- Design an experiment that tests the mealworms' responses to various types of foods.
- Compare the mealworms' responses to different foods.
- Infer why mealworms prefer some foods over others.

Possible Materials

20 mealworms
plastic storage box
pan balance
cheesecloth
gram masses
hand lens
forceps
20 g bran flakes
20 g dry oatmeal
20 g sugar-coated corn flakes
20 g broken, unsalted wheat crackers
water

Safety Precautions

Return all mealworms to your teacher at the end of the experiment. Dispose of the cereals as directed by your teacher.

DESIGN YOUR OWN INVESTIGATION

Plan the Experiment

1 Examine the materials provided. Which materials will you use? How will you use them?

2 Agree upon a way to test your hypothesis. Write down what you will do at each step.

3 Assign tasks to members of the group.

4 Design a table for recording your data. Decide when data will be measured and recorded.

Check the Plan

1 Determine where you will put the different foods in the plastic box. How will you calculate how much food the mealworms have eaten?

2 Decide where to place the mealworms in the box. Be sure to discuss how to move the mealworms back to their starting place so that the experiment can be repeated several times.

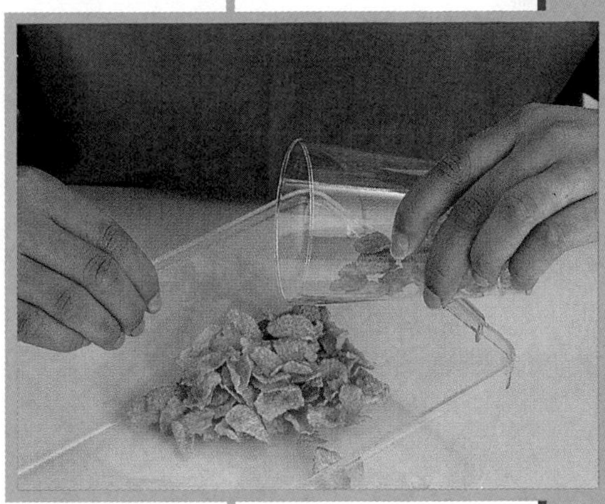

3 Before you start the experiment, have your teacher approve your plan.

4 Carry out your experiment. Complete your data table *in your Science Journal.*

Analyze and Conclude

1. **Use Numbers** Calculate the total number of mealworms that preferred each food.
2. **Use Numbers** Calculate the mealworms' daily average of food intake for each food type.
3. **Conclude** Which type of food did most mealworms prefer? Did this support your hypothesis? Explain.
4. **Infer** Infer why the mealworms were attracted to a particular food.

Going Further

Predict whether mealworms might be attracted to other food choices. Design an experiment to test this prediction. Test the prediction.

How Animals Digest Food

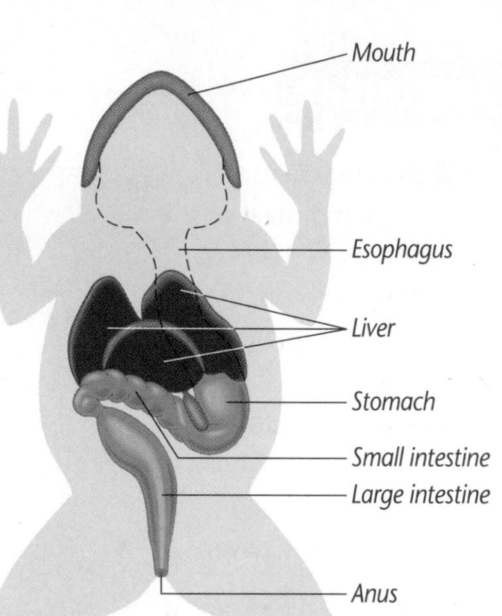

Figure 9-3

A Food enters through the mouth. The frog's tongue enables it to grab whole insects.

B Food passes through a series of organs in the digestive system. Enzymes in the stomach and small intestine break the food down chemically. The digested food is absorbed and used throughout the body.

C Undigested materials are expelled as waste through the anus.

Locating food is one thing, but once an animal has the food it needs, it has to break it down into substances it can use. This is done through the process of digestion. Most many-celled animals have digestive systems. In a digestive system, food is broken down mechanically and chemically as it passes through different parts of a specialized body tube. These animals have two body openings, a mouth and an anus, and food moves in only one direction. **Figure 9-3** describes how one animal, the frog, digests food.

What happens when an animal doesn't have a complex digestive system like the frog's? Some organisms, such as sponges, feed by filtering water that flows through the pores in its body. **Figure 9-4** shows how another organism, the starfish, feeds.

Figure 9-4

A Starfish use their tube feet to obtain food, such as clams, mussels, and worms. Here, the starfish attaches its tube feet to both halves of a mussel shell and pulls until the shell opens.

B The starfish pushes its stomach out through its mouth and spreads the stomach over the food. Enzymes secreted by the stomach turn the food into a soupy liquid, which is taken into the stomach.

C Then, the starfish pulls its stomach back into its body and digestion continues.

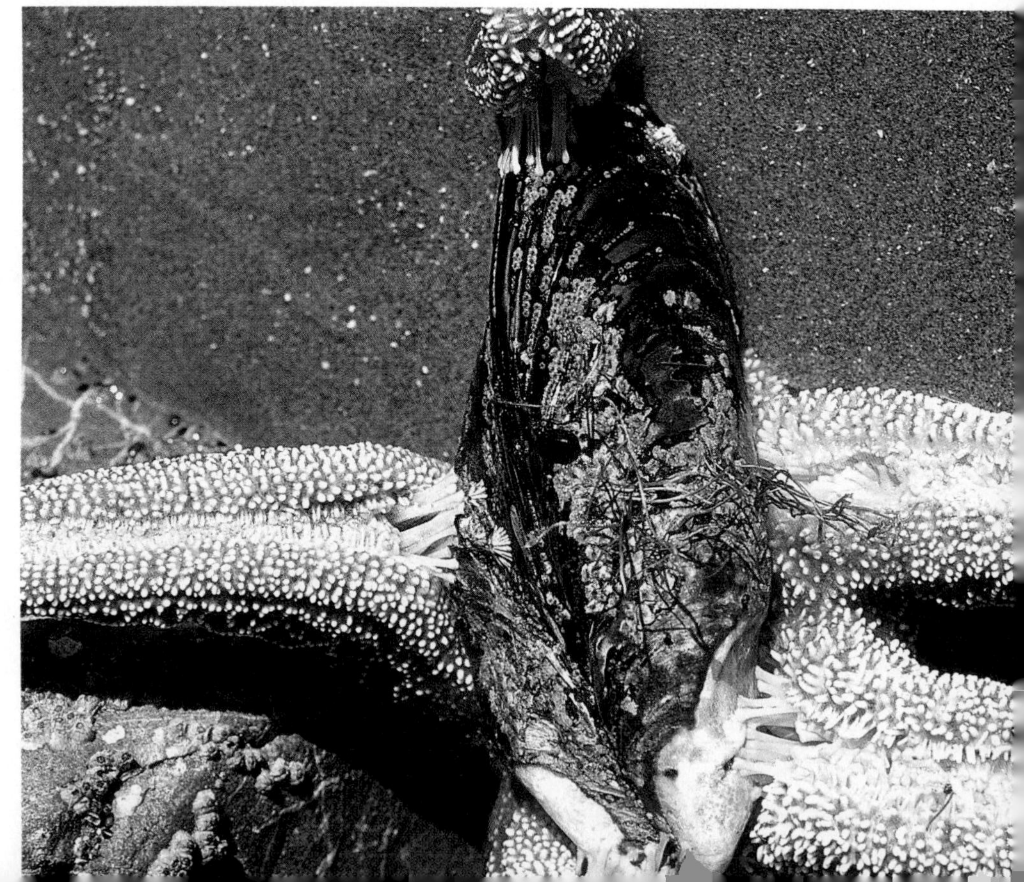

How Scientists Classify Animals

As you can see, there are many different features to consider when looking at animals. Scientists use these different characteristics to place animals into groups.

■ Invertebrates and Vertebrates

Try this simple activity. Reach around and run your fingers down the middle of your back from neck to waist. Describe what you feel.

When you ran your hand down your back, you felt a backbone. Biologists use the characteristic of having or not having a backbone as a way to separate members of the animal kingdom into two groups. Most animals in the living world don't have backbones. These animals belong to an enormously large group known as the invertebrates. An **invertebrate** is any animal that doesn't have a backbone. Worms, clams, jellyfish, flies, and spiders are examples of invertebrates.

You belong to the smaller group of animals that do have backbones. You are a **vertebrate**, an animal that has a backbone. **Figure 9-5** shows examples of different groups of vertebrates and invertebrates.

SKILLBUILDER

Making and Using Graphs

This bar graph gives you some idea of the relative number of species of invertebrates and vertebrates that biologists have identified. How many species of invertebrates are shown by the graph? Which group of animals is most abundant? Which group has the fewest number? If you need help, refer to the **Skill Handbook** on page 657.

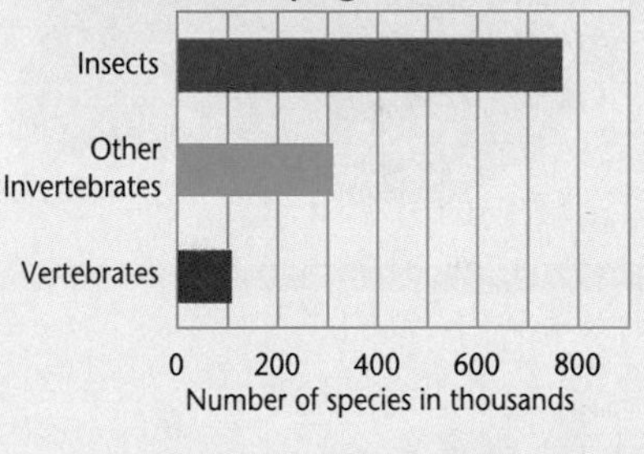

Figure 9-5

Vertebrates

Frogs *Lizards* *Fish* *Rabbits* *Birds*

Invertebrates

Clams *Flies* *Spiders* *Sponges* *Snails*

Figure 9-6

Organisms have one of three basic body plans.

A Radial symmetry is seen in a hydra where tentacles surround a central point, the mouth. There appears to be no left or right, front or back.

B Butterflies show bilateral symmetry. They have distinct left and right sides.

C Organisms, such as sponges, which show no recognizable symmetry, are described as asymmetrical.

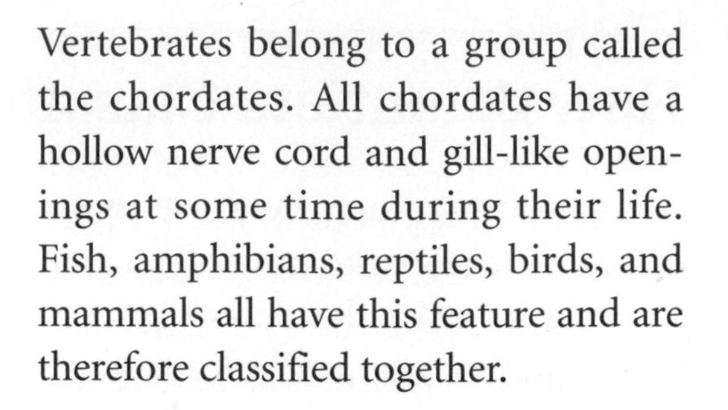

Vertebrates belong to a group called the chordates. All chordates have a hollow nerve cord and gill-like openings at some time during their life. Fish, amphibians, reptiles, birds, and mammals all have this feature and are therefore classified together.

Body Plans

Biologists also look at each animal's basic body plan, or how body parts are arranged, when describing and classifying an organism. Body plan is the animal's symmetry. In **Figure 9-6**, you can learn about different body plans.

Physics CONNECTION

Creature Features

Building models of animals can help you understand their adaptations. How can you combine serious science with fun arts and crafts? Just ask biomechanics researcher Mimi Koehl from the University of California at Berkeley.

Biomechanics

Biomechanics is the field of science in which scientists ask how living organisms are affected by the laws of physics. By studying the physical environment an animal lives in, scientists can begin to explain why animals are shaped in a certain way and why they behave as they do. For example, the shapes of fish and

Malaysian flying frog

Skeletons: A Means of Support

Have you ever watched a tall building under construction? Steel beams provide the support for the walls, floors, and roof. Animals also have support systems called a skeleton. Remember when you felt your backbone? The backbone is part of your internal support system. But skeletons may be internal or external.

Internal and External Skeletons

Figure 9-7 shows an example of an **endoskeleton**, a skeleton that is within an animal's body. All vertebrates have endoskeletons. Endoskeletons, such as

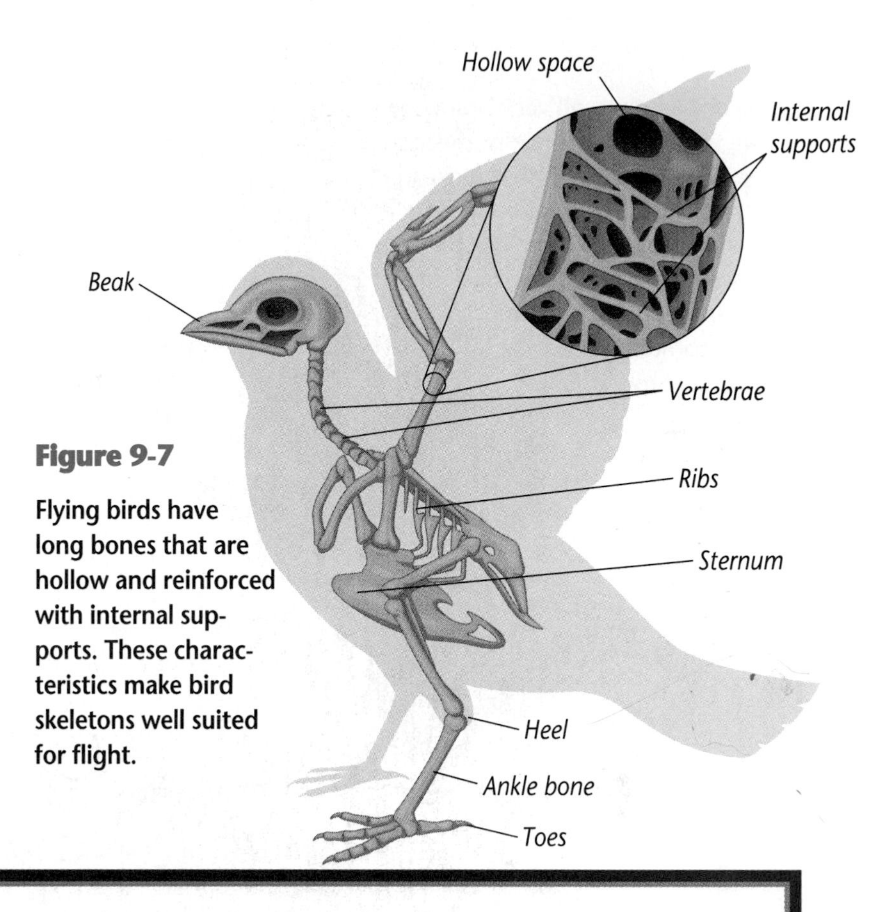

Figure 9-7

Flying birds have long bones that are hollow and reinforced with internal supports. These characteristics make bird skeletons well suited for flight.

dolphins allow these animals to swim through water with little resistance.

But explaining animal structure is not always so easy, especially with live animals or animals that have become extinct.

Flying Frogs

Dr. Koehl has worked with biologist Sharon Emerson of the University of Utah to explain the structure of a flying amphibian—the Malaysian flying frog. Dr. Emerson has studied this tiny frog in its native habitat. Dr. Emerson wanted to know whether this frog's interesting adaptations, such as large webbed feet, had anything to do with the frog's gymnastic abilities.

Koehl and Emerson made several realistic models. They also made individual legs, "hands," and feet of nonflying frogs.

To investigate whether the frog's shape is related to its acrobatic abilities, Koehl and Emerson tested their model frogs in a small wind tunnel. The wind tunnel allowed the researchers to investigate how wind resistance affects the frog as it flies through the air. They also replaced parts of the model with the interchangeable nonflying-frog parts to see how these affect wind resistance.

From the experiments, Koehl and Emerson observed that the frog's adaptations, such as its webbed feet, helped it control how it moved through the air much like a parachutist controls direction during a fall. They concluded that the flying frog's shape is not so much beneficial to flying as it is to how it controls its fall.

You Try It!

Go to the library and learn about the adaptations of some of your favorite animals. Read about their behaviors in their natural environments. How are your animal's adaptations related to its behavior?

Figure 9-8

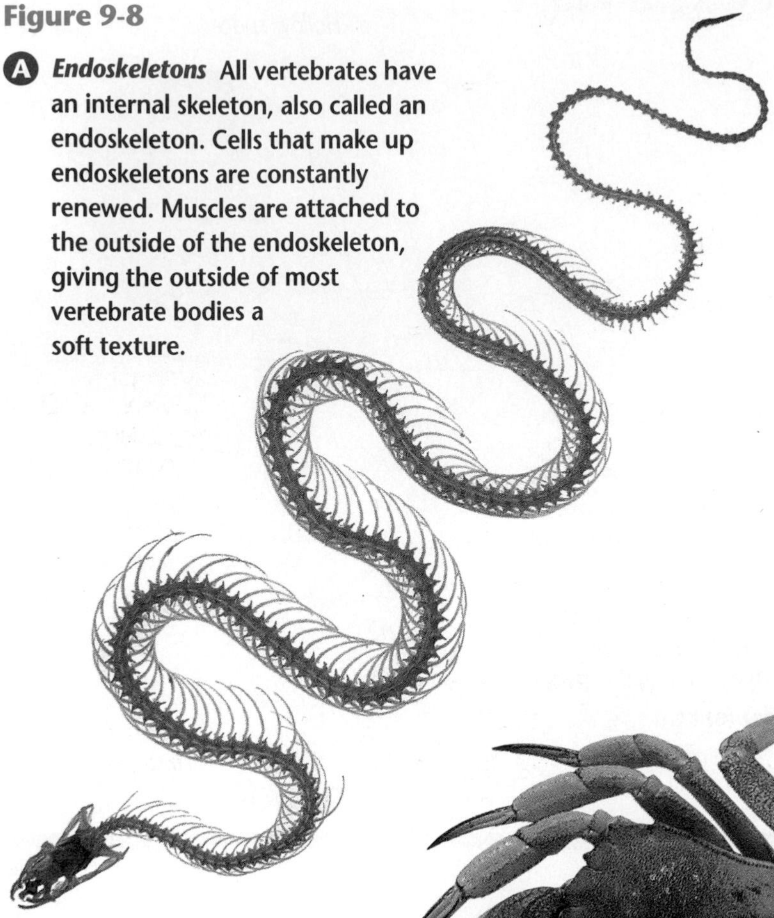

A ***Endoskeletons*** **All vertebrates have an internal skeleton, also called an endoskeleton. Cells that make up endoskeletons are constantly renewed. Muscles are attached to the outside of the endoskeleton, giving the outside of most vertebrate bodies a soft texture.**

B ***Exoskeletons*** **The shell of a crab is its exoskeleton. This outside skeleton protects the animal's internal organs from loss of fluids and supports its body. The crab sheds its exoskeleton every few weeks as it grows, and a new one develops underneath. The internal organs and the muscles of crayfish, lobsters, shrimp, crabs, ants, bees, and beetles are attached to the inside of the exoskeleton.**

your own, are made of bone, but sharks and some fish have endoskeletons made of cartilage.

Some animals have an internal skeleton that is neither bone nor cartilage. Animals such as jellyfish and earthworms maintain their form because of fluids contained under pressure in compartments in their bodies.

Many invertebrates such as the crab in **Figure 9-8B**, have an **exoskeleton**, a support system on the outside of the body.

In this section, you've thought about characteristics that separate animals from other groups of living things. You also learned that animals are classified in different ways based on body structure adaptations. In the next section, learn how different animals reproduce.

1. An adult sponge is an animal that doesn't move from place to place. It's attached to one spot on the ocean floor. Why can you still consider it an animal?
2. Classify each of the animals listed as vertebrate or invertebrate. Which of the animals has an endoskeleton? Which of them has an exoskeleton?

   bee mouse robin ant deer
3. **Apply** If you found a fossil of an organism with a backbone, what characteristics would you know about the organism?

9-2 Reproduction and Development

How Animals Reproduce

Have you ever stopped at a pet shop to look at puppies, rabbits, and kittens? By the time these animals get to the store, they're already several weeks old and changing rapidly. As you laugh at their actions, you're not thinking about the important processes of reproduction that took place to make these young animals. Reproduction in animals is either sexual or asexual. Each process is characterized by certain adaptations. For example, eggs are an important adaptation in reproduction for many animal groups. In the Explore activity below, observe an egg to identify features that help chickens and other birds to survive as a species.

Section Objectives

- Distinguish between sexual and asexual reproduction.
- Trace the stages of complete and incomplete metamorphosis.

Key Terms

fertilization
regeneration
metamorphosis

Explore! ACTIVITY

What's in a bird egg?

What To Do

Take a close look at a chicken egg to learn something about the typical parts of a bird egg.

1. Open a chicken egg into a shallow bowl.
2. Use a hand lens to take a close look at the shell. How do you suppose a shell is helpful to the developing bird?
3. With the help of the diagram of the egg, identify the parts inside the egg.
4. *In your Journal,* infer a function for each part you see in the egg.

Shell membrane
Yolk
White
Shell
Air space

Sexual Reproduction

Physics

Many animals have evolved behaviors that promote sexual reproduction. The coqui frog in Puerto Rico makes a sound like its name (ko-*kee*) to attract a mate. The sound can be as loud as 108 decibels. Find out what a decibel is and why 108 of these would be deafening.

Animal groups that reproduce sexually have separate male and female individuals. In sexual reproduction, sperm from a male unite with one or more eggs produced by a female in a process called **fertilization**. In animal groups, fertilization may be external or internal.

External Fertilization

Reproduction results in a generation of new individuals that are like their parents. Different animal species may produce one or many new individuals at one time. For starfish, sea urchins, fish, frogs, and other water-inhabiting animals, huge numbers of eggs and sperm are usually produced at one time. These organisms are dependent on water to carry out fertilization. During external fertilization, the female releases eggs into the water. The male then releases sperm, which swim to the eggs. In each instance, all of the eggs are usually fertilized.

Internal Fertilization

During internal fertilization, a female produces one or more eggs that are kept in the body. The male then deposits sperm in a fluid into the female's body. The sperm swim to and unite with the eggs. Organisms that have fertilized eggs that undergo development in the female's body generally produce smaller numbers of offspring. Organisms that undergo internal fertilization are not usually restricted to living in or near water to accomplish fertilization.

Egg

Egg-producing ovaries

Figure 9-9

A ***External Fertilization*** **Among organisms that reproduce through external fertilization, water is a key factor. Female fish release large numbers of eggs into the water. The male fish release large numbers of sperm that swim to the eggs and fertilize them.**

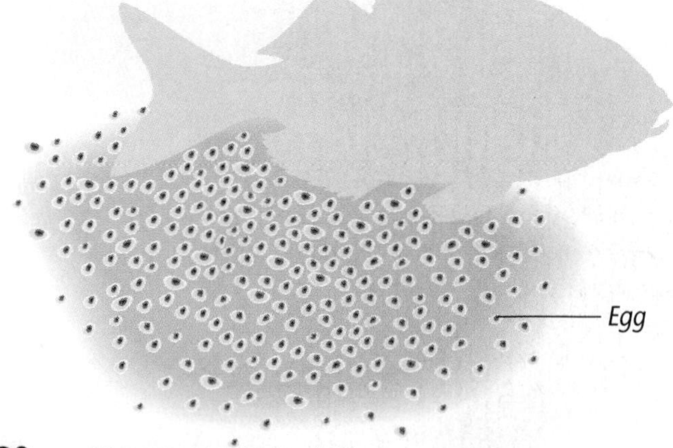

B ***Internal Fertilization*** **During internal fertilization, eggs remain in the female. While less dependent on water for fertilization than fish or other aquatic animals, sperm from the male moves in a fluid through the female reproductive system toward the egg. Once fertilized, an egg develops in the female, as with humans, or may be laid with a protective shell, as with alligators and ducks.**

Asexual Reproduction

Asexual reproduction is the production of a new organism from just one parent. No eggs or sperm are exchanged. Among animals, asexual reproduction occurs in many invertebrates, such as the aphids in **Figure 9-10**.

Hydra and sponges can reproduce by an asexual process called budding. During budding in hydra, as shown in **Figure 9-11**, one or more new individuals form on the parent organism. At some point, the new organism breaks off from the parent. The new organism has the same characteristics as the parent.

Regeneration

A few animals form whole new body parts by regeneration. **Regeneration** occurs when an animal regrows a missing part or regrows from only a portion of the original body. Regeneration may also be a form of asexual reproduction when whole new individuals develop. Sponge growers cut large sponges into smaller pieces and throw the pieces back into the ocean. Each separate piece grows into a larger sponge in as little as eighteen months.

Figure 9-11

Ⓐ Budding is a form of asexual reproduction. During budding, a small growth, or bud, forms on the parent hydra.

Developing bud

Ⓑ The bud continues to grow until it develops all of the characteristics it needs to survive on its own.

Ⓒ Eventually, the bud breaks off from the parent and lives independently. How does the new hydra compare with its parent?

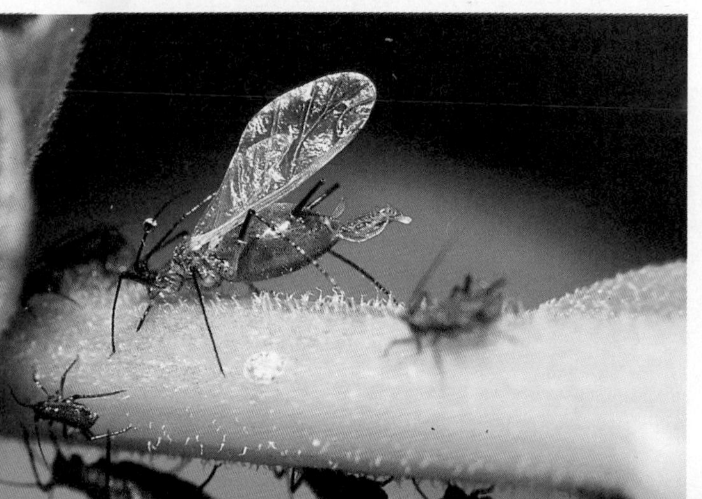

Figure 9-10

Aphids are insect pests commonly found feeding on rose bushes. Aphids reproduce almost continuously by asexual means, and for most of the year, produce only female offspring.

Animal Development

Development of a fertilized egg into an adult varies in the animal world. Animals such as birds and mammals have young that look very similar to the adult form of their species, so changes during their development are not too dramatic. For example, kittens have many of the characteristics that an adult cat has. But many young animals at first look nothing like their parents. What happens to these animals as they progress to adulthood?

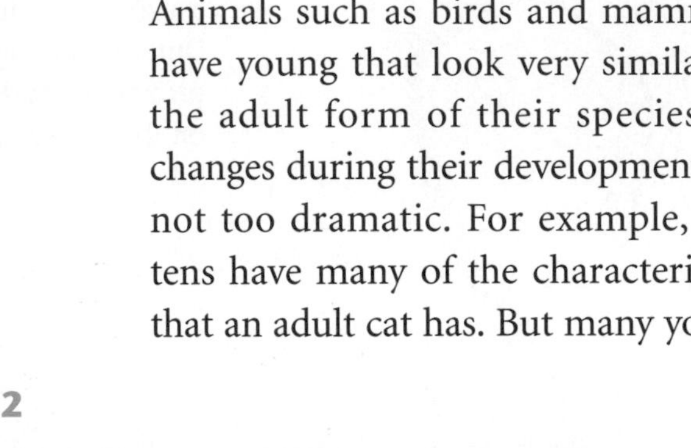

Metamorphosis

During development, many members of the animal kingdom undergo extensive changes in form. The changes in form that organisms undergo in their life cycles are called **metamorphosis.** *Meta-* means after or beyond and *morpho* means form. One familiar example is the frog in **Figure 9-12.** On this page and the next, you can see the changes that frogs undergo. Other organisms change form completely as they grow from egg to adult. Two types of metamorphosis are known in insect life cycles—complete and incomplete. In the Find Out activity that follows, take a look at the stages of metamorphosis that occur during the development of fruit flies.

Figure 9-12

A The female frog lays up to 3000 eggs, which are fertilized by the male's sperm after the egg mass has been laid in water.

B Metamorphosis is chemically controlled by substances called hormones. After about two weeks, the fertilized eggs of frogs hatch into a larval stage called a tadpole.

C The tadpole lives in water, has a long tail, and uses gills to take in oxygen from the water.

Four weeks old

D As the tadpole grows, its tail begins to be absorbed. Legs form and lungs develop.

Six weeks old

Find Out! ACTIVITY

How does a fruit fly change as it develops?

Changes in form are easy to observe in fruit flies because they go through their life cycle in a short period of time.

What To Do

You will observe different stages of development in live fruit flies.

1. From your teacher, obtain a vial containing food and fruit flies in different stages of development.
2. Using a hand lens and without opening the vial, observe the fruit flies.
3. Use the diagrams below as a guide to identify different stages of development.

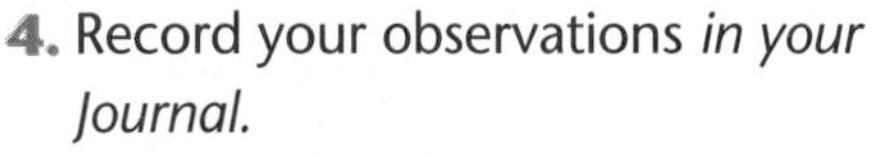

4. Record your observations *in your Journal.*
5. Repeat your observations every day for two weeks. Record changes that you see.

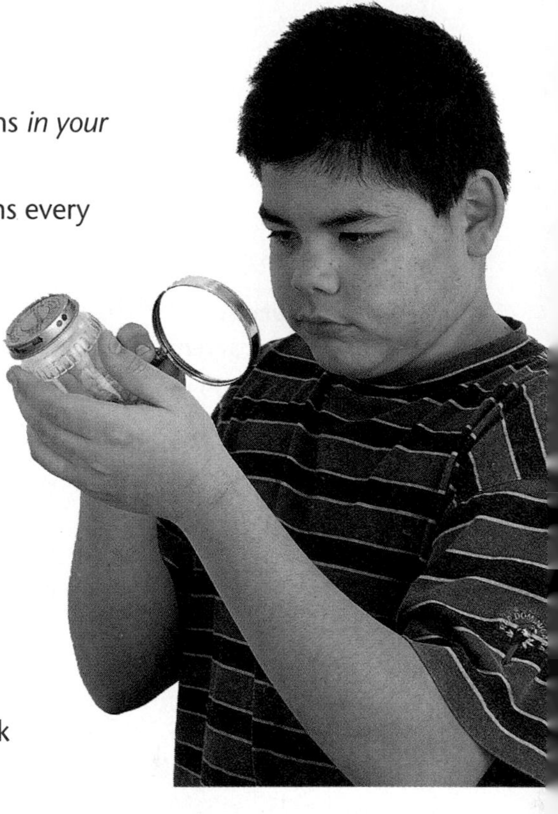

Conclude and Apply

1. How many stages did you observe? Describe all the stages of development that you observed.
2. Draw each stage and arrange them in the order in which you think development occurs.

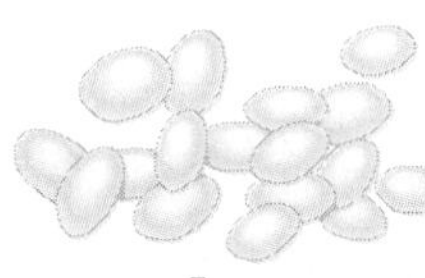

Eggs

Larvae

Pupae

Adult

Nine weeks old

E **The young frog's tail continues to be absorbed and the frog begins spending more time on land than in the water.**

Twelve weeks old

Adult frog

F **A mature frog has no tail, lives on land, breathes air, and eats insects rather than algae.**

STAGE 1 Egg

STAGE 2 Larva

STAGE 3 Pupa

Figure 9-13

A ***Complete Metamorphosis*** begins about seven days after an egg is fertilized. The caterpillar egg develops into a larva which chews the egg case open and stretches out, as in Stage 2.

B Once hatched, a caterpillar eats several times its body weight in one day. As it grows, the larva molts—its exoskeleton splits and a new one forms. Just before its last molt, the mature larva attaches itself to a twig or leaf to prepare for the pupa stage.

C The third stage in the metamorphosis is the pupa. The caterpillar spins a covering from a silken thread it produces. The larva now enters the pupa stage. During this time, chemicals called hormones cause vast changes to take place that result in a complete change in form inside the pupa.

Complete and Incomplete Metamorphosis

Insects exhibit two different kinds of metamorphosis. The distinct and different stages of development that you saw in the Find Out activity tell you that fruit flies undergo complete metamorphosis. Butterflies also undergo complete metamorphosis. **Figure 9-13** across the top of this page and the next shows how completely different the adult stage in a butterfly is from the larval stage.

Other animals change form too, but the changes are less distinct. In contrast to complete metamorphosis, incomplete insect metamorphosis involves three stages. As you can see in **Figure 9-14**, grasshoppers undergo incomplete metamorphosis. First, eggs hatch into nymphs, which look very similar to the adult, only smaller. Periodically, nymphs molt and grow larger. Once wings develop, the grasshoppers are mature.

Figure 9-14

STAGE 1 Eggs

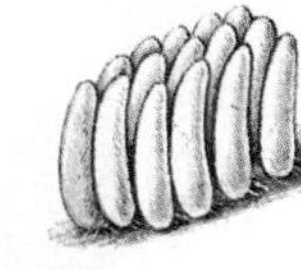

A ***Incomplete Metamorphosis*** begins as the grasshopper egg hatches and a nymph (as in B) emerges. The nymph is an immature form that looks like an adult grasshopper, only much smaller.

STAGE 2 Nymph

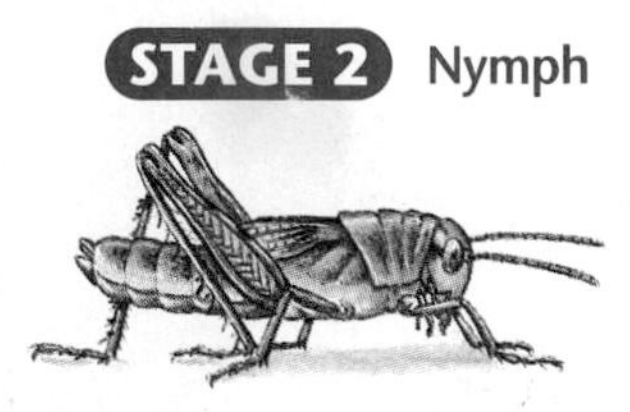

B The nymph, which has undeveloped reproductive organs and lacks wings, molts five or six times as it grows and develops.

STAGE 3 Adult

C It takes 40 to 60 days for a nymph to become a mature, winged, adult grasshopper that can reproduce.

STAGE 4
Adult

E The wings reach full size about 30 minutes after the butterfly has emerged. After about an hour, the insect is ready to fly in search of food. Unlike the caterpillar, the adult butterfly does not eat leaves. Instead, it drinks nectar from flowers.

D In the last stage of metamorphosis, the insect splits open its covering and emerges. The adult insect—a butterfly—unfolds its wings and flutters them, thus pumping blood into its veins.

Survival During Development

Animals have evolved with a variety of adaptations that enable young to survive to adulthood. Some of these adaptations involve reproducing in large numbers, shells, or internal development. Eggs and larvae are common sources of food for other animals. As a result, these stages are frequently destroyed by changes in the environment, such as drying or lack of food. How do these species survive? Animals that develop through the process of metamorphosis seem to reproduce in large numbers. In contrast, birds, and reptiles reproduce in smaller numbers. These species have adapted ways to protect their young as they develop outside the female's body. After fertilization, a protective shell forms around an egg. The shell keeps the egg from drying out.

Most mammals develop within the female's body. Internal development provides protection for the embryo.

1. Compare sexual and asexual reproduction. Is there an advantage to sexual reproduction?
2. Compare and contrast complete and incomplete metamorphosis.
3. **Apply** In what way does an organism that reproduces by internal fertilization have an advantage over one that reproduces by external fertilization?

Adaptations for Survival

Section Objectives

- Explain how adaptations allow animals to survive on Earth.
- Give examples of some animal adaptations.

Key Terms

cellular respiration
metabolism

Surviving Where You Are

Would you expect a fish to survive in a forest? Of course not. Fish have adaptations that make them better suited for life in water. Birds, bears, beetles, and butterflies also have characteristics that make them suited for their environment. Consider the characteristics of each of the environments and the adaptations of animals in each area in the following Explore activity.

Explore! ACTIVITY

Does an animal's environment tell you something about its adaptations?

What To Do

Study the pictures showing the different environments where organisms live.

1. *In your Journal,* make a chart with the headings *Tundra, Desert, Grassland,* and *Rain Forest.*
2. Under each heading, write a description of the area from what you see in the pictures.
3. Brainstorm a list of the kinds of adaptations animals would probably have to have to survive in each of these environments? Include this list in your chart.

Desert in Alamo Canyon, Arizona

Grasslands of southern Brazil

Alaskan tundra in fall

Rain forest in Venezuela

Physical Adaptations

It's fairly easy to conclude that an organism living in a rain forest might have some adaptations that differ from an organism that lives in the arctic tundra. An adaptation is any characteristic that increases an organism's chances for survival. Adaptations may be structural, like bird beaks. Others are harder to detect. For instance, cows have symbiotic bacteria that produce the enzyme that allows them to digest cellulose. Even behaviors can be considered adaptations.

■ Body Structure Adaptations

Remember the Find Out activity you did that involved bird beaks? The beak is only one adaptation that birds have. The activity could have been done using the birds' feet as well, as **Figure 9-15** shows.

Bird feet are an example of an adaptation that involves the animal's body structure. An anteater's tongue and the teeth of a deer are also body structure adaptations. Beaks, teeth, feet, and tongues are all body structures. Are there any adaptations you can think of inside the body?

■ Internal Body Adaptations

Internal adaptations may be structural and chemical. One internal adaptation found in animals is the organ used to obtain oxygen. Most organisms require oxygen for respiration. **Cellular respiration** occurs inside the body's cells when oxygen combines with digested food to release energy from chemical bonds in food.

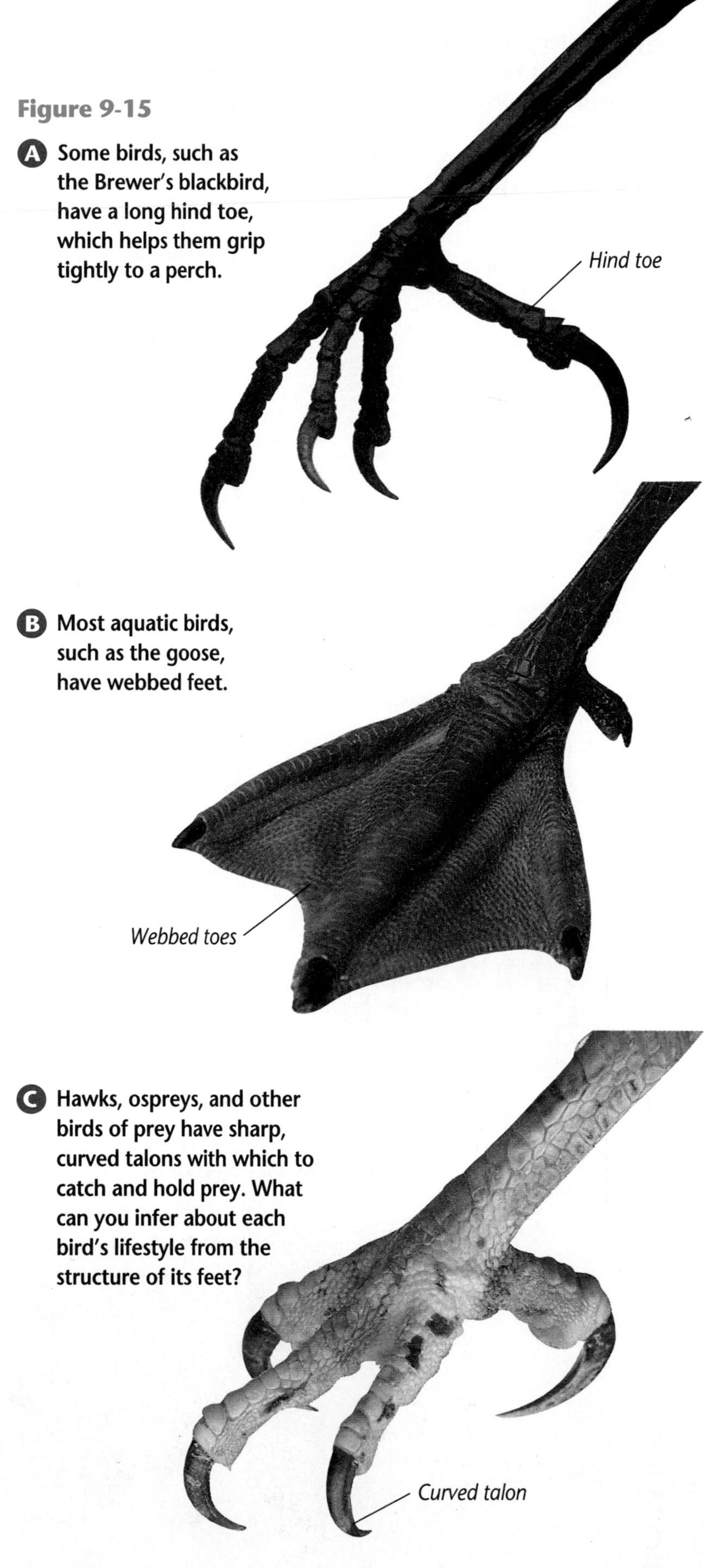

Figure 9-15

A Some birds, such as the Brewer's blackbird, have a long hind toe, which helps them grip tightly to a perch.

B Most aquatic birds, such as the goose, have webbed feet.

C Hawks, ospreys, and other birds of prey have sharp, curved talons with which to catch and hold prey. What can you infer about each bird's lifestyle from the structure of its feet?

Figure 9-16

A As water passes over the gills, capillaries within them absorb oxygen dissolved in the water. The blood carries the oxygen to body cells, where it is used in cellular respiration.

B One of the waste products of cellular respiration is carbon dioxide. Carbon dioxide is picked up from cells by the blood and carried to the gills where it is passed back into the water.

Gills

■ Adaptations for Breathing

In the animal kingdom, there is a tremendous variety of ways in which organisms take in oxygen for cellular respiration. **Figure 9-16** shows a fish with gills, which it uses to remove oxygen from water. Insects have small openings along the sides of their bodies through which air containing oxygen enters. Most amphibians have lungs but they can also obtain oxygen through their skin. And of course, humans obtain oxygen through air breathed into lungs.

Cellular respiration is one of the chemical changes that goes on in an organism. The total of all of the chemical changes that take place in an

Konrad Lorenz

Konrad Lorenz was a famous scientist who used his sense of sight to observe animals. Lorenz was a founder of the science of ethology—the study of animal behavior.

Lorenz thought that in order to learn about animal behavior, an animal must be observed in its natural environment. Before Lorenz, scientists had mainly studied animal behavior in laboratories.

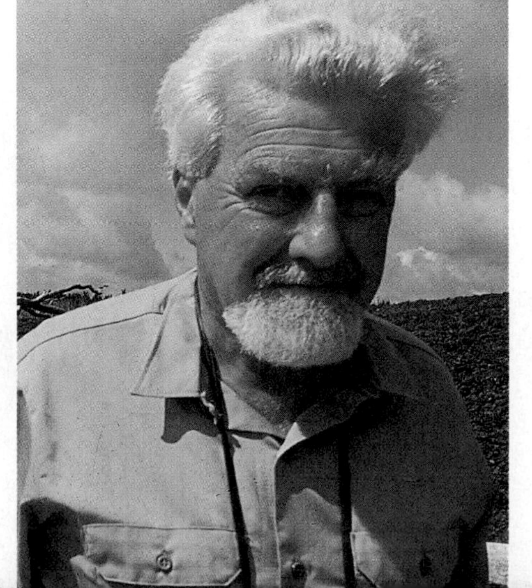

Konrad Lorenz

The Importance of Observation

Lorenz devoted much of his time to watching colonies of birds, including geese. From these observations came one of his most important discoveries. In 1935, Lorenz concluded that if a mother goose is not present when her baby geese hatch, they will consider the first moving object they see to be their mother.

organism is its **metabolism.** During the metabolism of food, heat is released. The faster food is broken down, the greater the amount of heat energy released. Why do you suppose you get warm when you exercise? Could this be related to increased metabolism from increased muscle action?

Human Adaptations for Respiration

Not all organisms adapt to the same conditions in the same way. People who live in high mountain areas such as in the Andes of South America where there is less atmosphere have been found to have larger hearts that circulate blood more quickly. They also have more red blood cells to carry oxygen than people who live at sea level. But, some people who live in similar conditions in Tibet do not have these adaptations.

Behavior Adaptations

Animals demonstrate many kinds of behavioral adaptations. A bluejay squawks or shrieks if a cat comes too close to its nest site. Some bugs quickly skitter away when a light shines on them. The set of responses an organism exhibits to changes in its environment is its behavior. In the Investigate that follows, you will see how an earthworm reacts to several changes in its surroundings.

Will Anyone Do?

Lorenz found that if the moving object happened to be himself, the baby geese would follow him as if he were their mother. He found this to be true with ducks, too, as in the photograph below. Lorenz called this behavior *imprinting.* Imprinting is an animal instinct in which the animal becomes attached to another organism at a critical time soon after birth or hatching. Imprinting is important because in order for baby animals to survive, they must recognize a mother who will feed and protect them.

Lorenz continued his work in animal behavior and, in 1973, was awarded the Nobel prize for his work. Lorenz died in 1989.

You Try It!

Choose an animal to observe for a week and keep a diary of the animal's activities. What conclusions can you make about the animal's behavior from your observations?

INVESTIGATE!

Earthworm Behavior

How can you determine the effect some conditions have on an earthworm? In this activity, you will observe some earthworm characteristics and infer how they enable the earthworms to survive.

Problem

How is an earthworm adapted to live in soil?

Materials

hand lens
vinegar
live earthworms in slightly moist soil
500 mL beaker
toothpick
flashlight
shallow pan
paper towels
cotton swab
water

Safety Precautions

Earthworms can be released into the soil when you have completed your investigation. Earthworms are valuable because they aerate and mix soil as they move through it.

What To Do

1. Copy the data table *into your Journal.*
2. Open the container to be sure some of the earthworms are on the top of the soil. Shine the flashlight on the worms. Record how the worms react.

Data and Observations	
Condition	Response
Light	
Fingers	
Touch-front	
Touch-back	
Vinegar	

A

B

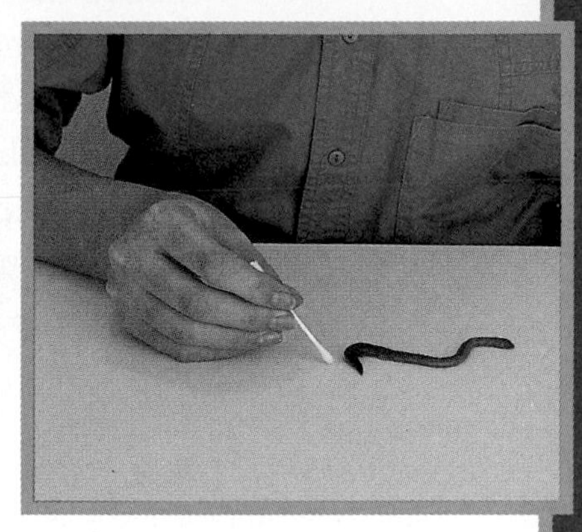

C

3 Moisten your hands and remove an earthworm from the container. **CAUTION:** *Use care when working with live animals.* Keep your hands moist while working with the earthworm. Hold the worm gently between your thumb and forefinger. Observe its movements and record them in the table.

4 Rub your fingers gently along the body. With a hand lens, ***observe*** the small hair-like bristles that you feel.

5 With the toothpick, gently touch the worm on the front and back ends. Record your observations.

6 Dip the cotton swab in vinegar. Place it in front of the worm on a wet paper towel. *Do not touch the worm with the vinegar.* Record what you observe.

Head end

Ringlike segments

All earthworms are made up of many segments. They have no legs, and it is sometimes difficult to tell which end is the head. The head is the end closest to the thick, heavy band on the worm's body.

Analyzing

1. What happens when light is shined on the earthworms?
2. How does the earthworm react to touch?
3. How does the earthworm react to the vinegar?

Concluding and Applying

4. ***Infer*** how the earthworm's reaction to light is an adaptation for living in soil.
5. How are the bristles an adaptation for living in soil?
6. **Going Further** ***Design an experiment*** to find out how the earthworm reacts to different temperatures.

As you review your results from the Investigate activity, you should notice that the bristles are a structural adaptation. The responses the earthworm made to light, touch, and vinegar are behavioral adaptations. Just as body structure can aid survival, different kinds of behavior can also determine if an organism will survive.

Figure 9-17

An animal may defend its territory to protect its food supply or a mate. Defending its territory, a dog may growl, bark, and bare its teeth. How does this behavior differ from a dog greeting someone familiar?

Mating Behaviors

Many animals take part in activities that attract members of the opposite sex. These behaviors also ensure that both animals are ready to mate at the same time. The peacock spreads his feathers to attract the peahen. Some insects release chemicals that attract members of the opposite sex. Other insects rub their legs or wings together to produce sounds that attract mates.

Many behavioral adaptations are ways for animals to communicate. In addition to marking their territory and finding mates, animals communicate to warn of danger, give directions for finding food, and maintain social order within a group.

Protective Behaviors

Look at **Figure 9-18**. Can you see any animals? Some adaptations protect animals from being seen as they hunt or from being attacked and eaten by other animals. Camouflage is an adaptation that allows an animal to

How Do We Know?

Do some animals rely on one another's behavior?

Some behaviors are helpful to more than one species of animal. For example, the frog-eating bats in parts of Central and South America hunt frogs at night. Researchers know that the bats use sound to find the frogs. But how do the bats distinguish between poisonous and nonpoisonous frogs?

A Batty Experiment

The researchers set up two speakers and a frog-eating bat in a large cage. One speaker broadcast the mating call of a poisonous frog. The second speaker played the mating call of a nonpoisonous frog. The bat always flew toward the sound from the nonpoisonous frog. The researchers concluded that not only did the bats use sound to find the frogs, but the bats used the sound to distinguish poisonous and nonpoisonous frogs. These bats show a feeding behavior that is dependent on the mating call behavior of frogs.

hide by blending into its surroundings. The stripes of a tiger or a zebra are one type of camouflage. A chameleon can turn different shades of green and brown as it moves through vegetation. A mouse or a snake can stay safely hidden when they lie motionless in leaves on a forest floor, as seen in **Figure 9-18.**

You have learned about several adaptations animals have that allow them to survive in their environment. Some of these adaptations are physical, such as specific beaks, feet, or claws. Other adaptations are behaviors that help animals communicate or find food. Without these adaptations, animal groups would not survive.

Figure 9-18

A The white-footed mouse is not easily seen because its coloring blends well with the ground color. This adaptation provides some protection from predators while the mouse feeds on leaves, seeds, nuts, berries, and insects.

C The copperhead's skin pattern is similar to the patterns made by the sticks and leaves through which it slithers.

B Tigers hunt many different animals in various environments. The patterns on their coats allow them to blend with many surroundings and hunt undetected.

check your UNDERSTANDING

1. How do these adaptations increase the chance for the animal or the animal's species to survive?
   a. eyesight of an owl
   b. whiskers of a cat
   c. courtship dance of a bird
   d. blending into environment
2. Give an example of an adaptation in body structure and explain how it helps the organism survive.
3. **Apply** When a honeybee locates a source of nectar, it flies back to the hive and performs a special dance. What type of adaptation is this? How is it useful for the bees?

NATIONAL GEOGRAPHIC

SCIFACTS

Can male animals give birth?

Unlike most fathers in the animal kingdom, the male sea horse is the one who gets pregnant and gives birth. After a female deposits eggs in the male's brood pouch, he fertilizes them and gives the developing embryos protection and nourishment. About 21 days later, he expels his young in a long and exhausting labor. Depending on the species, the offspring will number from as few as four to as many as a world-record 1572.

Sea horses mate for life and reinforce their bonds with ritual "greetings." Each morning the female visits her pregnant partner. Both sexes brighten in color and then twirl around a sea grass shoot, holding on to it with their tails.

Various species of the genus *Hippocampus* are found in the coastal waters of six continents. A legal global trade of 20 million sea horses annually–primarily for medicines, aquariums, curios, and food–could lead to the widespread collapse of sea horse populations.

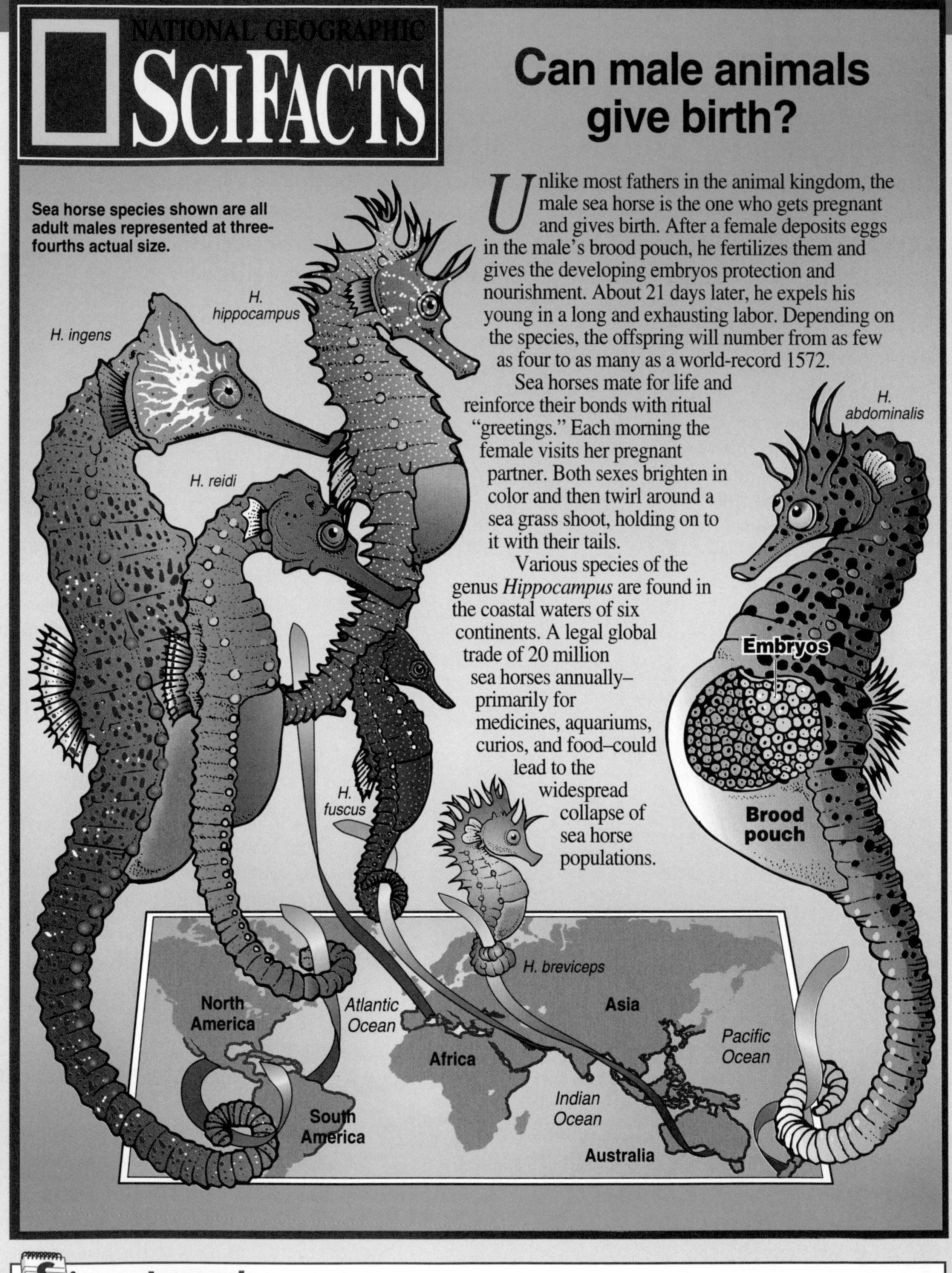

Science Journal

Think about why very small animals are important to life. *In your Science Journal,* write a poem about sea horses or another small animal after researching information about that animal.

EXPAND your view

HISTORY CONNECTION

Domesticating Animals

Paintings in caves show that animals were tamed, or domesticated, thousands of years ago. Once people settled into communities and learned how to plant crops, they also learned to use animals as a source of meat, milk, and wool, and to tame them to perform tasks.

Using Tame Animals

The first animal to be domesticated was the dog. People bred them for jobs, such as guarding and hunting.

Later, people saw advantages in using tame sheep and goats to supply meat, milk, and wool. Cattle, pigs, and donkeys were soon domesticated, too. The Anasazi, prehistoric Native Americans of the American Southwest, domesticated turkeys for food and clothing. They used their feathers to make robes and blankets.

What Do You Think?

What can you tell about the people who made the drawings shown in the picture? What can you tell about the animals?

Do Birds Have Knees? Do Ladybugs Sneeze?

Sometimes poets use absurd images to convey ideas. Find and read the poem "A Love Song" by poet Raymond Richard Patterson (Adoff, Arnold, ed. *Black Out Loud: An Anthology of Modern Poems by Black Americans*).

What do you think is the answer to the poet's initial question? How did your knowledge of animals help you determine the answer to the questions?

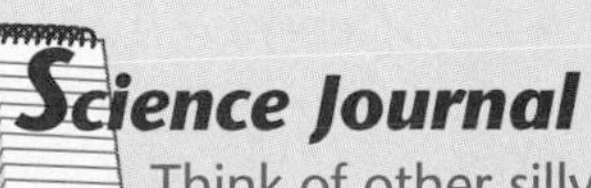

Think of other silly images of animals. *In your Science Journal* write and illustrate a picture book to share with a younger child. Use a question like those in the poem on each page of your book.

Teens in SCIENCE

Jessica Knight

Jessica Knight, a 16-year-old student at the North Carolina School of Science and Mathematics, wanted to know more about planarians. She wondered what would happen to planarians if they were exposed to various amounts of light.

Researching a Question

By reading about experiments conducted on planarians, Jessica learned that a fragment of planarian about the size of a period on this page could regrow into a complete planarian within two weeks. She also learned that, when exposed to too much light, cancerous cells grow in some planarians. Maybe, she thought, planarians could teach us something about the changes caused in cells by ultraviolet light, an agent which is thought to cause cancer.

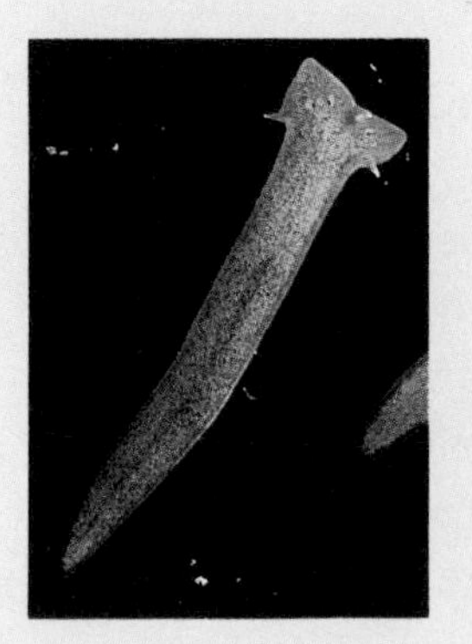

Two-headed planarian

The Experiment

For her experiments, Jessica chose *Dugesia tigrina*, a brown planarian that has a primitive nervous system.

Using a dissecting microscope for close observation, Jessica sliced them apart in a variety of ways. Then she watched how they regenerated missing parts. "Depending on how you cut them," Jessica says, "you can come up with two heads on one end, or a tail on each end, or head on each end, or a head coming out the side."

Collecting the Data

After weeks of observing and videotaping regeneration in planarians, Jessica was ready to study the effects of various amounts of ultraviolet light on regeneration and cancer growth. She planned to use a light meter and calculations to determine how much light the planarians actually receive.

What levels of light affect regeneration? How does light affect regeneration? What levels cause tumors? How much light kills the planarians? Jessica believes she will have answers to these questions when she has completed her experiment. She thinks that damage caused by the ultraviolet light will be comparable to damage ultraviolet light does to human skin.

What Do You Think?

Do you think planarian research could someday show scientists how to treat wounds in humans?

chapter 9
REVIEWING MAIN IDEAS

Science Journal

Review the statements below about the big ideas presented in this chapter, and answer the questions. Then, re-read your answers to the Did You Ever Wonder questions at the beginning of the chapter. *In your Science Journal,* write a paragraph about how your understanding of the big ideas in the chapter has changed.

1 **A diet of flying insects satisfies this frog's need for energy.** ***How does this activity characterize it as an animal?***

2 **An animal has one of two main kinds of support—inside the body and outside the body.** ***What are these two types of support called, and what are some examples of animals having each type?***

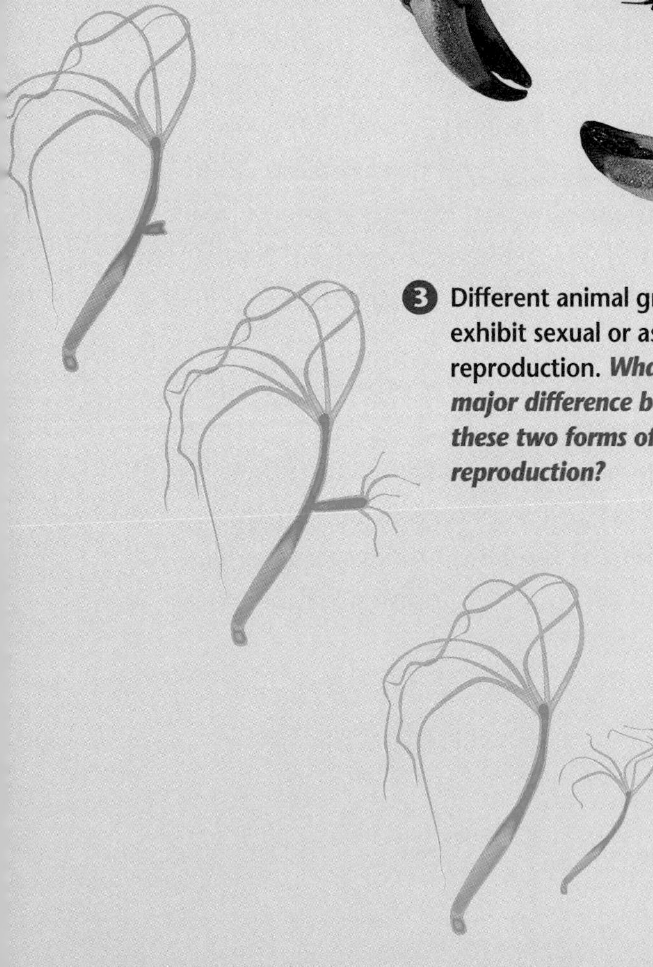

3 **Different animal groups exhibit sexual or asexual reproduction.** ***What is the major difference between these two forms of reproduction?***

4 **Foot structure, coloring, and behavior are examples of animal adaptations.** ***How do adaptations help animals survive in their environments?***

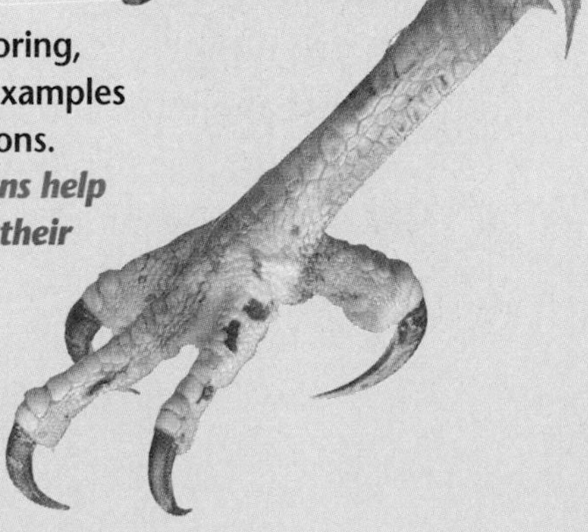

chapter 9
CHAPTER REVIEW

Using Key Science Terms

cellular respiration
endoskeleton
exoskeleton
fertilization
invertebrate
metabolism
metamorphosis
regeneration
vertebrate

1. What is the relationship between the following pairs of terms?
   metabolism and cellular respiration
   metamorphosis and regeneration
   endoskeleton and exoskeleton
   vertebrate and invertebrate
2. Using a dictionary, research the meaning of the roots *endo-* and *exo-* and explain how knowing those meanings helps you understand the meaning of the terms *endoskeleton* and *exoskeleton.*
3. What term in the list above is used to explain how organisms release energy?

Understanding Ideas

Answer the following questions in your Journal *using complete sentences.*

1. What is the difference between plants and animals in terms of how they obtain energy?
2. How is the skeleton of a bird different from the skeleton of a bee?
3. What are the stages of complete metamorphosis in a butterfly?
4. Explain what type of symmetry humans have.
5. What does fertilization accomplish in a sexually reproducing organism?

Developing Skills

Use your understanding of the concepts developed in this chapter to answer each of the following questions.

1. **Concept Mapping** Complete the concept map using these terms: *one parent, sexual, asexual, two parents.*

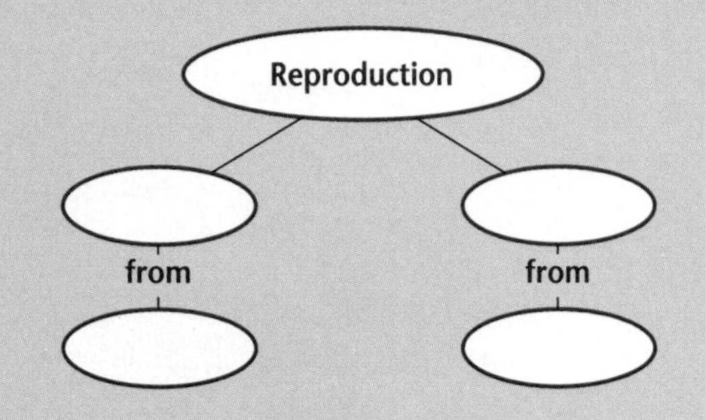

2. **Making and Using Graphs** Make a pie graph of the species of arthropods.

Class of Arthropod	# of species
Arachnids	100 000
Crustaceans	25 000
Insects (known)	700 000

3. **Comparing and Contrasting** Repeat the mealworm investigation on pages 282 and 283 using different food types. Use aspartame (a sugar substitute), pieces of apple, or molasses. Compare the results of this activity with those made in the original activity.
4. **Interpreting Data** Change the type of food or temperature used for raising fruit flies in the Find Out activity on page 293 to see how development of the larvae might be affected.

chapter 9
CHAPTER REVIEW

Critical Thinking

In your Journal, *answer each of the following questions.*

1. Compare and contrast the advantages and disadvantages of sexual and asexual reproduction.
2. Why do animals that develop inside the parent produce fewer eggs than those animals that develop externally?
3. What characteristic puts humans in the same group as snakes but in a different group from worms?
4. Give a specific example of how behavior can increase an animal's chance for survival.
5. Suppose a bird hatched with a beak that was shaped differently from beaks of other birds in the same species. Would this be helpful or harmful? Explain.

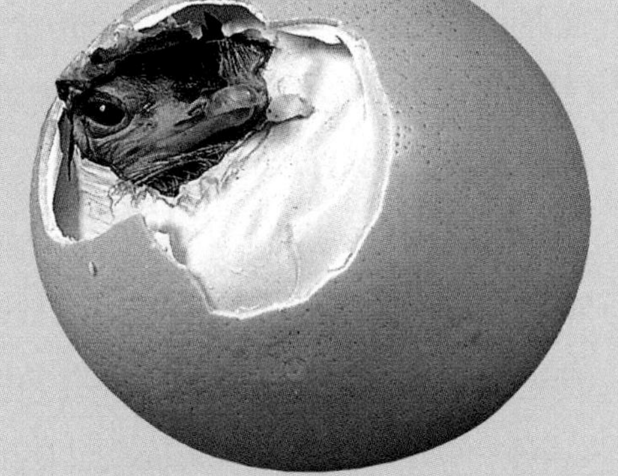

Problem Solving

Read the following problem and discuss your answers in a brief paragraph.

1. Suppose a female fish lays 100 000 eggs in a season. The male's sperm can fertilize 60 percent of the eggs. How many fertilized eggs are there?
2. After fertilization, 90 of every 100 of the fertilized eggs are eaten by other animals. Now how many eggs are left?
3. An additional 20 percent of the remaining eggs are destroyed when the water temperature gets too cold. How many eggs actually hatch?
4. If only half of those fish actually live to be adults, calculate the total number that survive.

CONNECTING IDEAS

Discuss each of the following in a brief paragraph.

1. **Theme—Stability and Change** Explain how a keen sense of sight is an adaptation for survival.
2. **Theme—Scale and Structure** Discuss whether complete metamorphosis is an advantage over incomplete metamorphosis?
3. **Theme—Systems and Interactions** Why is a tumbleweed not an animal even though it moves from place to place?
4. **A Closer Look** Kittens are born with their eyes shut and do not see their mothers for the first few days. How might imprinting take place between cats and their kittens?
5. **Physics Connection** How can experimenting with models of animals help you understand their adaptations?

CHAPTER 10

Plant Life

Did you ever wonder...

- Why leaves of many plants turn bright colors in the fall?
- What roots are for?
- Why insects are attracted to flowers?

Science Journal

Before you begin to study about plants, think about these questions and answer them *in your Science Journal*. When you finish the chapter, compare your journal write-up with what you have learned.

When was the last time you and your friends got together for a movie? After reading the newspaper ads, you chose the show. You paid for your ticket, rushed to the concession stand, and then looked for several seats in a row. The lights went out, and you enjoyed two hours of laughter, tears, or thrills.

Unless the movie title was The Eggplant that Ate Chicago, the last thing on your mind was "plants." But think about all the ways plants were involved. Trees provided the material for the newspaper, ticket, popcorn box, and soft drink cup. Popcorn—first used by Native Americans—is the seed of a plant. The flavoring in your drink came from plant parts. Even your clothes or the seat covers may be made of cotton grown in India. In this chapter, you will find out about plants and their roles in your life.

▶ ***In the activity on the next page, explore some of the characteristics that make a plant, a plant.***

Explore! ACTIVITY

What's for lunch?

What To Do

1. With your classmates, bring in items to make a salad. Many different items can be included, such as carrots, lettuce, beans, peppers, and cheese.
2. Before you put your salad together, identify the items that are plants. What makes them plants?
3. How are the plant items in your salad different from foods that aren't plants? List the differences *in your Journal.*
4. Were some salad ingredients made from plants? What about the salad oil or dressing?

What Is a Plant?

Section Objectives

- List the traits of plants.
- Describe the structures and functions of roots, stems, and leaves.

Key Terms

xylem
phloem

What Makes a Plant a Plant?

Have you ever taken a walk in the woods or in a park with trees and flowers? Maybe someone you know has a garden. Your neighbor may grow herbs in a kitchen window. Most certainly you've seen weeds growing at the sides of roads. Trees, flowers, vegetables, herbs, and weeds are all plants.

Nearly all animal life depends on plants. If there were no more plants, animals would not go on living for very long. You know that you are an animal. But do you know what makes you different from a plant?

Remember that all organisms can be grouped according to their traits. In the previous chapter, you learned that all animals share certain traits. Plants, too, have traits in common. These traits separate plants from the other kinds of living things.

Figure 10-1

Plant types differ widely from one another, but most plants share the following three characteristics:

A **Plants don't depend on other organisms for their food. Instead, they make their own food.**

B **Plants are usually green.**

C **Plants usually don't move around. Most plants have roots or rootlike structures that hold them in the ground. There are several different kinds of roots shown in the photographs on these two pages.**

Tap roots are thickened roots that store food for the plant. Carrots are examples of tap roots.

Fibrous roots are branched and spreading. These roots can go very deep into the ground. This African violet has fibrous roots.

Plant Structure

If you were asked to draw a plant, you'd probably draw one similar to the plants shown in **Figure 10-1.** Most plants you're familiar with have roots, stems, and leaves. Take a look at these structures in the following activity.

Explore! ACTIVITY

Are all roots, stems, and leaves alike?

What To Do

1. Obtain several plants from your teacher. Look at the plants carefully. Can you identify the roots of each plant?
2. How are all the roots alike? How are they different?
3. Compare and contrast the stems and leaves of the plants, too. Record your observations *in your Journal.*

You can see from the Explore activity that roots, stems, and leaves are not all alike. Yet each structure of the plant has a specific function that helps keep the plant alive.

■ Roots

Suppose you took a walk to observe plants in your neighborhood. You might see trees, potted plants in windows, and dandelions in sidewalk cracks. But you actually saw only about half of each plant! You saw only the parts of the plants that are aboveground. You probably did not see any roots. Most plant roots are below the surface of the ground. The root systems of some plants are as large or larger than the rest of the plant. Why must root systems be so large?

Roots have two important functions. All the water and minerals used by a plant enter the plant through its roots. Roots also anchor the plant in the soil. Without roots, a plant could be blown away by wind or washed away by water. Sometimes roots also store food. When you eat carrots or beets, you are eating roots with stored food.

Plants, like this cactus, that live where there is little rainfall have compact root systems that are close to the surface of the ground. These roots quickly absorb water from dew or rain.

Figure 10-2

Stems **carry out several functions. They support the above-ground parts of a plant.**

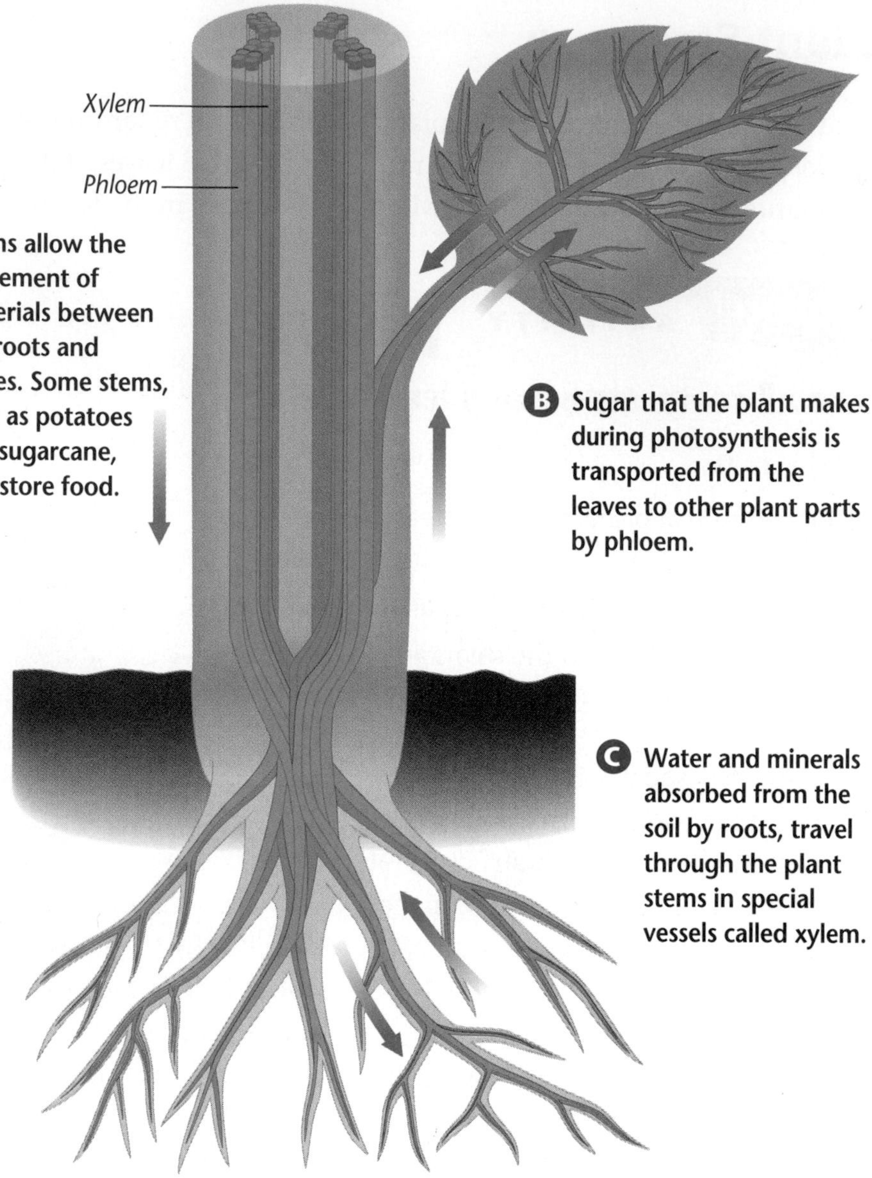

A **Stems allow the movement of materials between the roots and leaves. Some stems, such as potatoes and sugarcane, also store food.**

B **Sugar that the plant makes during photosynthesis is transported from the leaves to other plant parts by phloem.**

C **Water and minerals absorbed from the soil by roots, travel through the plant stems in special vessels called xylem.**

Stems

Stems have several jobs in keeping a plant healthy. They support the plant, store food, and allow for the movement of materials through vessels called xylem. **Xylem** is made of tubelike vessels that transport water and minerals up from the roots through the stem to the leaves of a plant. Xylem is dead and is what we call wood. The second type of vessel–phloem–is alive. **Phloem** is made of tubelike vessels that move food from the leaves to other parts of the plant. **Figure 10-2** shows where xylem and phloem are located in a teabush.

Leaves

Did you notice different kinds of leaves in the Explore activity? Leaves come in all shapes and sizes. A cactus has sharp spines, while a holly's leaves are dark, shiny, and prickly. One pine's needles are long and thin, yet another's are short and thick. No matter what shape and size leaves are,

Figure 10-3

Leaves **are protected—top and bottom—by a thin layer, called the epidermis. A waxy coating called the cuticle sometimes covers the epidermis and protects the plant from drying out.**

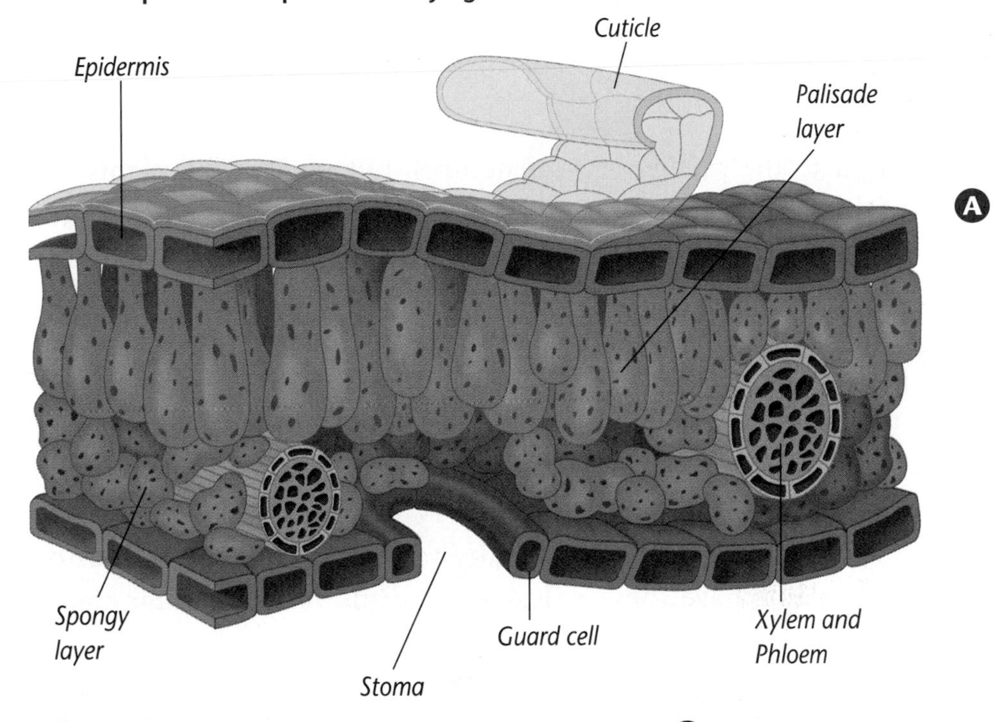

A **Two different layers are located between the upper and lower layers of the epidermis. The palisade layer, where most food is made, is just below the upper layer of the epidermis. A spongy layer is located between the palisade layer and lower layer of the epidermis.**

C **The spongy layer contains many air spaces as well as the xylem and phloem that transport water, minerals, and food to and from the leaves.**

B **Materials needed by the plant, such as water, oxygen, and carbon dioxide, pass in and out of the leaf through small openings called stomata. Guard cells around each stoma control the size of these openings.**

they are the plant's organs for trapping sunlight and making food. You can see the structure of a typical leaf in **Figure 10-3**. Notice the jobs of the different parts of the leaf as you study the figure.

In this section, you read about the traits that set plants apart from other organisms. You've also seen some of the structures many plants have. In the next section, you will find out how to use these structures to group plants.

1. List the traits of plants.
2. What are the main functions of roots, stems, and leaves?
3. Which tissue transports water in a plant?
4. How does carbon dioxide enter a plant?
5. **Apply** Why would a cactus usually have a thick, waxy coating covering the stem just like some leaves do?

Classifying Plants

Section Objectives

- Compare and contrast vascular and nonvascular plants.
- Compare and contrast plants that produce seeds in cones with those that produce seeds in fruits.

Key Terms

nonvascular plant
vascular plant

Nonvascular Plants

When you went to the movies at the beginning of this chapter, you discovered one way you could classify plants—by their usefulness. Scientists, however, determine which groups to place plants in by observing their structures.

In the last section, you looked at and described some typical plants. Each had roots, stems, and leaves. You may think that all plants have these structures, but look at the plants in **Figure 10-4**. They don't have the structures you might associate with plants. The mosses and liverworts in **Figure 10-4** belong to a group called nonvascular plants.

Recall from the last section that xylem and phloem are tubelike vessels that carry water, minerals, and food throughout the roots, stems, and leaves of a plant. A **nonvascular plant**

Figure 10-4

Mosses and liverworts are examples of nonvascular plants. Notice that they don't have flowers or cones, which means that they cannot produce seeds. Instead, mosses and liverworts reproduce by spores. You will learn more about this method of plant reproduction later in this chapter.

is a plant that lacks tubelike vessels to transport water, minerals, and food. Nonvascular plants also lack roots, stems, and leaves. They do have rootlike fibers—stalks that look like stems—and leaflike green growths. Study the traits of the mosses and liverworts in **Figure 10-4**. How do mosses and liverworts reproduce? Where do they live?

Mosses and liverworts are often the first plants to grow in areas that have been ravaged by fire. They also grow on newly formed rocks such as those found in lava beds. As the plants grow, their rootlike fibers move into small cracks in the rocks' surfaces. Mosses release chemicals that actually begin to break down the rocks. As these plants grow and die, the decaying plant material adds nutrients to the newly formed soil. Eventually, other plants are able to survive in the same area.

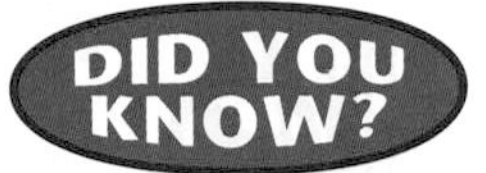

During World War I, doctors used peat moss as a dressing for soldiers'wounds. The high level of acid of the moss prevented bacteria from growing in the wounds.

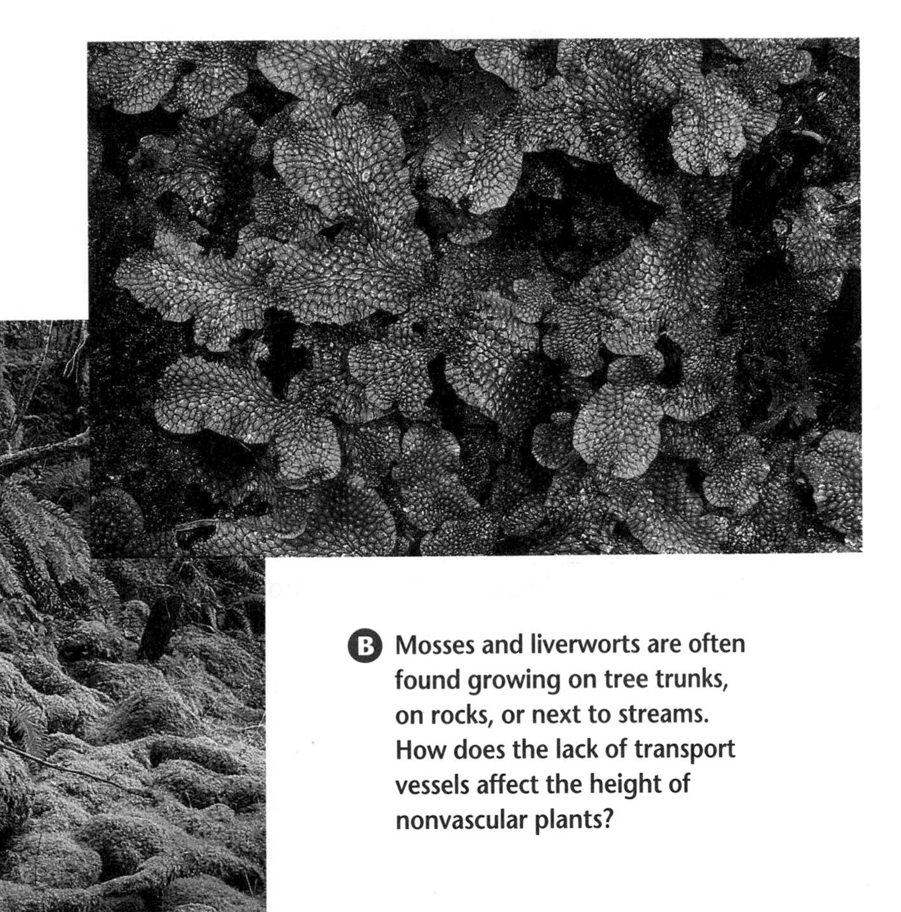

A Because nonvascular plants aren't able to transport water efficiently, they must live in moist areas.

B Mosses and liverworts are often found growing on tree trunks, on rocks, or next to streams. How does the lack of transport vessels affect the height of nonvascular plants?

Seed Plants

By far the largest group of plants on Earth consists of the seed plants. Over 235 000 species of seed plants have been discovered. Like ferns, seed plants are vascular—they have vascular tissue. Seed plants are different from both nonvascular plants and seedless vascular plants because they have roots, stems, and leaves and grow from seeds. As you do the following Explore activity, you will discover what's in a seed.

What's in a seed?

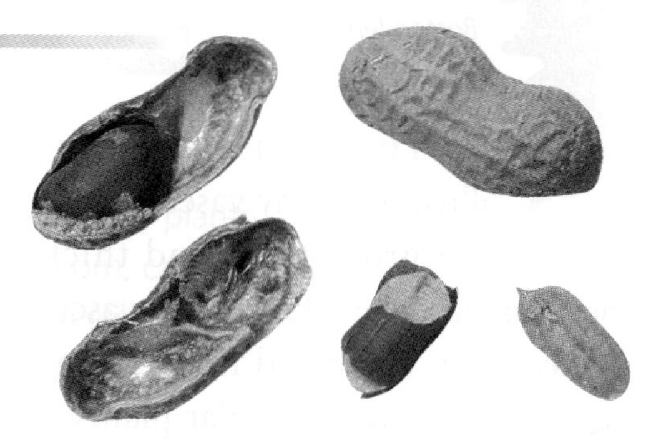

What To Do

1. Use a peanut that's still in its shell. Open the shell to expose the seeds.
2. Take the reddish-brown covering off one of the seeds. Carefully pull apart the two halves of the seed. Examine the halves with a hand lens. Which part of the seed is the young plant?
3. Find the parts that you think would become stem, leaves, or roots. *In your Journal,* summarize what you think the rest of the seed is used for.

Figure 10-6

You just saw that a seed contains an undeveloped plant and stored food. Each seed contains everything needed to produce a new plant. While all seeds may have the same function, they are produced by two different groups of plants—the gymnosperms and the angiosperms.

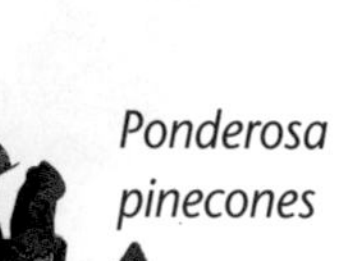

Ponderosa pinecones

Ponderosa pine tree

Gymnosperms

Both the oldest trees and the tallest trees alive today are gymnosperms. Gymnosperms are vascular plants that produce their seeds on cones. The word gymnosperm means "naked seed" and is very descriptive because the seeds of these plants are not protected.

Figure 10-6 shows an example of a gymnosperm. You may know most of the plants in the gymnosperm group by the name evergreen because they remain green throughout the year. You are probably most familiar with the different types of evergreens, such as the pines, firs, and spruces.

■ Angiosperms

One of the best parts of a summer picnic is biting into a cold, juicy watermelon. Watermelons and many of the other foods you eat are examples of angiosperms. An angiosperm is a vascular plant in which the seed is enclosed and protected inside a fruit. You will learn more about how seeds form in both angiosperms and gymnosperms in the next section.

Angiosperms are also known as flowering plants. The variety of flowering plants seems endless. Stately oaks and graceful dogwoods, delicate rice and hearty corn plants, colorful bird-of-paradise and white yucca flowers are a few examples.

You've just read about the major classification of plants into nonvascular plants, vascular plants that have no seeds, and vascular plants that produce seeds. In the next section, you'll discover how each of these plants reproduces.

Figure 10-7

check your UNDERSTANDING

1. Explain the differences between a vascular plant and a nonvascular plant.
2. Why is a pine tree placed in a different group from a cherry tree?
3. **Apply** You notice some beautiful flowers in a field. There are yellow flowers, white flowers, and purple flowers. What can you tell about the kinds of plants they are part of?

10-3 Plant Reproduction

Section Objectives
- Trace the stages in the life cycle of a moss.
- Describe the structure and function of a flower.
- List methods of seed dispersal.

Key Terms
pollination

Plants from Plants

What is the first picture that comes to mind when you hear the word *nursery?* Most of us usually associate babies or young children with that word. However, sometimes the word is associated with plants. A plant nursery is where you can go to buy plants. In most cases, the plants you buy are young. You might walk through large greenhouses full of young plants as you decide which ones to buy. Where do all the plants come from?

Find Out! ACTIVITY

How can you grow new plants?

Sometimes new plants can grow from plant parts. Try this activity to see how you can grow a new plant.

What To Do

1. Take a cutting from a philodendron plant. Include part of the stem and one or two leaves.
2. Place one end of the stem in water.
3. Observe the cutting for a week or two.

Conclude and Apply

1. What happens to the cutting after several weeks?
2. How is what you have observed similar to what happens when you plant a seed? Record your observations *in your Journal.*

Asexual Reproduction

Some angiosperms can reproduce from their roots, stems, or leaves. Reproduction of new plants from roots, stems, or leaves is called vegetative reproduction. The new plants that result are identical to the parent. **Figure 10-8** shows several plants that reproduce by vegetative reproduction. Which of these plants develops new plants from the roots and which develops new plants from the stems?

Figure 10-8

A **Onions, daffodils, and potatoes all reproduce from the stem of the plant. Onions and daffodils produce bulbs, the part of the stem from which new plants originate. The potato itself is a thickened stem.**

Onion

Daffodil

Willow tree

B **The roots of the sweet potato, blackberry, or willow develop shoots that grow into separate plants.**

C **Some plants, such as strawberries, grow runners—stems that grow across the top of the soil and touch down at points. New plants grow where the runner touches the ground. Other plants develop underground stems, called rhizomes, that push through the ground to become new plants. Lawn grasses can reproduce this way.**

Strawberry plant

Sexual Reproduction

Recall from Chapter 9 that animals have both sexual and asexual reproduction. In sexual reproduction, the new organism develops from two parents. Sexual reproduction in plants involves the production of either spores or seeds.

■ Reproduction by Spores

Nonvascular plants, such as the mosses, and seedless vascular plants, such as ferns, reproduce from spores. Follow the life cycle of a moss in **Figure 10-9** to see how it reproduces.

■ Seeds from Flowers

Instead of producing spores during sexual reproduction, many plants produce seeds. Pine trees and other gymnosperms produce seeds on cones. Angiosperms produce seeds within flowers. In the following activity, you'll study the parts of a flower to see where seeds are produced.

Figure 10-9

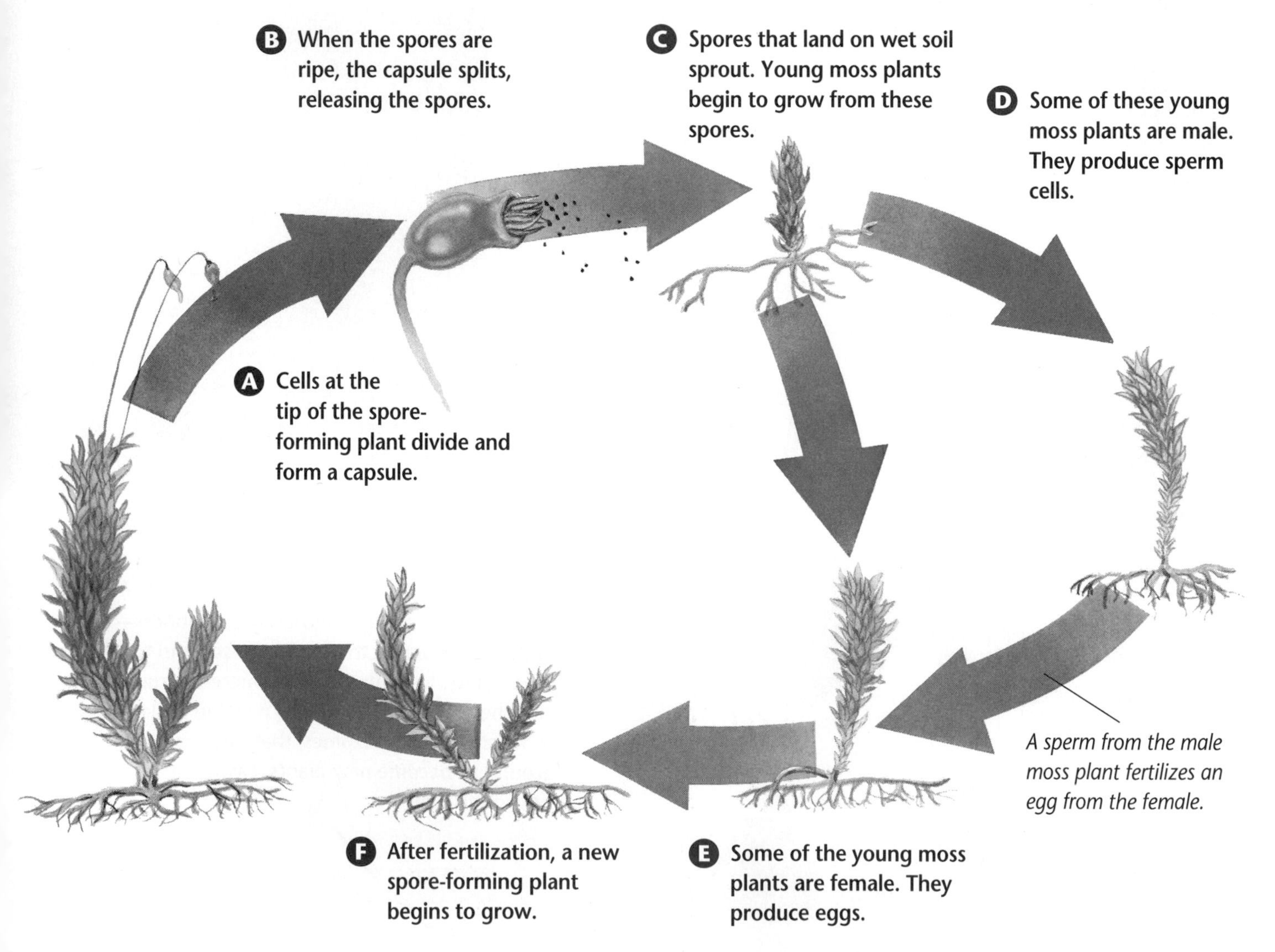

Find Out! ACTIVITY

What are the parts of a flower?

Flowers are more than pretty things for us to enjoy. A flower allows a plant to carry out the important job of reproduction.

What To Do

1. Examine the flower your teacher will give you. Use the illustration to see how the parts are arranged.
2. Remove the outer row of leaflike parts called the sepals. The structures inside the sepals are petals. Remove the petals.
3. Next, locate the stamens, the thin stalklike structures with expanded tops. Remove the stamens.
4. Look at the stamens with a hand lens. Observe the top part called the anther and the stalk called the filament.
5. Tap the anther against a piece of black paper to knock out the pollen grains. Examine the pollen grains with a hand lens.
6. The structure that remains is the pistil. The stigma is at the top. The stalklike part is the style. The ovary is the swollen base of the pistil. Use a scalpel to cut across the ovary. **CAUTION:** *Always be careful with sharp instruments.* Use a hand lens to look at the inside of the ovary.

Conclude and Apply

1. What functions might the petals have?
2. How is the stigma adapted for trapping pollen grains?
3. How might pollen travel to the stigma?
4. *In your Journal,* diagram and label the parts of a flower.

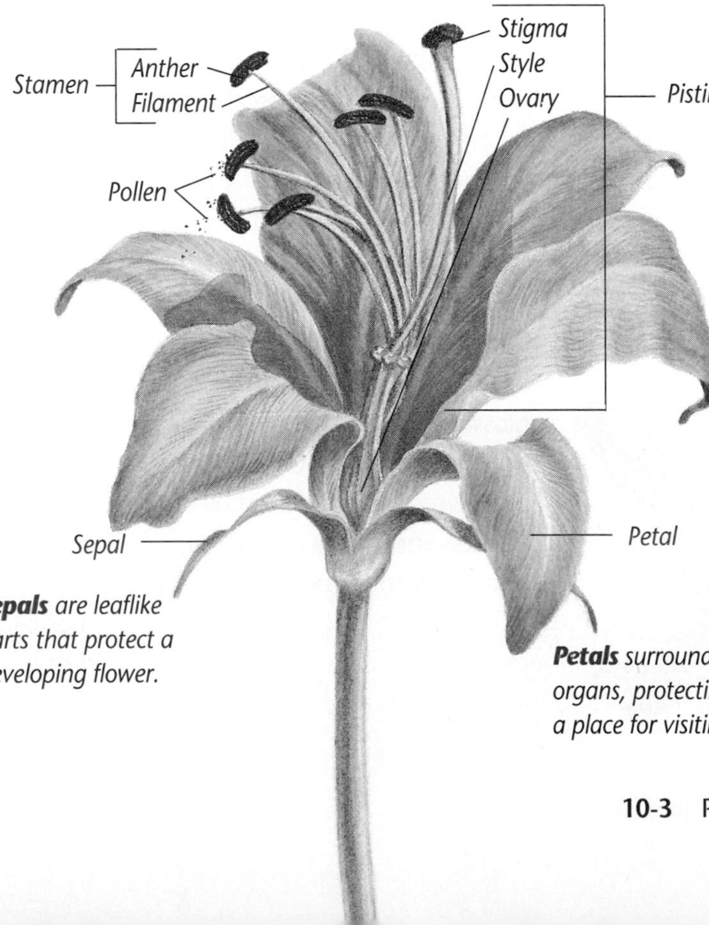

Stamen
Anther
Filament
Pollen
Stigma
Style
Ovary
Pistil
Sepal
Petal

***Stamens** are the male reproductive organs. Each stamen has a slender stalk with a thick anther on top. Pollen grains form in the anther. Sperm develop in the pollen grains.*

The pistil** is the female reproductive organ. The pistil includes a sticky stigma, a stalklike style, and a swollen base called the **ovary.

***Sepals** are leaflike parts that protect a developing flower.*

***Petals** surround the reproductive organs, protecting them and providing a place for visiting insects to land.*

How Do We Know?

Pollinating Flowers

Scientists used movie cameras to show how pollination happens. They took pictures showing a bumblebee climbing into a flower. As the bee climbs in, you can see an anther full of pollen coming down on its back. As the bee leaves, flecks of pollen grains are sticking to its body. These grains are left on the stigmas of other flowers it visits.

What did you notice when you looked inside the ovary? You should have seen tiny structures that resemble seeds. However, these structures are not actually seeds. When the eggs inside these structures are fertilized, seeds will then develop. Each structure produces one seed.

Seed Development

Before a seed can develop in a seed plant, a pollen grain must be transferred from the male to the female. In angiosperms, wind, insects, birds, or other animals may transfer pollen from the anther to the stigma. When pollen lands on the stigma, it forms a tube that grows down through the style and into the ovary. Sperm from the pollen grain travel through the tube and unite with the egg contained within the small structures inside the ovary. The transfer of pollen grains from the stamen to the stigma is called **pollination**.

The shape, size, and color of flowers are important factors in how they are pollinated. For example, large, brightly colored flowers may attract insects that pollinate the flowers. Night-blooming flowers may have

a Closer Look

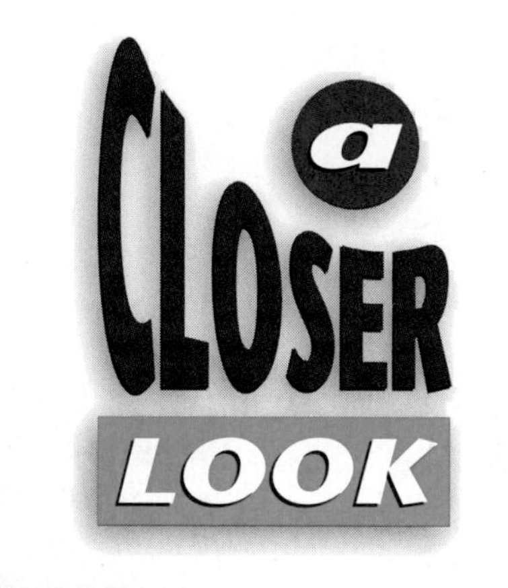

Advertising in the Real World

"Wanted: Insect, bird, bat, or other animal to carry pollen from male to female plant. No experience necessary, but must be able to follow instructions. Benefits competitive."

An ad like this might work for plants if insects and other animals could read. But plants have better ways of attracting willing workers. The color of the blossom may attract a particular pollinator. About 80 percent of all flowers are pollinated by insects, and the rest by wind, birds, and mammals. Which insect or mammal comes to a flower depends on what the flower looks and smells like. For example, hummingbirds are attracted to big, showy, red flowers like the hibiscus for their nectar.

Of Birds and Bees

Bees sometimes go to red flowers, too. That's because of the scent they put out, but not because of the red color. Bees see mostly blue, lavender, and yellow colors, so those are the colors of flowers to which bees travel. White attracts flies or night-flying insects and bats, depending on the scent.

strong scents that attract pollinators such as bats. And those flowers that are pollinated by the wind may be pale in color or white, have small petals, or maybe no petals at all. Can you think of any wind-pollinated flowers?

Figure 10-10 shows the parts of a seed. The seed contains an embryo plant, food for the embryo, and a protective seed coat. Remember the peanut you examined earlier in this chapter? You could identify the young plant and its food. In the following activity, you'll investigate the relationship between soaking the seed coat and the time it takes the seed to begin to grow.

Figure 10-10

Each seed is a complete growing environment for the embryo plant inside. The seed provides food until the young plant can produce its own, and the seed coat provides protection until the new plant gains size and strength.

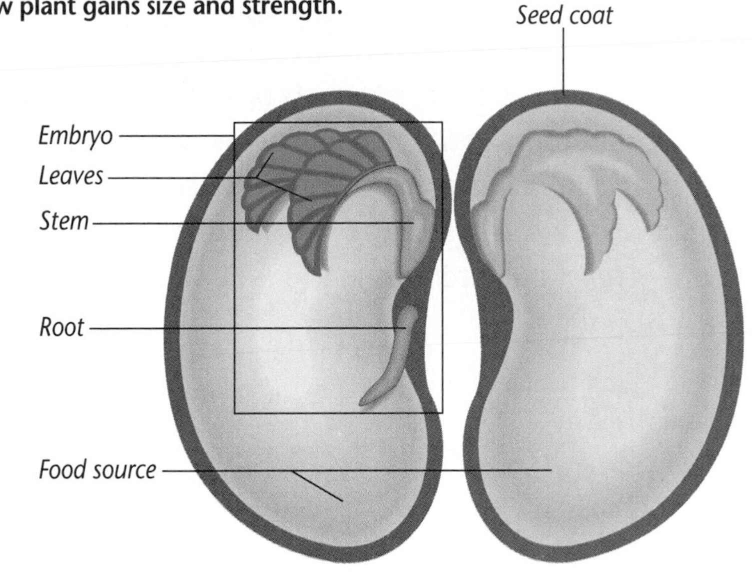

Most birds have poorly developed senses of smell. That's why hummingbirds are attracted to color. Bright red flowers are attractive to hummingbirds.

Once a pollinator is attracted to a flower, the appearance of the flower sometimes contributes to the pollination process. On the blossom, there might be a cluster of dots or a color pattern visible to insects.

You Try It!

Design your own flower that would attract a particular type of pollinator. Use color or scent or both. Mark the flower with patterns that might help lead the pollinator to the pollen. Be sure to include the stamen (male) and stigma (female) parts so pollination can take place. You may either draw your flower or make a model flower from colored tissue paper. How might a flower pollinated by the wind differ?

DESIGN YOUR OWN

INVESTIGATION

They're All Wet

You know that seed coats protect seeds, but a plant embryo cannot grow until this coat breaks open. In this activity, you will soak seeds in water to observe what effect this has on the seeds' coats. You will also observe whether soaking the seeds affects the time it takes them to sprout.

Preparation

Problem

How does soaking affect the time it takes seeds to sprout?

Form a Hypothesis

As a group, form a hypothesis about what might happen to seeds that are soaked in water for various lengths of time.

Objectives

- Predict the effect soaking has on the time it takes seeds to sprout.
- Infer what function water plays in the seeds' ability to sprout.

Materials

6 small cups (paper or plastic)
12 radish seeds
12 watermelon seeds
12 bean seeds
paper towels

DESIGN YOUR OWN
INVESTIGATION

Plan the Experiment

1 Examine the materials provided by your teacher. Then design an experiment that uses these materials to test the effects of different soaking times on seeds.

2 Plan a data table in your Science Journal for recording your observations.

3 Because your test may last several weeks, assign daily tasks to all members of the group. Who will observe the seeds each day? Who will record the observations?

Check the Plan

Discuss and decide upon the following points and write them down.

1 Have you allowed for a control in your experiment? What is it?

2 How long will you conduct your test? How will you observe the sprouting seeds without injuring the seeds?

3 Make sure your teacher approves your experiment before you proceed.

4 Carry out your experiment. Record your observations.

Analyze and Conclude

1. **Compare and Contrast** Which seeds sprouted first? Last?
2. **Infer** What can you infer about the types of seeds and the times it took for them to sprout?
3. **Separate and Control Variables** Why did you soak the seeds for different amounts of time?
4. **Interpret Data** Infer what function water played in this experiment.
5. **Draw a Conclusion** How does soaking time affect the time it takes for a seed to begin growing? Did your observations support your hypothesis?

Going Further

Predict what would happen if you used tea or lemon juice as a soaking solution.

Figure 10-11

Fruits and seeds are dispersed by animals, wind, water, and sometimes people.

A Fleshy fruits, such as oranges and tomatoes, are filled with water and sugar. Animals are attracted to these fruits, eat them, and may spit out the seeds or disperse them in their wastes.

B Winged "helicopters" of the maple and silky dandelion seeds are carried away by the gentlest breezes.

C Sticker or burr type fruits, like those of the common thistle, may stick to animals or the clothing of people and be carried far away from the original plant.

D Many fruits and seeds of plants growing near water, such as the coconut, contain air chambers that allow them to float and be carried for miles in water.

Seed Dispersal

Imagine what would happen if all seeds began to grow close to the parent plant. The young plants would compete with the parent plant, and with each other, for light, water, soil, and nutrients. The dispersing of seeds away from the parent plant helps reduce the competition for these resources and gives each plant a better chance of survival.

You and even your pets disperse seeds. Small seeds may stick to your shoes. Hooked seeds may stick to your dog's fur or to your clothes. In the next section you will learn how plants get the energy they need to produce flowers and seeds.

1. Trace the life cycle of a moss.
2. How does the seed of an angiosperm develop?
3. What is the function of flowers?
4. List two ways seeds can be dispersed.
5. **Apply** Suppose you're eating a piece of watermelon, and you spit out some of the small, black structures contained in the fruit. What part of the plant are you eating? How are you helping the plant reproduce?

10-4 Plant Processes

Transpiration

Remember the last time you took part in a physically active game? It may have been aerobics in gym class, a soccer game, or simply chasing your dog around the yard. Think about how your body reacted. Your face was probably flushed, and you breathed hard. You're used to the idea that people and other animals breathe. But the idea that gas exchange also happens in plants may seem a little strange. The next activity will allow you to observe this exchange indirectly.

Section Objectives

- Explain the role of stomata in gas exchange in plants.
- Compare photosynthesis and respiration.

Key Terms

transpiration
photosynthesis
chlorophyll

Find Out! ACTIVITY

Where does the water come from?

Who ever heard of a sweaty plant? Yet, plants do release water vapor as a part of the gas exchange that they undergo. This activity will give you a clue how.

What To Do

1. Obtain two plastic bags, two potted seedlings, petroleum jelly, and water from your teacher.
2. Pour the same amount of water into the pots of both plants.
3. Label one bag "petroleum jelly" and the other bag "no petroleum jelly."
4. Put one seedling in the bag labeled "no petroleum jelly." Seal the bag and put it in a sunny window.
5. Rub petroleum jelly on the bottom of all the leaves on the second plant. Put this seedling in the other bag. Seal the bag and place it next to the first plant.
6. Wait several hours or until the next day and observe the bags.

Conclude and Apply

1. In which bag did water droplets collect?
2. *In your Journal,* explain where the water came from.
3. What did the petroleum jelly prevent from happening?

Interpreting Scientific Illustrations

Stomata are located on leaves. Look at **Figure 10-12**. Where are the stomata located on this leaf? What is one reason for this location? In pond lilies, the leaves float on the water. Where would you expect the stomata to be on pond lily leaves? For help refer to the **Skill Handbook**, page 667.

How does gas exchange take place in plants? Study **Figure 10-12**. It shows how gases move into and out of leaves, and how water vapor is given off by the stomata as these gases are exchanged. Water is absorbed by roots and is transferred up to the leaves through xylem vessels. Once in the leaves, most of the water evaporates. The water vapor is released from inside the leaf through the stomata. The loss of water vapor through the stomata of a leaf is called **transpiration**. Plants lose large amounts of water every day through the process of transpiration. This water is a major source of the water vapor in air.

Think about the Find Out activity you just completed. Water formed inside one bag. It formed when water vapor that transpired from the plant collected on the inside of the bag. The other bag had little or no water. Recall that you rubbed petroleum jelly on the bottom of this plant's leaves. Based on what you know about the structure of a leaf, what did the petroleum jelly do? Where do you think most of the stomata are located on a leaf?

Chemistry CONNECTION

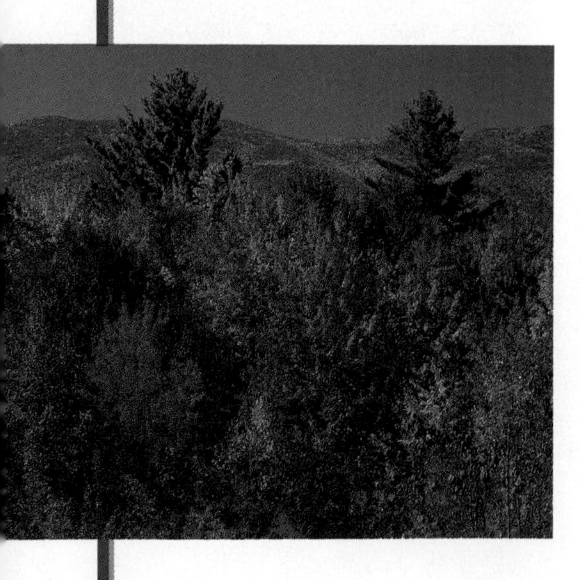

In Living Color

In the fall, the leaves of many shrubs and trees change from their familiar green to shades of red, yellow, orange, and brown. This happens because such plants are breaking down chlorophyll in colder weather. The lack of chlorophyll shows us other pigments present in the leaf that we can't normally see. Some of these pigments transfer energy from sunlight to chlorophyll.

Chromatography

You can reveal the pigments in a leaf by a technique called chromatography. This technique uses a solvent that causes the pigments to separate. The pigments travel up a piece of paper, each pigment stopping at a different place. The more soluble a pigment is, the farther up the paper it travels.

What To Do

1. Obtain a piece of filter paper at least 15 cm long.
2. Use a pencil to mark two X's 2 cm from the bottom and 1.5 cm from the sides of the filter paper. Use the Figure as a guide.
3. Use a dropper to add pigment to the paper strip between the two X's you

Figure 10-12

Plants release water vapor through openings in the leaves called stomata. Each stoma is surrounded by two guard cells that regulate the size of the opening.

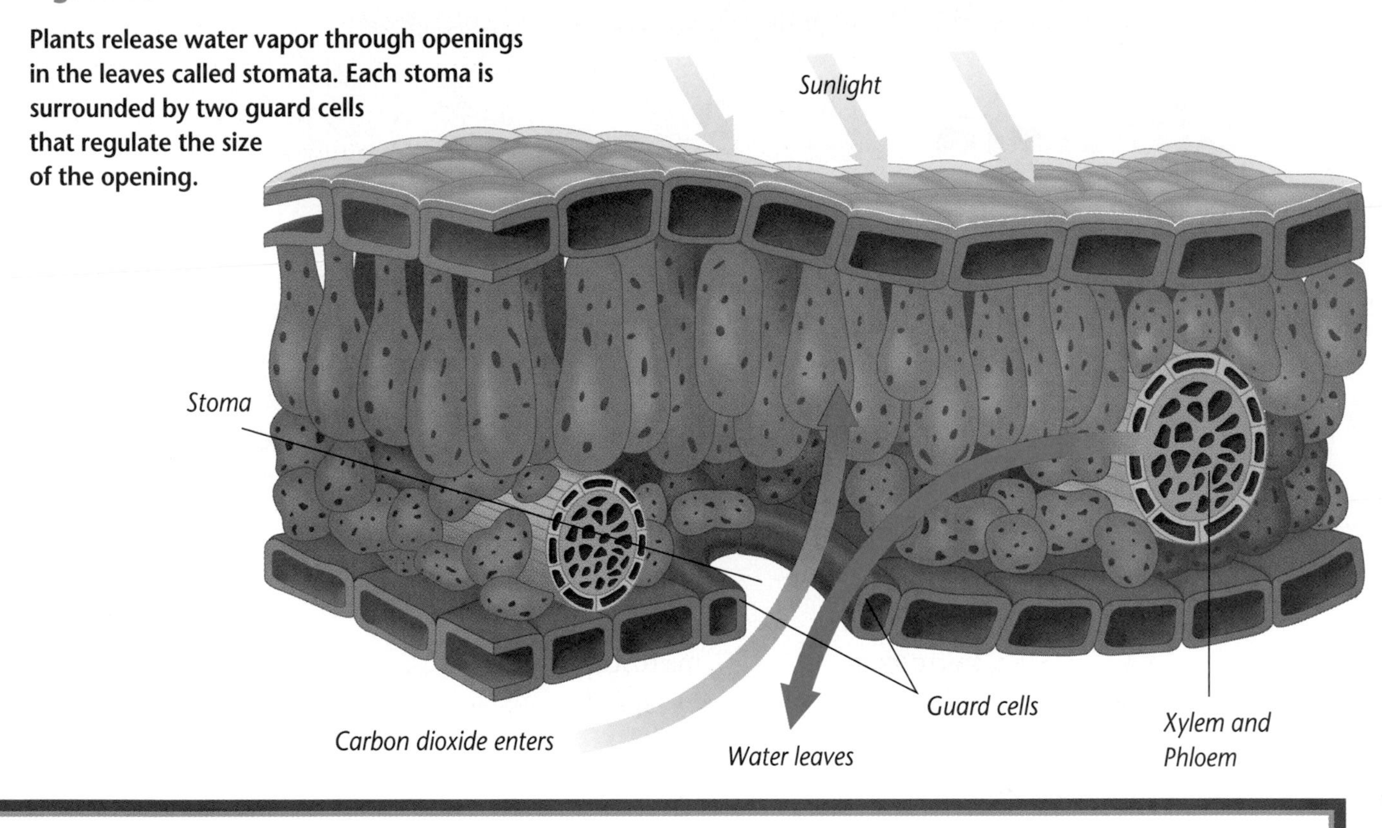

made. Allow the spot of pigment to dry.

4. Continue to add pigment to the paper until you have a dark spot, about 20 drops.
5. Using the Figure as a guide, roll the end of the filter paper around a straw. Fasten the filter paper around the straw with a paper clip.
6. Remove the paper and straw assembly from the jar. Add solvent to a height of 0.5 cm in the jar.
7. Rest the straw across the top of the jar, with the paper dangling into the solvent. Make sure the bottom end of the paper strip *just* touches the solvent.
8. Do not shake or move the jar for at least 15 minutes.
9. Remove the paper strip from the jar. This is your chromatogram.

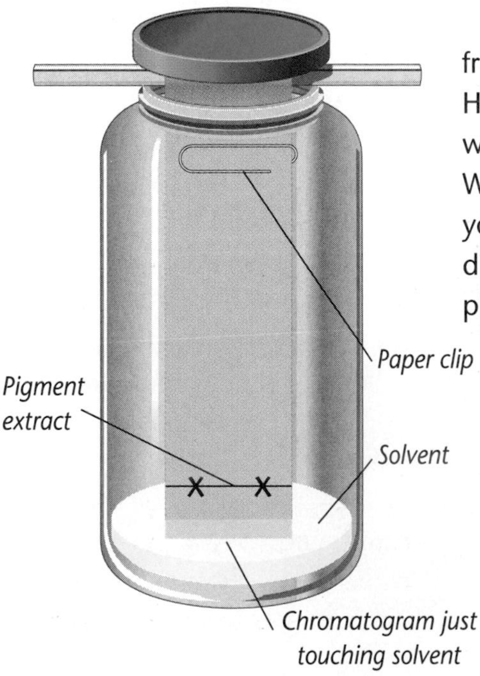

10. Notice the different bands of color on the chromatogram. Each color band is a different pigment.

What Do You Think?

The solution you tested came from a green plant—spinach. How many different pigments were in the solution you tested? What colors were they? How do you think your results would differ if you used a different plant solution?

INVESTIGATE!

Stomata

You learned that stomata are openings through which oxygen, carbon dioxide, and water pass. In this activity, you will learn what stomata look like and how they work.

Problem

How do stomata work?

Materials

lettuce	dish
water	coverslip
microscope	microscope slide
salt solution	forceps
paper towel	pencil

Safety Precautions

Use care handling the microscope.

What To Do

1. Copy the data table *into your Journal.*
2. From a dish of water containing lettuce leaves, choose a lettuce leaf that is stiff from absorbing the water.
3. Bend the leaf back and use the forceps to strip off some of the transparent tissue covering the leaf. This is the epidermis (see photo ***A***).
4. Prepare a wet mount of a small section of this tissue (see photo ***B***).
5. Examine the specimen under low and then high power of the microscope (see photo ***C***). Draw and label the leaf section in your data table.
6. Locate the stomata. Count how many are present and how many are open. Record these numbers in your data table.

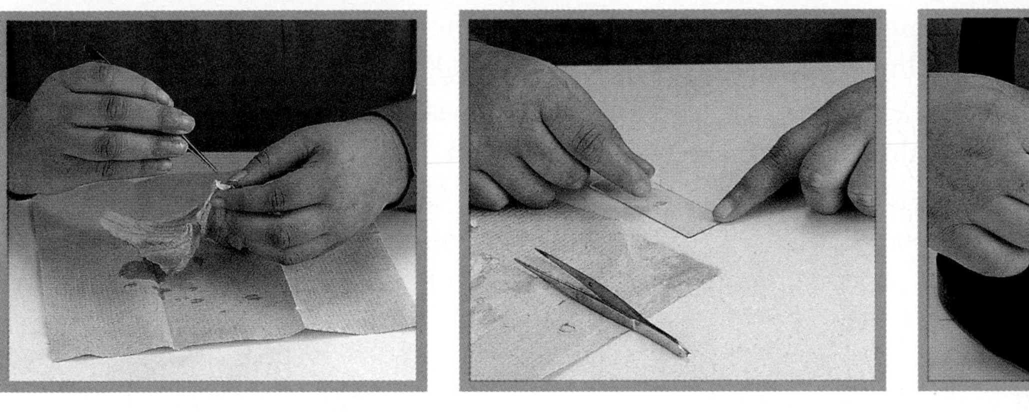

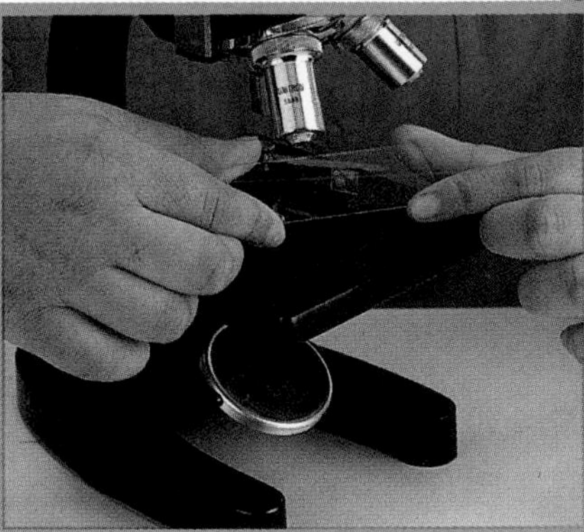

A B C

7 Place a paper towel at the edge of the coverslip and draw out the water. Using a dropper, add a few drops of salt solution at the edge of the coverslip. The salt solution will spread out beneath the coverslip.

8 Examine the preparation under low and then high power of the microscope. Draw and label the leaf section in your data table.

9 Repeat step 6.

Data and Observations		
	Water Mount	Salt Solution
Number of Stomata		
Number of Open Stomata		
Drawing of Leaf Section		

Analyzing

1. ***Describe*** the guard cells around a stoma.
2. How many stomata did you see in each leaf preparation?
3. ***Calculate*** the percentage of the stomata open in water and in salt water. Which type of water had a higher percentage of open stomata? Which had a lower percentage of open stomata?

Concluding and Applying

4. ***Infer*** why the lettuce leaf became stiff in water.
5. ***Infer*** why more stomata were closed in the salt solution.
6. **Going Further** ***Predict*** what would happen if you soaked the lettuce in a stronger salt solution. Would more or fewer stomata close?

Photosynthesis

You know that animals are consumers. Almost all consumers depend on plants, either directly or indirectly, for food. Almost all plants, on the other hand, do not depend on other organisms for food. They produce their own.

Plants produce food in a series of chemical reactions. The energy for these reactions comes from sunlight. **Photosynthesis** is the process in which plants use light to produce food. During photosynthesis, plants use sunlight to change water and carbon dioxide into sugar and oxygen.

Chlorophyll is a green pigment in plants that traps the light from the sun. Plants are green because chlorophyll absorbs the blue, violet, and red parts of the light spectrum. It reflects green light, so plants appear green to us.

Let's look at what happens to the products formed during photosynthesis. Some of the sugars formed are used by the plant for its own life processes, such as growth. Some sugar is stored. When you eat carrots or potatoes, you are eating stored food.

Some of the oxygen that forms during photosynthesis is used by the plant itself. Some oxygen passes out of the leaves through the stomata. This oxygen may eventually be used by other organisms for respiration. The carbon dioxide produced by other organisms during respiration is used by plants to make food during photosynthesis. In this way, photosynthesis and respiration are linked in a never-ending cycle that provides energy to all living things.

Figure 10-13

The processes of photosynthesis and respiration are linked. Some of the end products of each process are the starting products for the other process.

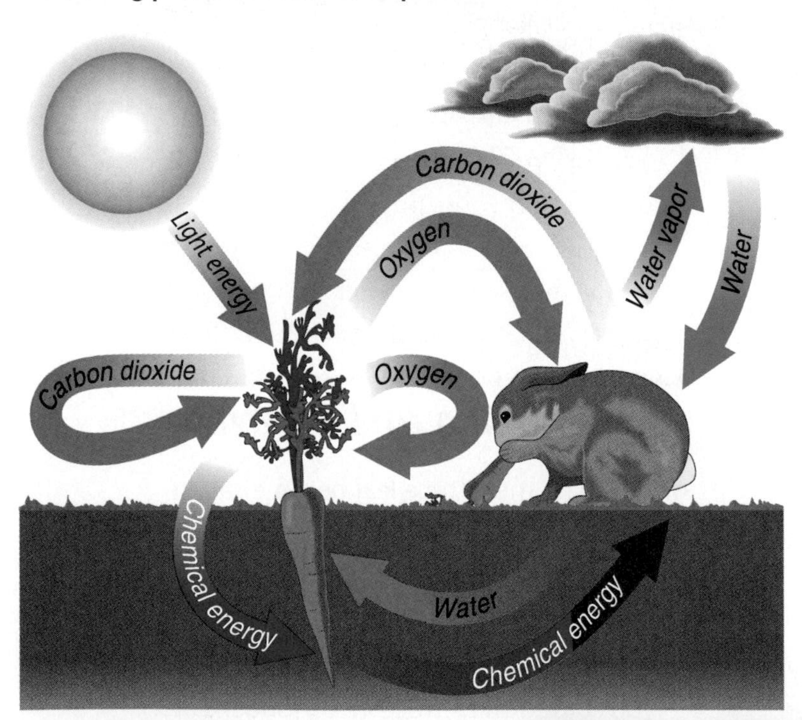

check your UNDERSTANDING

1. What role do stomata play in gas exchange in plants?
2. What are the starting and end products of photosynthesis and respiration?
3. What is the role of the green pigment chlorophyll in photosynthesis?
4. **Apply** How is all life on Earth dependent on sunlight?

Green Plants vs. Industrial Growth

Like animals, plants can be harmed by the actions of humans. Laws are sometimes used to protect endangered species—animals or plants whose existence is threatened. In what ways are plants threatened, and by whom?

Most people have heard about the threat to tropical rain forests. In Central and South American countries, these diverse forests are being cleared to create new agricultural land for growing populations and to provide lumber. Many South American people depend on these cleared lands for growing crops, even though the soil is not very rich.

Global Warming

Scientists hypothesize that continued destruction of the rain forests will contribute to a condition known as global warming.

This map shows surface temperatures on Earth. The warmer areas are shown in red, while the cooler areas appear in blue.

Global warming is a rise in average atmospheric temperatures. When certain gases, like carbon dioxide, build up in Earth's atmosphere, they trap heat that normally escapes through the atmosphere. This raises temperatures. Carbon dioxide is produced when the trees are burned as people clear the rain forests. Adding to this is the loss of the trees that use carbon dioxide in the process of photosynthesis. Earth's plants play a major role in regulating carbon dioxide levels in the atmosphere.

Untapped Resources

The loss of rain forests and other forested areas is harmful in other ways, too. You may wonder why it would matter to us if some obscure plant species ceased to exist. So far, only five percent of the plant species in the world have been analyzed for their potential as medicines. Plants that hold cures for diseases could disappear before we ever get a

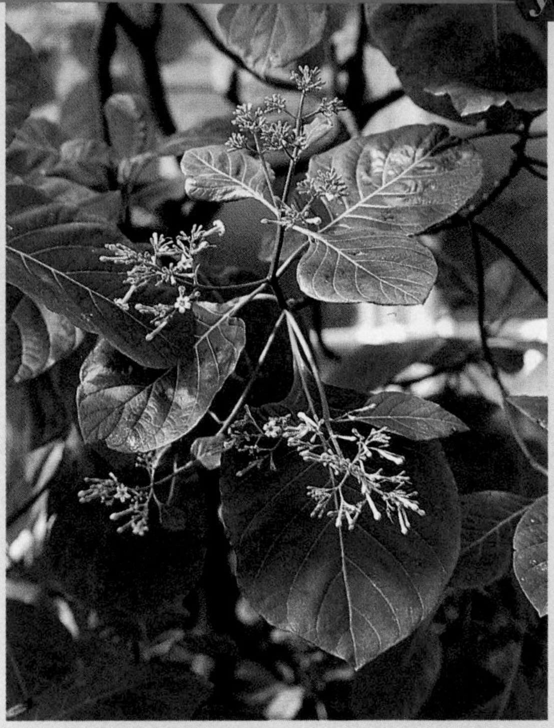

chance to find them. Rain forests are particularly important because they contain nearly half of the world's species of plants and animals. This diversity is important in maintaining Earth's fragile ecological balance.

Threats from Industry

Wild plant species face additional threats in industrialized parts of the world. Here, threats come from the introduction of exotic species, diseases, insect pests, and water and air pollution. Environmental changes that affect plants usually affect all living creatures. Some plants will not grow where air pollution exists. If the air is not good enough for them, is it good enough for us?

Before the Industrial Revolution in England, most peppered moths were white. Their white color enabled them to blend in with the lichen-covered bark of the trees. As the Industrial Revolution came into full swing, soot killed the lichens and blackened the trees. Then black peppered moths became dominant. After Britain passed laws to clean the air, lichens returned, and white peppered moths again became common. The lichen served as an indicator of environmental health. An environmental change sufficient to cause the black peppered moth to be more common must have been both widespread and long-lasting.

Environmental Monitors

Plants are in touch with their environment and are an indicator of the quality of our environment. In fact some people think plants can feel pain and pleasure the way animals can. No scientific evidence exists for this. But plants do send and receive electrical signals within their tissues. Scientists have attached electrodes to leaves and shown that changes in the quality or amount of air, light, or water in a plant's environment make differences within the plant's voltages.

NASA's Mission to Planet Earth (MTPE) is tracking global vegetation and temperature changes using satellite data. Download satellite images of an equatorial forest during several weeks. See if you can identify any changes in the images.

An **urban forester** is someone who looks out for the trees in a city. Fighting tree diseases such as oak wilt and educating the public about them are part of the job. An urban forester studies botany and chemistry and attends forestry school. Local, state, and federal governments hire foresters.

The Soil-Less Garden

Growing plants in nutrient solutions in tanks instead of in soil is called hydroponics. It comes from Latin words that mean to work the water. Hydroponics was first developed in California in 1929, by Dr. W. F. Gerische.

Growing plants in greenhouses in nutrient solutions has advantages. If soil is unsuitable, or at a premium in an area, or if there are diseases in the soil, hydroponics is a good alternative. It works with a wide variety of plants, including tomatoes, lettuce, and carnations.

Variations on a Theme

Two methods of hydroponic gardening are commonly used. In the original method, plants grow in a shallow, watertight container that holds the nutrient solution. Wood fiber, peat, or some other growing medium is supported by a wire framework a few centimeters above the surface of the liquid. Seedlings are set into the growing medium with their roots in the nutrients held in the shallow container. The nutrient solution must have air circulated through it, and must have its pH checked regularly. The solution needs to be completely changed every 10 to 14 days.

A more popular method uses a layer of sand or gravel along with the nutrient solution. The sand or gravel, which is the growing medium, is held in individual

pots or in rectangular containers. The nutrient solution may be fed from the top or pumped up from the bottom and allowed to drain back for reuse.

One difficulty with hydroponics is that nutrient solutions must be checked and adjusted daily. The nutrients used are essentially the same ones found in fertile soil, or in fertilizers. However, great care must be taken that the nutrients remain in the proper concentration and are aerated so the plants can take them in.

What Do You Think?

Do you think vegetables grown in a hydroponic garden would taste any different from those grown in soil? What plants might not be suited to hydroponic growing?

HISTORY CONNECTION

Ancient Medicinal Plants

Around 4000 years ago, a Chinese emperor put together a book that described more than 300 medicinal plants. Early Sumerians and Egyptians used plants for healing. Later the Greeks and Romans also provided additional information about medicinal plants.

During the Middle Ages, monks in Europe studied and translated ancient texts about healing herbs. Every monastery had a Physick Garden for growing the herbs. Such gardens later became common at castles, courts, and hospitals.

By the 13th century, there was a system of classifying plants. New books were written giving herbal prescriptions for illnesses. Eventually, scientists learned to isolate the healing ingredient and to make more of it.

Early forms of drugs, such as aspirin and insulin, can be traced to medicinal plants used by Native Americans. In the 1940s and 1950s, chemist Percy Julian, shown in the photo, developed drugs from chemicals in soybeans. His synthetic cortisone is used by arthritis sufferers today.

What Do You Think?

If you were a scientist, how much attention would you pay to ancient beliefs?

Sunkissed Flowers

You learned that plants need sun in order to live and grow. "Sunkissed: An Indian Legend," as told by Alberto and Patricia de La Fuente (Peña, Sylvia Cavazos, ed. TUN-TA-CA-TUN), illustrates the importance of the sun to all living things—especially to the survival of plants.

A legend is a story that has been passed along from earlier times. It may be partly true or simply an imaginative way of explaining some of the things that took place in nature. Obtain a copy of "Sunkissed: An Indian Legend" and read its explanation of how one kind of flower, the Margarita, was changed for all time by a special kiss from the sun.

Science Journal

In your Science Journal write a short legend that tells why a certain kind of flower is like it is today. Just choose a flower and let your imagination take over!

REVIEWING MAIN IDEAS

Science Journal

Review the statements below about the big ideas presented in this chapter, and answer the questions. Then, re-read your answers to the Did You Ever Wonder questions at the beginning of the chapter. *In your Science Journal*, write a paragraph about how your understanding of the big ideas in the chapter has changed.

1. Plants are either vascular or nonvascular. Nonvascular plants and some vascular plants, such as the fern, reproduce by spores. Most vascular plants, such as the poppy, reproduce by seeds. ***How do the plants in the photographs reproduce?***

2. Cones are the reproductive organs of gymnosperms. Flowers are the reproductive organs of angiosperms. ***What are the parts of the flower shown here?***

3. Transpiration, respiration, and photosynthesis are processes carried on by all plants. Photosynthesis and respiration are plant processes that provide the food and energy needed for plant growth. Transpiration is water loss from the leaves of plants. ***How are photosynthesis, respiration, and transpiration related?***

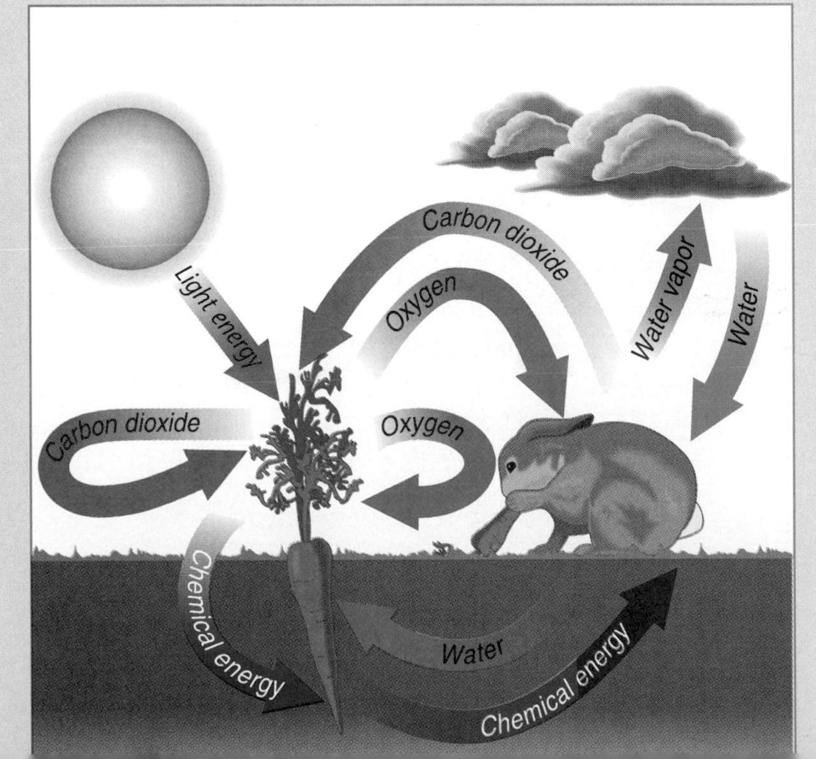

chapter 10
CHAPTER REVIEW

Using Key Science Terms

chlorophyll	pollination
nonvascular plant	transpiration
phloem	vascular plant
photosynthesis	xylem

Each of the following sentences is false. Make the sentence true by replacing the italicized word with a word from the list above.

1. *Phloem* is made up of vessels that transport water and minerals throughout a plant.
2. A *vascular* plant lacks xylem and phloem.
3. The process by which pollen grains move from the stamen to the ovules is *transpiration.*
4. *Xylem* is the green pigment in plants that traps light.
5. The process in which plants use light to produce food is *transpiration.*
6. The loss of water vapor through the stomata of a leaf is called *pollination.*
7. A *nonvascular* plant has xylem and phloem.
8. *Chlorophyll* are vessels that transport food throughout a plant.

Understanding Ideas

Answer the following questions in your Journal *using complete sentences.*

1. Why is the palisade layer in leaves important?
2. Where might you find nonvascular plants living? Why?
3. Explain the difference between an angiosperm and a gymnosperm.
4. List some ways pollen may be transferred.
5. What happens to the products formed during photosynthesis?

Developing Skills

Use your understanding of the concepts developed in this chapter to answer each of the following questions.

1. **Concept Mapping** Complete the concept map of the life cycle of a moss.

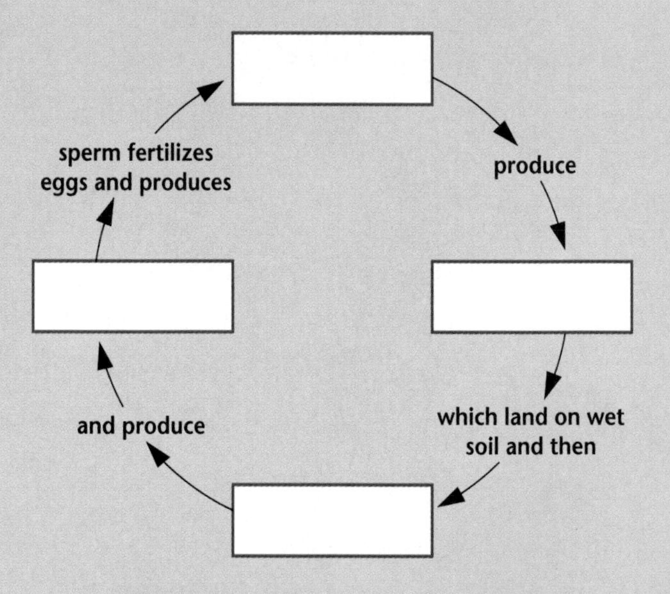

2. **Observing** Repeat the Explore activity on page 320, using a lima bean and a corn seed. Identify the young plant, the stored food, and the seed coat in each seed.
3. **Observing and Inferring** After doing the Explore activity on page 331, observe how sunlight affects transpiration. Water two potted seedlings and cover and seal each of them in a plastic bag. Put one plant in the sunlight and a box over the other plant. After two days compare the amount of water inside the bags. How does sunlight affect transpiration?

chapter 10

CHAPTER REVIEW

Critical Thinking

In your Journal, *answer each of the following questions.*

1. What is the function of the sticky fluid that is produced on pine cones?
2. In nonvascular plants, why are the spore-producing plants dependent on the gamete-producing plants?
3. What two features of a leaf help prevent water loss?
4. Why do flowers that are pollinated at night often have a strong scent?
5. Some birds pollinate when they feed on nectar from flowers. Look at the birds shown in the picture. Which one probably feeds on nectar? How can you tell?

6. Which plant do you think loses more water through transpiration, a plant with few, small, leaves, or one with many, larger, leaves? Explain your answer.
7. Describe how the structure of seeds helps plants reproduce.

Problem Solving

Read the following problem and discuss your answers in a brief paragraph.

Dawn went with her grandmother to buy seeds to plant in the garden. She noticed that the package of zinnia seeds she wanted to buy said that the seeds were 95 percent viable. Her grandmother explained that viable meant living. She said that 95 out of 100 seeds would sprout and grow.

They purchased the seeds and headed home to plant them around the border of their garden.

How could Dawn and her grandmother find out if the seeds they planted were viable? List the steps you would take to determine if a seed is viable.

CONNECTING IDEAS

Discuss each of the following in a brief paragraph.

1. **Theme—Scale and Structure and Systems and Interactions** What are some traits and processes that plants share with animals?
2. **Theme—Systems and Interactions** Why is photosynthesis important for maintaining Earth's present atmosphere?
3. **Theme—Systems and Interactions** List three ways plants affect your life.
4. **How It Works** Compare and contrast two methods of hydroponic gardening.
5. **Science and Society** Why is the preservation of the Amazon rain forest so important?

CHAPTER 11

ECOLOGY

Did you ever wonder...

- What's going on when bread gets moldy?
- Why our oxygen supply doesn't get used up?
- Why penguins don't live in your neighborhood?

Science Journal

Before you begin to study about ecology, think about these questions and answer them *in your Science Journal*. When you finish the chapter, compare your journal write-up with what you have learned.

Have you been to the zoo recently? If so, you know that modern zoos keep animals in areas that resemble their natural surroundings. Just as it would in nature, the zoo giraffe finds its food in tall trees that grow in a grassland, while zebras and wildebeests graze on the grass.

How can different types of living things survive in the same area? How do these living things interact with the nonliving world around them? Start exploring the interaction of living things with the activity on the next page.

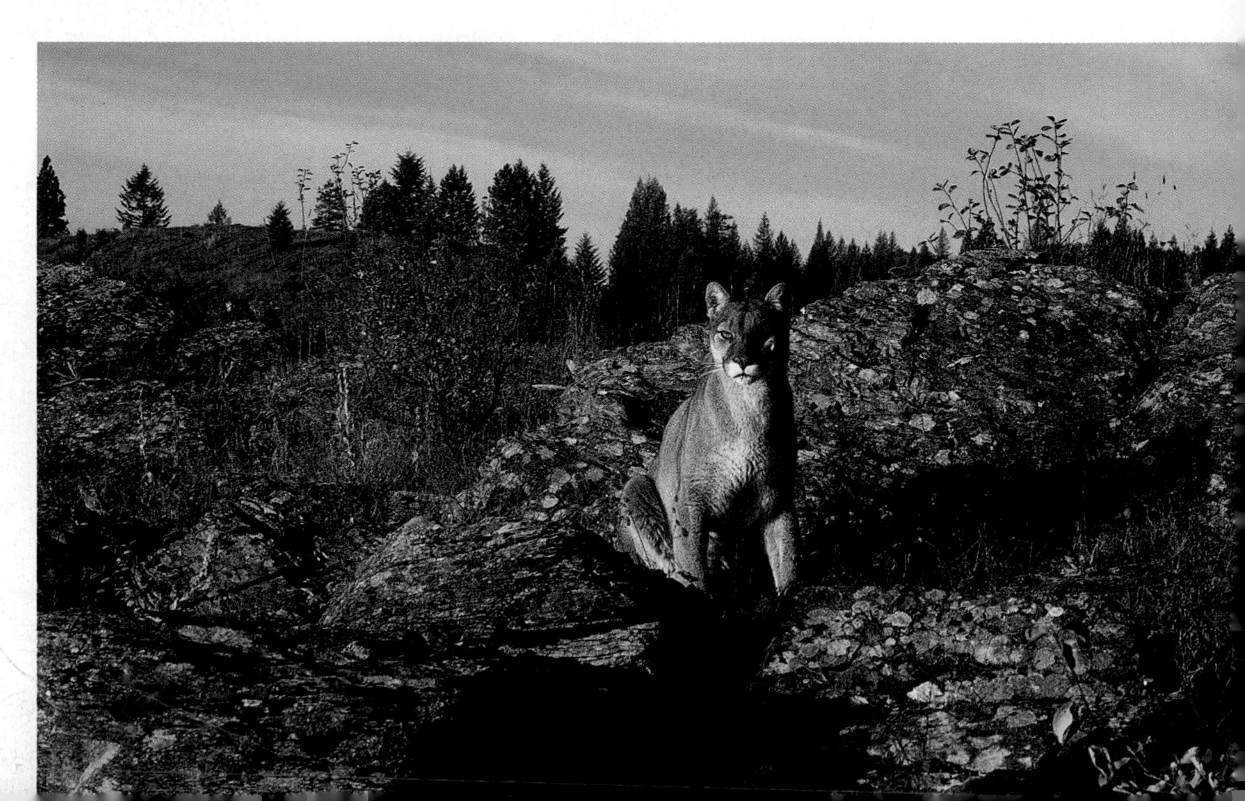

Explore! ACTIVITY

What would you discover on a neighborhood safari?

What animals and plants live and grow in your neighborhood? How might these living things interact? Go on a neighborhood safari or expedition with two friends and find out.

What To Do

1. Choose a small area near your school to study local plants and animals. Try to find out where they live, how they get what they need to live, and how they are influenced by the nonliving parts of their surroundings.
2. *In your Journal,* write your observations or make drawings of what you see.
3. Compare your findings with those of other groups.

11-1 What Is an Ecosystem?

Section Objectives
- Distinguish between populations and communities.
- Distinguish between habitats and niches.
- Describe the structure of an ecosystem.

Key Terms

habitat, population, community, niche, ecosystem

Living Things and Their Natural Surroundings

You may sometimes move through your daily activities without thinking about your surroundings. In school, you spend much of your day in rooms interacting with classmates and teachers. After-school activities bring you in contact with different groups of friends and acquaintances. Your location may shift from school to an outdoor playing field, local shopping center, or the busy sidewalk that leads you home. You may not notice the yellow tulips in a pot on a neighbor's porch or the footprints left by a raccoon as it ran through a muddy flowerbed.

Each day you move into and out of many different surroundings. Explore your surroundings in the activity that follows.

Explore! ACTIVITY

In how many different surroundings do you carry out your everyday activities?

Sometimes we're not even aware of all the places we visit in a day or of the living things that surround us in those places.

What To Do

1. For one day, *in your Journal* record the different places in which you work, play, and live. Record the plants, animals, or other organisms you interact with. List the nonliving parts of each place too, such as air, noise, sunlight, or artificial light.
2. Be sure to explain how you interact with each living and nonliving part of your surroundings. For example, did you drink any water? Eat a piece of fruit? Ride a bicycle?
3. Next, think of how separate places might be related or connected to each other. How might something that happens in one place have an effect on another place?

Environment and Habitat

As you filled out your Journal, you became aware of the many different living things that you interact with each day. No matter where you are, you interact with plants, animals, and other organisms. But you also interact with nonliving things. You breathe in oxygen, feel the warmth of the sun, or brace yourself against the force of the wind. You are surrounded by your environment. The environment consists of everything around an organism.

Think back to the Journal you kept. You may have been in several different environments. School, a soccer field, a movie theater, a bus or subway car, a grocery store, or a crowded beach are some examples. Now think of the place where you live. The particular place where an organism lives is its **habitat**. Your habitat might be your neighborhood or local community. A starfish may live in an underwater cave. A rattlesnake's habitat may be a canyon in the desert.

Figure 11-1

A Organisms live in many different kinds of habitats. The eagle's habitat, for example, includes both land and the air.

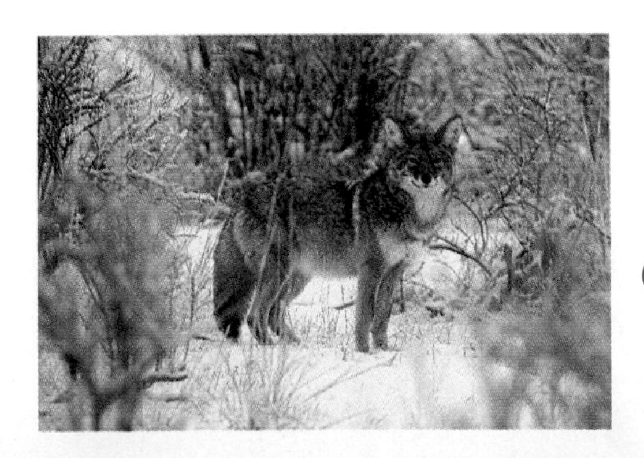

B The coyote lives in a variety of land habitats including deserts, mountains, and prairies.

C The mallard's habitat is this small pond and the grassy area near the water's edge.

D The sea is the habitat of the octopus.

Populations and Communities

Figure 11-2 shows some of the animals that live on the grasslands of Africa. Each individual animal within each group is a member of a population. A **population** is a group of individuals of the same species that live in an area at the same time.

Choose one of the environments you recorded in the Explore activity. What animal and plant populations live there?

As you study the different populations in **Figure 11-2**, notice that they interact with each other. Together, these populations form a community. A **community** is made up of all the populations that live and interact with each other in an area.

Think of the community in which you live. What are five populations that live and interact with you? Describe the relationships you have with each other.

How do different populations share the same habitat? This next activity will show you.

Figure 11-2

A In this natural habitat, large herds of zebra and wildebeest can be found next to a smaller number of giraffes.

B Bushes in the grassland provide shelter for birds.

C The zebras all belong to the same population. What other populations are shown?

Find Out! ACTIVITY

Can three different bird species share the same habitat?

How can different animals share the space in which they live and feed? This activity will help you understand.

What To Do

1. Copy the diagram of the tree *into your Journal.*
2. Develop a key to show each of the three species of warblers.
3. Use your key to fill in the diagram of the tree to show where each species of bird spends most of its time feeding. The following observations will help you. The Cape May warbler feeds in areas 1a and 2a. The Bay-breasted warbler feeds in areas 3a, 3b, 3c, and 4c. The Myrtle warbler feeds in areas 3b, 3c, 5c, and 6c.

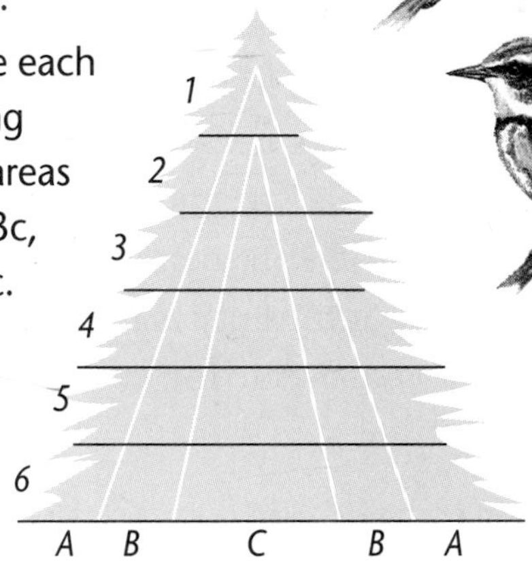

Conclude and Apply

1. In which parts of the tree does each warbler feed? Which birds share some parts of the tree?
2. How can three bird species feed in the same tree?

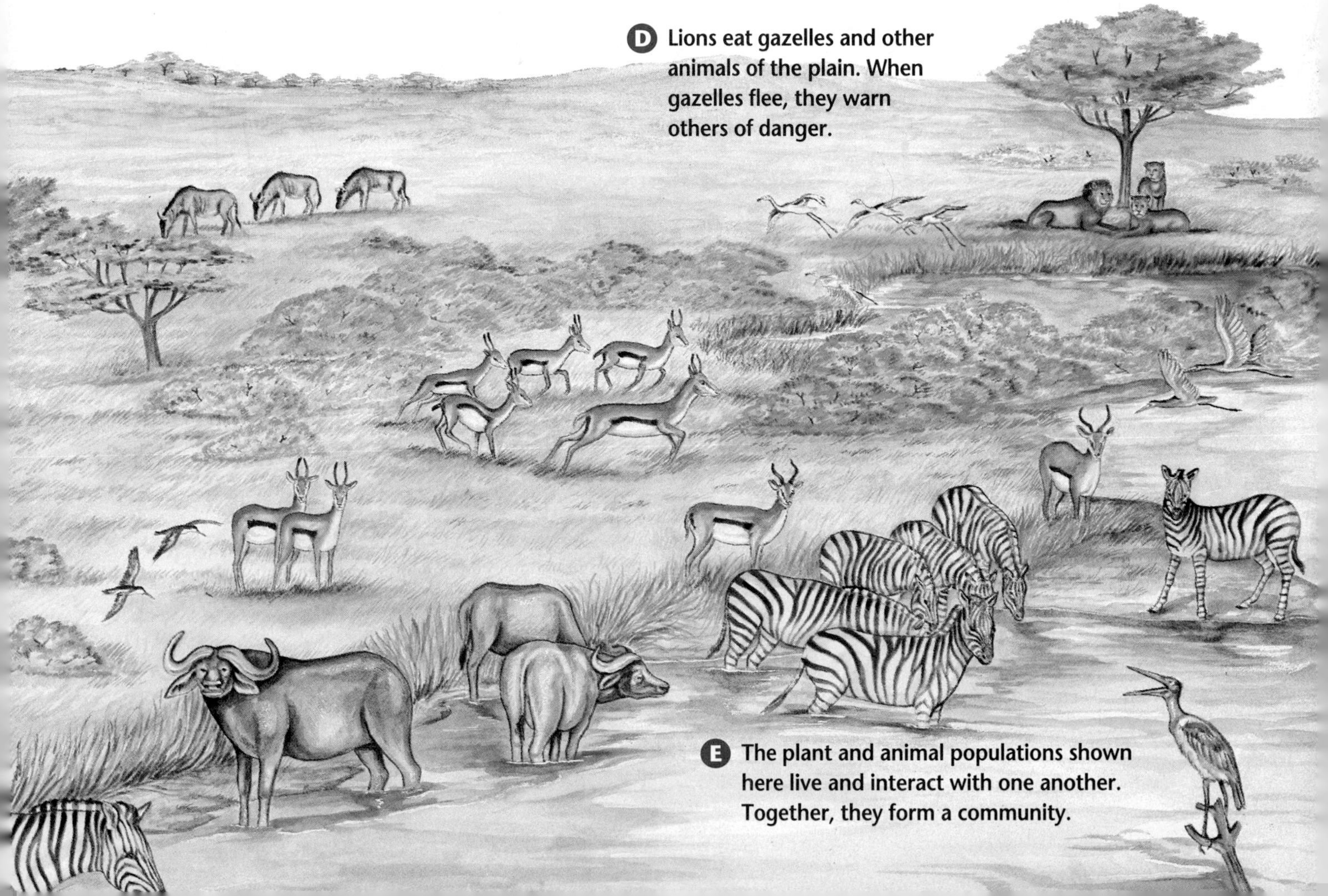

Bay-breasted warbler

Cape May warbler

Myrtle warbler

1
2
3
4
5
6
A B C B A

D **Lions eat gazelles and other animals of the plain. When gazelles flee, they warn others of danger.**

E **The plant and animal populations shown here live and interact with one another. Together, they form a community.**

Niches

In the Find Out activity you saw how feeding areas within a habitat could be divided so that several species could share the same living space.

If you observe other communities in nature, you will find the same thing. Many populations can live in the same area because each species fills a specific role in the community. The role of an organism within its community is the organism's **niche**. A barn cat, for example, fills a certain role in a farm community by eating mice and rodents. An organism's habitat is part of its niche. What an organism eats, when it eats, and where it eats are also part of its niche. Look back at the Find Out activity. You could describe part of the Cape May warbler's niche by saying that the Cape May warbler feeds at the top outer branches of a tree. The way an organism reproduces and raises its young are part of its niche, too. **Figure 11-3** gives other examples of niches.

Figure 11-3

A Zebras feed on the tall, coarse grasses, wildebeests feed on the leafy center layer, and the small gazelles feed on the tender new shoots.

C Lions also share this community but unlike the other animals mentioned on this page that eat plants, lions eat other animals.

B Hippos spend the hot days in the water and graze on grass at night. Gazelles, zebras, and wildebeests graze during the day.

D No two plants or animals meet their needs in exactly the same way. Each species fills a particular niche within the habitat. In this way, species can exist together in the same community.

Elements of an Ecosystem

You've learned that organisms interact with each other in communities. They also interact with nonliving things in their environment. These relationships form an ecosystem. An **ecosystem** is a community of organisms interacting with one another and with the environment. A rotting tree stump is a small ecosystem, as you can see in **Figure 11-4**.

Cities, redwood forests, polar regions, and oceans are examples of larger ecosystems. How would you describe your ecosystem? As you continue through this chapter you'll learn about how organisms interact in an ecosystem. You'll find out about how the roles different organisms play all contribute to the ecosystem's changes and stability.

Figure 11-4

A rotting tree stump is a small ecosystem. Here insects, bacteria, and other organisms all interact with one another.

check your UNDERSTANDING

1. Give an example of a population of plants.
2. What is the difference between a population and a community?
3. What is the difference between a niche and a habitat?
4. **Apply** Describe the niche you fill in your community. Identify how this niche benefits two other populations that share your community.

Organisms in Their Environments

Section Objectives

- Describe a food chain and its relationship to a food web.
- Explain how natural cycles are important in the environment.

Key Terms

decomposer
food chain
food web

Food Producers and Consumers

In Chapter 9, you learned that all animals consume other organisms for food. These animals may consume other animals, plants, or plants and animals. In Chapter 10, you saw that plants produce their own food. Think back to the organisms at the beginning of this chapter. Which organisms are consumers? Which are producers? Producing or consuming food is one of the major niches an organism fills. It's one of the major ways in which organisms interact within their environments.

Explore! ACTIVITY

How do organisms get their food?

What To Do

1. Below is a list of organisms that you might find if you took a walk around your school.
2. Study the list and classify the organisms into two groups: those that can make their own food and those that cannot make their own food.

cactus	fern	earthworm
gerbil	student	geranium
moss	bird	fish
grass	ant	butterfly
spider	squirrel	tree

3. Which organisms did you classify as producers? Which did you classify as consumers? Answer the questions and record your observations *in your Journal.*

Decomposers

Now look at the organisms you classified in the Explore activity as consumers. Some consumers, such as gerbils, eat only plants. Other consumers, such as spiders, eat only animals. Still other consumers eat both plants and animals. Which type of consumer are you? Are all humans the same type of consumer?

In the first section, you learned that each organism has its own niche. One kind of consumer, called a decomposer, has an especially important niche within the community. A **decomposer** is an organism that gets its food by breaking down dead organisms into nutrients. As a result, nutrients within dead organisms are recycled back into the environment. Study **Figure 11-5** to learn more about decomposers.

Have you ever seen mold on a rotting log or on an old tomato? These organisms, called fungi, are decomposers. Most bacteria are decomposers, too.

Producing, consuming, and decomposing to obtain food are ways organisms interact. Do the next Investigate to see some of the relationships in an ecosystem.

Figure 11-5

A Perhaps you've seen mold on a rotting log or on a spoiled fruit or vegetable. That mold and these mushrooms are members of the fungus kingdom. Most fungi are decomposers—they get their food by breaking down dead organisms into nutrients.

B Many types of bacteria are also decomposers. In compost heaps, bacteria break down dead plant material into the nutrients that living plants need.

INVESTIGATE!

What Do Owls Eat?

Owl pellets are made of indigestible things an owl has swallowed, including fur and bones. These pellets form in an owl's stomach and then the owl coughs them up. Examining an owl pellet can tell you much about what is going on in a small part of the owl's ecosystem.

Problem

What role do owls play in their ecosystem?

Materials

water
forceps
coverslip
magnifying glass
cardboard
bowl
glass slide
light microscope
owl pellet
glue

Safety Precautions

Use care when handling microscope slides and coverslips. Dispose of all materials properly.

What To Do

1. With your group design a way to investigate what an owl pellet is made of and what its contents are. You should make a display of the contents of the owl pellet. After your plan has been approved by your teacher, carry it out.
2. *In your Journal,* write a short summary of your design and of what you found the contents of the owl pellet to be. Use the table on page 355 to help you identify the contents of the owl pellet.

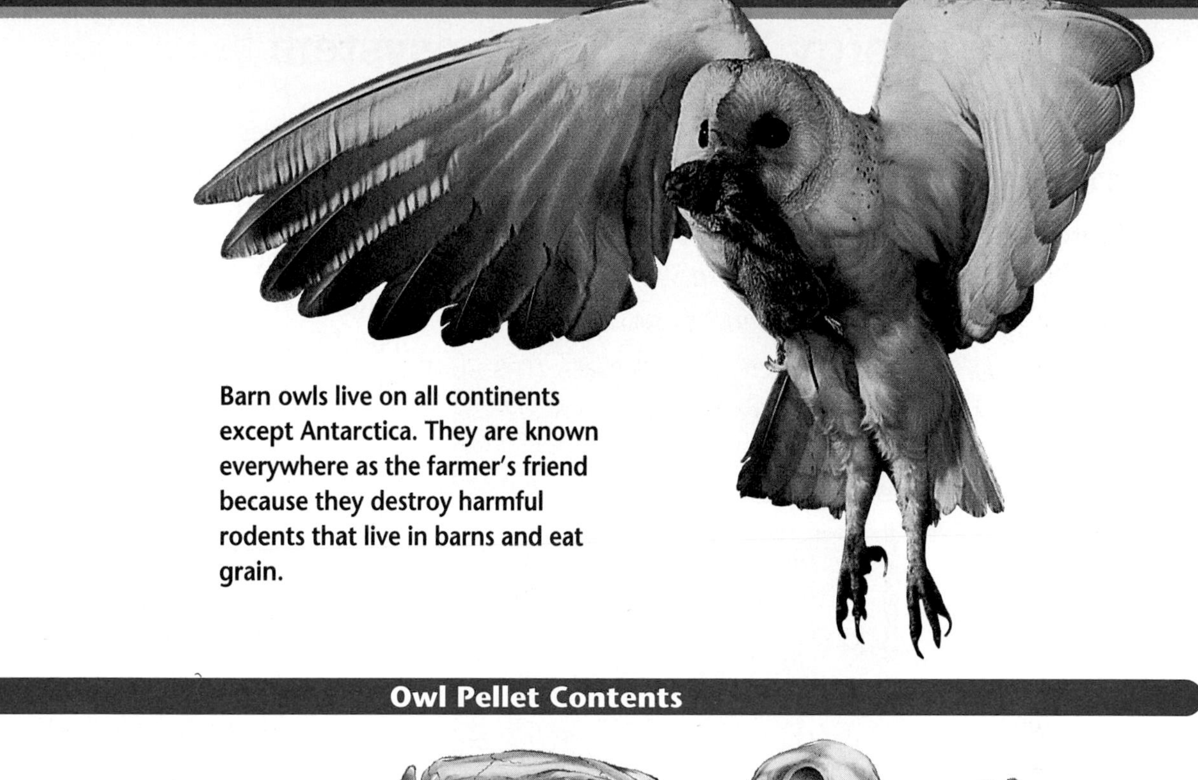

Barn owls live on all continents except Antarctica. They are known everywhere as the farmer's friend because they destroy harmful rodents that live in barns and eat grain.

Owl Pellet Contents

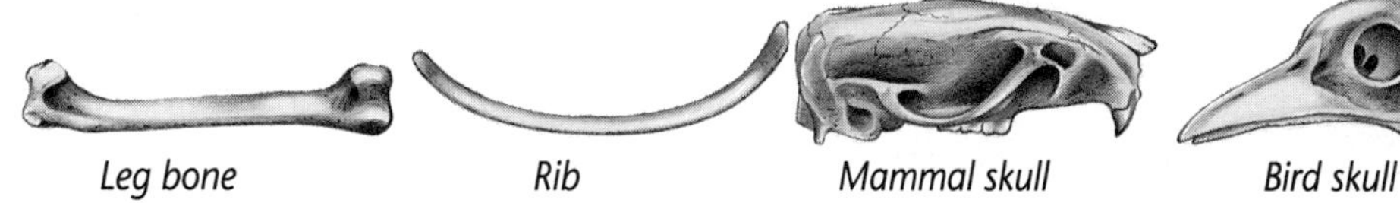

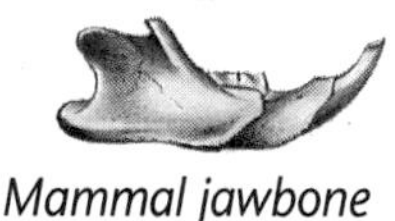

Leg bone *Rib* *Mammal skull* *Bird skull* *Mammal jawbone*

Analyzing

1. What made up the outside of the owl pellet?
2. What did you see inside the pellet? How many of each kind of thing were there?
3. What role does an owl play in its ecosystem? Is it a producer or a consumer? How do you know?
4. Describe the niche of an owl. Include where the owl lives, when it feeds, and what it eats. Describe the niche of an owl's prey. How are the two similar? How do they differ?

Concluding and Applying

5. If one owl pellet is produced each day, ***estimate*** the number of organisms eaten by the owl in a single day. Estimate the number of organisms an owl needs to eat to survive for one year.
6. **Going Further** ***Design an experiment*** to figure out what might happen to the population of owls if there were a sudden explosion in the population of mice.

Energy Flow in an Ecosystem

Figure 11-6

A Plants use sunlight to produce food in the form of sugar. Plants store the food they make in their roots, leaves, and stems.

B A mouse eats the plants. Some of the food in the plants is stored in the mouse's body. The mouse's body changes some of the food into energy to run, eat, and breathe.

C The snake eats the mouse. The mouse supplies energy for the snake to live.

D Hawks eat a variety of small animals including snakes. The hawk's body uses the energy gained from the snake to carry out its life processes. This flow of food energy from one organism to another continues throughout the food chain.

Whether you observe a small part of an ecosystem, such as in the last activity, or an entire large ecosystem, such as the ocean, you'll find feeding relationships among the organisms. Food is required for the life processes of every organism, whether it is a producer, a consumer, or a decomposer. How do producers, consumers, and decomposers interact?

Remember that through the process of photosynthesis, plants use light energy from the sun to make food. This chemical reaction changes water, carbon dioxide, and light into sugar and oxygen. The sugar is food that can be stored and used later by the plants.

When animals—consumers—eat plants, the energy in the plants is passed to the animals. These animals are then eaten by other animals, which in turn may also be eaten. Each time, food energy passes from one animal to the next. Energy is also passed on when decomposers break down dead organisms. Each organism in this relationship is like a link in a chain. A **food chain** is a model of how the energy in food is passed from organism to organism in an ecosystem.

Figure 11-6 shows the elements of a simple food chain. Plants produce food for themselves which is stored in roots, stems, and leaves. Animals eat plants, and the animals are, in turn, eaten by other animals. In this way energy from the sun is distributed throughout an ecosystem.

Food Webs

A feeding relationship in a single food chain is simple. However, most organisms get their food from more than one source. For example, a bear eats fish, berries, honey, and insects. An owl eats different kinds of rodents and snakes. Sometimes one food source can provide food for many different organisms. For example, grass is eaten by rabbits, cattle, deer, and horses. Thus, an organism can belong to several different food chains. When related food chains are combined, a food web is formed. A **food web** is the combination of all the overlapping food chains in an ecosystem. **Figure 11-7** is an example of a food web.

Consumers with varied diets—in other words, those that belong to a fairly large food web—have a better chance of survival than those with limited diets. If something happens to disturb one supply of food, the consumer can obtain food from another food chain in the web.

Sequencing

Study the list of organisms below. Decide in which sequence (or order) they should be placed to make the most likely food chain. If you need help, refer to the **Skill Handbook** on page 653.

bass
insect larvae
person
crayfish

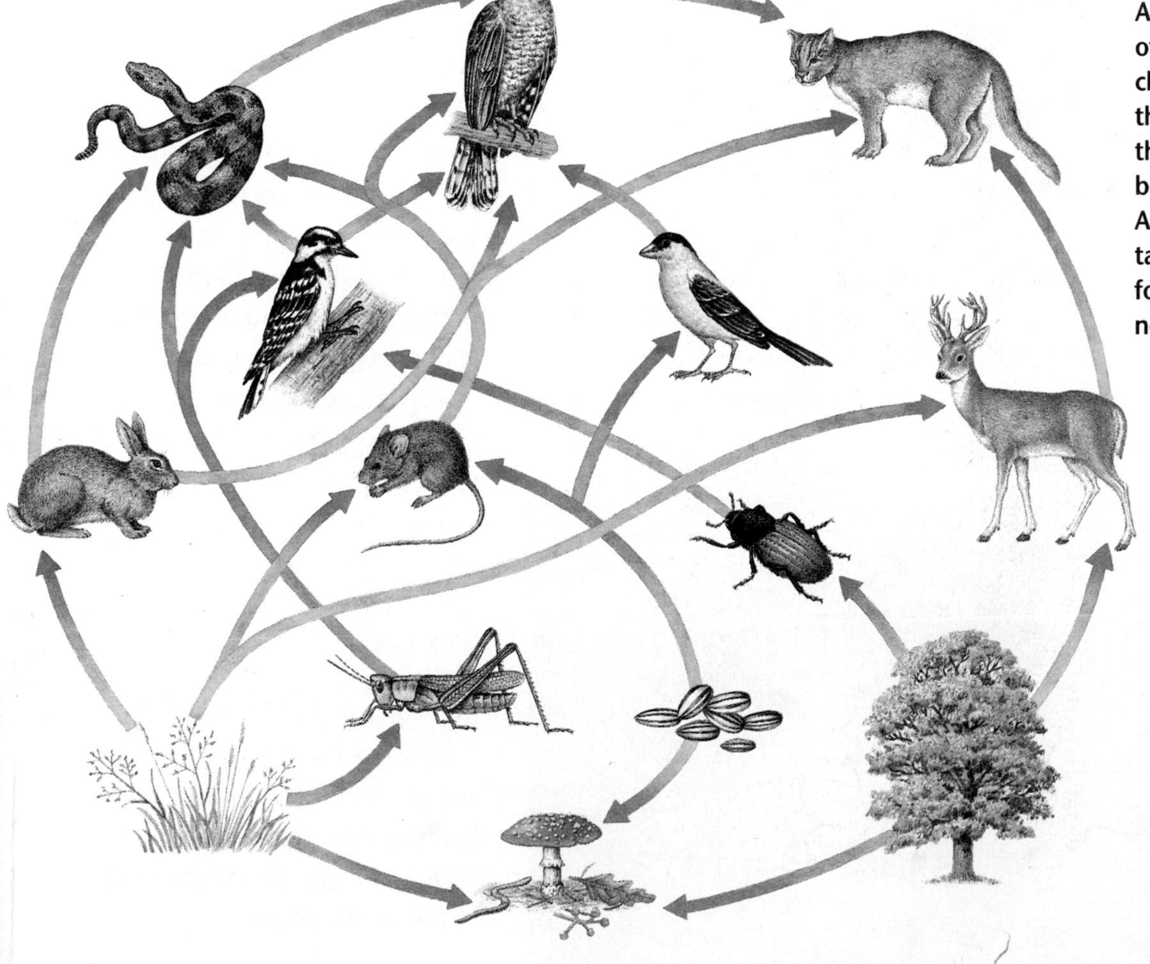

Figure 11-7

A food web is a model of the overlapping food chains in an area. Follow the food chains that the seed-eating bird belongs to in this web. Are grasshoppers important to hawks in this food web? Why or why not?

Physics

Scientists know that matter can be neither created nor destroyed. Use this information to explain why recycling of materials is essential to life on Earth.

Natural Cycles

Organisms need a constant supply of energy to live. The sun provides the energy that flows through most of the food chains in our world.

Organisms also have other needs for survival, including water and nutrients. These needs are met from a limited supply of Earth's natural resources. Unlike energy from the sun, these resources aren't continually replaced. Instead, they are constantly being used and recycled. Without the recycling of materials, organisms would quickly run out of the water and nutrients they need.

■ Water Cycle

Energy from the sun causes water in Earth's oceans to evaporate. Hot air rises and carries water vapor up into the cooler atmosphere. Here water vapor forms clouds. Water falls from the clouds as rain or snow. Plants absorb water from the soil. Animals drink water or obtain it by eating plants. Both plants and animals use or store some water and return the rest to the environment. Plants release water through their leaves. Animals release water with waste products. Water evaporates, and the cycle continues.

Chemistry CONNECTION

Oxygen Makers

Earth's atmosphere provides some essential ingredients for life: oxygen, carbon dioxide, nitrogen, and water vapor. Earth's original atmosphere consisted of ammonia, carbon dioxide, carbon monoxide, hydrogen, methane, nitrogen, sulfur dioxide, and water vapor, but very little oxygen. Earth's current atmosphere is about 21 percent oxygen. So where did all the oxygen come from?

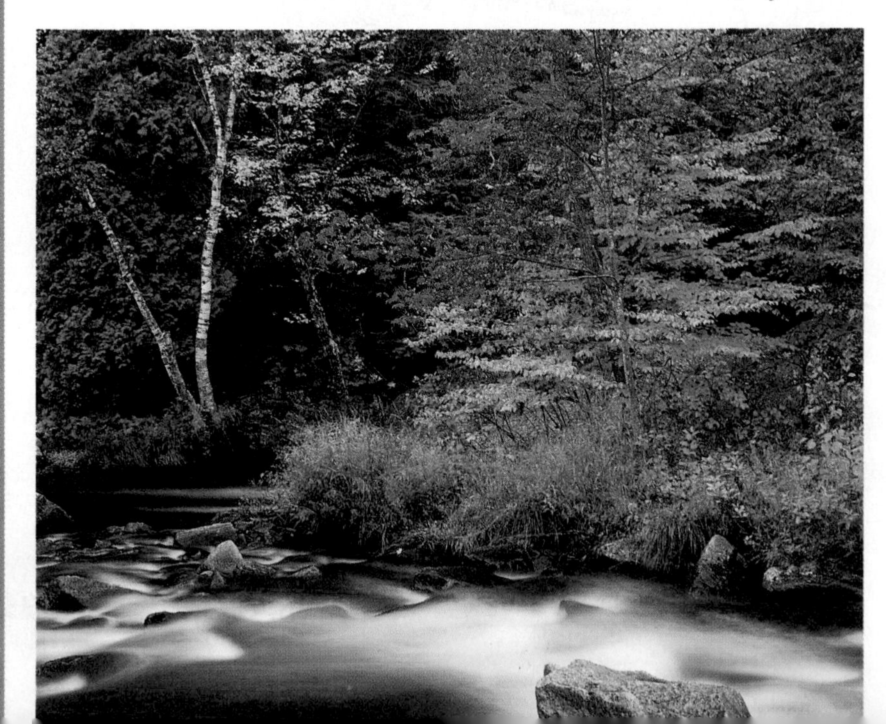

You learned that oxygen is a product of photosynthesis—the process by which plants and some bacteria and algae absorb carbon dioxide from the air, combine it with water in the presence of sunlight to convert it to sugar, and then release oxygen into the air. The oxygen content of Earth's atmosphere began to increase about 2.3 billion years ago, when cyanobacteria and algae started growing in the ocean. In a way, we owe

■ Nitrogen Cycle

Nitrogen is an element used by most organisms to build proteins and other body chemicals. While most of the atmosphere is made of nitrogen, organisms can't use this form of the element. Instead, plankton in water and bacteria in the soil and in the roots of bean and pea plants change the gas into a form that can be taken in and used by plants. Animals get nitrogen by eating either plants or animals that have eaten plants. The nitrogen is returned to the soil when animals release waste products or when dead organisms decay. **Figure 11-8** shows the nitrogen cycle.

Figure 11-8

In the nitrogen cycle, nitrogen passes from the atmosphere to living things, then back again to the atmosphere.

Nitrogen is changed to forms plants can use by lightning

Bacteria convert nitrogen back to gas

Bacteria change nitrogen into forms plants can use

Bacteria

our existence to bacteria and algae.

The ability of plants to convert carbon dioxide into oxygen is one reason why people are so concerned about our vanishing forests. So far, scientists have not found a way to make photosynthesis occur outside living organisms.

You Try It!

You can observe the results of photosynthesis.

Materials

small live plant
deep basin or pan
tall, narrow glass container or test tube
water hose or a bucket full of water

What To Do

1. Take your materials to a sunny location.
2. Fill the basin with water.
3. Fill the glass container to the brim.
4. Completely cover the open end of the container or test tube with your thumb.
5. Place the container upside down in the basin and remove your hand, without letting air inside.
6. Thread a runner of the plant into the container while keeping the open end of the container completely submerged. Don't cut the runner from the plant!
7. Leave the setup in the sun several hours. Record what you observe when you return. How might it be related to photosynthesis?

■ Oxygen-Carbon Dioxide Cycle

At this moment, plants, animals, and most other organisms are removing oxygen from the atmosphere. Why hasn't Earth's oxygen supply been used up? The answer is that oxygen is recycled.

Remember from Chapter 10 that during respiration, plants and almost all other organisms take in oxygen and release carbon dioxide. Carbon dioxide also enters the atmosphere when decomposers break down dead organisms. However, during photosynthesis, plants take in carbon dioxide from the air and release oxygen.

Figure 11-9

A **During respiration, plants and almost all other organisms take in oxygen and release carbon dioxide into the air. During photosynthesis, plants take in carbon dioxide from the air and release oxygen.**

B **Together the processes of photosynthesis and respiration continually recycle oxygen and carbon dioxide.**

Lately, many people have become concerned with another way in which carbon dioxide is released. Sometimes dead organisms do not decay. After millions of years, they turn into fossil fuels such as coal. When the fossil fuels are burned, carbon dioxide is released. The use of fossil fuels has greatly increased since the 1800s. Thus, the amount of carbon dioxide in the atmosphere has also increased. Continued use of fossil fuels is changing the delicate balance of Earth's atmosphere.

Another human activity that can affect the oxygen-carbon dioxide cycle is cutting down Earth's rain forests. This can result in less oxygen being produced and released into the air because there are fewer plants to carry out photosynthesis.

Natural recycling that occurs on Earth ensures that living things will be able to obtain the materials needed for life.

1. Explain the relationship between a food chain and a food web.
2. Is it possible to find a food chain that includes only a producer and decomposer? Explain your answer.
3. Describe what might happen if the water cycle was interrupted.
4. **Apply** Identify a meat or fish product that you've recently eaten. Construct a food chain that shows the feeding relationships that preceded your eating the product. Place yourself at one end of the food chain.

11-3 How Limiting Factors Affect Organisms

Requirements for Life

Section Objectives
- Identify some limiting factors.
- Describe adaptations of organisms to limiting factors.

Key Terms
limiting factor

At the zoo, you'll notice that animals are displayed in different environments. Some animals, such as some penguins, are housed behind glass, where the temperatures can be kept cool during hot weather. Others, such as rattlesnakes, are found in hot, dry display areas. Still others, such as bats, are literally kept in the dark. Why do all these different animals have such different requirements?

Plants and other living things also are found growing in different conditions. Why might this be? Do the activity that follows to begin exploring what factors might limit growth.

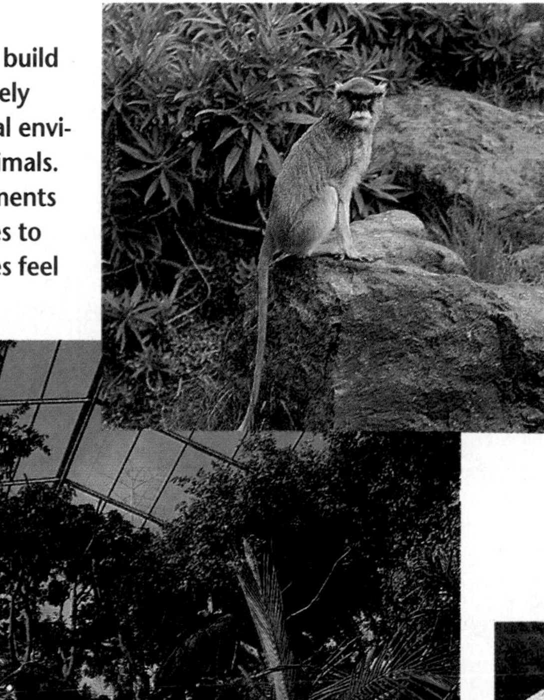

Figure 11-10

A Many modern zoos build enclosures that closely resemble the natural environments of the animals. Jungle-like environments with plenty of places to climb make primates feel at home.

B The natural environment of this bamboo viper snake is hot and dry. Here the snake is kept in a glass enclosure with air that is just the right temperature and has just the right moisture content to keep the snake healthy.

C Birds are kept in roomy aviaries filled with plants that would grow in the bird's natural habitat.

D Animals, such as polar bears, that need a certain temperature to survive may be kept in glass enclosures where temperature can be easily monitored.

DESIGN YOUR OWN
INVESTIGATION

How Do Molds Grow?

Molds are fungi that can feed on just about anything. Think about where molds grow in our environment. Do they grow everywhere or are there factors that limit the growth of molds?

Preparation

Problem
What basic factor limits the growth of molds?

Form a Hypothesis
As a group make a hypothesis about what factor seems most important in encouraging the growth of mold.

Objectives
- Identify factors that encourage growth of mold.
- Evaluate data.
- Determine which factor is a strong limiting factor to the growth of mold.

Possible Materials
6 small paper cups
hand lens
labels
mold source (teacher supplies)
spray bottle of water
plastic wrap
cotton swabs
dry potato flakes
dry macaroni
sugarless, dry cereal
other dry saltless, sugarless food

Safety Precautions

After transferring the mold source, wash your hands thoroughly. All surfaces in the experiment in touch with microorganisms should also be washed thoroughly. Do not inhale, taste, or touch material from the mold source. If you have a mold allergy, do not handle the mold.

DESIGN YOUR OWN
INVESTIGATION

Plan the Experiment

1 Examine the materials provided and decide how you will use them to test the group's hypothesis.

2 What is the limiting factor that you are testing? How will it be introduced in the experiment?

3 A small amount of food at the bottom of each cup is enough to feed mold. To introduce mold into each cup, rub a moist cotton swab across the dish of growing mold, then rub the cotton swab across the surface of the food in each cup. Try to put the same amount in each cup.

4 Mold grows over a period of days. Checking mold growth day by day should be taken into account in making your plan and your data table.

Check the Plan

1 How will you keep the environment in your experimental cups from change or contamination?

2 Where will you keep your experiment? Is it a neutral environment? Are the conditions for all the cups the same?

3 How long do you think it will take the mold to grow? How often will you check the experiment? Make certain that each observation is recorded in your data table.

4 Before your begin the experiment, have it approved by your teacher.

5 Carry out your experiment and record your data.

Analyze and Conclude

1. **Compare and Contrast** In which cups did you see evidence of mold growth? In which cups was there no mold growth?
2. **Infer** Determine whether there is a factor that limits the growth of mold.
3. **Interpret Data** Did mold grow faster on one particular food?
4. **Draw a Conclusion** If you wanted to package food to sell, what is one way you could prevent mold from spoiling your product?

Going Further

Moisture is a limiting factor in mold growth. What other factors can you test to see if they limit mold growth?

Figure 11-11

A Many types of penguins require a cold, wet habitat and could not survive in the hot, dry habitat that is home to the pinto chuckwalla.

■ Limiting Factors

As you worked on the Investigate, you found that mold grew better on certain materials and under certain conditions. What might have happened if you had placed the materials in the refrigerator? Mold would still have grown, but much more slowly.

Environmental factors help determine whether an organism can live in the environment. Think about a shark. Will a shark survive in the ocean or a lake? You know that most sharks live in the ocean. Sharks are saltwater organisms, and most species of sharks can't survive in a freshwater lake.

Now think about plants. Cacti grow in dry areas such as deserts. Too much water will kill them. A **limiting factor** is any condition that influences the growth or survival of an organism or species.

Limiting factors can be nonliving, environmental conditions, such as temperature, wind, chemicals in the soil, amounts of light and water, as well as pollution in the water or air. Limiting factors can also be the relationships between living organisms in a community. You'll see what kinds of relationships can be limiting as you continue to read the chapter.

B Lack of moisture is a limiting factor for orchids, which need a lot of moisture to live, but not for cacti, which are adapted to thrive in a hot, dry habitat.

Nonliving Limiting Factors

You saw that molds need water to grow. What kinds of limiting factors affect other living things?

Temperature

Every organism has a set of conditions that are best for survival. For example, most organisms can survive if the temperature falls within a certain range. For example, some fish in a freshwater aquarium carry on life processes in water that is room temperature (22°C). They can live in water that's 5.5 degrees warmer or colder. If the water's temperature goes beyond that 11-degree range for too long, the fish die.

Sunlight

The amount of direct sunlight an ecosystem receives is another limiting factor. Go to a greenhouse or a store that sells plants. A tag with instructions for proper care is often included with each plant. Bright, direct light kills some plants. Other plants thrive in it. Study **Figure 11-12** to learn more about sunlight as a limiting factor.

Rainfall

The amount of rainfall in an environment is also a limiting factor. Generally, each ecosystem has an average level of rainfall. Many factors work together to determine that level. If rainfall doesn't meet that level over a long period of time, plants die. Can you infer what happens to the animals, including humans, in the ecosystem?

Figure 11-12

For many plants, sunlight can be a limiting factor.

A Bright, direct sunlight kills some plants. Other plants thrive on it. Impatiens grow best when planted in shady areas.

B If you want petunias to thrive, you must plant them in sunny to partly sunny areas.

C Zinnias grow best in full sun.

Figure 11-13

More than half of the animal and plant species in the world live in the rain forest ecosystem. A great many species have adaptations that help them deal with limiting factors in the rain forest ecosystem.

The harpy eagle soars high above the upper canopy hunting for monkeys and sloths for food.

Spider monkeys eat mostly nuts and fruit from the forest.

Spider monkeys live in the upper canopy. They use their tails to swing from branch to branch.

The scarlet macaw uses its strong beak to eat nuts and seeds.

Sloths use their long curved claws as hooks to help them move within the trees or to hang upside down.

Boas, which grow to giant size in the rain forest, stalk tree frogs and iguanas for food.

Climbing plants and vines grow and twine around the trees and bushes in the understory.

The largest animals in the ecosystem live on the forest floor. This South American jaguar's coat helps it blend into the habitat and hide from its enemies.

Ocelots hunt birds and monkeys in the lower canopy and rabbits and small deer on the forest floor.

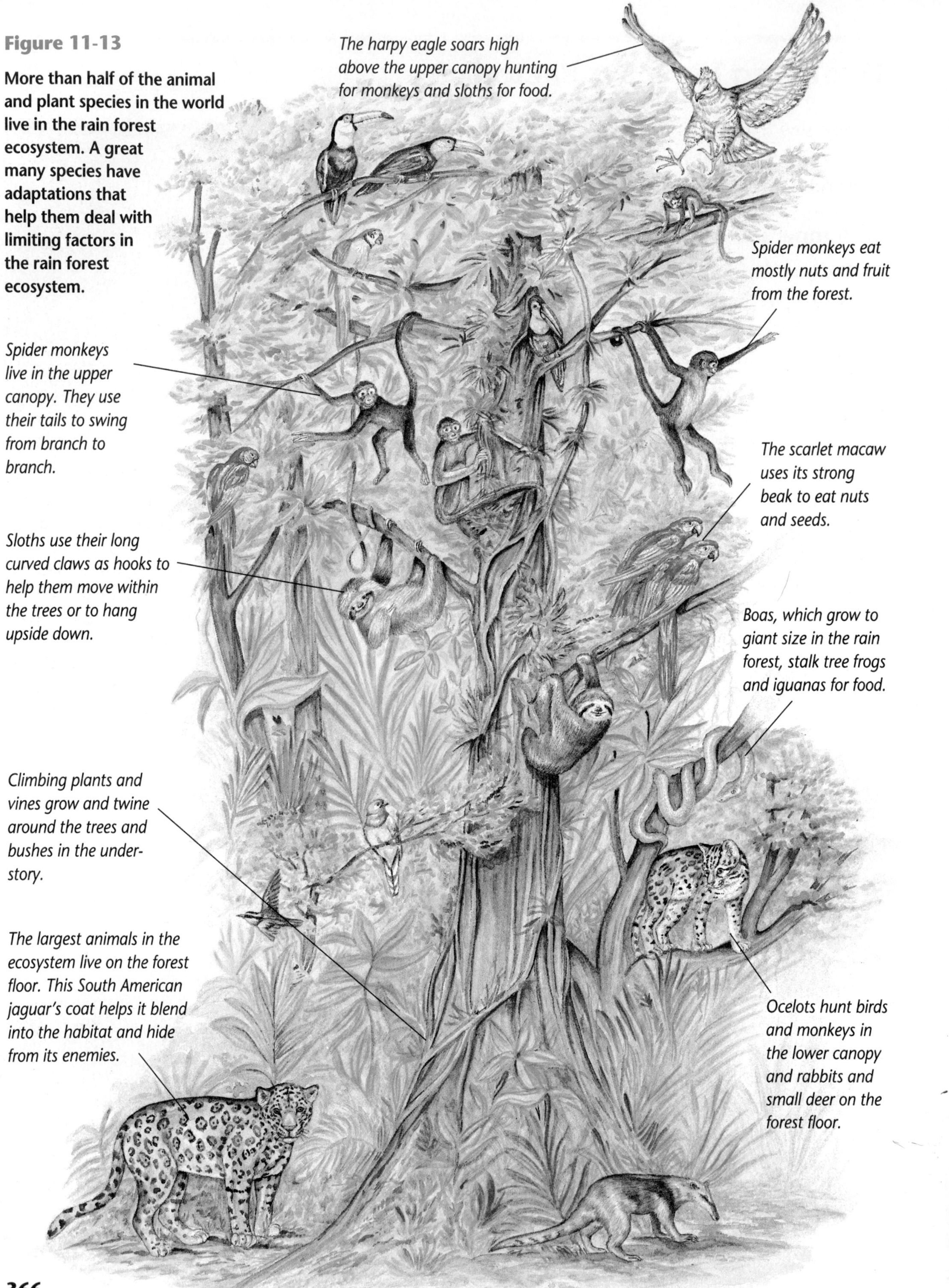

Other Organisms as Limiting Factors

You've learned about some non-living limiting factors. Now, find out how relationships between living organisms can be limiting factors.

■ Competition

Recall that in Section 11-1 you learned that each organism fills a niche in its community. Competition results when two organisms try to fill the same niche. The organisms compete for food, shelter, water, and other needs until one organism is forced to leave the area or dies.

One example of competition as a limiting factor is what happens to wildlife as humans move into an area. Humans build houses, cut down trees, pave roads—activities that greatly change the environment. Many animals are forced to live elsewhere. **Figure 11-13** shows other examples of competition.

■ Predator-Prey Relationship

A close look at a food chain can provide a clue to another behavior-linked limiting factor. Animals that catch and eat other animals are called predators. See **Figure 11-14** for one example of predators. The animals predators eat are called prey. The predator-prey relationship has an effect on the size of populations of both predators and prey. How many predator-prey relationships can you find in **Figure 11-13**? Usually the numbers of predators and prey within a community will stay about the same. But look at **Figure 11-15** to see what happens when the size of one population changes. You'll notice that as the mouse (prey) population rises, the number of owls (predator) also rises. At some point the large owl population will eat so many mice that only a few will be left. Without enough mice to eat, the owl population will decrease. What do you think will happen next to the size of each population?

Figure 11-14

Lions hunt in groups. Working together, they are able to kill prey larger than themselves, such as wildebeests and zebras. Cooperative hunting also allows each individual lion to expend less energy in the hunt.

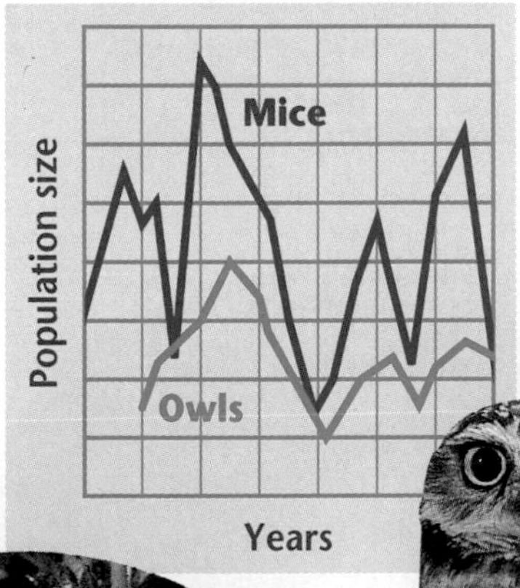

Figure 11-15

Owls are predators of mice. The chart shows how the populations of mice and owls change over several years. Notice that as the number of mice (prey) rises, the number of owls (predator) also rises.

How Organisms Are Adapted

The success of an organism within its environment depends on how well it's adapted to that environment. An adaptation is a characteristic that increases the chance of an organism to survive in its environment. **Figure 11-16** shows one example of a plant adapted to a certain environment. Look back at **Figure 11-13** and see how many adaptations to rain forest conditions you can spot.

■ Plant Adaptations

Lack of rainfall in a desert is a limiting factor for many types of plants. Why do cacti grow successfully in a desert environment? You'll recall from Chapter 10 that a cactus plant is adapted in two ways. First, its extensive root system quickly absorbs any water that may fall during a rainstorm. Second, its stems and leaves prevent the loss of water. The waxy covering called the cuticle prevents water loss through the stem. The leaves of the cactus are long, sharp spines. Because there is less leaf surface area, less water is lost through the spines than would be with other types of leaves.

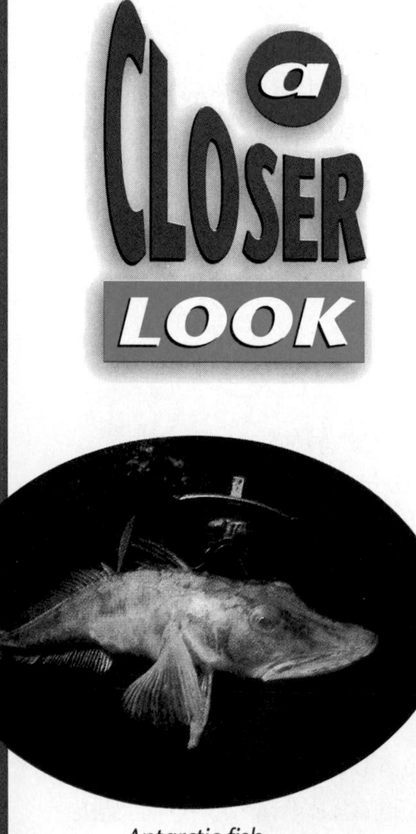

Antarctic fish

How Wide Is Life's Comfort Zone?

You probably adjust the temperature of your home by using heaters and fans or air conditioners. How much heat and cold could you endure if you had to?

Many life-forms can't adjust the temperature where they live. How much heat and cold can living beings endure?

Cold

In Antarctica's McMurdo Sound, the water temperature ranges from -1.4°C to -2.15°C. Yet fish live and thrive in McMurdo Sound. Most of them are a kind of perchlike fish. How do they keep from freezing? Their bodies have evolved the ability to produce compounds that act like strong antifreeze. Most other fish freeze when their body fluids cool to about -0.8°C, but McMurdo Sound's perchlike fish freeze only when their temperature goes down to about -2.2°C. McMurdo Sound very rarely gets that cold, so these fish have the habitat largely to themselves.

Heat

The prizewinner so far for surviving high temperatures is archaebacteria, a kind of microorganism that can grow at temperatures up to 110°C. Archaebacteria inhabit the waters near undersea volcanic vents.

■ Adaptations to Low Light

Plants in rain forests are adapted to different limiting factors. Lower levels of the rain forest receive very little light. Any nutrients in the topsoil are quickly absorbed by the roots of tall trees, so the soil has few nutrients. Plants called epiphytes grow high up on the branches of the taller trees. They grow in the top layers of the forest and get water from the air and nutrients from decaying plant matter near their roots. In addition, growing high in the branches of a tree also exposes the plant to greater amounts of sunlight.

Figure 11-16

A **The silversword plant grows high in the craters of extinct volcanoes in Hawaii. During the day it's exposed to strong ultraviolet light. At night it's exposed to extreme cold.**

B **The leaves of the plants have small hair-like projections that serve to protect the plant both from the cold and from the ultraviolet light.**

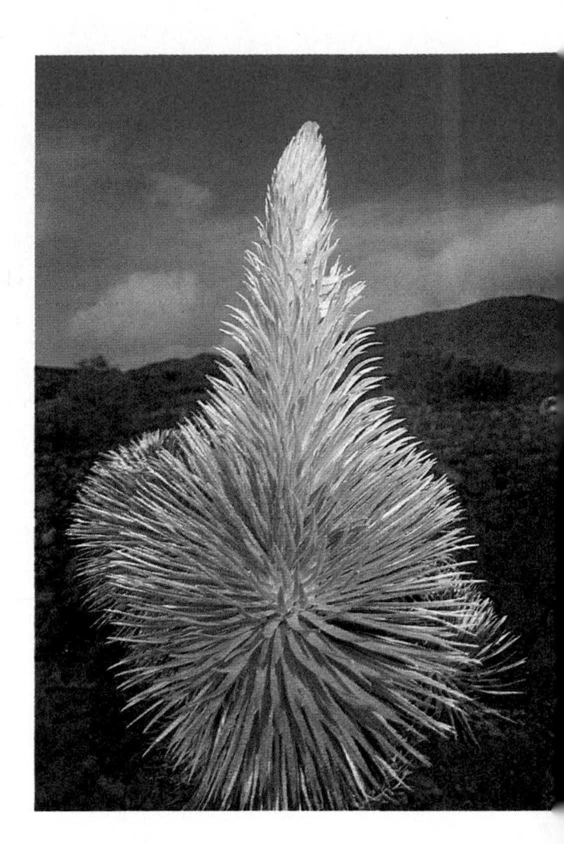

Other Challenges

The high temperature isn't the only challenge these microbes have mastered. When volcanic gases dissolve in seawater, they make it very acidic. Some archaebacteria live in water with a pH of 1 or less—more acidic than stomach acid. Other archaebacteria prefer water with a pH of 11.5—nearly as basic as the ammonia in household cleaners.

Some of these can also survive in solutions that are 36% salt. (For comparison, Atlantic and Pacific Ocean seawater is about 3% salt, and the Great Salt Lake is about 25% salt.)

That's not all; some archaebacteria even grow in the very deepest parts of the sea, at tremendous pressures.

From the cold ocean depths to the heat of volcanic vents—in strong acids or bases or salts—even the most extreme habitats can contain life.

What Do You Think?

Consider what kind of life-support suit you would need to visit Antarctic perchlike fish or archaebacteria where they live. Describe the extremes such a suit would have to protect you from.

In what other places—places that we now think to be uninhabitable—might we someday find living organisms?

Lake bed stained by the growth of Archaebacteria.

Figure 11-17

The camel's body is well adapted to its desert habitat.

Camels can shut their nostrils and lips tightly to keep out blowing sand.

Camels have two long toes on each foot. The two toes are connected by a broad cushion-like pad. The pad allows the camel to walk on sand without sinking, much like snow-shoes allow a person to walk on snow.

Thick eyebrows shade the camel's eyes from the bright desert sun and long lashes help keep out blowing sand.

Camel's knees have tough, leathery pads of skin, which cushion the impact and protect the camel from the burning hot sand when the camel kneels to rest.

Animal Adaptations

Just as plants are adapted to various environments, animals are also adapted. In **Figure 11-17** you can see how a camel is adapted to life in a desert environment.

Animals that live in very high mountain areas of the world also have adaptations to several limiting factors. For example, as you climb to higher elevations, the temperature drops and the amount of oxygen in the atmosphere decreases. Animals that live in this environment, such as the llama are protected against the cold and high altitudes.

If you were an astronaut orbiting Earth, you'd be able to see the white polar caps, the blue oceans, the brown deserts, and the green grasslands. Even at that distance you'd see that Earth is home to a variety of ecosystems. But only a closer look shows you how much the characteristics of each ecosystem influence the lives of the organisms that live there.

check your UNDERSTANDING

1. What effect would placing a plant in a closed box have on its growth? What limiting factor(s) is (are) involved?
2. Why would competition among organisms increase when resources are limited?
3. Would the adaptations of a cactus help or harm the plant if it were placed in a wet environment? Why?
4. **Apply** Limiting factors exist for humans as well as other organisms. Suppose you were on a camping trip in a desert. Make a list of the limiting factors you'd need to deal with. Identify the equipment you'd need to protect yourself from these limiting factors.

Teens in SCIENCE

One for All, and All for Trees

Have you heard about The Tree Musketeers? No, they don't carry swords or fight bad guys. But in their home town of El Segundo, California, these young people are real heroes.

Planting Trees

The Tree Musketeers began when several girls met in a Brownie Scout troop. "We were studying ecology," explains one of the founding members, Sabrina Alimahomed. "We learned how trees help clean the air and create rain. Since our state has an air quality problem and a drought, we felt that we could help by planting some trees."

Sabrina explains how the organization works. "The Tree Musketeers teaches people how to plant and care for trees," she says. "We got started by planting one tree, and the organization just grew from there. When we first heard about pollution, many of us felt frightened. We'd all assumed that because we were children, we didn't have to worry about things like the environment yet. But now we know that children need to care about the planet, too. Grown-ups always tell us that we can do anything if we set our minds to it. So, we decided to save the world."

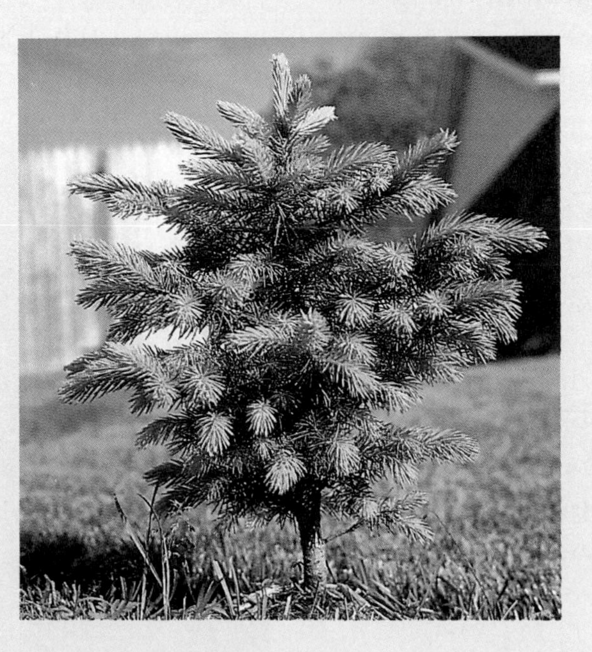

There's no doubt about how valuable trees are to the environment. Trees not only help produce the oxygen we breathe, they also help prevent soil erosion, and control noise pollution by absorbing sound.

Saving Ecosystems

Over the years, more than 300 children have participated in The Tree Musketeers. Hundreds of trees have been planted.

Sabrina continued, "We hope that our work in The Tree Musketeers will continue to help both children and adults realize that when it comes to saving our planet, every person makes a difference."

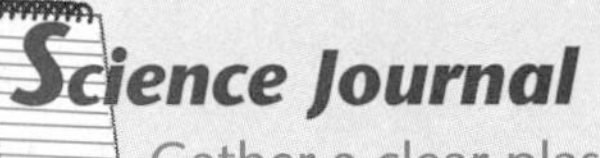

Science Journal

Gather a clear plastic bag and some string. On a hot, sunny day, tie a small plastic bag around a few leaves hanging on a low tree branch. Leave the bag for a few hours. Now measure the amount of moisture that has collected on the inside of the bag. Record your results and observations *in your Journal.*

Science and Society

Saving Chesapeake Bay

You may have studied estuaries in geography or in a science class. An estuary forms where a river enters the sea, creating a mixture of fresh water and salt water. Chesapeake Bay is the largest estuary in the United States. The bay stretches 185 miles from the north where the Susquehanna River enters, to the south between Cape Charles and Cape Henry in southeastern Virginia.

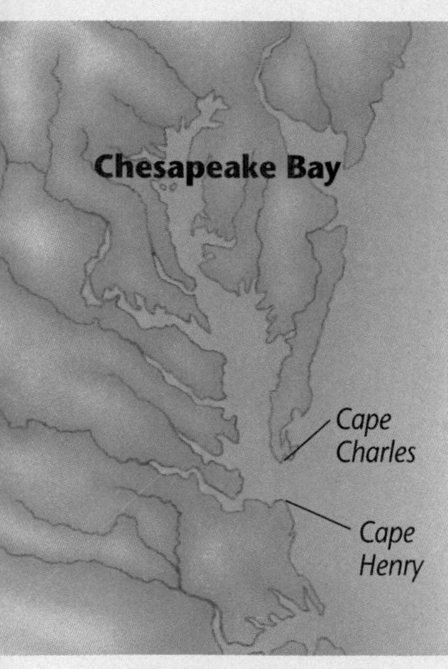

Location of Chesapeake Bay

Life in Chesapeake Bay

Chesapeake Bay is probably best known for the enormous number of crabs and oysters pulled from its waters. In addition to the large amount of aquatic life, the bay is host to many other animals.

The bay and its 7000 miles of shoreline are home to many water birds, including Canada geese, green-backed heron, snowy egrets, and the largest population of ospreys found in the United States.

Pollution Threatens the Bay

Forty-six major rivers and hundreds of tributaries carry fresh water to Chesapeake Bay. But the "fresh" water is really far from fresh. It's full of chemical runoff (contaminated water) from factories, sewage plants, and farms. These chemicals can cause diseases in fish and shellfish.

The Threat from Algae

But that's only one of the problems. Where water circulation is low—in narrow parts of rivers and estuaries—an overabundance of plant nutrients can cause problems, too. When runoff contains nitrates and phosphates, such as those found in fertilizers, the algae in the water

Osprey

feed on them and reproduce more rapidly. Curtains of these plantlike protists have been known to grow as much as three feet thick! This keeps the sun from reaching any oxygen-producing algae below.

When the nutrients in the water have been used up, the algae die and begin to decay. Rather than solving the problem, the decomposing algae make the situation even worse. The decaying process uses up the oxygen in the water, and the lack of oxygen makes it hard for fish and other aquatic organisms to survive.

Blue crab

DDT: Still a Threat

Polluted waters take a toll on water birds, too. From the 1950s to the early 1970s, runoff containing the pesticide DDT caused widespread contamination. Organisms can't eliminate DDT from their systems. The chemical becomes more concentrated in their body tissues with each step up the food chain.

Here's how DDT moved through one food chain in Chesapeake Bay. Runoff contaminated plants and organisms in the water. Fish ate these plants and organisms, or absorbed DDT directly through their skins. Birds ate the contaminated fish. When ospreys ate fish containing DDT, they produced eggs with shells so thin that the chicks were crushed beneath their nesting parents. Because of this, the osprey's breeding population fell to about 1000 pairs. However, since the United States banned DDT in 1972, the osprey population in the bay has doubled.

Clean Up Underway

Efforts by the states of Maryland, Virginia, and Pennsylvania to clean up the bay have concentrated on wastewater treatment and regulation of development near its waters. Treating sewage more thoroughly than required by law, limiting construction and the use of concrete and asphalt, and finding ways to keep soil and chemicals out of the water may help save the bay.

interNET CONNECTION

The Environmental Protection Agency is involved in federal cleanup efforts at Chesapeake Bay. Use the World Wide Web to find information on the cleanup program that might also have an application in your area.

REVIEWING MAIN IDEAS

Science Journal

Review the statements below about the big ideas presented in this chapter, and answer the questions. Then, re-read your answers to the Did You Ever Wonder questions at the beginning of the chapter. *In your Science Journal,* write a paragraph about how your understanding of the big ideas in the chapter has changed.

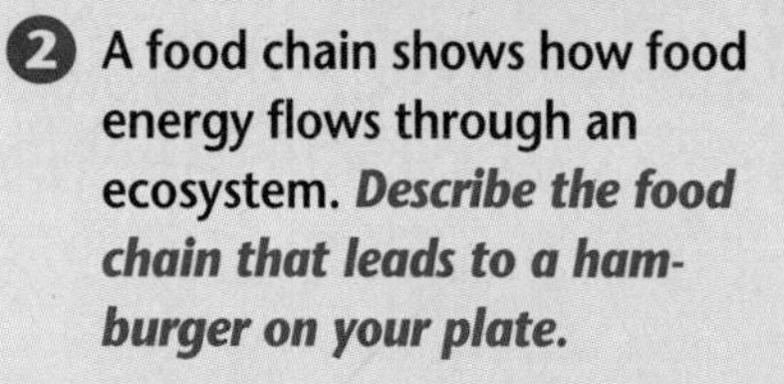

1 A community of organisms interacting with the nonliving environment is an ecosystem. ***Describe conditions and organisms in a pond ecosystem.***

2 A food chain shows how food energy flows through an ecosystem. ***Describe the food chain that leads to a hamburger on your plate.***

3 Many materials, such as water, oxygen, carbon dioxide, and nitrogen, are constantly being recycled through the environment. ***Why is it necessary for water, oxygen, and nitrogen to be recycled?***

4 An organism's survival is related to how well it is adapted to the environment. Limiting factors, which may be living or nonliving, influence the survival of an organism or a species. ***Describe how a camel is adapted to its environment.***

chapter 11
CHAPTER REVIEW

Using Key Science Terms

community
decomposer
ecosystem
food chain
food web
habitat
limiting factor
niche
population

For each set of terms below, explain the relationship that exists.

1. niche—habitat
2. population—community
3. food chain—decomposer
4. food chain—food web
5. limiting factor—ecosystem

Understanding Ideas

Answer the following questions in your Journal *using complete sentences.*

1. What is the relationship between a population, community, and ecosystem?
2. Explain why producers and decomposers are important.
3. What is the source of the energy that flows through most of the food chains on Earth?
4. List three examples of limiting factors.
5. Give an example of how a living thing might be adapted to survive despite limiting factors in the environment.

Developing Skills

Use your understanding of the concepts developed in this chapter to answer each of the following questions.

1. **Concept Mapping** Using the following terms complete the concept map of limiting factors: *adaptations, competition, light, nonliving, predator-prey, rainfall.*

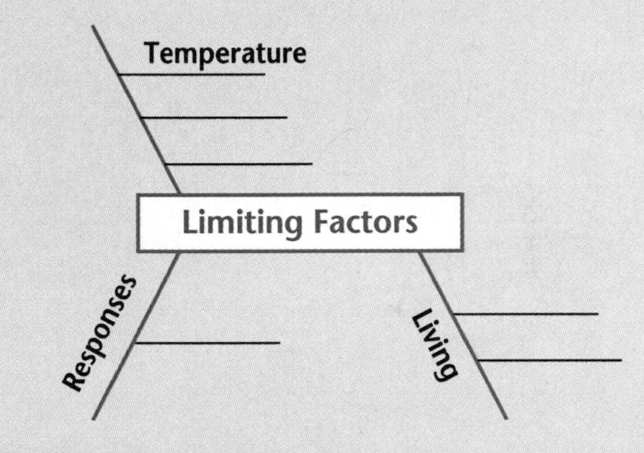

2. **Sequencing** Look at the food web on page 357. Follow the food chains of a snake and a hawk.
3. **Separating and Interpreting Data** Change the amount of water or temperature used for growing mold in the Investigate on pages 362-363 to see how growth might be affected.

Critical Thinking

In your Journal, *answer each of the following questions.*

1. Give examples of situations when too much or too little of a material becomes a limiting factor.
2. Explain why natural cycles are important in the environment.

3. Explain why two species cannot occupy the same niche at the same time.
4. Describe the niche of a cow.
5. What effect would humans have if they tried to kill all the bark beetles in this community with a chemical?

Problem Solving

Read the following problem and discuss your answers in a brief paragraph.

Large areas of the rain forest are being destroyed each year. This loss of habitat means fewer animals can live in the remaining area. You are a biologist trying to predict how long the habitat can support three animal populations.

1. Animal A currently has a population of 100. Each year its population doubles. How large will its population be after 1 year, 2 years, 3 years, and 4 years?
2. Animal B has a population of 50. Each year its population triples. How large will its population be after 1 year, 2 years, 3 years, and 4 years?
3. Animal C has a population of 25. Each year its population quadruples. What is its population after 1 year, 2 years, 3 years, and 4 years?
4. Right now the area in the rain forest that you are studying can provide food for 10 000 animals. Because of continued habitat destruction, that number is reduced by 10 percent a year. Find out how many animals the habitat can feed after 1 year, 2 years, 3 years, and 4 years.
5. In which year will the total population outstrip the food supply?

CONNECTING IDEAS

Discuss each of the following in a brief paragraph.

1. **Theme—Energy** How does a food web show the relationship between organisms in an ecosystem?
2. **Theme—Energy** What role does sunlight play in an ecosystem on Earth?
3. **A Closer Look** Describe ecosystems that you are a part of. How are they alike and different?
4. **Science and Society** How are food webs related to the spread of poisonous chemicals and other pollutants in an ecosystem?

unit 3
UNIT REVIEW

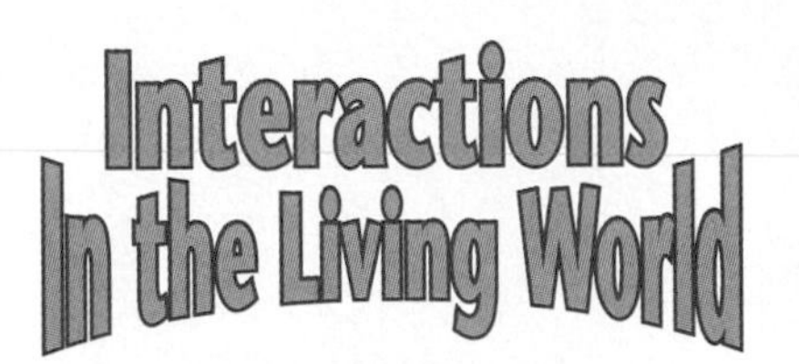

In this unit, you classified organisms as plants or animals using characteristics such as the ability to move about freely and search for food and water.

You learned how plants manufacture their own food using sunlight and that animals then rely on this stored food in plants to survive. You also saw how plants and animals form an important part of the oxygen-carbon dioxide cycle.

Try the exercises and activity that follow—they will challenge you to use and apply some of the ideas you learned in this unit.

CONNECTING IDEAS

1. Trace the pathway of water from soil, through a vascular plant to its leaves, and back again to the soil. Explain what processes occurred in which plant parts, both inside and outside the plant. Relate the processes inside and outside the plant to their effects on the ecology of the plant's habitat.
2. Obtain samples of a wide variety of objects from your teacher. Design a classification scheme that will enable you to classify living and nonliving things. Decide if other groupings are needed to further classify the living things and the nonliving things.

How Might Salt Be a Limiting Factor?

What To Do

Design an experiment that will determine if radish seedlings will grow in salt. Be sure to keep all factors except the amount of salt constant. The amount of salt given to the plants will be the only variable in your experiment. Record your design *in your Journal.*

UNIT 4

Changing Systems

This wonderland of stone arches, boulders, and basins in Arches National Park shows the shaping power of nature. Here, what was a sandy seafloor millions of years ago, is now a rocky desert ridge. In this unit, learn how wind, water, shifts in temperature, and movements of Earth can change the planet's physical appearance and affect its ecology.

NATIONAL GEOGRAPHIC

try it!

Erosion by running water can occur slowly or rapidly. What are some factors that affect how rapidly water erodes Earth's surface?

What To Do

1. Place a layer of small rocks in the bottom of one pan and a layer of sand in the bottom of another.
2. Fill a pitcher full of water.
3. Tilt each of the pans at a 10 degree angle and slowly pour the contents of the pitcher into the raised end of the pan.
4. Predict what will happen to the rocks in the pan. Test your prediction.
5. Now, predict what will happen to the sand in the other pan. Test your prediction.
6. Set up the pans again.
7. Predict what will happen to the rocks and sand in the pans if you pour the water rapidly. Test your predictions. Be sure to set a large container under the pans to collect overflow.

CHAPTER 12

MOTION

Did you ever wonder...

- Why you have a sensation of moving backward as you sit in a car while one next to you is pulling away from a traffic light?
- Why your stomach feels funny when you're on a roller coaster?
- Why you feel pulled outward when riding around a curve in a bus?

Science Journal

Before you begin your study of motion, think about these questions and answer them *in your Science Journal.* When you finish the chapter, compare your journal write-up with what you have learned.

The first visit to the amusement park each summer is the best. This year, the high point of the visit is the new sky ride. Did you notice that as the chairs of the sky ride start forward, you feel pushed backward into your seat? Did you also notice that as the ride stopped for new passengers, you slid forward a little? Do you remember how the roller coaster went faster and faster as it went downhill? These are some of the effects of motion that we'll be exploring in this chapter.

▶ ***In the activity on the next page, explore some of the ways you could describe a position to someone else.***

Explore! ACTIVITY

How would you tell someone where you are?

Almost every day you have to tell someone where somebody or something is. How do you go about it?

What To Do

1. With your pencil, make a dot somewhere along the top edge of a sheet of unlined paper. Describe *in your Journal* the location of the dot on your paper.
2. Put a second dot on the same sheet of paper.
3. In your own words, describe its position and compare the location of the first dot with that of the second.
4. Ask a friend to read only your journal description and from the description, try to place two dots on another piece of paper to look like yours.
5. Repeat this exercise with lined paper and then with graph paper.
6. Does your ability to tell someone where the dots are improve each time? Why do you think this is so?

12-1 Position, Distance, and Speed

Section Objectives

- Specify the position of an object.
- Find the distance along a path.
- Determine the average speed of a moving object.

Key Terms

position
distance
average speed

Position and Motion

One of the best things about going to an amusement park is going there with friends. Sometimes, however, not everyone can arrive together—you need to decide where and when people are to gather so that no one gets left out. As an example, you might specify at 2:00 P.M. by the front gate, or perhaps by the merry-go-round at noon.

■ Position

In the Explore activity, you tried to describe the location or position of a dot on a sheet of paper. If you described the position of the dot by saying how far it was from the top and side edges of the paper, you were using points along the edges of the paper as reference points. The **position** of an object must always be described by comparing it to a reference point. By the time you did the exercise with graph paper, all you had to do to describe your position to a friend was to say something like "over five squares from the left edge and down six squares from the top."

Where you are located is your position compared to a reference

Figure 12-1

To describe the position of something, you must have a reference point. This amusement park is located just outside the center of Calgary, Canada. Many of the food booths are just in front of the large Ferris wheel. The large Ferris wheel is to the left of the smaller Ferris wheel. Find the merry-go-round in the photo. Can you describe its position without referring to any other object in the photo?

point. A reference point might be the base of a Ferris wheel during your trip to the amusement park. A reference point could also be in front of a certain store in a mall or by the door of a particular building on a farm. The main thing is that everyone needs to know what the particular reference point is in order to locate his or her position.

■ Motion

What if you walk from the water slide to the tilt-a-whirl? Doesn't your position change? When you change your position you experience motion. You could describe your change in position to a friend in terms of the number of steps you took walking from the water slide to the tilt-a-whirl. For your friend to be able to take the same walk, however, you would also have to say in what direction you walked. For example, you could say that you walked 75 steps north and then 100 steps west. The direction of motion can be described using compass directions or using the number of degrees in a circle. Let's explore how you might describe both the direction and distance of motion by using just a map.

Explore! ACTIVITY

How can you use a map to help describe motion?

What To Do

1. Using the figure shown, determine what distance and in what direction you must travel along the paths to go from the Tunnel of Love to the House of Terror.
2. What direction describes the path you would take when moving from the Ferris wheel to the Tunnel of Love?
3. Where do you end up if you travel directly west 50 meters from the Ferris wheel?

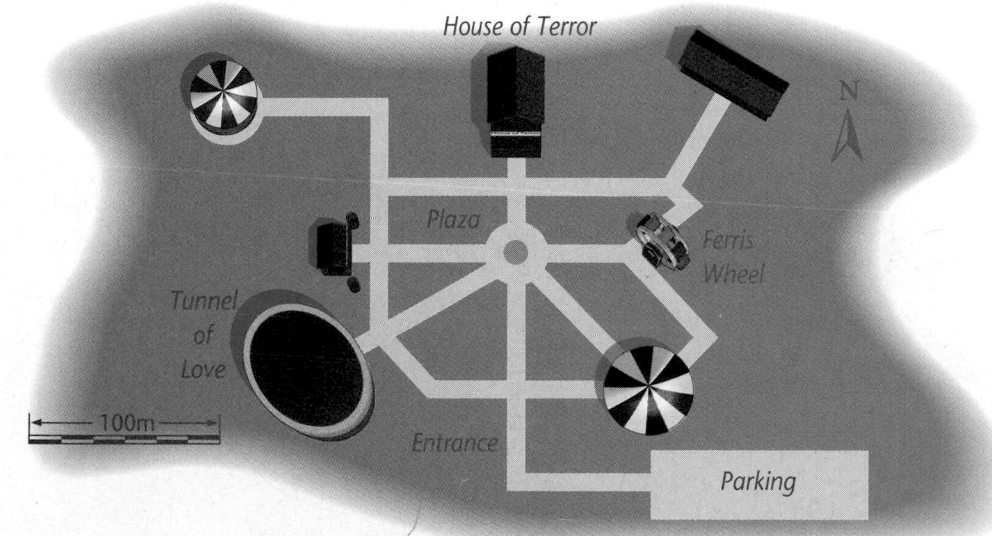

Distance Along a Path

When you walk through the amusement park, you change your position with every step you take. In doing so, you travel a certain distance. **Distance** is how far you travel along a path while you change your position. You've seen that a distance can be measured using just about any units—the number of steps, or the number of city blocks, for example. In science, we usually use SI units. The SI unit for measuring distance is the meter, abbreviated m.

Walkers and joggers wear a small device to record the distance that they travel. If you measured your distance as you walked between rides, food booths, and shows, you might find that you had covered several thousand meters (1000 meters = 0.6 mi).

Figure 12-2

If you wanted a snack at the amusement park, you might walk 250 m from the merry-go-round to the snack bar. Walking back along the same route, you would travel another 250 m to return to your starting point. The distance along the path between those two points is 250 m; the total distance to the snack bar and back is 500 m.

Life Science CONNECTION

How Fast Do Animals Move?

All animals have specialized structures that allow them to move in different ways and at different speeds.

Animals can move on land, on water, under water, and through the air. They can move their whole bodies or just some of their parts. Animals can walk, run, leap, jump, climb, and dig. Most birds can run, walk, fly, glide, soar, swim, or waddle on land. Snakes can slither. Squids and scallops can move by jet propulsion.

For vertebrates, animals with backbones, movement requires muscles attached to movable bones, and energy. The faster an animal moves, the more energy it uses. For invertebrates, animals without backbones, movement requires

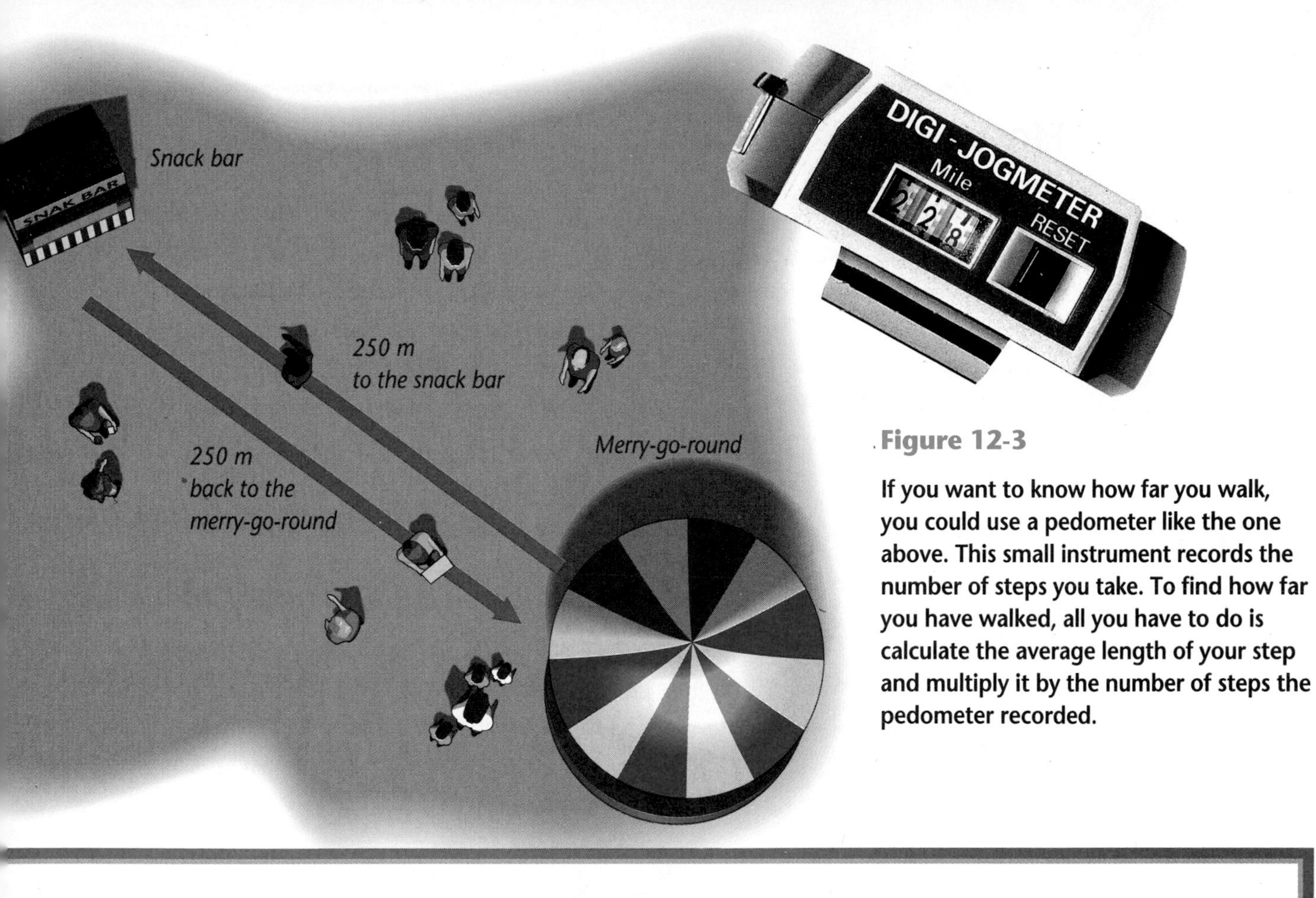

Figure 12-3

If you want to know how far you walk, you could use a pedometer like the one above. This small instrument records the number of steps you take. To find how far you have walked, all you have to do is calculate the average length of your step and multiply it by the number of steps the pedometer recorded.

other adaptations, such as waving hairs, wings, siphons, and sometimes many legs.

Does it surprise you that, generally, the larger the animal, the faster it can move? Does it also surprise you that swimming is the most energy-efficient way for an animal to move? Flying requires more energy, because the bird must overcome gravity. What animals do you think can move with the highest speeds?

The chart provides the fastest speeds ever measured for a variety of animals. Keep in mind that the greatest speed that an animal is capable of can only last a short amount of time. For every animal, there is a preferred speed that is usually far less than its top speed.

Speeds of Animals

Mammals		Birds		Amphibians	
cheetah	26.7 m/s	vulture	17.0 m/s	frog	1.5 m/s
racehorse	19.1 m/s	ostrich (running)	18.0 m/s	**Fish**	
blue whale	18.0 m/s	penguin		tuna	20.0 m/s
dog	16.0 m/s	(swimming)	3.5 m/s	flying fish	10.0 m/s
rabbit	15.7 m/s	duck		salmon	3.0 m/s
cat	13.4 m/s	(swimming)	0.7 m/s	**Invertebrates**	
human	12.0 m/s	**Reptiles**		locust	4.5 m/s
squirrel	2.0 m/s	lizard	6.7 m/s	dragonfly	22.0 m/s
		turtle	2.0 m/s	ant	0.03 m/s

Which animal has the fastest top speed? The slowest? How many times around a circular track could a rabbit run for every one circuit of a turtle?

What is your school record for the 50 or 100 meter dash? What is this speed in meters per second? How does this compare with the human top speed? What is your best speed in the 50 or 100 meter dash? How does this compare with the fastest human?

How Fast Is Fast?

Figure 12-4

The distance traveled by the roller coaster in a certain time is its average speed.

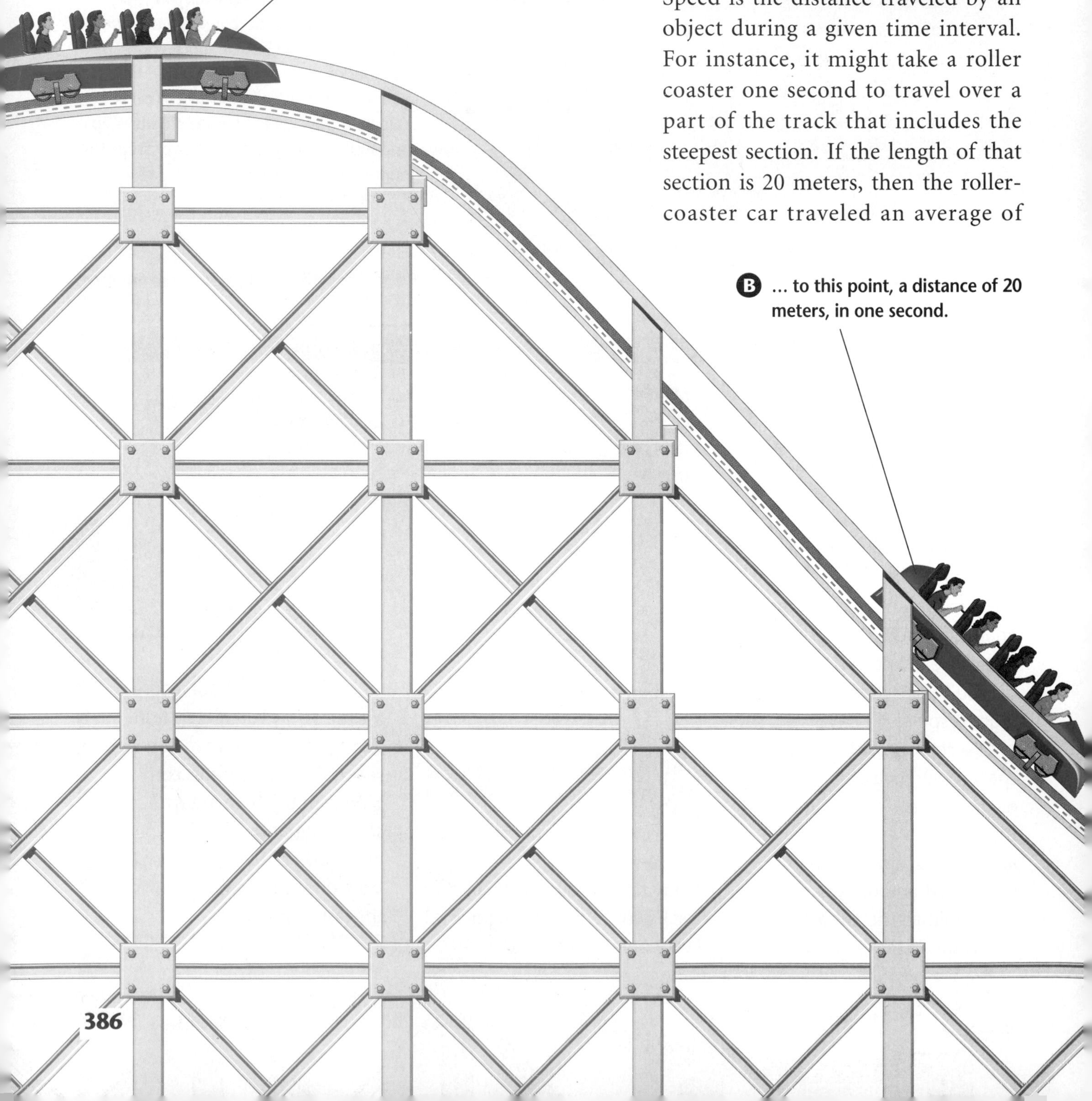

A The roller coaster travels from this point ...

B ... to this point, a distance of 20 meters, in one second.

Perhaps one of the most exciting rides you recall from your trip to the amusement park is the roller coaster. Up, down, around—first fast, then slow, then really fast.

One of the things that changes the most on a roller coaster is the speed. Speed is the distance traveled by an object during a given time interval. For instance, it might take a roller coaster one second to travel over a part of the track that includes the steepest section. If the length of that section is 20 meters, then the roller-coaster car traveled an average of

20 meters per second over that section. Walking around the amusement park might give you an average speed of around 1 meter per second, if you're not in much of a hurry.

■ Average and Instantaneous Speed

Suppose that in one hour, while walking around the amusement park, you run to catch up with some friends, stop to talk, buy some cotton candy, and watch the reptile show. Like most moving things, you do not maintain a constant speed during your walk. Even though your motion isn't constant, it is possible to find your average speed.

The **average speed** is found by dividing the total distance traveled by the total time required to travel the distance. That is,

$$\text{average speed} = \frac{\text{total distance}}{\text{time interval}}$$

In the next activity, you will find your average walking speed.

Which is the fastest roller coaster has often been subject to dispute. Speeds are frequently exaggerated for commercial reasons, but one of the fastest is the Magnum XL-200 at Cedar Point Park, Sandusky, Ohio. It has a vertical drop of nearly 59 m and attains a speed of 32 m/s.

D **The roller coaster doesn't travel at a constant speed all of the time that it goes around the tracks. Sometimes it goes faster, sometimes more slowly. If you know that the roller coaster takes 3 minutes to complete its course and the tracks measure 1170 meters from start to finish, what is the average speed of the roller coaster?**

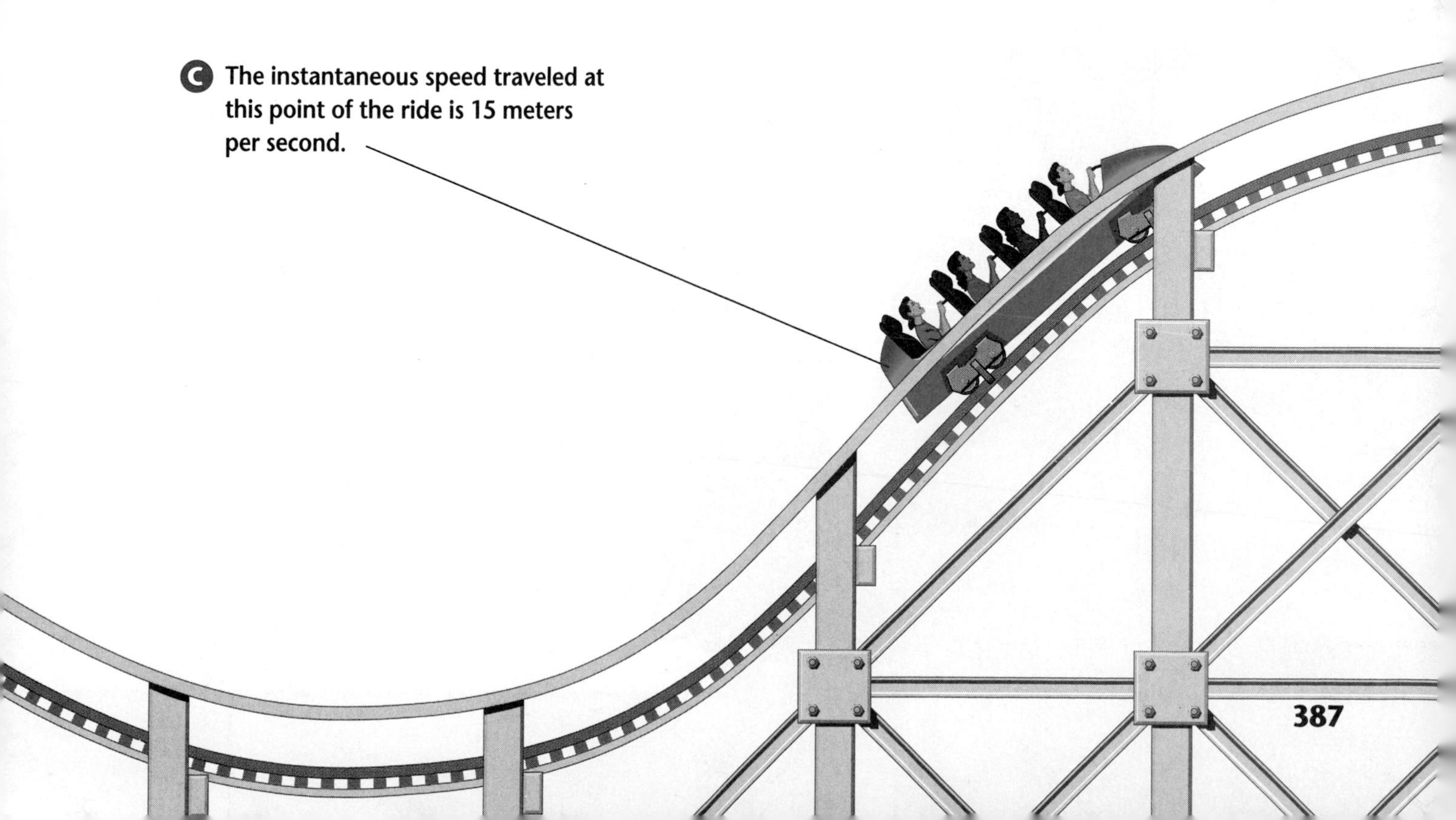

DESIGN YOUR OWN
INVESTIGATION

Average Walking Speed

When you walk, do you feel more comfortable walking barefoot, in sandals, or in athletic shoes designed for walking or running? Have you ever wondered what your average speed is when you walk?

Preparation

Problem

Can the type of foot gear you wear increase your average walking speed?

Form a Hypothesis

As a group, form a hypothesis predicting what foot gear will increase average walking speed for each individual in your group.

Objectives

- Measure speed and find averages for each individual.
- Compare foot gear for walking speed.
- Graph and interpret your data.

Materials

meterstick
masking tape
stopwatch
shoes, boots, and sandals

DESIGN YOUR OWN
INVESTIGATION

Plan the Experiment

1. This is a group activity. Each group should test its hypothesis by designing a test procedure. Write it out step by step.
2. Speed is measured in meters per second (m/s). To find average speed, you need to know the distance traveled and the length of time each individual walked.
3. A walkway of a definite size is needed to conduct tests of the hypotheses. How long will your test track be?
4. How many trials will you conduct for each individual wearing a particular type of shoe? Testing someone 5 times is more reliable than testing once.
5. What foot gear will each individual wear? Should all the individuals tested by one group wear similar foot gear? Make certain that shoes, boots, and sandals are free from mud and dirt.
6. Design data tables *in your Science Journal* or on a spreadsheet for recording your data.

Check the Plan

1. What is your control in this test?
2. What are your variables?
3. Who will collect the data?
4. Make certain your teacher approves your plan before you proceed.
5. Carry out the experiment, make observations, and record the data.

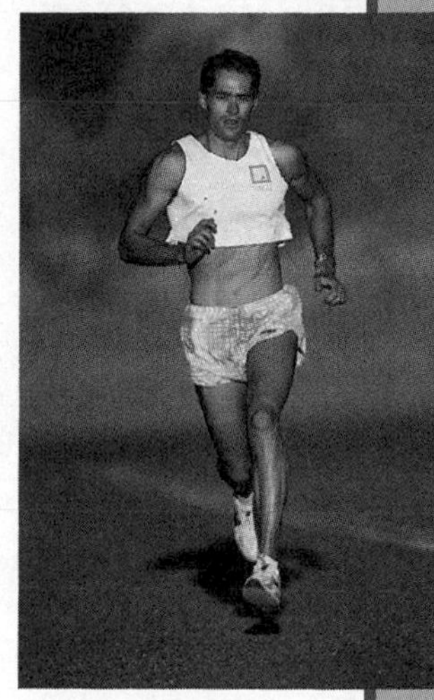

Pete Kain swims, cycles, and runs as a triathlete. If you knew the time and the distance he covers in each event, would you be able to find Pete's average speed as a triathlete? How?

Analyze and Conclude

1. **Analyze** Was your hypothesis supported by the data? Use your data to explain why or why not.
2. **Interpret** What foot gear produced the fastest average speeds in your group?
3. **Analyze** Use all the class data to make bar graphs of individual speeds in each type of foot gear. This can be done on a spreadsheet. When you have a graph for each type of foot gear, analyze each one to find out who was the fastest walker in all the different shoes. Was there a foot gear that caused some individual to walk slower while others walked faster?
4. **Infer** What would happen to your average walking speed if your running shoes had wet mud on them or they were worn down?

Going Further

If your have a suitable track, test which brand of running shoe increases average speed the most.

Figure 12-5

The numbers under each figure indicate the speed of that runner at the instant the photo was taken. Are these photographs a record of average or instantaneous speeds?

As you saw in the Investigate activity, the speed of an object at any one instant may not be the same as the object's average speed. Instantaneous speed is the rate of motion at any given instant. A car's speedometer shows instantaneous speed. In the fable of the tortoise and the hare, the hare's instantaneous speed could be much greater than the tortoise's speed. Which animal had the faster average speed? How do you know?

Walking around an amusement park, riding a roller coaster, driving a car, riding a skateboard, even orbiting planets—all involve a motion during an interval of time. For each motion, we can determine the object's average speed over the path taken by dividing the total distance traveled by the time interval.

The average speed of a moving object tells you how rapidly it travels but it does not tell which way the object goes. In the next section, you will learn how to combine speed and direction to describe an object's motion.

check your UNDERSTANDING

1. In your own words, describe what is meant by (a) position and (b) distance.
2. How could you measure the distance of your path from home to school?
3. List the information you need to calculate the average speed of a car traveling from your house to school.
4. **Apply** Florence Griffith Joyner set a world record by running 200 m in 21.56 s. What was her average speed?

12-2 Velocity

Displacement and Velocity

Section Objectives

- Distinguish between displacement and distance.
- Find the average velocity of a moving object.
- Distinguish between velocity and speed.
- Use the concept of relative velocity.

Key Terms

displacement
average velocity
relative velocity

Have you ever ridden on a merry-go-round or carousel? Usually, a ride on the carousel involves 15 or 20 turns in a circular path. You may ride for three or four minutes, but you get on and off at the same place. Despite all of the trips around in a circle, you really haven't gone anywhere at all.

Displacement

Displacement is the net change in position of an object. A round trip to the store, like the round trips on the carousel, produces a displacement of zero because you end up where you started.

Displacement is described by both a distance and a direction. Distance is the length of the path only. Look at the map on page 392. To say that you live 16 kilometers from the amusement park is not necessarily helpful to another person. Sixteen kilometers could be anywhere in a circle of radius 16 kilometers from the amusement park. To make it more understandable and useful to others, you need to specify which way. As shown by the map, home is 16 kilometers south of the amusement park.

Suppose you drove to and from the amusement park. The odometer of the car measures the distance the car has moved. As with walking, the round trip measures a distance of 32 kilometers. Your displacement is still zero. Is there a way to describe motion that takes displacement into account?

Figure 12-6

The round trip around a Ferris wheel produces a displacement of zero because you get off the ride at the same point that you got on.

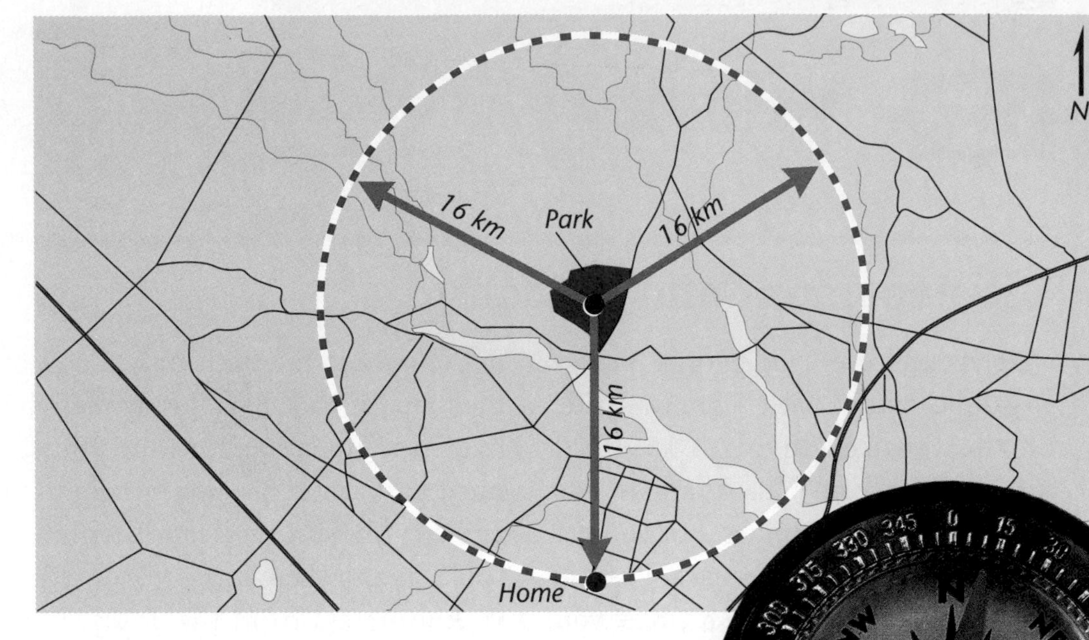

Figure 12-7

A To say that you live 16 kilometers from the amusement park is not necessarily helpful to another person. Sixteen kilometers could be anywhere in a circle of radius 16 kilometers from the amusement park.

B Other people will understand your directions more clearly if you give both a distance and a direction. For example, home is 16 kilometers south of the amusement park.

Making and Using Graphs

The table gives the stopping distances for different speeds. Graph the points with the speed in m/s along the horizontal axis and the stopping distance in meters along the vertical axis. Connect the points with a smooth line.

Using the graph, determine how much braking distance increases when the speed increases from 4 m/s to 8 m/s. If you need help, refer to the **Skill Handbook** on page 657.

Speed (m/s)	Braking Distance (m)
2	1.0
4	2.3
6	4.2
8	6.9
10	10.0

Average Velocity

A measure of motion that tells you how fast and which way an object moves is velocity. You learned in the first section that the average speed of an object depends on the distance traveled within a certain time. Now that you know the difference between distance and displacement, do you think there could also be a measure of how fast an object moved over a certain displacement? There is! The measure of such motion is called **average velocity**.

Calculating an average velocity is similar to calculating an average speed. We are concerned here with the total displacement, which includes distance and direction rather than the total distance traveled. To find average velocity:

$$\text{average velocity} = \frac{\text{total displacement}}{\text{time interval}}$$

Relative Velocity

Have you ever sat in a car at a traffic light and felt you were moving backward? When you looked at other objects outside the car you realized that it was the car next to you moving forward.

The same effect can happen at the amusement park on a double roller coaster with a double track. While waiting for your car to move, the car in the roller coaster next to yours starts moving. You think that you are moving in the opposite direction.

This is an example of **relative velocity.** Relative velocity is the velocity of one object determined from the view, or frame of reference, of another object. Either one or both of the objects may be moving relative to some third object.

Explore! ACTIVITY

What is relative velocity?

What To Do

1. Send a battery-powered toy car along the length of a sheet of paper.
2. Observe the motion of the car.
3. Can you predict what will happen if you send the car along the paper while a friend pulls the paper on the table in the direction of the motion of the car? Try it!
4. Describe the car's motion.
5. Now, observe the motion of the car when the sheet is moved in a direction opposite to that of the car's. What do you see?

In the Explore, the car moved over the paper and over your desktop. The car's motion over both the paper and desk top was the same as long as the paper didn't move. As soon as you made the paper move, however, the car's motion over the desktop was not the same as its motion over the paper. When you describe the motion of the car or any object, you have to compare it to something else—in this case, either the desktop or the paper. The motion that you describe depends on your frame of reference, or what you are comparing the car's motion to. We usually use Earth as our frame of reference. For example, you speak of your motion to and from school in terms of the distance and direction you travel on the surface of Earth. We don't always use Earth as our frame of reference, however.

Figure 12-8

(A) **An astronaut working outside a space shuttle would use the shuttle as her frame of reference. If the astronaut and shuttle are moving in the same direction around Earth at the same orbit speed, then their relative velocity would be zero. In this case, the astronaut would say that she is motionless compared to the space shuttle.**

(B) **On the ground, however, NASA controllers would describe both the astronaut's and the shuttle's orbit speed as about 40 000 kilometers per hour, using Earth as their frame of reference.**

Around and Around We Go

Although we generally express our velocity relative to Earth, we can get some interesting information if we consider our velocity relative to other locations. For example, you know that Earth rotates once every 24 hours. When you stand still, your velocity relative to Earth is zero, yet you are moving as Earth rotates. If a friend were suspended above the North Pole in a spaceship and looking down at Earth, what would your friend observe your velocity to be?

The circumference of Earth at the equator is about 25 000 miles (40 000 km). This means that if you were standing at a

The photograph to the right was taken with a camera pointed at the North Star and with the shutter left open about four hours. The white lines are tracks made by stars as Earth rotated beneath them.

An astronaut making repairs to an object in space would use a different reference point to determine her velocity than a person tracking on the ground. Her only frame of reference is the shuttle.

1. A man walks 2 km due west, then turns around and walks 3 km due east. What distance does the man walk? What is the man's displacement?
2. Explain whether it is possible for a car's average velocity to be zero even if the car traveled a distance of 200 km.
3. An airplane flying toward the west has a speed of 200 km/h. What is the plane's velocity?
4. A student decides to have some fun on a moving walkway at the airport. The walkway moves to the north with a speed of 2 m/s, and the student walks at the same speed in the same direction. What velocity would a person standing next to the walkway measure to describe the student's motion?
5. **Apply** If the same student sees a friend standing next to the walkway and wants to remain at rest relative to that friend, at what velocity (speed and direction) should he or she walk?

point on the equator, you would move 25 000 miles in 24 hours as Earth rotates. That's about 1040 mi/hr (1674 km/hr). Your friend in the spaceship would observe you moving in a circle at that speed.

What is the speed of Earth as it revolves around the sun? Let's find out!

Use your math skills to figure out how fast Earth would appear to be moving if you observed it from the sun. Although Earth's path or orbit around the sun is not a perfect circle, we can get a rough idea of our speed assuming that it is.

1 The circumference of a circle can be calculated using the equation $c = 2\pi r$ where c = circumference, r = the radius of the circle and $\pi = 3.14$. The average distance from Earth to the sun is about 93 000 000 miles (149 700 000 km). This is the radius of the circle or orbit that Earth travels around the sun. Calculate the circumference of the circle.

2 Earth travels this distance, c, in one year (365 days). How far does Earth travel in one day?

3 What is the speed of Earth in miles/hour?

4 Why do you think it might become more important to use relative velocity as we increase our travel in space?

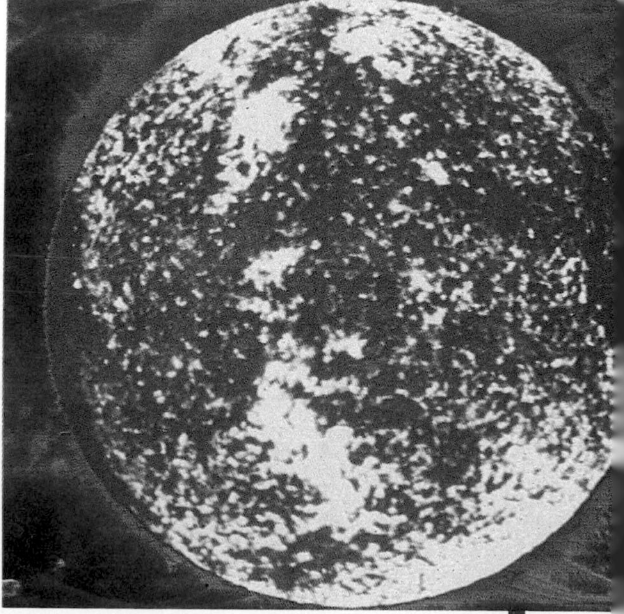

Acceleration

Section Objectives
- Distinguish between velocity and acceleration.
- Determine acceleration from velocity change and time.

Key Terms
acceleration
average acceleration

Changing Velocity

Have you ever enjoyed an absolutely smooth ride? Surely not at the amusement park, where half of the fun comes from sharp turns, moving up and down, and spinning around in circles.

When the velocity of an object changes, the object accelerates. You often do not sense your motion when you are moving at a constant velocity. You do, however, sense motion when you accelerate. Anyone who has ridden on a roller coaster knows about acceleration. When the car takes off quickly from rest, you feel as though you are being pushed back in your seat. When the car's brakes are suddenly applied, you may feel as if you are moving forward. Even in the family car, you move forward if the car stops suddenly. These are everyday examples of acceleration.

When you are moving along in one direction at a constant speed, but then turn quickly to the right or left you feel a push outward. This is another example of acceleration. Since velocity involves both speed and direction, to change your velocity requires that you change either one or the other. Thus, acceleration can be produced by changing your speed (how much) or by changing your direction of travel (which way), or both.

Figure 12-9

A You can sense motion when you accelerate. When your bumper car takes off quickly from rest, you feel as though you are being pushed back in your seat.

B When the bumper car bumps into another car and comes to a sudden stop, you feel yourself being pushed forward.

You often use the word acceleration in conversation when you speak of something speeding up. Did you know you would be equally correct to refer to an object that is slowing down as accelerating? Astronauts undergo large accelerations when they take off from Earth. This is due to their large change in velocity as they move from Earth to their position in orbit around Earth. For this reason, astronauts have comfortably padded seats. When the shuttle and the astronauts return to Earth, they need to slow down. This slowdown is referred to as a negative acceleration.

Acceleration is the rate at which velocity is changing. Because velocity can change by changing either the speed or direction of motion, you can accelerate by changing speed, direction, or both. For an example, suppose you are on a water slide. Both your speed *and* acceleration change as you move over different parts of the slide.

Figure 12-10

Suppose you are on a water slide and speeding up as you move. Your speed changes by 1 meter per second for every second that you move. Your acceleration is 1 meter per second per second, or 1 m/s/s.

A If the slide were steeper, you would gain speed more rapidly—say 2 meters per second for every second that you slide down. Your acceleration along the slide would be 2 m/s/s.

B Each instant on the slide your acceleration changed. Your velocity and your acceleration change every time you go over a bump.

C The acceleration at each instant is called the instantaneous acceleration.

INVESTIGATE!

Instantaneous Acceleration

Have you ever wondered how quickly you can accelerate? You can make an accelerometer that will allow you to measure the instantaneous acceleration of moving objects.

Problem

How can you measure instantaneous acceleration?

Materials

protractor
10 to 12 cm length of string
heavy button

What To Do

1. Copy the data table *into your Journal.*
2. Assemble the materials as shown in the pictures (see photos ***A*** and ***B***).
3. Hold the protractor upside down. When taking a reading, hold the protractor level. With the weight hanging freely, the string should line up with the 90-degree mark on the protractor.

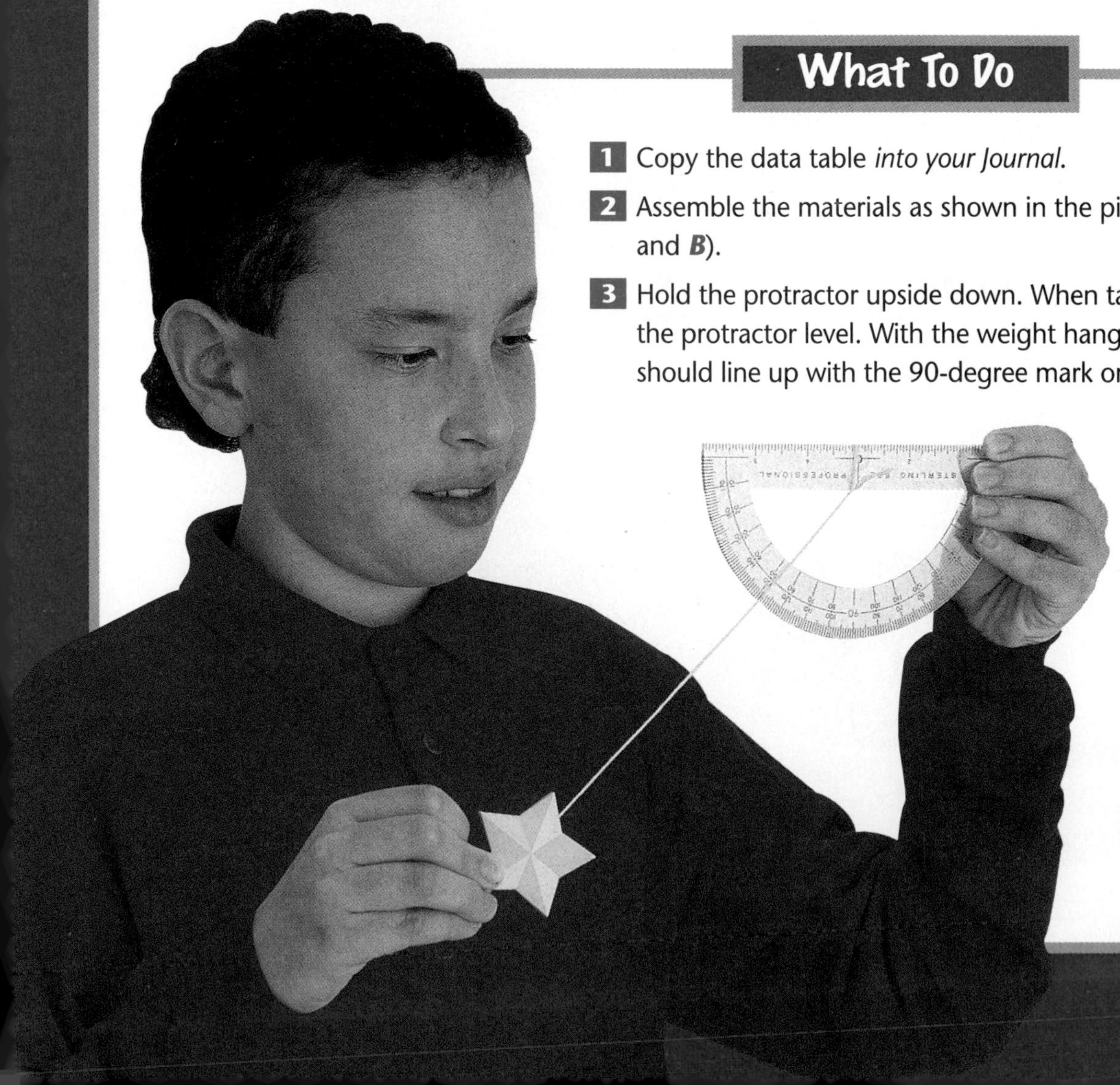

A

B

Moving Object	Acceleration m/s/s
90°	0
80°	1.7
70°	3.6
60°	5.7
50°	8.2
45°	9.8
40°	12
30°	17
20°	27
10°	56
0°	—

Conversion Chart

4 Hold the accelerometer at arm's length in front of your face with the numbers facing you. Quickly move the accelerometer to one side. Observe the maximum angle of the string measured by the protractor. In what direction does the string move? What can you infer about the direction of acceleration? Try moving the accelerometer quickly to the other side. What does this tell you?

5 Use the conversion chart to convert the angle reading on the accelerometer to an acceleration in meters per second per second.

6 Hold the accelerometer level and begin to run. Have a friend run with you and read the angle. Enter this data in the table.

Data and Observations

Moving Object	Acceleration m/s/s

Analyzing

1. In what direction does the string move in comparison with the direction you move when you speed up? Describe.

2. How did the string behave as you slowed down?

Concluding and Applying

3. Describe the position of the string while you were moving with constant velocity.

4. **Going Further** Predict whether or not loose objects in an accelerating car would tend to move in the same direction of the string, or in the opposite direction.

Figure 12-11

A If a go-cart on a straight, level track speeds up from 0 to 3 m/s in 8 seconds, the car's average acceleration is:

Average acceleration = change in velocity/time interval

$$= \frac{3/\text{m/s} - 0 \text{ m/s}}{8 \text{ s}}$$

= 0.375 m/s/s along the track

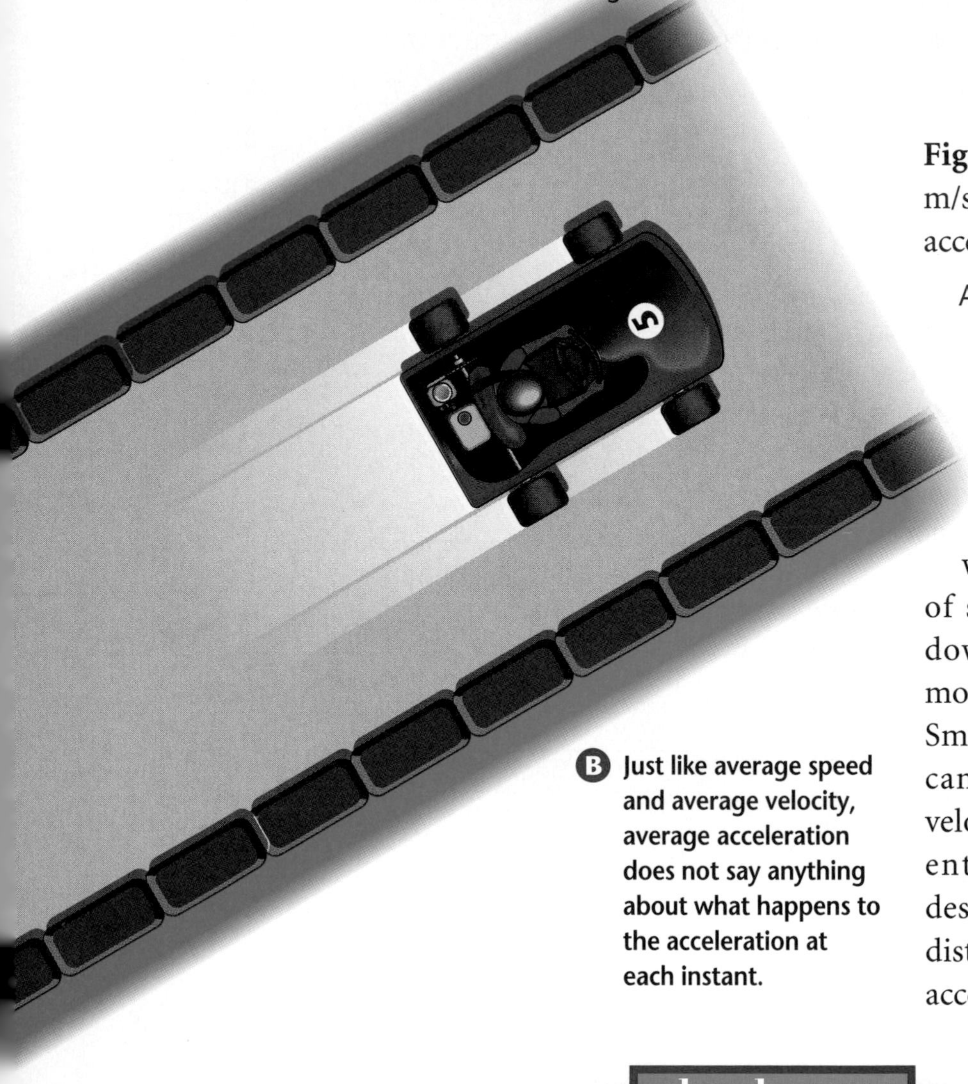

B Just like average speed and average velocity, average acceleration does not say anything about what happens to the acceleration at each instant.

■ Average Acceleration

Calculating average acceleration is similar to finding average velocity. **Average acceleration** is the change in the velocity divided by the time interval during which the change occurs:

Average acceleration = change in velocity/time interval with a certain direction

For example, if the go-cart in **Figure 12-11** speeds up from 0 to 3 m/s in 8 seconds, the go-cart's average acceleration is:

Average acceleration equals the change in velocity divided by the time interval (3m/s – 0 m/s)/8 s = 0.375 m/s/s along the track

Every day of your life, you move in a variety of different ways and experience acceleration of some kind. Whenever you slow down, speed up, turn a corner, or move in a circle, you are accelerating. Smooth rides at a constant velocity can be interrupted by a change in velocity. When observing the different motions around you, try to describe them in terms of position, distance, displacement, velocity, and acceleration.

1. A car moves with a constant velocity of 15 m/s north. What is the car's acceleration?
2. What must happen to the velocity of an object when the object is accelerating?
3. Explain how it is possible for an object to be accelerating if it is moving with constant speed.
4. **Apply** Calculate the average acceleration of a car that increases its velocity along a straight line from 10 m/s to 21 m/s in 7 seconds.

12-4 Motion Along Curves

Changes in Position: Displacement

A long roller coaster has many curves and bends. Obviously, if you were in a hurry to get from one place to another, a path like the one described by the tracks of the roller coaster would not be the quickest way to go! You can easily see that a straight line is a shorter route.

Recall that you find displacement along a straight line by subtracting the starting position from the finishing position and noting direction of the motion. But how do you find displacement between two points along a curved line, a winding road for example?

Section Objectives

- Distinguish between a displacement and a distance along a curved path.
- Find the average velocity for motion along a curved path.
- Recognize situations for which there is an acceleration, called the centripetal acceleration, even when the speed is constant.

Key Terms

centripetal acceleration

Find Out! ACTIVITY

How is displacement along a curved path measured?

Look closely at the drawing. It shows both the actual path and the displacement of a train along an amusement park track. What is the train's displacement for this trip?

What To Do

1. Use the scale at the bottom of the diagram to determine the length of the displacement.
2. Use a protractor to measure the direction. Record your measurements *in your Journal.*

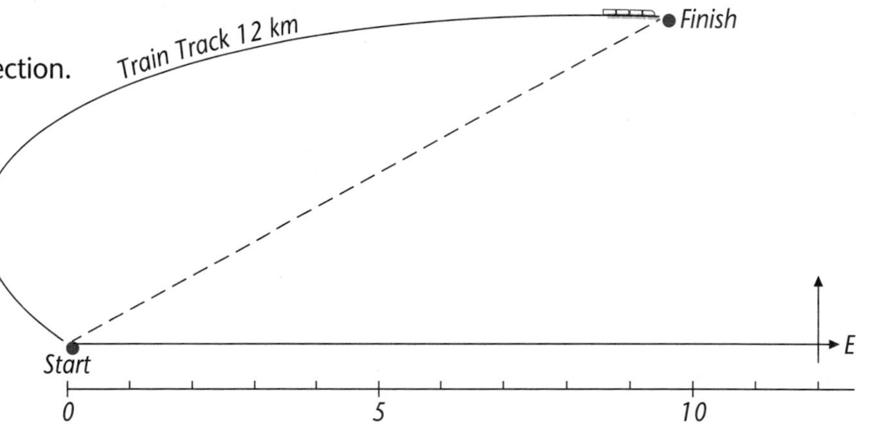

Conclude and Apply

1. What is the average velocity if the train completes the trip in 3 hours? Divide the total displacement by the time interval.
2. Is the distance along a curved path always greater than the displacement between the start and end points?

You learned in the Find Out that displacement along a curved path is measured along a straight line connecting the start and end points. If you travel on a curved road from one town to another, your displacement will be the distance, measured along a straight line, between the two towns. The actual distance you traveled along the curved road will be greater than the displacement.

Figure 12-12

A **Imagine planning an automobile trip from Falmouth to New Bedford, Massachusetts. The only route possible is a curved and hilly highway around Buzzards Bay.**

B **Once you arrive at New Bedford, your displacement is the distance measured along a straight line between the two towns.**

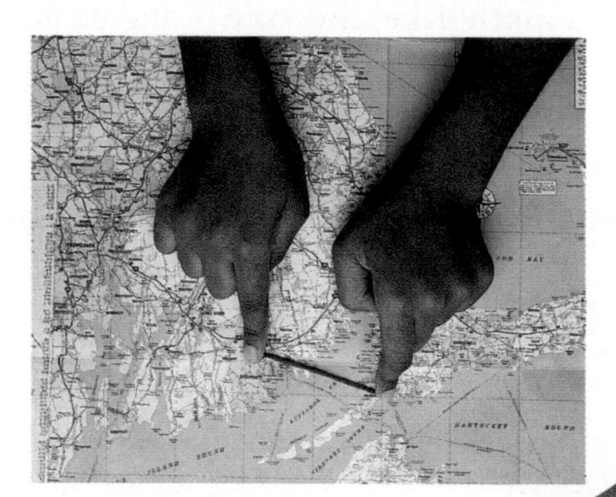

C **Will the actual distance you travel be greater than or less than your displacement?**

Centripetal Acceleration

If you were traveling on a curve, in which direction would you accelerate? In the next exercise you will explore the direction of acceleration along a curved path.

You are already familiar with the effects of acceleration. When a car speeds up, you feel pushed backward. As an elevator starts upward, you feel pushed downward. By such experience, you know you are accelerating in a direction opposite to that in which you feel pushed. Therefore, in circular motion, since the push feels outward, acceleration must be inward. A device that shows direction inward when moving in a circle is the bubble accelerometer. In the next activity you will see how the device directly shows acceleration.

Connect to...

Life Science

Centrifuges spin materials in a circle. They are used to separate blood cells from plasma, cream from milk, and for concentrating viruses. Make a drawing of a centrifuge and explain how it works.

Explore! ACTIVITY

What is the direction of acceleration of an object moving along a circular path?

What To Do

1. Fill a test tube with water. There should be 1 cm air space at the top after a stopper has been inserted into the test tube.
2. When you turn the test tube on its side, you will have a bubble accelerometer. Hold the test tube level and accelerate it to the right. Which way did the bubble move relative to the acceleration? Now lay the test tube on the radius of a record turntable. After attaching the test tube securely with masking tape, start the turntable rotating at its slowest speed. Which way does the bubble move? Could you use this bubble accelerometer to detect acceleration for other objects that can move in circular paths?

Bubble
Test tube with water and air bubble
Turntable

In the Explore, the inward motion of the bubble shows that the acceleration is directed toward the center of the turntable. The direction of the acceleration of an object moving along a circular path is toward the center of the circle and is called **centripetal acceleration**.

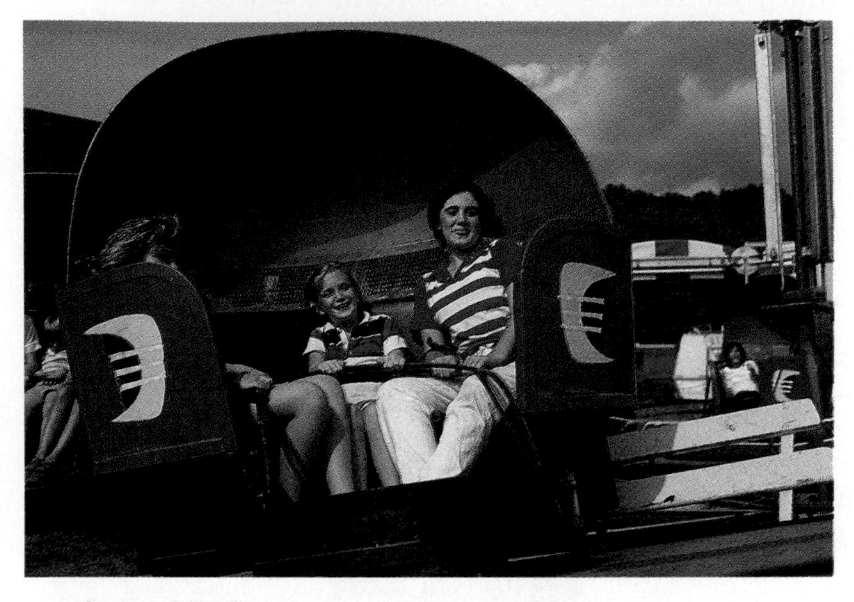

Figure 12-13

On a tilt-a-whirl, you spin around in a small circular path. At the same time, your small cart is sweeping in a larger circular path. At times, the acceleration would result in your being flung against the side of the cart so that you could be accelerated the same as the cart.

You've had a busy day at the amusement park. You have learned some amazing things about objects that travel in circular paths. Now you're hungry. You've really worked up an appetite. To get to the ice cream stand as quickly as possible, you would take the straightest path. You calculate the displacement in the same way, whether the path traveled is straight or curved. Remember that displacement and not the distance along any path traveled is used to calculate average velocity. If you ride in a roller coaster at a constant speed on a curved track, you are continually undergoing centripetal acceleration. You are always accelerating toward the center of the curve or circle that you are traveling around.

As a satellite or space shuttle travels in its orbit around Earth, even when it has a constant speed, it is accelerating toward Earth. You will find out what the source of this acceleration is in the next chapter.

check your UNDERSTANDING

1. If you travel on a curved road from one town to another, your displacement is always different from your actual distance traveled. One is always greater. Explain how you would measure each and why one is greater. Draw a diagram to help you with your explanation.
2. Explain what you would need to know to find the average velocity for motion along a curved path.
3. Why is an object accelerating when it is moving in a circle at constant speed?
4. **Apply** Could you use a bubble accelerometer to study the centripetal acceleration of a moving car? Explain how you would do it.

HISTORY CONNECTION

History of Time

How precisely did people know the time before watches and electric clocks were invented? How did people organize their days before agreeing on a system?

When people first began to farm and build towns, about 10,000 years ago, the most important times to know were the seasons of the year. These were easy to measure by counting the days since the sun was highest in the sky in summer, or since the river flooded in the spring. People soon realized that the seasons repeated themselves about every 365 days.

As life in towns required cooperation among many different people, it became important to know the time of day. The position of the sun in the sky gave a clue, and this could be measured using the first clock, a shadow clock or sundial as shown in the figure. About 4000 years ago in Egypt, an early shadow clock was a post in the ground. If you stood looking at the post toward north, the post would cast a shadow toward the west, to your left, as the sun rose in the morning. At sundown, the shadow would be cast toward the east, to your right, as the sun set in the west. At any point in the day, the shadow would fall on a different position on the ground. This position told the time. During the day, the shadow's tip would move

from left to right in an arc to the north.

The shadow clock was only useful during the day, and people began to invent new clocks that would work at night too. One of these was the water clock. If you made a water jug with a small hole in the bottom, the water would slowly leak out and the water level would go down. The level of the water in the jug would tell you how much time had passed since the jug was filled.

The water clock worked fine during the summer, but not when the water froze during winter. This problem was solved by substituting fine sand for water. By about the year 800, the sand clock became the hourglass, a bottle with two compartments separated by a partition with a small hole in it. When the sand all fell through the hole to the bottom compartment, someone quickly turned it over so that the sand would flow the other way.

The water and sand clocks were inconvenient because someone always had to be there to refill the water or turn the hourglass over.

By the 1300s, accurate mechanical clocks were invented using a falling weight that turned an axle, indicating the time in hours. These were used in towns to ring bells so that everyone would know what hour it was. It was not until the 1600s that precise portable clocks using springs were used on sailing ships to help in navigation. These ships' clocks were later made much smaller so that everyone could carry a precise watch.

You Try It!

Build a shadow clock and measure its accuracy. Place a straight stick in the ground. At 8:00 A.M., place a small stone at the tip of the stick's shadow. At every hour after 8:00, place another stone on the shadow's tip. On another day, choose five times during the day and use your shadow clock to measure the time as accurately as possible. Compare the shadow-clock times with the actual time measured with a clock. What are the differences between the shadow clock times and the actual times? How much error would you make in estimating the time using the shadow clock?

Check your shadow clock a few times for the next few weeks. Do the shadow tips still match perfectly with your stones at selected times? Explain why.

Technology Connection

The Technology of Thrills

Ron Toomer gets motion sickness and hates to ride on roller coasters. He especially hates to ride on the Magnum XL-200 in Sandusky, Ohio, the world's largest roller coaster. The Magnum reaches a speed of 75 miles per hour and drops 210 feet on one of its downhill runs. When the cars reach the bottom, the riders are pressed into their seats with about as much force as astronauts taking off in the space shuttle. Ron Toomer is the engineer who designed the Magnum and 80 other roller coasters all over the world. He and the other engineers who design roller coasters have two important thoughts in mind when they begin to plan a new ride—how to make it safe for the riders, and how to produce as many thrills as possible.

Most roller coasters are now built from thick steel tubes. A team of engineers uses computers to calculate how strong the track has to be to stand up to the weight, speed, and forces of the cars as they climb, coast down, and go into loops upside down. For every foot of track, the computers calculate the car's velocity and its forces upward, downward, and sideways. New coaster cars are made with wheels above, below, and inside the tracks to keep the car from flying off into space when it goes upside down through corkscrew loops. After the roller coaster is built, computers monitor the speed of each car and apply several different brakes if the car begins to move too fast. The steel tracks and supports are checked for cracks with X-ray machines, and padded steel lap bars and belts keep the riders safely in their seats. For every new thrill built into a roller coaster, new safety features are added.

If Ron Toomer thinks of a new loop or twist that he would find terrifying, he knows that it will be popular with the public and his own kids. His fun comes from using his knowledge of mechanical engineering to create the most terrifying but safest roller coaster rides he can think of.

Using Computers

Take a survey of your classmates and friends to find out how many have ridden on a roller coaster, and how many of them would ride on one again. Ask what the roller coaster fans like about the rides. Using a spreadsheet, record your data and graph the results.

How Do You Paint Motion?

Italian painter Giacomo Balla painted Dynamism of a Dog on a Leash in 1912. He and his artistic friends at the time called themselves "futurists." They were tired of paintings that only showed objects and people at one instant in time like a snapshot. They believed that the future of the modern world would be full of machines in motion and they wanted a new way to paint moving objects that showed the excitement of their motion.

In this painting, which is shown on the right, the dachshund dog and its fashionable lady are shown with their feet in all possible positions as the dog trots down the street on its daily walk. Looking at the picture, you may get the idea that motion produces a blur to the eye. Single instants of time blend into one another because the eye and the brain cannot keep up with rapidly changing positions.

This painting was probably inspired by the first primitive movies that were made a few years earlier. These were a series of photographs of moving animals and people taken quickly, one after the other. Looking at one picture and then the next by flipping through the photographs lets you imagine the motion taking place. Balla painted the moving dog as if many of these photographs were added together in one place. The effect is to show changing positions over time in a single painting. This kind of painting was very unusual in 1912.

What Do You Think?

Do you think Balla was successful in capturing the rapid motions of the dachshund in this painting? Can you think of other ways that a painting or drawing can show motion? Draw a picture using one of these ideas.

chapter 12
REVIEWING MAIN IDEAS

Science Journal

Review the statements below about the big ideas presented in this chapter, and answer the questions. Then, re-read your answers to the Did You Ever Wonder questions at the beginning of the chapter. *In your Science Journal,* write a paragraph about how your understanding of the big ideas in the chapter has changed.

1. **Average speed is the total distance traveled divided by the total time required to travel the distance.** ***Who will win a race, the cyclist with the greatest instantaneous or average speed?***

2. **Average velocity is a quantity giving the total displacement divided by the time interval. It includes direction.** ***What factors must sailboats take into consideration about the wind in order to win a race?***

3. **Acceleration is a change in velocity that occurs over time.** ***If the girl on the right accelerates down the slide from 0 to 5 meters per second in 2 seconds, what is her average acceleration?***

4. **When an object travels along a curved path at a constant speed, its direction of motion is constantly changing.** ***What kind of acceleration is the object experiencing?***

CHAPTER REVIEW

Using Key Science Terms

acceleration
average acceleration
average speed
average velocity
centripetal acceleration
displacement
distance
position
relative velocity

Each phrase below describes a science term from the list. Write the term that matches the phrase describing it.

1. total velocity change divided by total time
2. ten miles per hour
3. ten miles per hour south
4. comparing your location to the location of a known point
5. acceleration of a point on the edge of a spinning compact disc.

Understanding Ideas

Answer the following questions in your Journal *using complete sentences.*

1. Why is the term "10 miles per hour" not a description of velocity?
2. How can the amount of your displacement be less than the distance you travel?
3. How can you determine if an object is accelerating?
4. What does an odometer measure?
5. If an object is slowing down, could you say that it is accelerating?

Developing Skills

Use your understanding of the concepts developed in this chapter to answer each of the following questions.

1. **Concept Mapping** You travel in a car to your grandmother's house. You want to know your average speed for the trip. Create an events chain to show how you would find your average speed.
2. **Making and Using Tables** The following are men's American record times for five running events: 100 m–9.85 s; 200 m–19.73 s; 400 m–43.29 s; 800 m–1 min 42.60 s; 1500 m–3 min 29.77 s. Use these data to make a table listing the event and average speed of each event. Do you notice any pattern in the table?
3. **Interpreting Data and Predicting** Use your results from the previous exercise to predict the average speed for the 1000 m race. Then use your prediction to estimate the record time.
4. **Making and Using Graphs** The data in the illustration below give the stopping distances for different car speeds. Plot these points on a graph with the speed in m/s along the horizontal axis and the stopping distance in meters along the vertical axis. Connect the points with a smooth line. Using your graph, determine how much the stopping distance

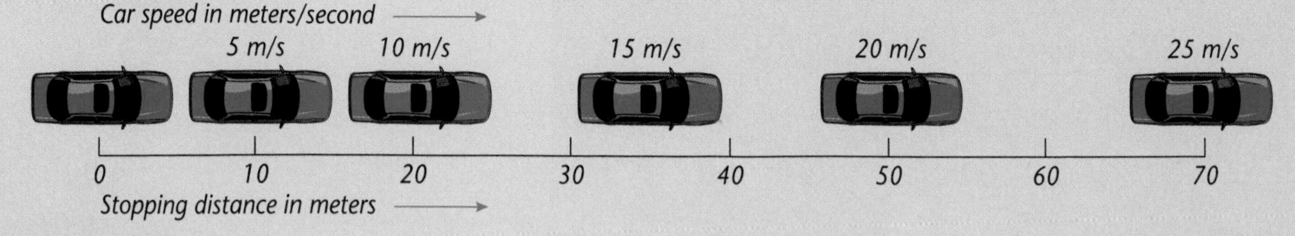

increases when the speed increases from 15 m/s to 20 m/s.

Critical Thinking

In your Journal, *answer the following questions.*

1. When does the distance along a path equal the displacement?
2. If two friends riding bicycles together both have the same velocity relative to Earth, what is their velocity relative to each other?
3. How might you determine the speed of your car if the speedometer broke?
4. When you enter some tollways, you are given a toll card that tells the location and time you entered. When you exit, the time on the toll card can be checked. Could a driver ever be issued a speeding ticket with this information? Explain.

Problem Solving

Read the following problem and discuss your answers in a brief paragraph.

Your friend lives in another city in your state and wants to visit you. Your friend just called and wants to know the shortest highway route between your two cities. All you have is your state map and a piece of string. Can you determine the shortest route with just the map and the string? Can you determine the displacement? Try it.

Obtain a map of your state and select another city on the map. Using a piece of string, how could you find the shortest highway route from your city to the one you picked? How would you determine the displacement involved?

CONNECTING IDEAS

Discuss each of the following in a brief paragraph.

1. **Theme—Stability and Change** Cruise control in a car keeps the car's speed constant. Does this necessarily keep the car's velocity constant?
2. **Theme—Systems and Interactions** If you are on a train or a plane with the window shades down, how do you know that you are moving? What could you do to find out if you are moving or not?
3. **A Closer Look** Who moves faster as Earth rotates, you or a person at the equator? Explain.
4. **History Connection** Compare and contrast three different methods of measuring time. What are the advantages and the disadvantages of each method?
5. **Technology Connection** In which position(s) on a roller coaster track do you experience centripetal acceleration?

CHAPTER 13

MOTION NEAR EARTH

Did you ever wonder...

- **Whether heavy objects fall to Earth more quickly than light objects?**
- **How satellites can stay in orbit?**
- **Why astronauts float around in the space shuttle?**

Science Journal

Before you begin to study about motion near Earth, think about these questions and answer them *in your Science Journal.* When you finish the chapter, compare your journal write-up with what you have learned.

Humans live only on Earth. We seldom stray far from its surface. You may have flown in an airplane, but that's still close to Earth. Some humans have gone to the moon. That may seem a long way from Earth, but compared with the distance to the other planets or the stars, it's not far at all.

Because we have spent nearly all of our time on Earth's surface, almost all our experience with motion has to do with the way objects move near or on Earth. When you shoot a basketball at a basket, you know the ball will fall back down. When you run down a basketball court, you know you are continually pushing off Earth and dropping back to it with each step.

How does motion close to Earth differ from what it would be in space? In this chapter, you'll explore motion on Earth and get an idea of how you would move elsewhere.

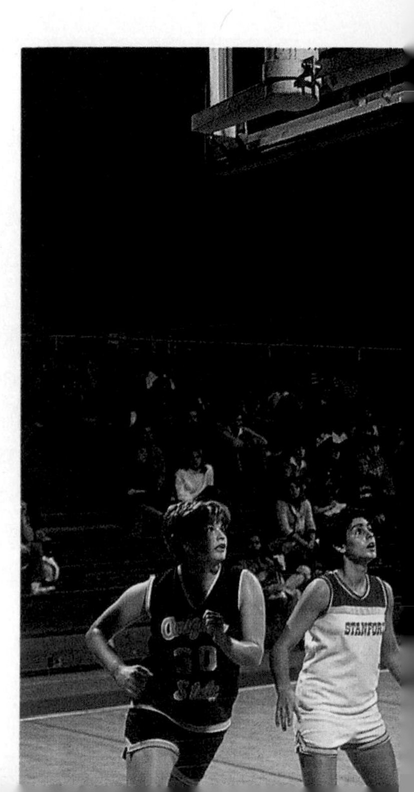

Explore! ACTIVITY

How do things fall?

You learned about motion in Chapter 12. Does the size or mass of an object affect its fall?

What To Do

1. Make two balls out of modeling clay, one about 1.5 cm in diameter and the other about 4 cm in diameter.
2. Determine which ball is heavy and which one is light.
3. *In your Journal,* predict which ball will fall more quickly when both balls are dropped from the same height at the same time.
4. Drop them at the same time from the same height.
5. Describe *in your Journal* how the balls landed.
6. Attach one of the clay balls to each end of a pencil. Hold this object high and drop it. Repeat the activity, varying the position of the balls.
7. Record *in your Journal* how the object fell and landed each time you dropped it.

13-1 Falling Bodies

Section Objectives

- Calculate the acceleration of a falling object given measurements of its position at various times.
- Describe the motion of an object as it falls freely toward Earth.

Key Terms

acceleration due to gravity

Describing How Things Fall

You experience falling objects every day. Raindrops or snowflakes may have fallen on you, and you may have seen leaves, seeds, or twigs fall from trees. When you jump, you always come back to Earth. What always brings you back to Earth when you jump? In this section, you will describe the motion of falling objects and learn that there is something similar about the motions of all falling objects, including yourself.

When Mass Varies

More than 2300 years ago, the Greek philosopher Aristotle was interested in the question—do heavy objects fall in the same amount of time as lighter objects? Aristotle, like others of his time, thought that Earth was the center of the universe and that objects with more mass would naturally rush more quickly to the center of the universe. Aristotle would have said that a large stone would fall more quickly than a small pebble.

In the early 1600s, the Italian scientist Galileo used experimentation to answer the question about falling objects. According to legend, Galileo dropped objects of different masses from the top of the Leaning Tower of Pisa to find out which would hit the ground first. See **Figure 13-1** to find out Galileo's conclusions.

Figure 13-1

A Although many doubt the accuracy of the legend that Galileo dropped objects from the top of the Leaning Tower of Pisa to find which would hit the ground first, Galileo did experiment with falling objects.

B From his many experiments, Galileo concluded that all objects should fall from the same height in the same time.

Find Out! ACTIVITY

Do heavier objects fall more quickly?

There are several ways to find out whether heavy objects fall more quickly than light objects. One way is to observe the motion of a pendulum.

What To Do

1. Make a pendulum by tying a 1 m length of string to two heavy bolts, nuts, or similar objects.
2. Hold the end of the string with one hand while you pull the objects, the pendulum bob, to one side about 25 cm with the other hand.
3. Release the bob and observe it closely.
4. Construct another pendulum the same length, using only one bolt, nut, or similar object.
5. Have a partner hold one pendulum while you hold the other. Start the pendulums swinging at the same time by pulling the bobs back about 25 cm and releasing them.

Conclude and Apply

1. What happened when the pendulums were released?
2. Which pendulum bob reached the bottom of the swing first? Did the heavy bob fall more quickly?

C **Leaves float and drift when they fall because of air resistance.**

As you saw in the Find Out activity, both bobs appear to reach the bottom of the swing at the same time. But you, like Galileo, couldn't really be certain whether the objects reached the bottom at the same time because they were moving too quickly. In the next activity, you have an opportunity to observe two balls of different masses, a baseball and a tennis ball, falling from the same height.

INVESTIGATE!

Acceleration of Falling Objects

Two falling balls were recorded by strobe photography. Six photographs were taken, each 1/10 of a second apart. Even though the balls are of different masses, they are falling at the same rate. Figure 13-2 is a drawing made from that photograph. At one side of the figure is a two-meter measuring stick. As each ball falls, there seems to be more distance between each succeeding image. You learned in Chapter 12 that distance traveled in a given time is a measure of speed. Therefore, if the balls are moving greater distances in the same period of time, they are speeding up or accelerating. Use Figure 13-2 to discover the acceleration of these two falling objects.

Figure 13-2

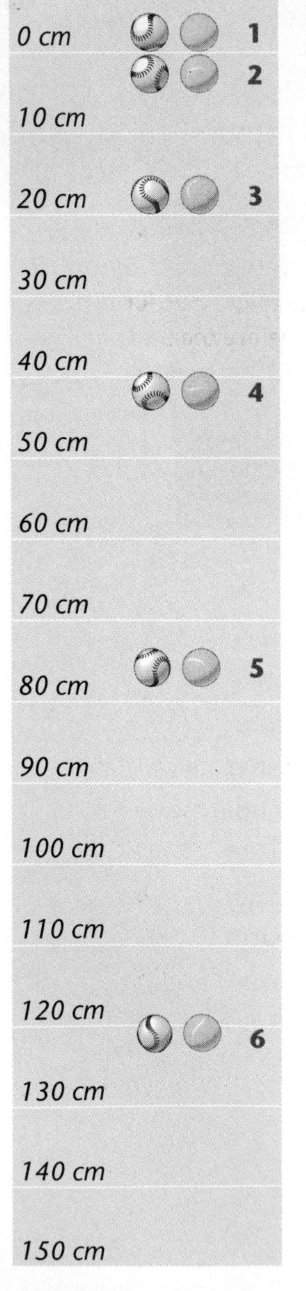

Problem

What is the acceleration of falling objects?

Materials

ruler data table **Figure 13-2**

What To Do

1. Copy the data table *into your Journal.*
2. Using the ruler as a guide, record the position of the first image of one ball as it starts to fall. Always ***measure*** the ball position from the same point on the ball.

Data and Observations

Image	Position (cm)	Distance Fallen (cm)	Average Velocity (m/s)	Time (s)
1				
2				0.10
3				0.20
4				0.30
5				0.40
6				0.50

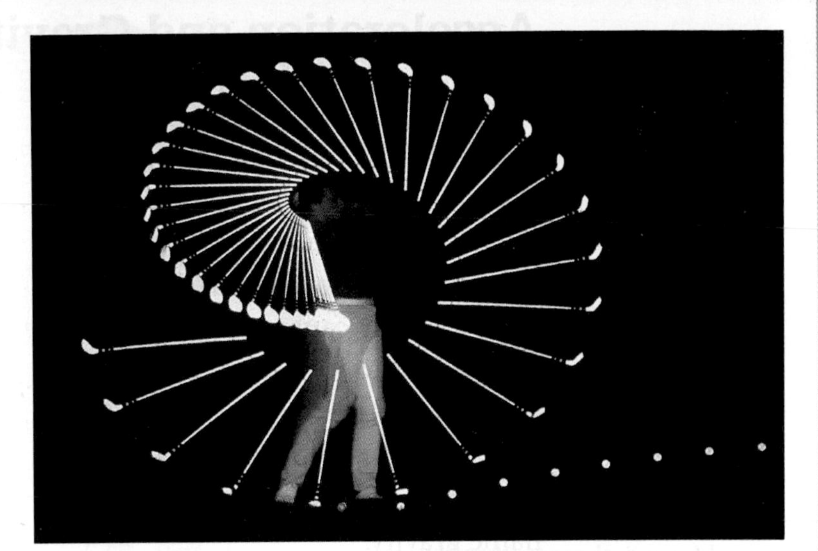

Harold E. Edgerton (1903-1990) developed strobe photography, which enables a photographer to take multi-image photographs of moving subjects. Each image in this photo was taken only a fraction of a second before the next.

3 Now, record the position of the second image.

4 ***Calculate*** the distance from the first to the second image by subtracting the position of the first image from the position of the second image. Record this distance in the table under Image 2.

5 The images were taken 1/10 of a second apart. Use this information to ***calculate*** the average velocity of the balls between the first and second image in meters per second by dividing the distance fallen (in meters) by 1/10 second.

6 Record the position of the rest of the images. Make sure you always measure to the leading edge of the ball.

7 Find the distance between each pair of images and the average velocity. Fill these in for the rest of the images.

8 The last column of the table shows the exact time the balls' velocity reached the average velocity. To calculate these times, we assumed the clock started at the time of the first image and that the ball reached average velocity halfway in time between any two images.

Analyzing

1. Did the velocity of the balls change as they fell? How do you know?
2. Make a bar graph of distance fallen versus time. ***Infer*** what the graph tells about the balls' positions as they fell.

Concluding and Applying

3. How much did the average velocity increase between the second and third images? Between the third and the fourth images?
4. **Going Further** ***Calculate*** the balls' acceleration. Find the acceleration between the image at 0.10 s and the image at 0.30 s by dividing the increase in velocity by the time interval in seconds. What was your result?

Acceleration on the Moon

Have you ever seen films of astronauts on the moon? If you have, you may have wondered why the astronauts seemed to float as they move from place to place. Why are astronauts on the moon able to jump up so high and then appear to float down?

The acceleration of gravity on the moon is less than the acceleration of gravity on Earth. Jumping astronauts on the moon reach a greater height before the acceleration of gravity slows them to a stop and causes them to fall back to the surface.

If you had the opportunity to play basketball on the moon, even Michael Jordan would be amazed at what you could do. Slam-dunking the ball would be simple because the lower acceleration due to gravity on the moon would allow you to jump higher.

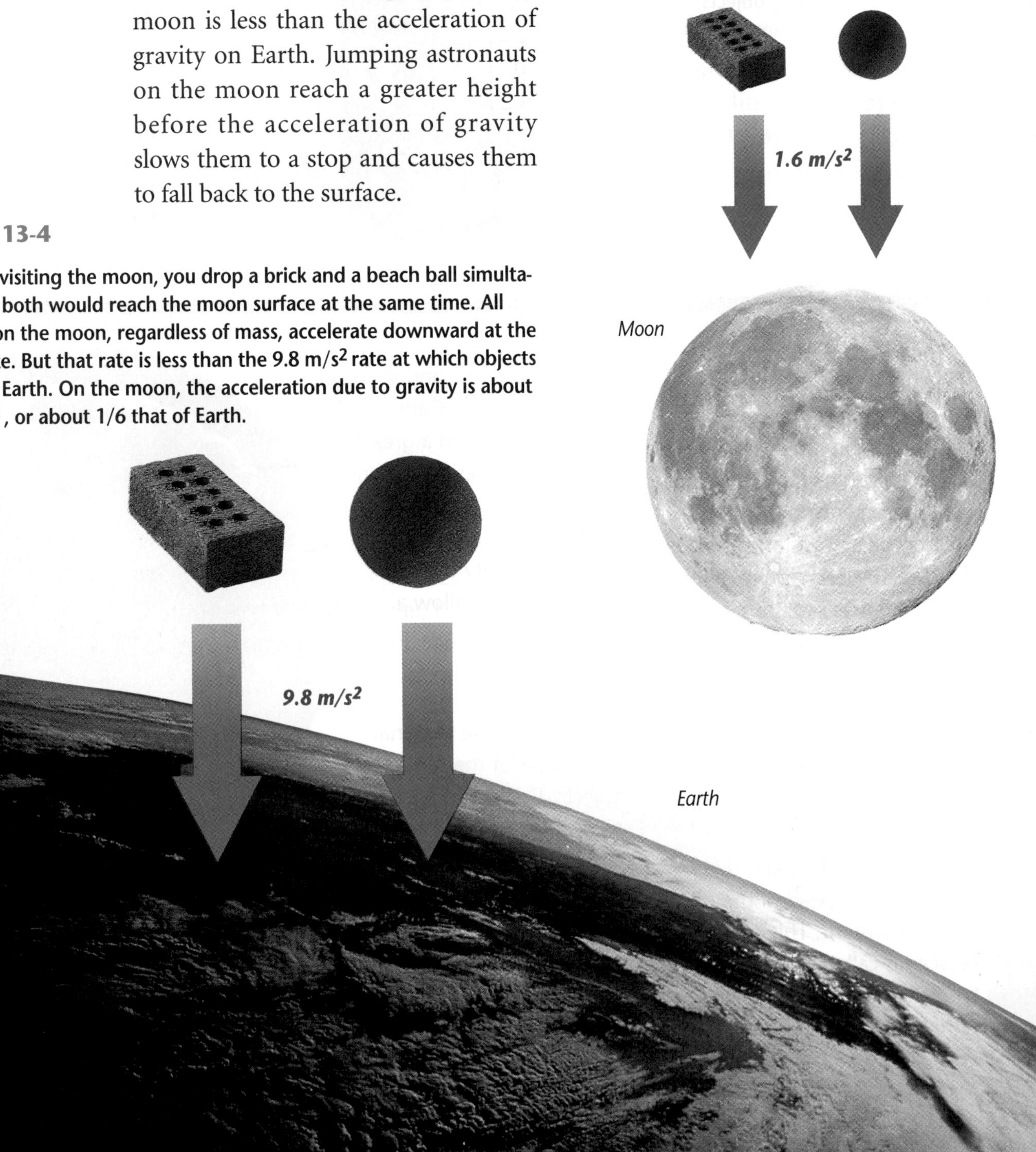

Figure 13-4

If, while visiting the moon, you drop a brick and a beach ball simultaneously, both would reach the moon surface at the same time. All objects on the moon, regardless of mass, accelerate downward at the same rate. But that rate is less than the 9.8 m/s^2 rate at which objects fall near Earth. On the moon, the acceleration due to gravity is about 1.6 m/s^2, or about 1/6 that of Earth.

Figure 13-5

One important thing that determines how hard you must push off the ground to get moving when riding on a skateboard is gravity.

SKILLBUILDER

Making and Using Graphs

Plot a graph of the results of Investigate 13-1. Put the average velocity of the ball on the vertical axis. Put the times that the ball actually fell at this velocity on the horizontal axis. Connect the points on the graph with a smooth line that goes all the way to the horizontal axis. Describe this line in words using the variables in your experiment (time and average velocity) in your description. If you need help, refer to the **Skill Handbook** on page 657.

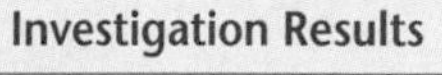
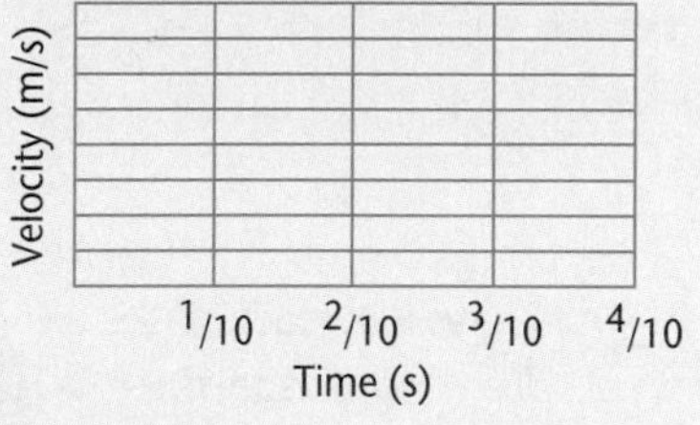

We experience gravity in our everyday activities. Gravity is important even as you walk or run.

Without air, heavy objects, light objects, and objects in between all fall with an acceleration equal to *g*. You now know at what rate of acceleration dropped objects fall at or near Earth's surface. What about when something is actually thrown, like when you throw a ball to the catcher to get a player out at home plate? Does this forward motion affect the way the object falls? In the next section, you will explore the kinds of motion that occur when an object is thrown.

check your UNDERSTANDING

1. Calculate the speed, in meters per second, of an object that has been falling from a building for eight seconds.
2. Explain in your own words how falling objects accelerate.
3. How could you show that the acceleration due to gravity of an object is a constant?
4. **Apply** Suppose an astronaut on the moon dropped a piece of rock from a height of 2 m and measured the time it took to fall to the moon's surface. Explain why a rock dropped from the same height on Earth would reach the ground more quickly than the rock dropped on the moon.

Projectile Motion

Section Objectives
- Describe the horizontal motion of a projectile.
- Describe the vertical motion of a projectile.
- Explain how vertical and horizontal motions of projectiles are independent.

Key Terms
projectile motion

The Motion of Projectiles

Everyone has, at one time or another, experienced projectile motion. What happens when you throw a stone or ball? The object will follow some curve through the air until it falls back down to Earth. Objects that are launched forward into the air, such as rockets, bullets, and satellites, are called projectiles. But even common objects, such as a soccer ball or baseball are projectiles. An object that is launched forward (horizontally) and then falls back to Earth is said to have **projectile motion**. How does such a thrown object move?

Figure 13-6

A Holding a basketball up to your chest, you fire the ball horizontally as hard as you can. The ball goes speeding away from your fingertips.

B At the exact moment that you let go of the ball, a friend drops a coin from the same height as you held the basketball.

C Both the coin and ball started from the same height. Both should fall at the same rate, but the basketball is moving forward as it falls. Does the forward motion of the ball affect the time it takes to fall?

Find Out! ACTIVITY

Does forward motion affect falling speed?

You can investigate the motion of projectiles by doing the following activity with a meterstick and two coins.

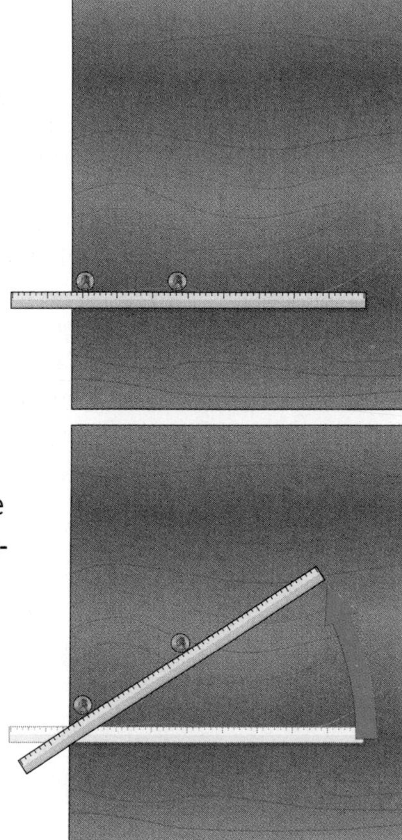

What To Do

1. Lay a meterstick on a table with approximately 20 cm extending over the edge of the table.
2. Place one coin next to the meterstick and close to the edge of the table.
3. Place a second coin 15 to 20 cm further up the meterstick. Both coins should be just a few millimeters from the stick.
4. Holding your finger on the meterstick at the edge of the table, quickly swing the meterstick so it pivots and pushes both coins off the table at the same time.

Conclude and Apply

1. Which coin flew off the table faster?
2. Which coin hit the floor first?
3. How did the motion of the coins differ as they were pushed off the table?

In the Find Out activity, both coins should have hit the floor at the same time, but it's difficult to see. The motion of the coins may have been too quick to let you analyze exactly what happened. Once again, we can use strobe photography to observe motion more accurately. The strobe photograph in **Figure 13-7** allows us to examine a similar experiment done with two golf balls.

As you can see, both balls are falling at the same rate. This means that a basketball fired from your hands horizontally will hit the ground at the same time as a coin dropped by your friend. How would you explain this?

Figure 13-7

A This strobe photograph shows the path of two golf balls. The red ball was dropped and the yellow one was fired horizontally.

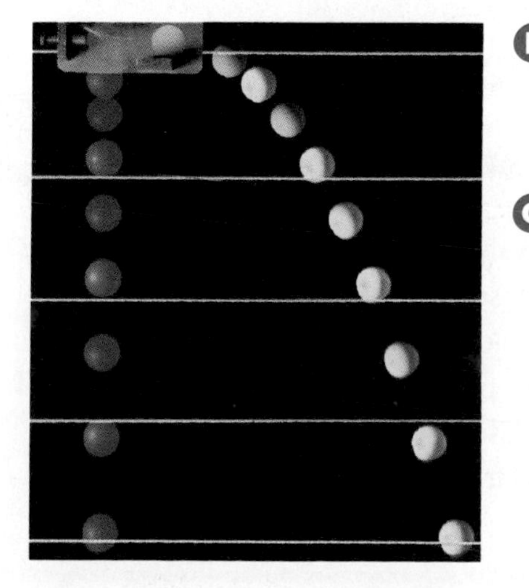

B The dropped ball fell straight downward. The fired ball moved horizontally as it fell.

C Both balls hit the ground at the same time. Both balls had a downward acceleration of 9.8 m/s^2. The forward motion of the yellow ball did not affect the rate at which it fell.

Horizontal and Vertical Components

We've been talking about projectile motion almost as if it were two separate motions. There's motion across the ground that we've been calling horizontal motion, and there's falling motion that we've been calling vertical motion.

Figure 13-8

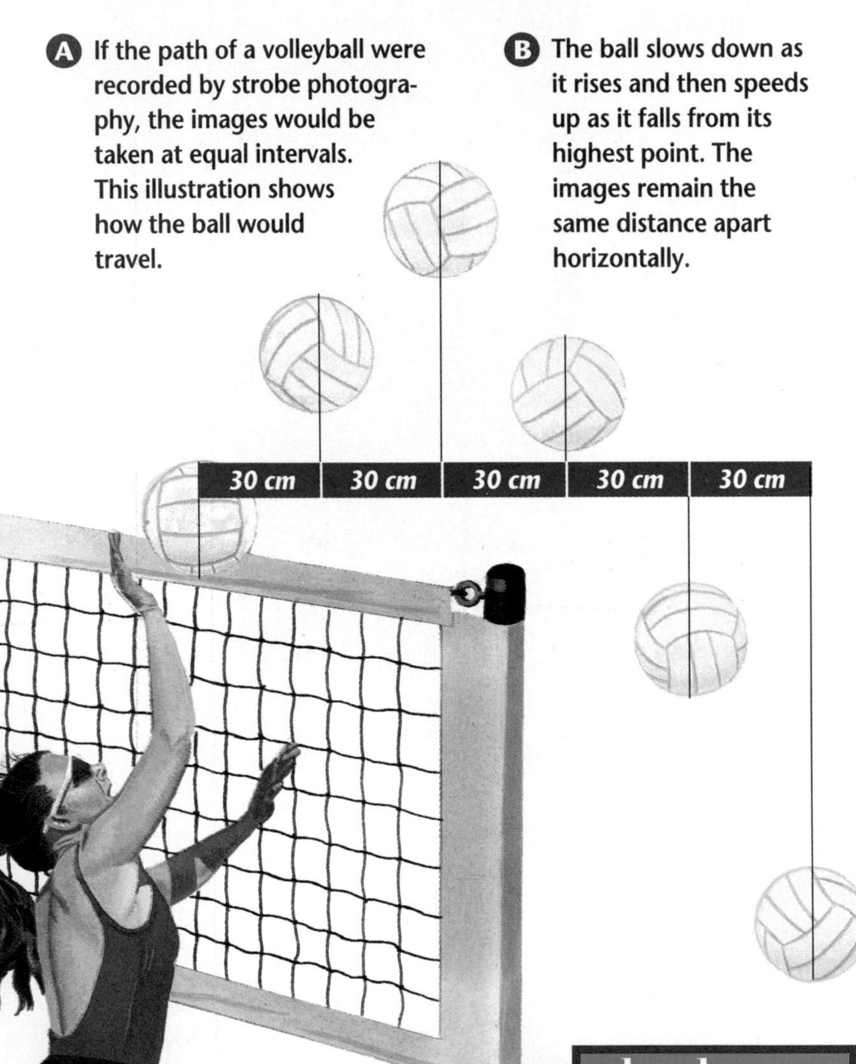

A If the path of a volleyball were recorded by strobe photography, the images would be taken at equal intervals. This illustration shows how the ball would travel.

B The ball slows down as it rises and then speeds up as it falls from its highest point. The images remain the same distance apart horizontally.

The horizontal part of a velocity is the horizontal component. Similarly, the vertical part of a velocity is called the vertical component. Every motion has both horizontal and vertical components, but each component acts as if the other were not present. We say that the vertical motion is independent of the horizontal motion. The vertical component has an acceleration equal to 9.8 m/s^2. The horizontal component has a constant velocity.

So far, you've only looked at the motion of projectiles fired horizontally. However, projectiles that are launched up into the air at an angle, like the volleyball in **Figure 13-8**, behave the same way.

Understanding the motion of projectiles was an important step in our quest to put objects into orbit around Earth. In the next section, you'll learn more about these objects and how they stay in orbit.

check your UNDERSTANDING

1. Describe three examples of a projectile not mentioned in this section.
2. Which object would hit the ground first, a baseball launched perfectly horizontally off the bat of a professional baseball player or a baseball dropped from the same height as the player's bat?
3. Explain how the motion of a basketball after a jump shot can be separated into vertical and horizontal components.
4. **Apply** Draw a diagram to show why a dart player has to aim above the target to hit the bull's-eye. Show the dart's path and the two kinds of motion involved.

13-3 Circular Orbits of Satellites

Newton's Prediction of Satellite Motion

Isaac Newton was born in 1642, the same year that Galileo died. Newton described, even back then, how a satellite could be put into orbit. It took another 270 years to develop the technology to send an artificial satellite into orbit. This satellite was *Sputnik I*, sent up by the Soviet Union on October 4, 1957.

How Projectiles Orbit Earth

Imagine Earth as perfectly round with no mountains or hills or air to slow or stop a projectile. Now, suppose you horizontally fire a projectile, perhaps a rifle bullet. The projectile moves horizontally and falls to the ground. But Newton had an interesting thought. Imagine that you throw something, or fire it, with enough velocity that it travels many kilometers. As it falls, it falls just enough to follow the curvature of Earth. It would fall until it circled Earth. This is shown in **Figure 13-9**. **Figure 13-10** shows how to calculate how fast a projectile would have to travel horizontally to orbit Earth.

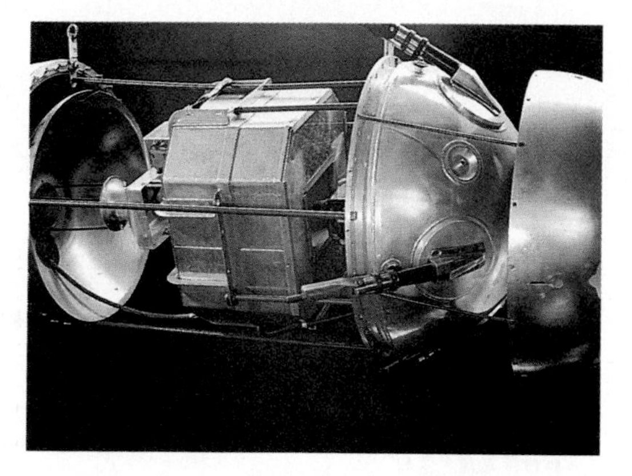

Sputnik I

Section Objectives

- Describe how a satellite is a projectile in free-fall.
- Connect weightlessness to free-fall.
- Explain satellite motion in terms of relative velocity.

Key Terms

weightlessness
stationary satellite

Figure 13-9

A A satellite is a freely-falling object. Because its horizontal motion combines with the downward motion due to gravity, the satellite circles or orbits Earth.

B A satellite has just enough horizontal motion to fall in a curved path around Earth and never hit it.

Earth

Figure 13-10

How fast would the satellite have to travel to continuously fall around Earth without hitting it?

A The satellite begins its vertical movement with a speed of 0 m/sec and accelerates downward at 7.8 m/s^2. At the end of 1 second, its average downward change in velocity for that second is 7.8 m/s divided by 2, or 3.9 m/s. So the satellite will fall 3.9 m during that second.

B Scientists have calculated that a projectile must travel 7.9 km horizontally in that second for its path to match the curve of Earth. Since there are 3600 seconds in one hour, this velocity is equal to

$$\frac{7.9 \text{ km}}{\text{s}} \times \frac{3\,600 \text{ s}}{1 \text{ h}} = \frac{28\,440 \text{ km}}{\text{h}}$$

A satellite must travel at 28 440 km per hour to continuously fall around Earth at the Equator.

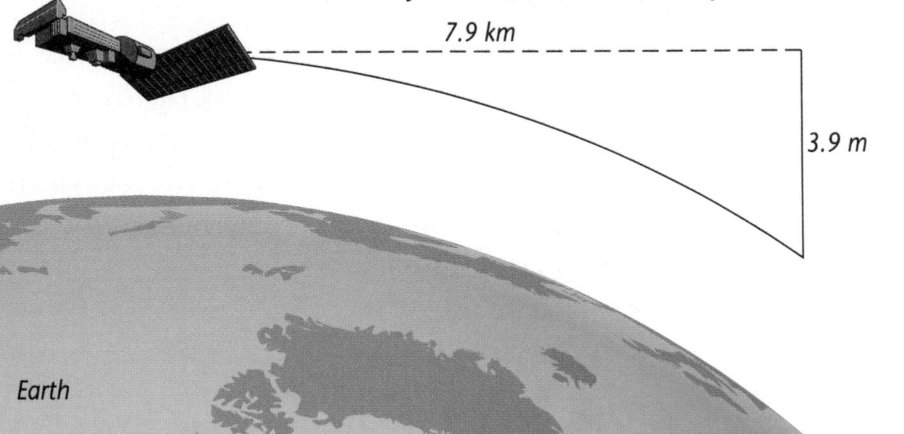

Life Science CONNECTION

Biological Effects of Weightlessness

On Earth, the force of gravity acts on everyone and everything. We call this downward force weight and measure it with a scale. Over time, the human body has adapted to the effects of gravity in this environment.

In an orbiting spacecraft, gravity still affects everything. Because everything is falling freely, however, the effect of gravity is different. If an astronaut stands on a scale in the spacecraft, the scale reads zero. For this reason, the astronaut is said to be weightless.

How do you think the human body would be affected by long periods of weightlessness? What happens when astronauts return to Earth's environment?

Areas of Concern

Our sense of balance depends upon gravity, but

Find Out! ACTIVITY

How did Sputnik I stay in orbit?

Sputnik I orbited about 516 km above Earth's surface. The satellite traveled at a horizontal velocity of 7.6 km/s. In each 7.6 km, it must fall toward Earth 4.18 m to stay in its orbit.

What To Do

1. Determine Sputnik's average downward velocity for one second.
2. Calculate the downward velocity at the end of that second.

Conclude and Apply

1. What is the relationship of average downward velocity to distance fallen in one second?
2. What is the acceleration due to gravity at this altitude?

The higher the altitude of a satellite's orbit, the lower the horizontal velocity required. This is because acceleration due to gravity is less further away from Earth. Perhaps you've seen pictures of astronauts floating inside a space shuttle as it orbits Earth. Why does this happen?

luckily, becoming disoriented in orbit has not become a major problem. Some astronauts did experience brief periods of nausea and disorientation, but these effects were short-lived.

All body functions are carefully monitored during a flight. The only factor that has shown a significant change is the pulse rate, which often increases during lift-off and space walks. In all cases, however, the rate has returned to normal in a very short time.

Returning to Earth

Upon return to Earth, some astronauts feel faint when they first stand up. Some Soviet cosmonauts found it difficult to adjust to the effects of gravity on Earth after 17 days in orbit. For several days, their arms, legs, and head felt as if they were very heavy. They also seemed to have less blood and some changes in the walls of their veins. The reasons are not yet clearly understood.

Other observed effects of weightlessness are the loss of calcium in the bones and the loss of body mass. So far, astronauts have quickly regained lost body mass after returning to Earth.

With every returning space flight crew, doctors are learning more and more about how the human body reacts to long periods of weightlessness.

What Do You Think?

After several months in space, the heart, muscles, and bones will adapt to the conditions of free-fall. What problems could arise for astronauts when they return to Earth after several months in space?

Weightlessness

Connect to... Life Science

How could astronauts exercise in space while experiencing weightlessness? Research several isometric exercises and tell why they would work on a spacecraft.

Why do we say that astronauts are weightless when in orbit? Have you ever jumped on a trampoline? **Figure 13-11** explains what happens when you jump on a trampoline.

In an elevator that starts downward rapidly, you may have a feeling that you suddenly weigh less. The floor of the elevator does not seem to push on your feet. When the roller coaster you're riding goes over the top of a hill at high speed, you feel lifted up and floating free—weightless.

These experiences occur when you are falling freely. Whatever the direction of your velocity, you are experiencing acceleration toward Earth in a free-fall. This is what we mean by **weightlessness.** If you could stand on a bathroom scale during this time, it would register zero.

Free-fall in Orbit

The satellites in orbit around Earth are in free-fall and that is why everything appears to be weightless aboard a satellite. The satellite and everything in it, including the astronauts, are all falling toward Earth with exactly the same acceleration. Satellites fall toward Earth and never really escape Earth's gravitational pull. The acceleration due to gravity is less for higher orbits. But such satellites still fall toward Earth, with some acceleration, even though it is less than 9.8 m/s^2. Have you ever looked up at the sky on a clear night and seen a bright spot moving across the sky? This may have been a satellite. Some satellites appear to move across the sky, and others do not. Why do some satellites appear to remain stationary?

Figure 13-11

From the time your feet leave the trampoline to the time at which they touch it again, you are experiencing weightlessness.

The Stationary Satellite

Imagine a satellite that always appears in the same position. A **stationary satellite** is placed in orbit around Earth at just the right altitude and just the right velocity so that it moves around its orbit once per day. It moves in the same direction as Earth is rotating. Relative to a person on Earth, this satellite has no motion.

Stationary satellites like the one shown in **Figure 13-12** are often used as communication satellites to relay radio messages from one city to others. For example, a stationary satellite placed over Lake George, Uganda could receive radio communications from Bombay and relay them to London. Stationary satellites are used to beam television transmissions of events live across the world.

You have learned in this section that satellites are constantly falling toward Earth as they orbit. You will find that the study of other falling bodies, such as a swinging pendulum, will help you understand much more about motion in many different areas of science.

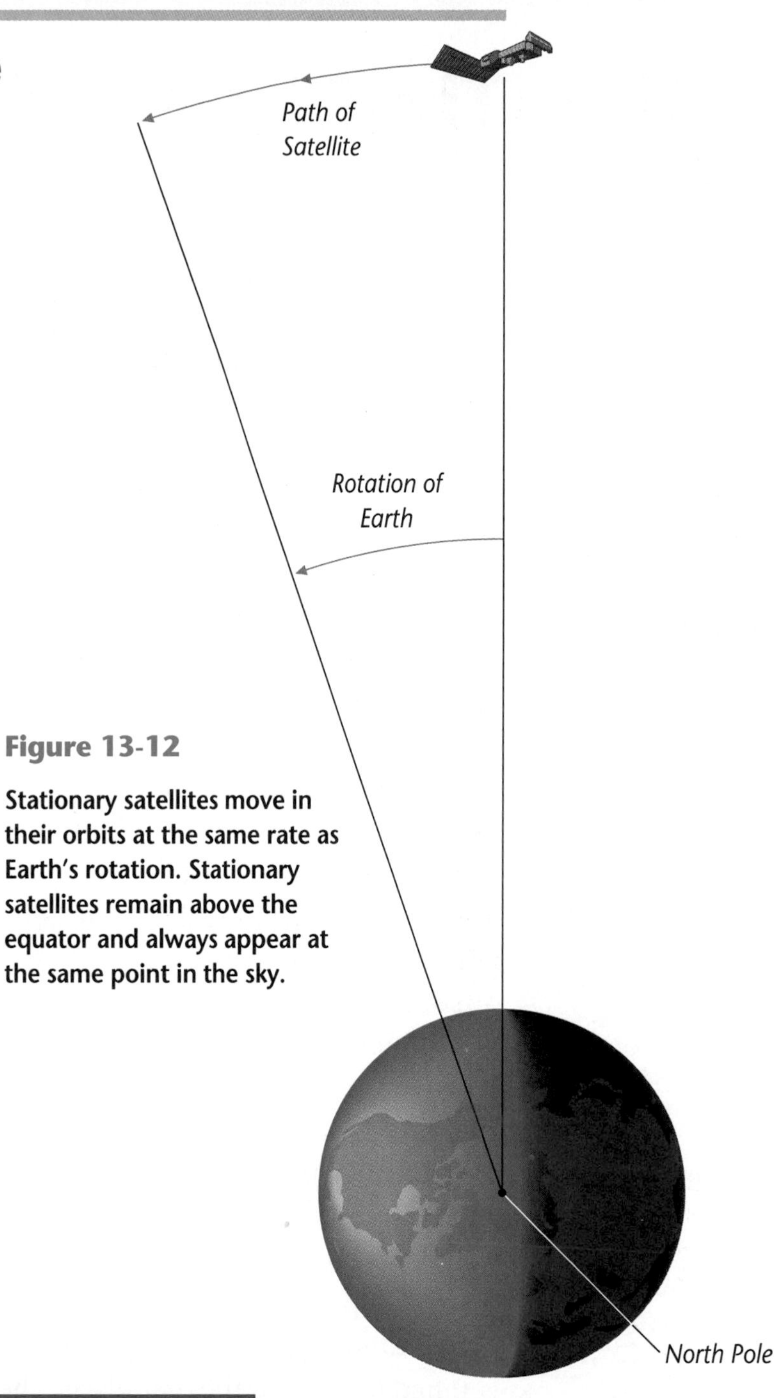

Figure 13-12

Stationary satellites move in their orbits at the same rate as Earth's rotation. Stationary satellites remain above the equator and always appear at the same point in the sky.

check your UNDERSTANDING

1. Explain how a satellite stays in orbit.
2. Imagine that you brought a bathroom scale into an elevator and stood on it. As you went down, what would you predict would happen to the weight it registers for you when the elevator first starts to move? Explain your answer.
3. Why would a stationary satellite always appear in the same location to you if you could see it from Earth?
4. **Apply** Could an astronaut in the space shuttle exercise by lifting weights? Explain.

The Motion of a Pendulum

Section Objectives

- Define the period of a pendulum.
- Define frequency, as it relates to periodic motion.
- Describe the relationship between the period of a pendulum, the mass of a bob, the length of the pendulum, and the amplitude of the motion.

Key Terms

period

Periodic Motion

Galileo is said to have watched a chandelier in a church slowly moving back and forth like a pendulum one day. He began to see that a pendulum's behavior would tell him something about how things fall on Earth. Earlier in this chapter you used a pendulum. You found that whatever the mass of the pendulum bob, the bob fell and reached the bottom of its swing in the same amount of time. Repeated motions such as those of a pendulum are called periodic motions. Let's begin to study the periodic motion of a pendulum by first observing and then defining the experimental variables.

Period

When you release a pendulum bob, it moves past the bottom and back up again to a position where it briefly stops. Then it reverses direction and swings back over to where you had let it go in the first place. The pendulum continues to swing back and forth. The time for the pendulum bob to swing over and back once is called the **period** of the pendulum. **Figure 13-13** illustrates the period of a pendulum.

Frequency

It is sometimes easier to use the number of times an object moves back and forth in one second, rather than how long it takes for one motion over and back. The number of times an object moves back and forth in 1 second is called frequency. We talked about the frequency of sound in

Figure 13-13

The period of the pendulum is the time the pendulum takes to complete one cycle. This pendulum's period is 2 seconds. What is the frequency of this pendulum?

Chapter 3. The process of moving over and back once is called a cycle. Frequency then is measured in cycles per second. Recall that a cycle per second is given the name hertz, abbreviated Hz. What is the frequency of a playground swing that swings back and forth once every 3 seconds? What is the frequency of a swinging door that swings back and forth once every 2 seconds?

■ Amplitude

As a pendulum moves toward its lowest point, note the distance the pendulum bob has traveled from the starting point to the bottom of the swing. This distance is called the amplitude. **Figure 13-14** illustrates three different amplitudes.

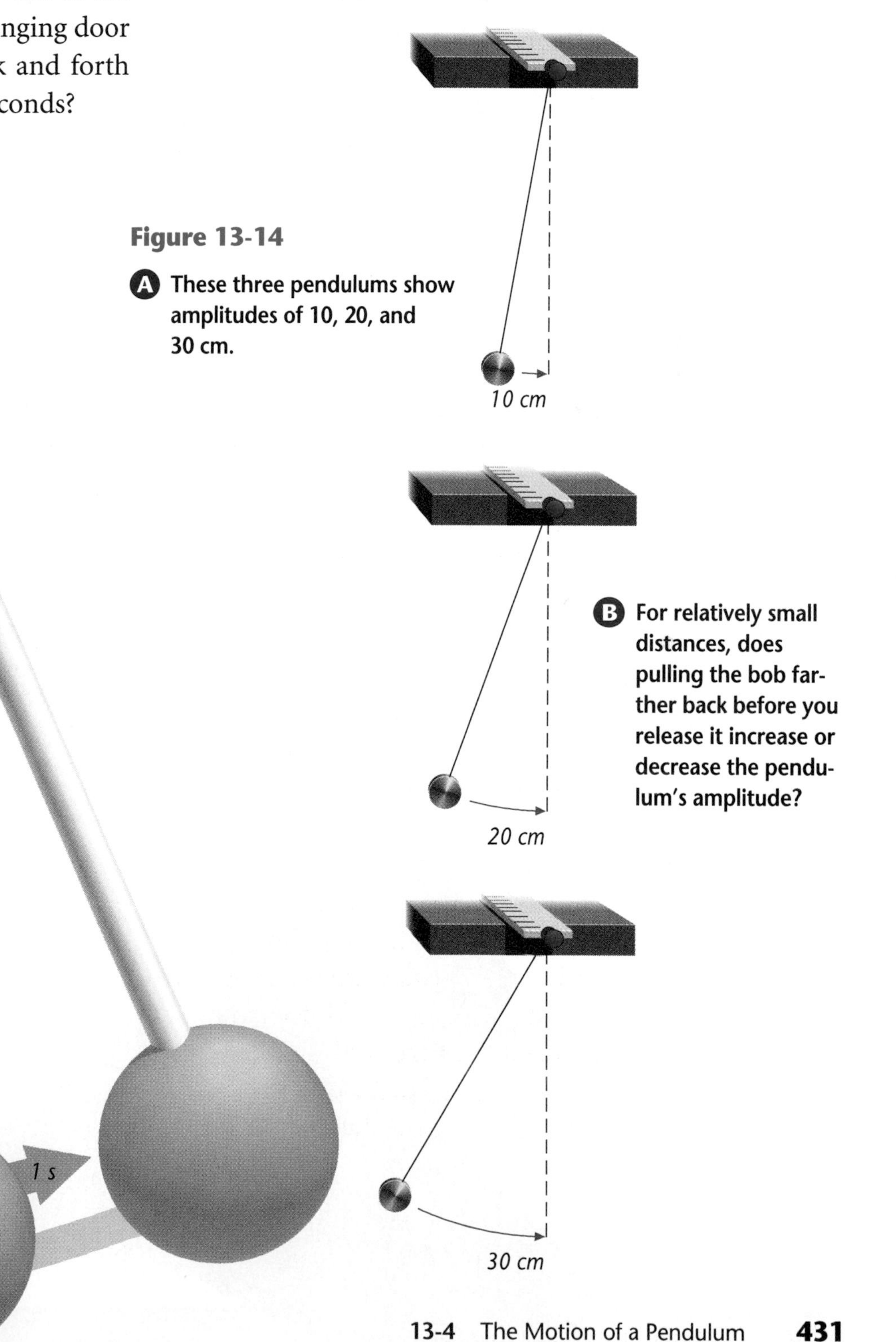

Figure 13-14

A **These three pendulums show amplitudes of 10, 20, and 30 cm.**

B **For relatively small distances, does pulling the bob farther back before you release it increase or decrease the pendulum's amplitude?**

DESIGN YOUR OWN

INVESTIGATION

The Period of a Pendulum

A classic example of periodic motion is a pendulum in a grandfather clock. How does a pendulum help a clock keep time? What variables affect a pendulum's motion?

Preparation

Problem

What affects the period of a pendulum?

Form a Hypothesis

Think about the length of the pendulum, the bob mass, and amplitude (pull-back distance) of the pendulum. How do you think changing these variables will affect the period of the pendulum?

Objectives

- Separate and control variables in an experiment.
- Predict the effect of different tests on the period of a pendulum.

Materials

ruler
string
masking tape
meterstick
metal washers
seconds timer

DESIGN YOUR OWN

INVESTIGATION

Plan the Experiment

1. Using the photo as a guide, explain how you will make your pendulum.
2. How will you measure the different variables?
3. Decide how you will vary each trial. The sample data tables will help guide you in your testing. Be sure you change only one variable in each trial.

Check the Plan

1. Prepare data tables *in your Science Journal* that are specific to your tests.
2. Have your teacher check your plan before you begin your experiment.

Data and Observations

Length = ___ cm		Mass ___washers
Pullback Distance (cm)	Time for 10 Swings (s)	Pendulum Period (s)

Amplitude = ___cm		Length = ___ cm
Pendulum Bob Weight (Number of Washers)	Time for 10 Swings (s)	Pendulum Period (s)

Amplitude ___ cm		Mass ___washers
Pendulum Length	Time for 10 Swings (s)	Pendulum Period (s)

Analyze and Conclude

1. **Compare** Summarize the results of your experiment and compare them with your hypothesis.
2. **Explain** Looking back at your comparison in the last question, explain the effect of changing the pendulum's bob mass, amplitude, and length on the pendulum period.
3. **Use Numbers** Draw a graph plotting the pendulum's period for the different string length. Using your graph, predict the pendulum's period for a string of 100 cm. What is the relationship between the change in length of string and the change in period?

Going Further

If you were building a pendulum clock, how would you build it to make sure the clock would be as accurate as possible?

Changing Variables

Figure 13-15

The steps shown model the process a scientist might use to discover what affects the period of a pendulum.

- ***State the problem as a question.***
  What affects the period of a pendulum?
- ***Decide which variables might make a difference.***
  length, mass, amplitude
- ***Choose a test variable. Keep all the other variables constant. Do several trials, changing the test variable in every trial. Measure the effects of the changes.***
  Constant: length, mass
  Varies: amplitude
- ***Choose a different variable to test and repeat the above step.***
  Constant: mass, amplitude
  Varies: length
- ***Choose a different variable to test and repeat the above step.***
  Constant: amplitude, length
  Varies: mass
- ***Analyze the results and decide which variable or variables make a difference.***

In the Investigate, you studied the effects of mass, amplitude, and length on the period of a pendulum. These three factors that you tested are called independent variables. The factor that depended on the value of the independent variable, the period, is called the dependent variable. An experiment is a procedure in which you hold all independent variables constant except one. **Figure 13-15** on the left shows one way to conduct an experiment.

■ Drawing Conclusions

Changing one independent variable at a time allows you to draw conclusions about the effect of that variable on what you're measuring, the dependent variable. If you had varied both length and mass at the same time, you would not know why the period changed. Experiments like these are used to discover the causes of the behavior of things you observe.

There are many other kinds of oscillations and vibrations that you will learn about later in this book. What you now know about the pendulum will help you understand their periods, frequencies, and amplitudes.

1. What's the difference between the frequency and the period of a pendulum?
2. Explain how you measure the frequency of the periodic motion of a pendulum. What units is frequency measured in?
3. If you wanted to change the period of a pendulum, which of the three variables you tested would you change?
4. **Apply** Give three examples of other objects or events that undergo periodic motion. How might you go about testing what affects the periodic motion of a guitar string?

HOW IT WORKS The Metronome

A metronome is a device that can be used to beat exact time for a musician. It works on the principle of the pendulum, which you have learned swings back and forth at a regular rate.

Adjusting the Tempo

As the rod in the metronome goes back and forth, it makes a ticking sound. The tempo, or rate of ticking, is adjusted by sliding the movable weight up or down the rod. Moving the weight away from the pivot produces a slower tempo. Moving the weight closer to the pivot produces a faster tempo. How is this similar to the rate of a pendulum?

A scale on the rod, or behind it, shows the number of swings per minute. For example, if you want one tick per second, you set the movable weight at 60. Where would you set it to get two ticks per second? How many ticks per second would you get if it were set at 90?

The First Metronome

The first metronome was probably made in 1815 in Amsterdam by an inventor named Dietrich Winkel. However, he did not get a patent for the device. In 1816, a German mechanic, Johann Maelzel, patented a similar device. Winkel went to court to get the patent rights. He won the court battle, but Maelzel's device was already widely used. In fact, many pieces of printed music have a notation, such as MM120, to indicate the tempo at which the composer wanted the music to be played. The MM stands for Maelzel metronome, and the 120 indicates the number of beats per minute.

You Try It!

Listen to several pieces of music. Using a second hand on a watch or a clock, determine at which number a metronome would have been set when these musical selections were played.

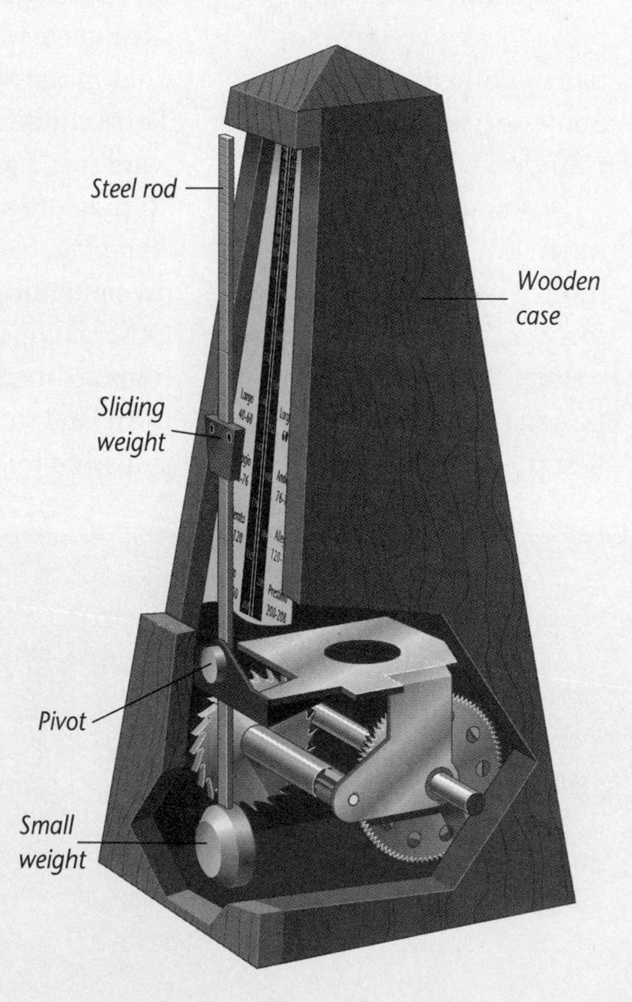

Science and Society

Weather Satellites

Can you think of any natural occurrence that affects people's lives as much as the weather does? Farmers depend on the weather for good crops. Floods, hurricanes, and tornadoes cause terrible damage and loss of life. Snowstorms often cause traffic problems.

It's no wonder, then, that much time, effort, and money is put into trying to forecast, or predict, what the weather will be like. Accurate forecasts could mean that problems caused by the weather would be less frustrating, damaging, and deadly.

Collecting Data

Meteorologists, people who study the weather, have many tools and instruments such as those shown in the picture to help them. To make weather predictions, meteorologists need to have a complete picture of conditions in the atmosphere. These conditions include wind speed and direction, air pressure and how it is changing, temperature, precipitation, and humidity. Observations of these conditions are made regularly from land stations, from ships and buoys at sea, and from airplanes and balloons in the sky. As you can imagine, gathering all the data from all parts of the world presents a problem.

In 1960, the United States government put into orbit *Tiros I*, the first artificial satellite equipped to take pictures of Earth's weather in detail. *Tiros III*, launched in 1961, was the first satellite to discover a hurricane over the Atlantic Ocean.

More recent developments include an advanced series of satellites called the *Tiros-N*. Besides observing weather conditions, these satellites collect data about infrared radiation in Earth's atmosphere.

There are two kinds of weather satellites. One kind orbits Earth in a low orbit—800 to 1400 kilometers—that passes over the poles. Because Earth rotates, low-orbit satellites pass over a different area on each orbit. The other kind of weather satellite has a very high orbit—36 000 kilometers.

Tiros-N *satellite*

At this height, the satellite goes around Earth in the same time it takes Earth to make one turn on its axis. In other words, the satellite is always over the same spot. Such satellites are so high, the pictures they take cover a large part of Earth's surface.

Weather Patterns

What kind of information can satellites gather? Satellites keep track of worldwide weather patterns. Weather patterns for big storms, such as hurricanes, can be identified and tracked so people can be warned.

Worldwide conditions such as snow and ice cover are easy to see on photos taken by satellites. Satellites also take pictures of the cloud patterns that occur during storms. The photo at the left shows one such cloud pattern. Besides taking pictures, satellites continually monitor the temperature of the water near the surface of the oceans.

Satellites collect information from their own instruments and relay it to ground stations for analysis. But they do more. The satellites also collect information from the thousands of land and water stations on Earth's surface. Instruments at these stations operate automatically, and the data they collect are transmitted by radio signal to a satellite. From there, the information is relayed to ground stations and analyzed by computers.

With this data-collecting system and high-speed computers to analyze the data, scientists continue to learn about the interaction of the air with land and the oceans. Researchers also learn about how the atmosphere gains and loses heat by radiation. In the future, patterns of weather behavior will be better understood, and long-range weather prediction may become more reliable.

Satellite photograph of a hurricane in the Gulf of Mexico

Use the World Wide Web to find out more about the American Meteorological Society and the topics they study. Explain which topics interest you and why.

Galileo

Galileo Galilei (1564–1642) began his career as a medical student, but soon gave up medicine for mathematics and the physical sciences. Early in his career, he studied and wrote about the motion of falling objects. His interests changed, though, when he heard about the invention of the telescope. He made one and used it to study objects in the sky. He observed the cratered surface of the moon, the "arms" of Saturn, the moons of Jupiter, the phases of Venus, and many stars that had not been seen before. Galileo found evidence that supported the Copernican (sun-centered) model of the solar system and thus cast doubt on the Ptolemaic 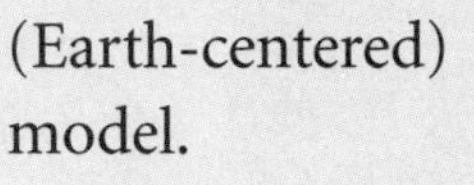 (Earth-centered) model.

He published his observations and conclusions. Because his ideas went against the teachings of his religion at that time, he was arrested and forced to deny his ideas.

Despite these setbacks, he continued his studies on motion. The results of his studies were published in a book entitled *Dialogues Concerning Two New Sciences.*

Galileo's studies of falling bodies, motion on an inclined plane, and projectile motion all helped give a better understanding of motion. Even though he seemed to understand what is now called inertia, his writings never included the idea of inertia. The same is true of acceleration. He wrote about it but didn't connect it with forces.

A replica of Galileo's telescope

You Try It!

Repeat one of Galileo's experiments. On a smooth, level floor, prop one end of a 30-cm ruler up about 2 cm. Let a marble roll down the ruler. After it gets to the floor, see how far it rolls in two seconds. Do this three times and find the average distance. Then use v = d/t to find the average speed. Change the slant of the ruler and repeat. What is the speed now? How would you explain the difference, if any?

REVIEWING MAIN IDEAS

Science Journal

Review the statements below about the big ideas presented in this chapter, and answer the questions. Then, re-read your answers to the Did You Ever Wonder questions at the beginning of the chapter. *In your Science Journal,* write a paragraph about how your understanding of the big ideas in the chapter has changed.

1 On or near Earth, the acceleration due to gravity is a constant 9.8 m/s^2. ***If an elephant and a mouse fell freely off a high wire at the same time, which would reach the net first?***

2 Projectiles have both vertical and horizontal movement. These objects move independently horizontally forward at a constant velocity and vertically downward at an increasing velocity because of the acceleration due to gravity. ***What motions do gymnasts and baseballs have in common?***

3 Satellites stay in orbit around Earth because of their horizontal velocity and the acceleration due to gravity. ***How does a satellite go to a higher orbit?***

4 The movement of a pendulum as it swings back and forth provides an opportunity to examine periodic motion and the variables affecting it. Pendulum length, not its mass or amplitude, determines the time it takes to swing back and forth once. ***How does increasing the length of a pendulum affect its period?***

Earth

chapter 13
CHAPTER REVIEW

Using Key Science Terms

acceleration due to gravity
period
projectile motion
stationary satellite
weightlessness

Each phrase below describes a science term from the list. Write the term that matches the phrase describing it.

1. throwing a ball
2. 9.8 m/s^2 at Earth's surface
3. appears not to move in the sky
4. seconds per cycle
5. condition of objects in free-fall

Understanding Ideas

Answer the following questions in your Journal *using complete sentences.*

1. What happens to the velocity of an object moving at constant acceleration?
2. Where might you experience weightlessness in your daily life?
3. If you saw a stationary satellite directly above your house at 6 A.M., where would you see it at midnight?
4. When a pendulum's length is increased, what happens to its period?
5. How long does it take for a stationary satellite to orbit Earth?
6. What method of photography is often used when analyzing objects in motion?

Developing Skills

Use your understanding of the concepts developed in this chapter to answer each of the following questions.

1. **Concept Mapping** Using the following terms, complete the concept map of the motion of a pendulum: *amplitude, frequency, length of string, mass of bob, period.*

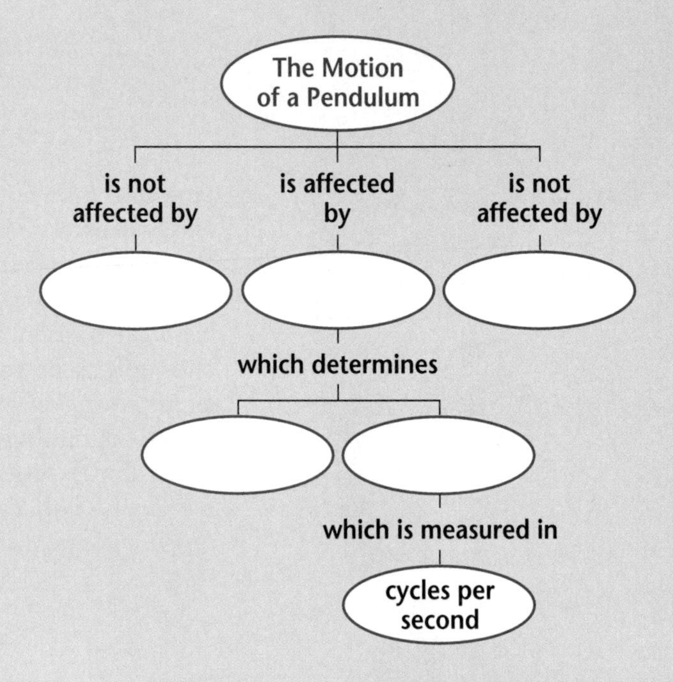

2. **Predicting** Use information from the Find Out activity on page 427 to predict the velocity of a satellite that orbits Earth at an altitude of 350 km.
3. **Interpreting Scientific Illustrations** In the diagram on the left, a rocket is fired from Earth in position 1. Describe what happens to its velocity in position 2. What do you think has to happen for it to go into position 3?

CHAPTER REVIEW

Critical Thinking

In your Journal, *answer each of the following questions.*

1. A flower pot accidentally falls from the balcony of a 12th-floor apartment. You see it smash on the ground 3 seconds later. What is its velocity just before it hits the ground?
2. You have two tennis balls. You allow one to drop straight to the ground. The other you toss 5 meters straight up into the air and then let it fall to the ground. Which ball is moving faster when it hits the ground? Explain why.
3. A punter punts the football at the 50-yard line, and the ball reaches its maximum height at the 30-yard line. Where will the ball land?

Problem Solving

Read the following problem and discuss your answers in a brief paragraph.

You are part of a space expedition that has just landed on an unexplored planet. One of your first assignments is to determine the acceleration due to gravity on this planet. You are in charge of the crew being sent to the surface.

1. What materials would you have your crew assemble in order to determine the acceleration due to gravity on this planet?
2. List the steps in the procedure that you would have the crew follow to calculate the acceleration due to gravity on this planet.

CONNECTING IDEAS

Discuss each of the following in a brief paragraph.

1. **Theme—Systems and Interactions** Why can some animals on Earth jump higher than humans, even though they are affected by the same gravity?
2. **Theme—Systems and Interactions** Do you think an accelerometer would work on a space shuttle? How do you think the accelerometer readings would change during and after lift-off, and finally in orbit?
3. **Theme—Stability and Change** Would the period of a pendulum be the same on the moon as it is on Earth? If not, why would it be different?
4. **How It Works** You and a friend are comparing metronomes. Yours has a sliding weight made of copper. Your friend's has a brass sliding weight. How does this affect the periods of the metronomes?
5. **A Closer Look** What is the relationship between a falling object's size, shape, and mass and the object's terminal velocity?
6. **Science and Society** How do weather satellites help weather forecasters?

Moving Water

Did you ever wonder...

- What happens to rain after it falls?
- How rivers form?
- Where well water comes from?

Science Journal

Before you begin to study about moving water, think about these questions and answer them *in your Science Journal*. When you finish the chapter, compare your journal entry with what you have learned.

Have you ever seen a raging, roaring stream like the one shown in the photograph below? Its rushing waters could take you on the most exciting ride of your life!

What if you could follow a tiny droplet of water? You might race with it down a swift stream, or you could follow a droplet as it lazily drifts down a gentle, quiet river. Eventually you might follow the droplet as it soaks into the ground. You might even find the droplet has made its way to a lake or to the ocean.

In the activity on the next page, explore how surfaces on Earth can affect what happens to water.

Explore! ACTIVITY

How do Earth's surfaces affect what happens to water?

Have you ever wondered why water flows the way it does? What happens to the rainwater that falls on grassy areas compared to rainwater that falls on a parking lot?

What To Do

1. Put waxed paper over some cardboard. Slowly pour some water onto the paper and tilt the cardboard.
2. Repeat the procedure, this time using paper towels. *In your Journal* describe what happens to the water in each case.
3. What is different about each surface?
4. How do these differences affect the way water moves?
5. What kinds of surfaces on Earth cause water to move in the ways seen in this activity?
6. *In your Journal* describe some examples that you have seen of how different surfaces affect the way water moves.

Water Recycling

Section Objectives

- Describe how water moves through the hydrologic cycle.
- Identify the processes involved in the hydrologic cycle.
- Demonstrate runoff.

Key Terms

hydrologic cycle
runoff

Water Cycle

Gray clouds roll in from the horizon, lightning flashes, thunder booms, and there you are—drenched by a sudden summer downpour. An hour later, the clouds have rolled past, the sky is bright blue, and puddles of rainwater are shimmering in the sunlight. Wait several hours more, and the puddles have disappeared. Where did the water go?

Find Out! ACTIVITY

How does water cycle through the environment?

What To Do

1. Obtain a large beaker, a small beaker, some plastic wrap, a marble, a rubber band, and a lamp.
2. Pour 2 cm of water into the large beaker. Then, place the small beaker upright in the center of the large beaker.
3. Cover the opening of the large beaker loosely with plastic wrap. Seal the wrap with the rubber band.
4. Put the marble in the middle of the plastic wrap. What do you think the marble does?
5. Place the beaker under the lamp or in direct sunlight for several hours.

Conclude and Apply

1. *In your Journal* describe what occurred after the beaker sat for several hours.
2. How does this activity help show what happens to water on Earth?

In the Find Out you saw how the liquid water went into the air as water vapor, a gas. You learned about liquids and gases in Chapter 4. Rainwater in puddles does the same thing. Did you see the water become vapor?

Let's follow what happens to a drop of water as it moves in a cycle from being vapor in the air to being liquid on Earth and from Earth back into the air just as the rainwater in the puddles. It is called the **hydrologic cycle**.

Figure 14-1

Hydrologic Cycle

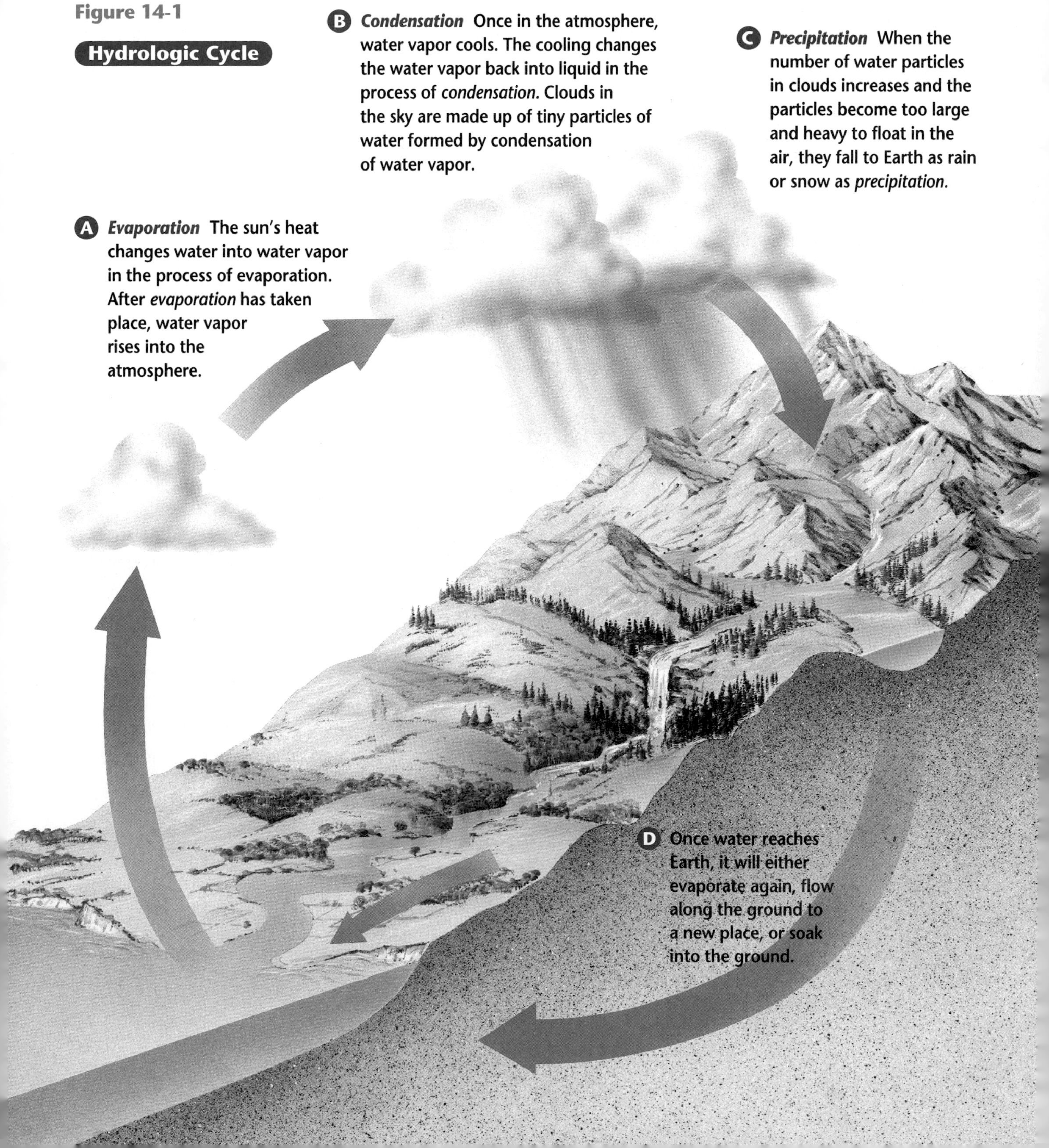

Runoff

Most people have spilled a glass of water sometime during their life. The glass topples over, and the water spills. If the water falls on a carpet, it quickly soaks in. If it spills on a tile floor, it forms a puddle. If the floor is uneven, the liquid soon flows toward the lowest spot.

Isn't this similar to what happened in the Explore activity? The water soaked into the paper towel but ran off the waxed paper.

This is also what happens to rainwater on Earth. Water soaks into the ground in some places but flows on the top of other surfaces. Water that flows and does not soak in is called **runoff**. Water that runs off will move along the ground and will eventually enter a stream.

What determines whether rainwater soaks into the ground or runs off? One factor is the ground itself. If the land is hard and smooth, like the waxed paper in your experiment or like rock in the real world, water will likely run off.

SKILLBUILDER

Sequencing

Sequence the events in the hydrologic cycle beginning with rain falling to Earth. If you need help, refer to the **Skill Handbook** on page 653.

Chemistry CONNECTION

Caves and Rock Formations

You have learned some of the ways in which water has the power to shape Earth. But not all of the features caused by the action of water can be explained by the force of its motions.

You may recall from studying about solutions that water is the most effective solvent known. It can bring about a chemical reaction that results in the formation of limestone caves.

A limestone cave or cavern is known as a solution cave. It forms when underground water slowly dissolves the rock.

This process begins when rainwater falls to the ground. Carbon dioxide, which is a gas, is absorbed from the surrounding air and mixes with water to form a chemical compound called carbonic acid. This acid is very weak, but it can dissolve certain types of rock, notably limestone.

The main ingredient in limestone is calcite, a mineral form of calcium carbonate. Carbonic acid reacts with calcium carbonate. When rainwater soaks into the soil, it sometimes flows into cracks within the limestone.

Figure 14-2

During the summer of 1993 flooding on the Mississippi River disrupted thousands of lives. Called one of the worst U.S. natural disasters of all times, the flooding caused an estimated 13 billion dollars in damages and killed 25 people.

A **This sequence of photos show the flooding of McBride, Missouri. A levee on the Mississippi River 14 miles away from the town broke at 2 A.M. The first photo was taken at 10 A.M. as residents evacuated their homes.**

B **The second photo was taken at 5 P.M. A boat patrols to make sure that everyone has left as the water rises.**

C **At 4 P.M. on the next day, 38 hours after the levee broke, this photo was taken, showing the water at its highest level in the town.**

What other factors affect whether rain soaks in or runs off? You know from experience that sometimes rains are fast, hard driving, and heavy. Light rain falling over several hours will probably have time to soak into the ground while heavy rain may run off because it doesn't have time to soak in.

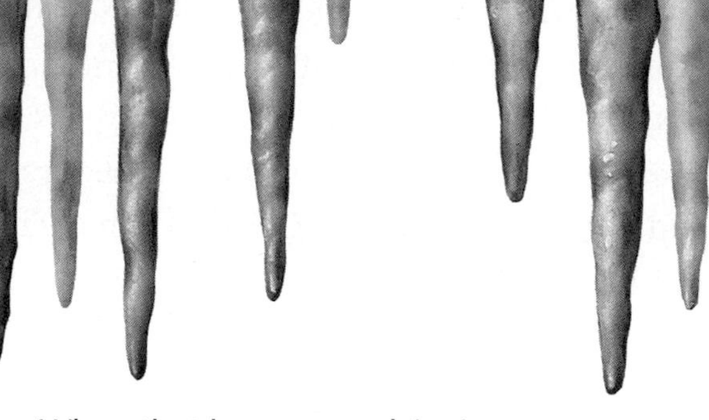

The carbonic acid slowly dissolves the surrounding rock, creating underground holes called caverns. Sometimes the ground above caves in, creating a sinkhole.

Have you ever visited one of these caverns? If so, you have probably seen rock formations hanging from the ceiling that look almost like giant icicles. These rock formations are called stalactites. Stalagmites are rock formations that rise from the floor.

A single stalactite may take thousands of years to form. When underground water dissolves limestone, it absorbs calcite. The stalactite begins as a single drop of water clinging to the roof of the cave. As the drop of water evaporates, it loses some carbon dioxide. When that happens, calcite is deposited on the end of the stalactite. The stalactite grows as other drops of water cling to the outside of the stalactite.

Every so often, a drop of water will fall on the ground, depositing some calcite on the cave floor. After many years, the calcite will form a stalagmite, which looks like an upside-down stalactite.

interNET CONNECTION

Information on the history and structure of Mammoth Cave is available from the National Park Service on the World Wide Web. Find out about the cave and describe an area in it that you would like to visit.

Figure 14-3

A Several factors determine how much water will soak into the ground and how much will run off. One factor is the ground itself. Water will run off of hard rocky land and soak into soft soil. Another factor is the slope of the land. Gravity pulls water down steep slopes.

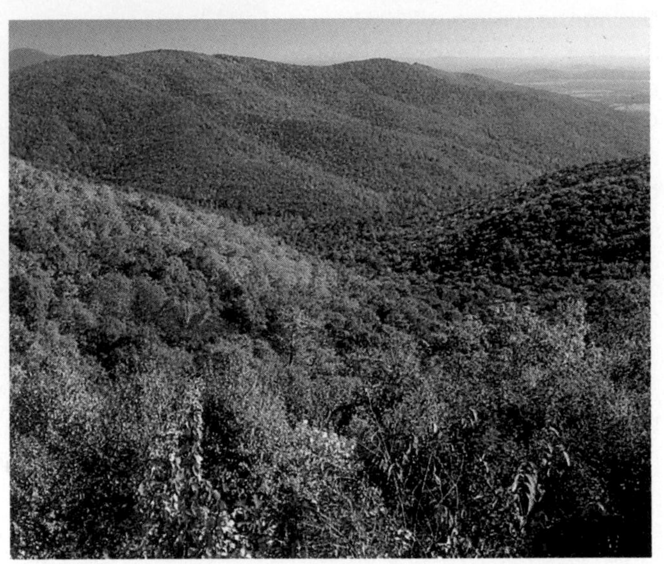

B Gentle rolling slopes and flat areas usually hold water until it either evaporates or sinks into the ground. The number of plants also affects runoff. Plants and their roots act like a sponge to soak up and hold water. Do you think the amount of moisture already in the soil affects runoff? Why?

Another factor that affects the amount of runoff is the slope of the land. You probably know that water flows downhill. This downward flow is due to Earth's gravity. Gently rolling slopes and flat areas usually hold water in place until it can evaporate or sink into the ground. Steep slopes, however, do not hold the water, and it runs off.

Do you think plants can affect runoff? Just like water running off a table, water on Earth tends to run off smooth surfaces. However, plants and their roots act like a sponge to soak up and hold water.

As you have read, there are many factors that affect runoff. A hard rain that falls on sloping, barren ground will probably run off. But a slow steady rain that falls on a level, grass-covered lawn will probably soak in and not become runoff. In the following sections, you'll learn what happens to water that soaks into the ground.

1. What supplies the energy for the hydrologic cycle?
2. What processes are involved in the hydrologic cycle?
3. How can runoff be decreased?
4. **Apply** Use the hydrologic cycle to explain why water can be described as recycled.

14-2 Streams and Rivers

Stream Development

Think of streams that flow near your home or streams you may have visited. Some streams are narrow, noisy, have steep sides, and flow swiftly. These streams may form white-water rapids or waterfalls. Other streams are wide and slow-moving. Why do streams develop differently?

Section Objectives

- Describe how and why streams form.
- Discuss characteristics of streams on steeply sloped land and streams on gently sloped land.

Key Terms

meander
drainage basin

Explore! ACTIVITY

What happens to rainwater that runs off?

Remember the storm you were caught in at the beginning of the last section? You never imagined that one storm could bring so much rain in so little time. Not all the rain collected in puddles, however. Where did all the rest of the water go?

What To Do

1. Place sand in a stream table to a depth of 4 cm, but leave one end of the table empty. Put a block under the end of the table that is full of sand so that it is lifted 2 or 3 cm.
2. Use a sprinkling can to sprinkle water in the sand on the upper side of the stream table. The sprinkled water will be like rain falling on Earth.
3. *In your Journal* record what happens.
4. Explain how the water forms streams in the sand? Where did the water settle?

■ Streams of Every Kind

As you saw in the previous Explore gravity causes water to flow downhill until it reaches the lowest point possible. Water flowing within a smaller channel is generally called a stream. Water in a larger channel is generally called a river.

Small streams eventually join together to form a larger stream. That larger stream will join with other large streams to form a river. Where do the rivers go? Do all rivers and streams have the same characteristics?

Streams that flow through steeply sloped areas run swiftly downhill. Such a stream may carve a narrow, steep, V-shaped valley because the running water wears away the stream bottom more than its sides. Streams on steep slopes may also form areas of white-water rapids or tumble over waterfalls.

Figure 14-4

Yellowstone National Park

A stream from a steep slope may eventually reach land that slopes very little. Or a stream may begin in such an area. A stream moving along a gradual slope flows much more slowly. Its valley is wide and low. The water has started to wear away the sides of the streambed, developing curves and bends in its path.

The curves in a river form because the speed of the water varies depending on the width of the stream channel. Water in wide, shallow areas of a stream is slowed down by the friction created with the bottom of the river. In deep areas, less water comes in contact with the bottom, so less friction results. Therefore, deep water can flow faster.

You can see that the river gently turns and curves as it moves along the gentle slope. This faster-moving water wears away the sides of the streambed where it flows more quickly, forming curves. A curve that forms in this way is a **meander**.

The broad, flat valley formed by a river on a gentle slope is called a floodplain. When the stream floods because of heavy runoff, it often covers part or all of its floodplain.

During the next Investigate you'll discover why streams have different characteristics.

The Yellowstone river, Yellowstone National Park

Figure 14-5

A Streams moving through flat or gentle slopes flow less rapidly than steep-sloped streams and flow in curves and bends.

B Curves in a river are formed when channels of deep water, free of the slowing force of friction from the stream bottom, flow faster than the rest of the water. This faster-moving water wears away the sides of the streambed, forming curves in the stream path.

INVESTIGATE!

Differences in Streams

You've seen how streams form, but do streams have different characteristics? During this Investigate you will make your own models of streams.

Problem

What factors do you think control stream characteristics? Think about what you know about streams. How would you make your own streams? How can you control the flow?

Safety Precautions

Wear an apron to protect your clothing.

Materials

2 pails	stream table
plastic hose	sand
2 screw clamps	blocks of wood

What To Do

Work with your group and plan ways to set up your stream table to form different streams. Show your plan to your teacher. If you are advised to revise your plan, be sure to check with your teacher again before you begin. Carry out your plan keeping in mind:

1. When you set up the stream table, dampen the sand.
2. By using a screw clamp on the supply hose you can adjust the flow of water.

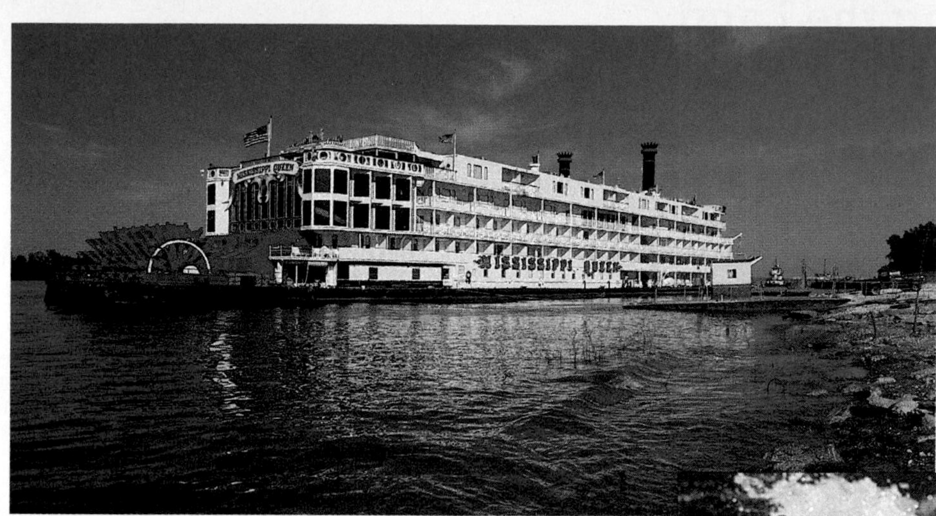

The broad, heavy bulk of the steamboat restricts its use to slow-moving, meandering rivers such as the Mississippi.

The light, narrow frame of a kayak makes it easy to guide in fast moving white water rapids, such as these on the Colorado River.

3 Do not make the reservoir end higher than the other end of the stream table.

4 Smooth out the sloping sand from the previous channel before forming another one.

Analyzing

1. How could the flow of water be increased?
2. How could the flow of water from the supply pail be slowed down?
3. Describe the channel that was formed when the sand end was high.
4. Describe the channel that was formed when the sand end was lower.

Concluding and Applying

5. ***Compare and contrast*** the two types of stream channels.
6. ***Determine the cause*** of the differences between the two channels you made.
7. **Going Further** What kind of stream channels would you expect to form on plains? What kind form in mountainous areas?

Draining the Land

The Ohio River at Cincinnati, Ohio

Figure 14-6

Most of the rain that falls between the Rocky Mountains and the Appalachians forms the Mississippi River drainage basin. The rain drains into small streams and rivers that eventually flow into the Missouri or Ohio Rivers. In turn, these large rivers flow into the Mississippi River.

Missouri R.
ROCKY MOUNTAINS
Mississippi R.
Ohio R.
APPALACHIAN MOUNTAINS
Mississippi River drainage basin

The Missouri River at Kansas City, Missouri

The Mississippi River at St. Louis, Missouri

The water in streams and rivers comes from rain or melted snow—that is, runoff.

All the water in a land area eventually flows down, or drains, into one stream. The area that a stream drains is called a **drainage basin**. Each stream has its own drainage basin.

The drainage basin of a large river usually includes the drainage basins of smaller rivers and streams. The largest drainage basin in the United States is the Mississippi River drainage basin. The Mississippi Basin is formed from most of the rain that falls between the eastern slope of the Rocky Mountains and the western slopes of the Appalachians.

All the streams and rivers in a major drainage basin form a river system. The Mississippi River system drains about one-third of the United States.

1. What causes streams to form and flow downhill?
2. Where are slow-moving streams most likely to be found?
3. Does water flow faster in wide or narrow channels?
4. **Apply** Why don't meanders form in streams on steep slopes?

Groundwater in Action

Into the Ground

In the previous sections we saw that some rainwater forms runoff and some rainwater goes into streams and rivers. Some of this rain water, however, soaks into the ground and seems to disappear. Where did the water go?

Section Objectives

- Explain how soil and rocks can be porous and permeable.
- Describe groundwater, aquifers, and the water table.
- Explain how groundwater is obtained from a well.

Key Terms

groundwater
aquifer
water table

Explore! ACTIVITY

How can the water level in the ground be changed?

What To Do

1. Fill a tub or stream table with sand and level it out. Pour water into the tub until the water is almost to the top of the sand.
2. Make a shallow hole in the sand so that you can see the water at the bottom of the hole. *In your Journal*, describe what this hole might represent.
3. Now, add more water to the sand. What happens to the level of the water in the hole? How can you change the level of the water?

As you observed, water that enters the sand moves from one place to another. There must be a lot of space between the fragments of sand. A drop of water that soaks into such ground would just seem to disappear because the ground has so much space within it.

Just watering a plant shows you how quickly water may soak into soil. Like most soils, the soil in which most houseplants are potted is made up of many tiny fragments. Some fragments may be sand-sized, some larger, and others smaller. The spaces among the fragments are called pores.

Permeability

Water that soaks into the ground collects in the pores and becomes part of the **groundwater**. In fact, it becomes part of a groundwater system.

Figure 14-7

Various kinds of soil allow water to pass through at different rates.

B Water drains easily through light sandy soil.

C Clay soil is dense and stops water from draining through.

A Peat soaks up and holds water.

Hot Springs and Geysers

In some locations beneath Earth's surface, underground water comes in contact with hot rock. When that happens, the water heats up. If the water then makes its way to the surface, a hot spring is formed. Usually, hot springs bubble gently and are only a few degrees warmer than the surrounding air.

In some cases, however, the underground water heats up so that it bursts violently through Earth's surface. These hot springs are called geysers.

Geysers exist in locations where there are vast underground passageways for the water to travel through. Usually, all of these connecting tunnels, as shown in the illustration, lead to a single opening on the surface.

The groundwater, from its contact with hot, underground rock, is heated to very high temperatures, causing it to expand to fill these tunnels.

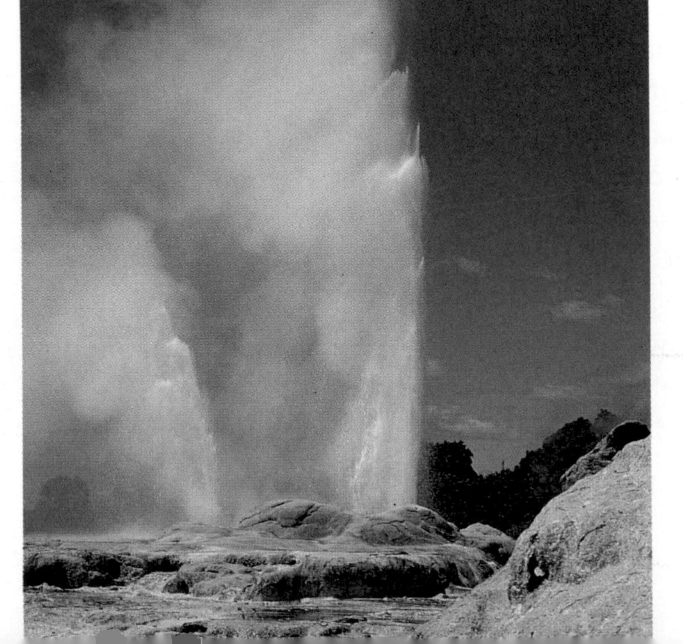

Pohuto and Prince of Wales Feathers geysers in New Zealand

Water that stays above the ground becomes part of a river system. A groundwater system is similar to a river system even though it lies within the ground. However, instead of having stream channels that connect different parts of a drainage basin, a groundwater system may have connecting pores that water can move through.

Soil or rock that has many connecting pores is said to be permeable. Water can pass through such ground materials easily. Soil or rock that has few or very small pores is less permeable. Water can't pass through it as easily. Some materials, such as clay, shale, and slate, have very small pores or no pores at all. Because water can't pass through these materials, they are impermeable.

How quickly water seeps into the ground depends on the permeability of that ground. Do you think water would seep quickly into hard-packed soil? How would permeability affect groundwater?

To understand how impermeable materials affect groundwater, think about a raincoat. You know that a raincoat is designed to keep rainwater from getting through. So the raincoat is impermeable to water. But other kinds of clothing might let some or all of the rainwater through.

In the next Investigation, you'll discover how different soils affect permeability.

This expanding water forces some of the water on top out of the ground, taking the pressure off the remaining water. The remaining water boils quickly, with much of it turning to steam. The steam shoots out of the opening like steam out of a teakettle, forcing the remaining water out with it. Once the geyser erupts, groundwater begins to refill the passageways, and the process begins again.

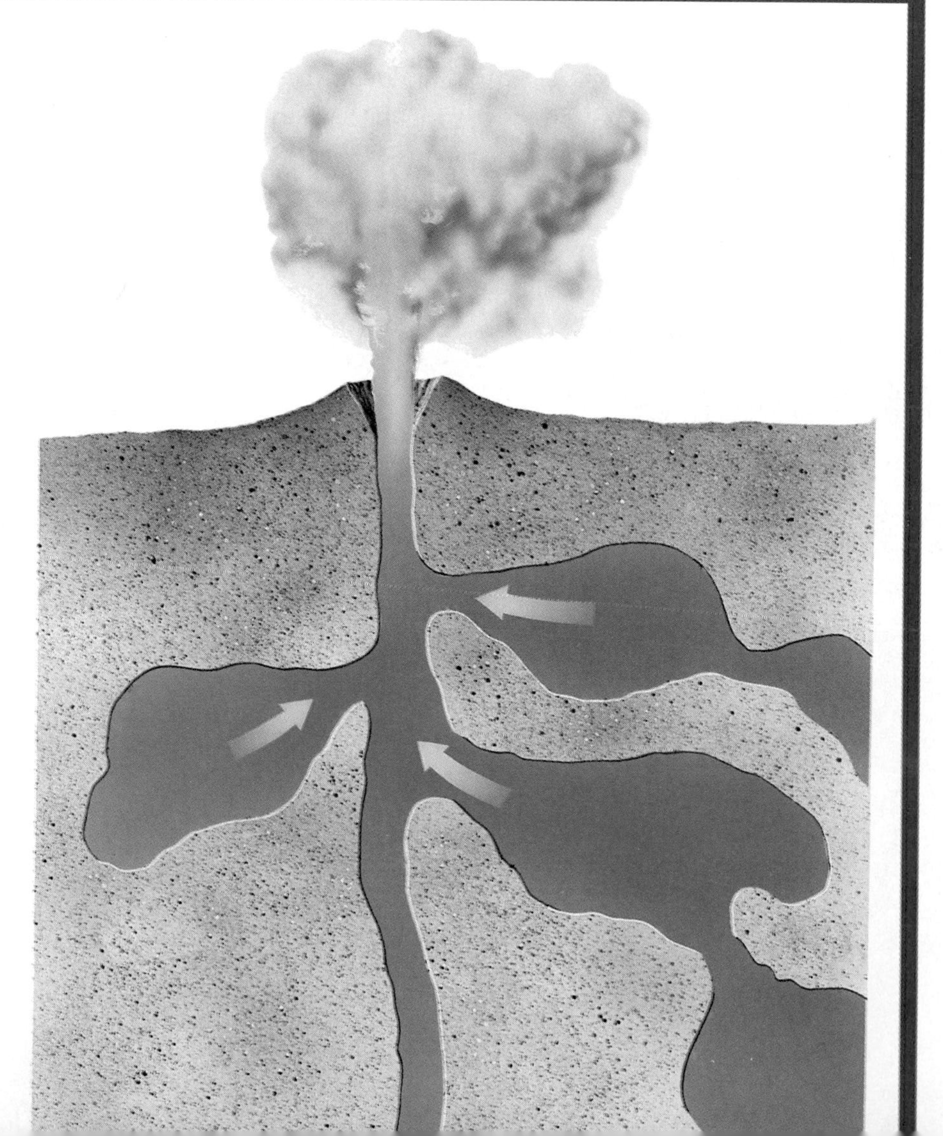

What Do You Think?

Some geysers follow a regular schedule. Old Faithful Geyser in Yellowstone National Park, for instance, erupts an average of once every 65 minutes. Can you explain why this happens?

DESIGN YOUR OWN
INVESTIGATION

Ground Permeability

There are many different kinds of soils. Soils that have a lot of connecting pores are characterized as permeable. Permeability affects how fast water can seep into the soil and flow through the ground.

Preparation

Problem
What factors determine how fast water seeps into different soils?

Form a Hypothesis
As a group, discuss what factors might influence different soils' permeability. Agree upon these factors, then make a hypothesis that can be tested in your investigation.

Objectives
- Predict and compare the permeability of different soils.
- Measure the time it takes for water to seep into different soils.
- Infer why some soils are more permeable than others.

Possible Materials
watch with second hand
25-mL graduated cylinder
four 600-mL beakers
water
metric ruler
permanent markers
potting soil, clay, sand, gravel

DESIGN YOUR OWN
INVESTIGATION

Plan the Experiment

1. Examine the materials provided by your teacher. Decide which materials you will use and how you will use them in your experiment.
2. Design a procedure to test your hypothesis. Write down what you will do at each step of your test.
3. Design a table for recording data.

Check the Plan

1. Review how you will combine the different materials to create "test soils." Will your combinations create different-colored and -textured test soils?
2. Have you determined how you will measure the water as it seeps into the soil?
3. Before you start the experiment, have your teacher approve your plan.

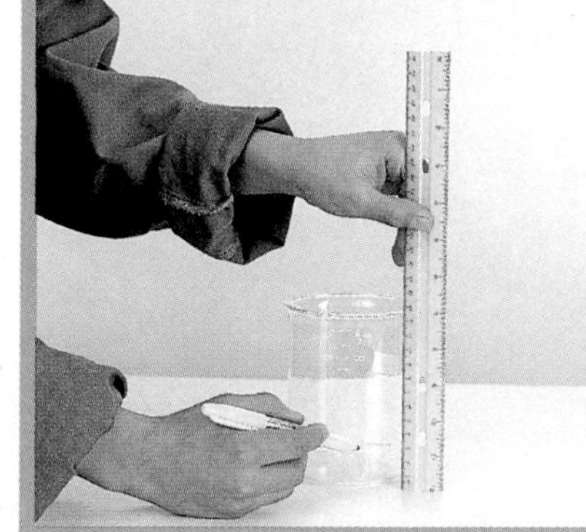

4. Carry out your experiment. Complete your data table *in your Science Journal* or on a computer spreadsheet.

Analyze and Conclude

1. **Measure** Measure the time it takes for the water in the beaker to permeate the soil. Compare your observations with your hypothesis and your predictions, and record these in your data table.
2. **Interpret Data** Which of the soils was least permeable? Most permeable? How did you tell?
3. **Infer** Infer why some soils are more permeable than others.

Going Further

Explain how permeability affects groundwater flow. Be sure to discuss runoff in your answer.

Figure 14-8

A Permeable, porous rocks, such as sandstone, allow water to pass through.
Granite
Sandstone
B Rock such as granite, which is neither porous nor permeable does not allow water to seep in.

Aquifers

How deep into the ground do you suppose groundwater can go? That depends on the permeability of the soil and rock. Groundwater will keep going down to lower levels until it reaches pores that are already filled with water. This water is resting on a layer of impermeable rock. When this happens, the impermeable rock acts like a dam, and the water can't move down any deeper. So the water begins to fill up the pores in the rocks above the impermeable rock. A layer of permeable soil or rock that allows water to move in and out freely is called an **aquifer**. Soils that contain sand or gravel and rocks like sandstones and limestones are often aquifers.

Why do you suppose aquifers are important to people? Aquifers are sources of water for many communities. In fact, if you do not live near a large river or a large freshwater lake, the chances are good that you get your water from an aquifer. Where does the water that you drink come from?

C When water moving through a permeable layer of rock reaches an impermeable layer, the water's downward motion is stopped. Once the pores to the permeable layer are filled, the water may move sideways through an aquifer—a permeable layer of soil or rock that allows water to move in and out freely. Soils that contain sand or gravel and permeable rocks are often aquifers.

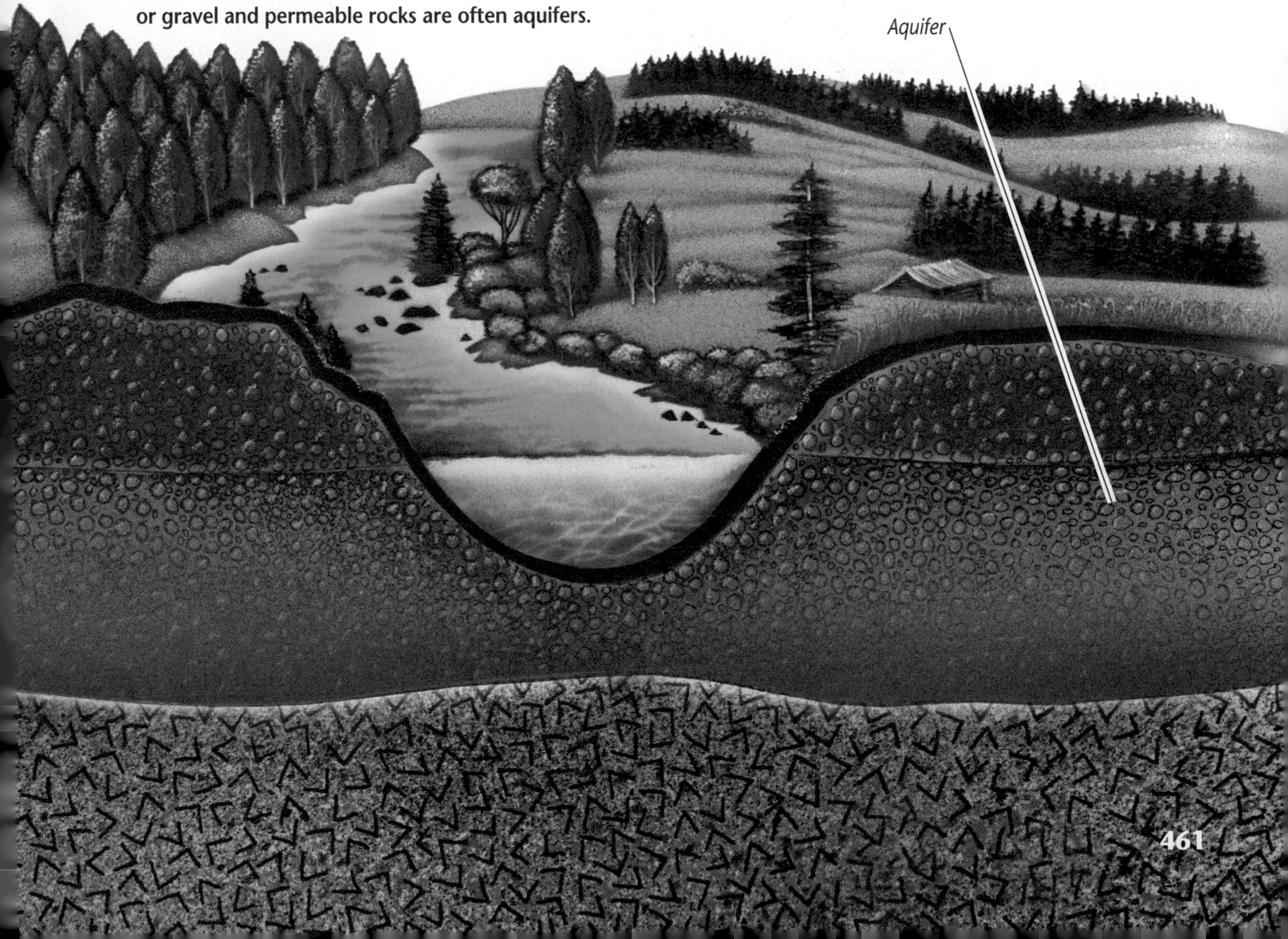

Wells and Springs

The water level in an aquifer may change from season to season. Recall the Explore activity you did at the beginning of this section. You discovered you could change the level of water in the aquifer you made. Knowing the level of water in the ground is important to many people because they get their drinking water from groundwater. Water wells are drilled down into the aquifers. Water from an aquifer flows into a well and then is pumped back up to the surface.

A well, as seen below, must go down past the water table to reach water. What is the water table? The **water table** is the top of the level where groundwater has collected in the ground. If the well is far enough below the water table, the well should provide a reliable source of cool drinking water in every season of the year.

During dry seasons, a well might dry up because the water table drops. The water table may also drop if too many wells are drilled in an area. In this instance, more water is taken out of the ground than can be replaced by rain. Unlike wells, most streams and

Figure 14-9

A When water from the aquifer flows into this well, it is pumped through pipes to the surface to provide drinking water. Why is knowing the depth of the water table during both normal and dry seasons important when digging a well?

B When water travels from a higher to a lower level and becomes trapped between two layers of impermeable rock, pressure builds up as the water attempts to reach the water table. If a well is drilled at that point, the pressure will push the water to the surface without pumping. Wells that flow without pumping are called artesian wells.

Aquifer

Water flows from an artesian well.

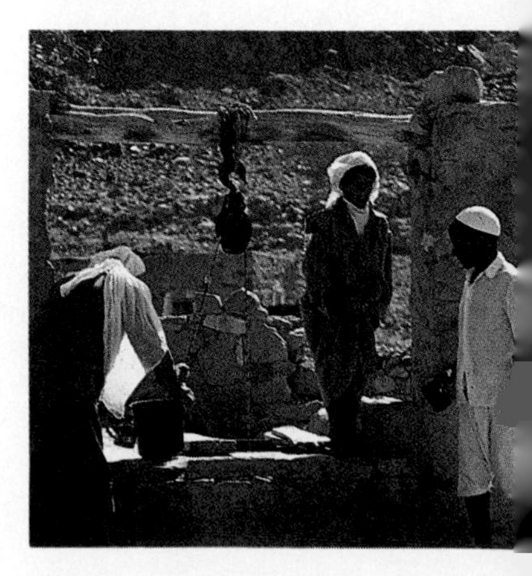

Drawing water from a well in Egypt.

Figure 14-10

Wherever the water table meets Earth's surface, groundwater may flow out of the rock or soil as seen in the photo on the left. These places where the water table is exposed are called springs. The photo above is of Mammoth hot springs in Yellowstone National Park.

rivers do not run dry in dry weather. One reason is that streams and rivers are usually lower in elevation than the surrounding land.

In some places, the water table meets Earth's surface. Groundwater simply flows out of the rock or soil at these places. Springs can be found on hillsides or any other place where the water table is exposed at the surface. Springs can often be used as a source of water.

You have taken a long journey through the hydrologic cycle. Rainwater can evaporate, run off to become rivers and streams, or seep into the ground to become groundwater. Rainwater can collect in aquifers and perhaps be pumped back up to the surface, where it once again moves through the cycle.

Recognizing Cause and Effect

Suppose you live in a town in which the population stays the same for many years. Then a number of new houses are built, and the population grows. The people in the town notice that the wells show signs of drying up. What could be the cause? What would be nature's remedy? If you need help, refer to the **Skill Handbook** on page 660.

1. How does rainwater enter the groundwater system?
2. How can rocks be both porous and permeable?
3. How can a well go dry? How can the well be made useful again?
4. **Apply** Explain how groundwater, aquifers, and the water table are related.

Science and Society

Water Wars

Water is an essential part of our everyday lives. In a single day, the average person in the United States uses 397 liters of water—that's enough liquid to fill up 1118 soft drink cans. We use water every time we take a shower, brush our teeth, or wash our clothes. We also use a lot of water indirectly. Many industries rely upon water to manufacture products such as paper and plastic. Farmers need water to irrigate the crops that produce the fruit and vegetables that we eat.

Where does all of this water come from? Some towns and cities get their water from nearby rivers, lakes, or underground wells. However, not everyone lives next to a source of fresh water, especially in the desert regions of our country. In many parts of the United States, communities are forced to get their water from other locations. Dams and pipelines are constructed to carry water from rivers that might be hundreds of kilometers away. Changing the natural flow of water in such a way is called water diversion.

There is, however, a problem with water diversion. When you take water away from a distant river, you leave less water for people who are living near the river. In some parts of the country, individuals, towns, and even states have gone to court to fight over water rights.

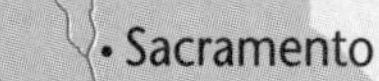

This irrigation system in Southern California is bringing water to a crop of beets.

For many years, California has been involved in a water dispute. Much of California's fresh water is supplied by the Sacramento River in the northern part of the state. Southern California, on the other hand, provides less than 20 percent of the state's fresh water.

Despite the fact that Southern California produces only a small amount of water, it consumes 85 percent of the water available in the entire state. Most of this water is used by farmers to irrigate their crops. Meanwhile, city dwellers in Northern California are facing severe water shortages. They want the government to pass laws that will restrict the amount of water used by the farmers.

In some parts of the world, water wars are on the verge of becoming full-scale wars. In the late 1980s, Turkey built a massive dam across the Euphrates River. The water in the dam's reservoir is used to irrigate crops and to generate electricity for almost half of the country. But Syria—Turkey's neighbor to the south—also depends upon water from the Euphrates. Syria has argued that the dam is stealing water away from its farmers. The dam has created tremendous tension between the two countries.

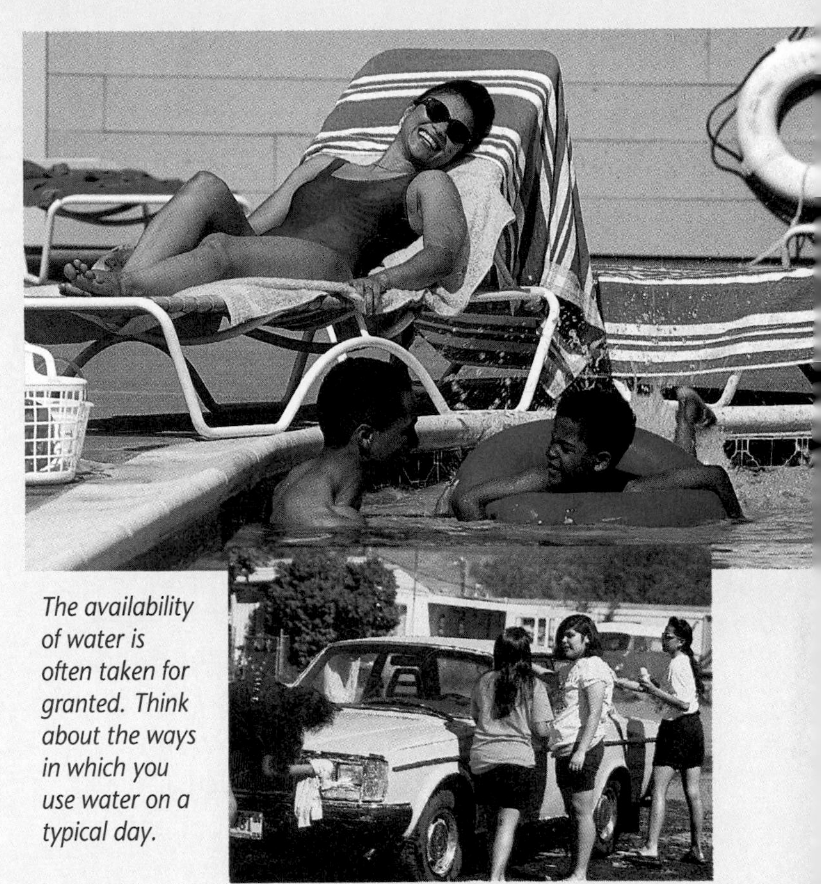

The availability of water is often taken for granted. Think about the ways in which you use water on a typical day.

What Do You Think?

Some people say that if cities made a concerted effort not to waste so much water, there would be plenty of water available for everyone. Do you agree? Can you think of a few simple things that you can do around your own home that will help conserve our supply of water?

Beets

Planning for the Next Floodwaters

A break in a levee at St. Louis

In July of 1993, the mighty Mississippi River flexed its muscles in the worst flood in North American history. The ordinarily lazy river became a raging monster, rising almost 150 feet over its banks and bulging to seventeen miles across in some places. It was called a "500-year flood," in the sense that a flood this bad occurs only about once every 500 years.

Water ripped apart buildings, bridges, roadways, and levees as if they were children's toys. Thousands of people were left without homes, and the cleanup will continue for years.

Only the most resistant vegetation survived the long-standing waters. Populations of mosquitoes and mayflies mushroomed. Wildlife—frogs, snakes, bobtail quail, pheasant, deer—were all displaced from their natural habitats.

Some of these effects last only a few years. Others will persist into the next decade. What makes a river flood? With all the technology we have at our fingertips, why can't we prevent disastrous floods?

How Floods Develop

Floods start with rain. Rainwater either soaks into the ground or runs off along the surface until it reaches a stream, river, or lake. This surface runoff is the main concern during a flood. The runoff floods the network of creeks, streams, and rivers on its way to the main river they feed into.

The Natural River

The land surrounding the Mississippi is wide and flat. For thousands of years, each time the river rose it spilled onto these wide flood plains. Tons of sediment left behind by receding water created the deep, rich soil that's coveted by farmers. Plentiful forests and wetlands absorbed excess rainwater like sponges, preventing smaller floods entirely and moderating the larger ones.

The Developed River

Flood walls and levees (tall, wide, protective walls often made of compacted soil) narrow the river channel and keep it from expanding onto its floodplains. Because it can't spread out, floodwater can only rise. Upstream the river backs up like a clogged drain, while downstream the waters move faster and push even harder on the levees.

Most of the original wetlands and forests have been developed by humans for farmland or urban centers. Towns and cities channel excess runoff to the river rather than absorbing it. And as time passes, disasters are costing more partly because there are more people in the way each time. With fast-growing river towns to consider, major floods seem more likely, not less.

Preventing Major Floods

Ideally, many of the levees should be moved back from the water's edge back about five miles along the whole length of the Upper Mississippi. That would work, but it would sacrifice valuable farmland and many towns and cities. Carrying out such a plan would carry economic costs perhaps even higher than those of the flood itself. Flood-plain management will have to use less sweeping measures.

One possible solution starts with a coordinated plan for the whole Upper Mississippi. Right now the region is an unorganized patchwork of private and local reservoirs, flood walls, levees, and locks. Each community has made its own decisions.

In comparison, the Lower Mississippi is protected by a unified flood-control system that hasn't failed since 1927 and didn't fail in 1993. But that system has storage and pass-through basins that add up to equal the area of the state of Indiana.

Can the Upper Mississippi states agree to put aside that much land? It would have to be surrounded by flood walls on the landward side. Some economists think part of the put-aside land could be farmed on a contingency basis. That is, as long as it isn't needed for overflow storage, it could be used for agriculture, but not for residences. One farmer working such land might be flooded out once in ten years; another once every other year. Crop insurance would have to make up for these losses.

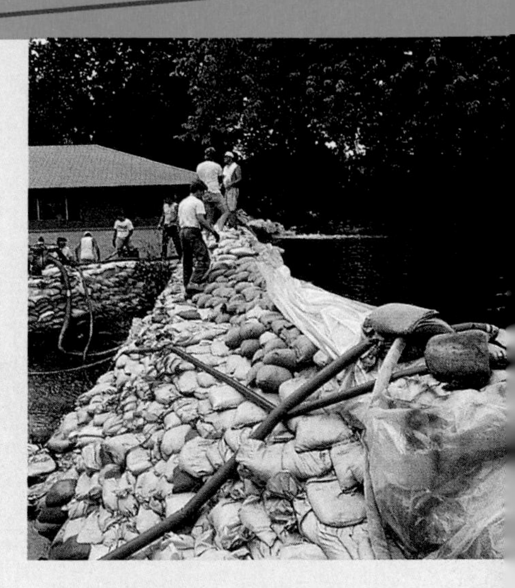

Sandbags are piled up to keep the Mississippi River back.

What Do You Think?

Only one thing is sure: no one who has had to shovel Mississippi mud out of his or her home wants to go through the flood of 1993 again. Take on the role of a farmer or someone who lives in the city. What would you decide to do to control floods? How would your decision affect others?

The narrow channel caused by the levees forces the river to back up, which pushes water upriver.

The river rises high and fast between the levees, which can then affect land areas downriver.

Teens in SCIENCE

The Clean Stream Team

How would you describe the city or town where you live? For 14-year-old JoAnna Gott, the answer is simple. "My town is beautiful. And that's the way we want to keep it."

JoAnna lives in Strafford, Missouri. The many nearby lakes, rivers, and streams are a large part of why people love to live in Strafford. So, it was only natural for JoAnna to get involved in a recent Urban Streams Festival held in her town.

"The festival was created to remind people to take care of our water. Right now we're lucky. Our water is clean. And that is a good reason to celebrate."

During the festival, residents of Strafford were encouraged to do more than think about water. They were urged to get involved in protecting this important resource. JoAnna's 4-H club accepted the challenge.

"We went to a park in town and painted a warning on all the storm drains. The storm drains are located along a road that runs through the park. Sometimes people have disposed of hazardous waste by pouring it down the storm drains."

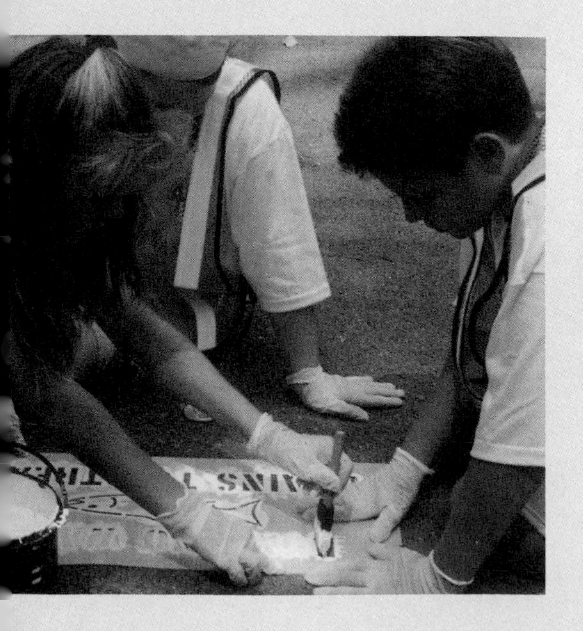

"People need to know what happens if they are careless. A person might think that a little old paint or household cleaner can't make that much difference in a big stream. But if the person actually thought about that poison running into their favorite stream, I don't think they would do it. Maybe this sounds silly, but I wish more people would think about how they would like it if they were a fish or some other animal that lives in the stream. I'd feel bad if someone dumped paint thinner down our chimney at home."

Science Journal

JoAnna loves her town. How about you? *In your Science Journal* make a list of the best and worst things about the city or town you live in.

Using your "best and worst" list as a guide, write a brief description of one thing that you could do to make your city or town a better place to live.

chapter 14

REVIEWING MAIN IDEAS

Science Journal

Review the statements below about the big ideas presented in this chapter, and answer the questions. Then, re-read your answers to the Did You Ever Wonder questions at the beginning of the chapter. *In your Science Journal,* write a paragraph about how your understanding of the big ideas in the chapter has changed.

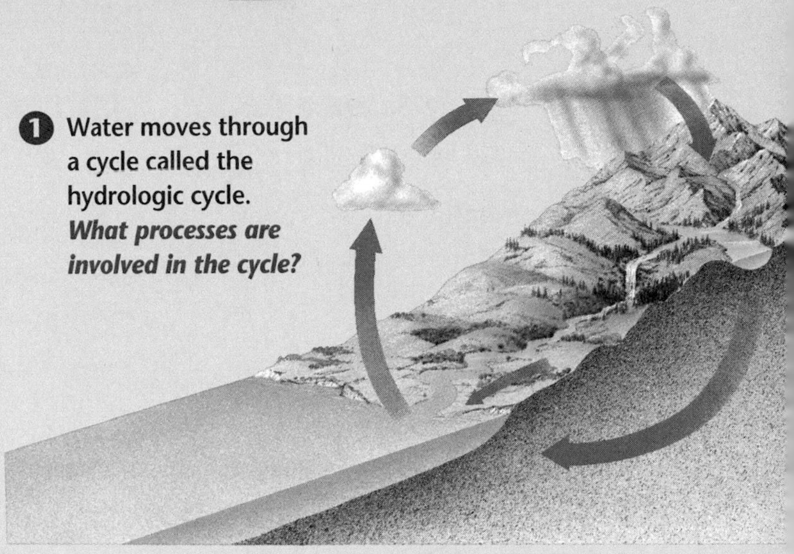

1. **Water moves through a cycle called the hydrologic cycle.** ***What processes are involved in the cycle?***

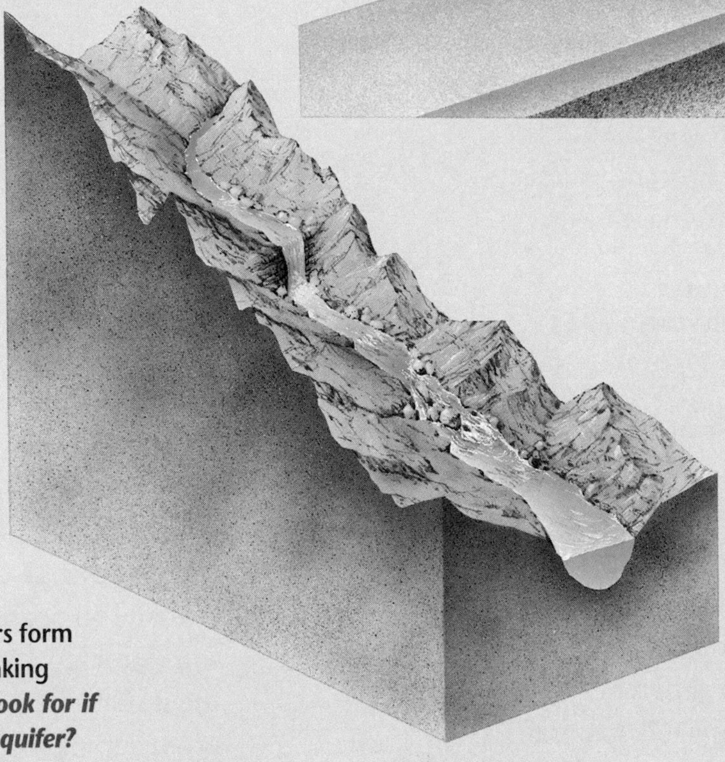

2. **Rivers and streams drain excess water from the land and thus form an important part of the hydrologic cycle.** ***Compare how rainwater runs off a steep slope and a flat area.***

3. **Groundwater and aquifers form important sources of drinking water.** ***What would we look for if we were looking for an aquifer?***

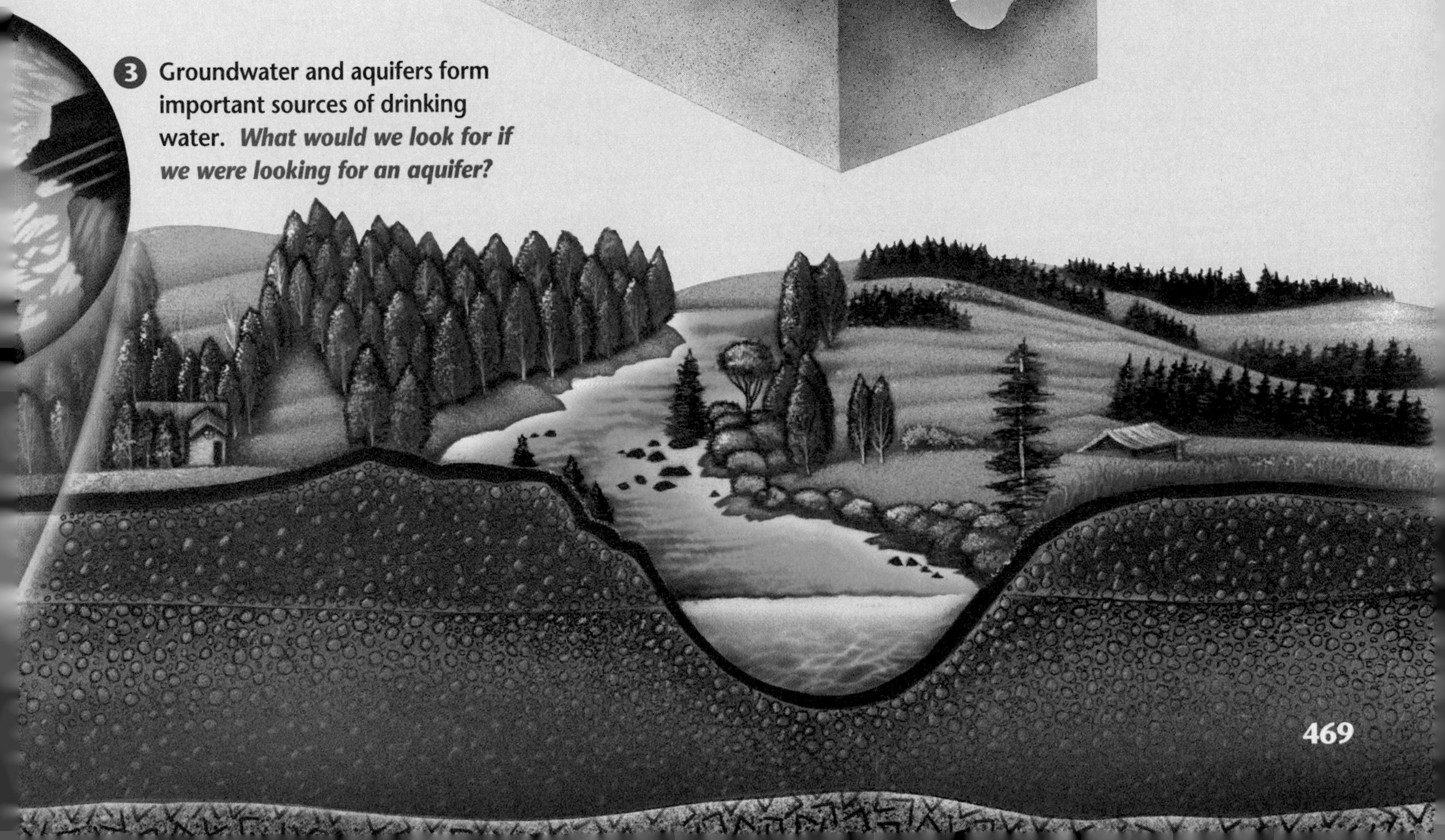

CHAPTER REVIEW

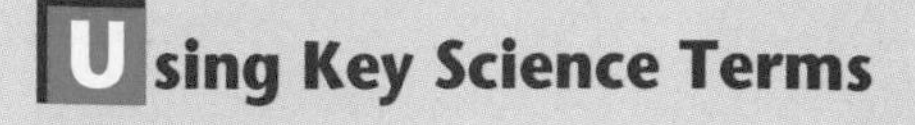

Using Key Science Terms

aquifer
drainage basin
groundwater
hydrologic cycle
meander
runoff
water table

For each set of terms below, explain the relationship that exists.

1. hydrologic cycle, runoff
2. groundwater, aquifer
3. runoff, drainage basin
4. water table, groundwater
5. meander, drainage basin

Understanding Ideas

Answer the following questions in your Journal *using complete sentences.*

1. What factors determine the amount of precipitation that becomes runoff?
2. Explain how meanders form.
3. What factors affect a river's ability to erode its bed?
4. Explain the difference between permeable and impermeable material.
5. Describe the movement of groundwater.

Developing Skills

Use your understanding of the concepts developed in this chapter to answer each of the following questions.

1. **Separating and Controlling Variables** You will need a stream table, watering can, sand, clay, humus soil, 3 liters of water, and a block of wood. Repeat the Explore activity on page 449 three times, using a different type of soil in the stream table each time. How does the rate of runoff vary with different soil types?
2. **Concept Mapping** Complete the concept map of precipitation.

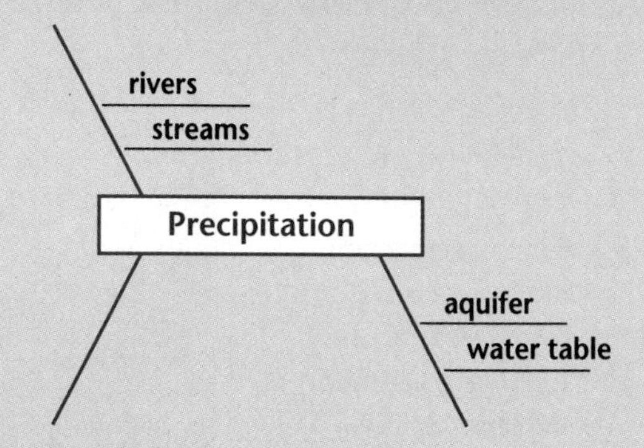

3. **Making and Using Graphs** Make a graph like the one below. You will need a stream table, a watering can, 9 liters of water, sand, clay, humus soil, a stop-watch, and 3 blocks of wood. Repeat the activity above creating three different slopes—one 15 degrees, one 30 degrees, and one 60 degrees—for each type of soil. Time how long it takes for most of the water to run off. Record your results on the graph. How does slope affect the runoff time for the different types of soil?

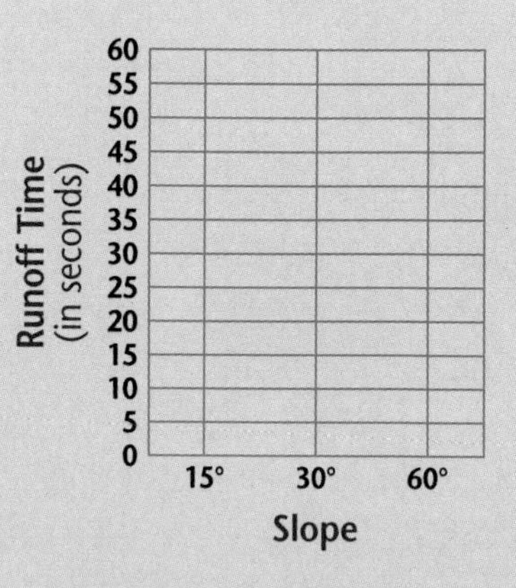

chapter 14 CHAPTER REVIEW

Critical Thinking

In your Journal, *answer each of the following questions.*

1. How can the level of the water table vary even when the groundwater is not disturbed by people?
2. Study the illustration. If a spring thaw suddenly melts a great deal of snow in the region labeled A, what do you think will happen to the river in the region that is labeled B? Explain your answer.

3. Compare a groundwater system with a drainage basin system.
4. What are the similarities and differences between a drilled well and a spring?

Problem Solving

Read the following problem and discuss your answers in a brief paragraph.

One way to test the permeability of different kinds of soil materials is to see how much time it takes water to flow through them. Suppose you had some water, a watch, some funnels lined with filter paper, some beakers, a graduated cylinder, and equal amounts of potting soil, marbles, and clay.

1. How could you set up an experiment to determine the permeability of each material?
2. Predict which material would be the most permeable. Least permeable?

CONNECTING IDEAS

Discuss each of the following in a brief paragraph.

1. **Theme—Systems and Interactions** What factors affect whether water will run off, evaporate, or soak into the ground at a certain location?
2. **Theme—Systems and Interactions** Earth has often been called a water planet. Based on what you've learned in this chapter, would you agree? Explain.
3. **Theme—Systems and Interactions** What is the relationship between the largest drainage basin in the United States and the kind of landform that is dominant in that region?
4. **A Closer Look** What role does groundwater play in the formation and eruption of a geyser?
5. **Economics Connection** How might the lessons learned from the Mississippi flood affect future development of wetlands?

CHAPTER 15

SHAPING THE LAND

Did you ever wonder...

- Why a river could be crystal clear at one time and murky brown at another?
- What causes rockslides?
- Where the piles of rocks along riverbanks come from?

Science Journal

Before you begin to study about what shapes the land, think about these questions and answer them *in your Science Journal.* When you finish the chapter, compare your journal entry with what you have learned.

Only two days ago, the river near Toshiko's house sparkled crystal clear. That was before the storms came and all the rain fell. Now the rock bridge she and her friends use to cross the river is covered with murky, chocolate-colored waters. Toshiko also notices that some of the river's bank has been washed away as well.

What caused the river to darken? What happened to the rock bridge? Will the riverbank look the same after the water retreats?

In this chapter, you will learn how forces in nature such as water and wind not only can change but can actually carry away parts of Earth.

Explore! ACTIVITY

How do sediments move from one location to another?

How many ways can you think of to move a pile of sediments, such as sand and gravel? Does nature move sediments in similar ways?

What To Do

1. Put a piece of waxed paper on a desk or table and place a small pile of sand and gravel on the paper.
2. Devise ways of moving the sand and gravel from one place to another without touching it. Record *in your Journal* how many different ways you can move the mixture.
3. Which type of sediment moved most easily? Did the type of sediment most easily moved change with the way you moved the sediments?
4. How do you think nature might use the same ways to move these sediments?

Gravity

Section Objectives
- Distinguish between erosion and deposition.
- Identify creep and slump as erosion caused by gravity.
- Describe rockslides and mudflows.

Key Terms
erosion
deposition
creep
slump
rockslide
mudflow

The Journey Begins

In the Explore activity, you may have tilted the wax paper because you realized that sediment can move by itself from a higher to a lower place. Now, think about sliding down a hill on skis in the winter or on roller skates in the summer. Gravity overcomes the force of friction, and you slip down the slope with very little effort.

Solid rock can be broken down into smaller pieces and changed into other materials as a result of weathering. When weathering occurs on hills and slopes, the resulting broken rocks can slide downhill just as you do. The wearing away of surface materials and the movement of the products of weathering from where they formed to a different location is **erosion.**

The four major causes of erosion are gravity, running water, glaciers, and wind. These are also known as agents of erosion. Throughout this chapter, you will discover how gravity, water, ice, and wind help erosion occur.

Eventually, your skis or roller skates come to a stop. In the same way, sediments will stop moving and pile up, or accumulate. This accumulation of eroded sediments is called **deposition.**

Figure 15-1

Throughout this chapter, you will discover how the four major agents of erosion—gravity, running water, glaciers, and wind—help erosion occur.

GRAVITY

RUNNING WATER

GLACIER

WIND

Slow Erosion

The next time you travel by car or bus, look along the roadway for trees, utility poles, or other objects leaning downhill. Trees and poles leaning downhill can be found in areas where freezing and thawing occur. As the ground freezes, small soil particles are pushed up by ice expanding in the soil. Then, when the soil thaws, it falls downslope, often less than a millimeter at a time. Several years of soil moving downslope very slowly can cause objects to lean. This slow movement of soil downhill is called **creep**. Creep as in **Figure 15-2**, gets its name from the way soil slowly creeps down a hill.

Sometimes one large mass of loose material or rock layers slips down a steep slope but doesn't travel very far. This slow mass movement of material is called **slump**. Slump occurs because the material under the slumped material weakened as in **Figure 15-3**.

Although such movements are slow, over time they can reshape the lay of the land. Valleys may gradually widen and the hills lining the valleys become more rounded and less steep.

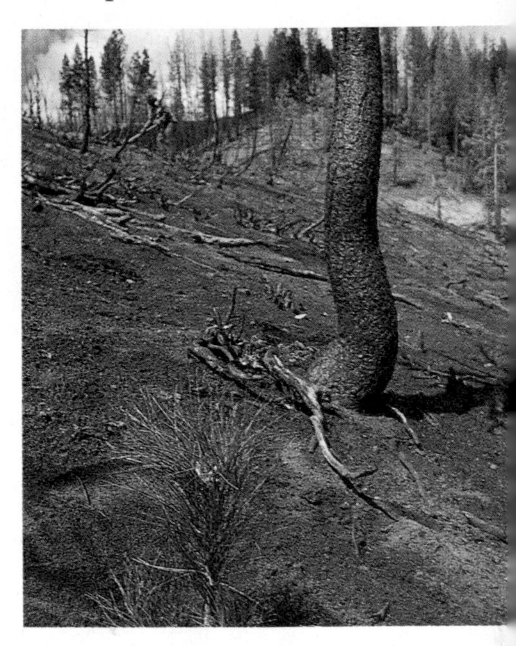

Figure 15-2

When you see objects, such as trees and fence posts, all tilting in the same direction, creep is occurring. Creep gets its name from the slow way soil falls downslope. It creeps!

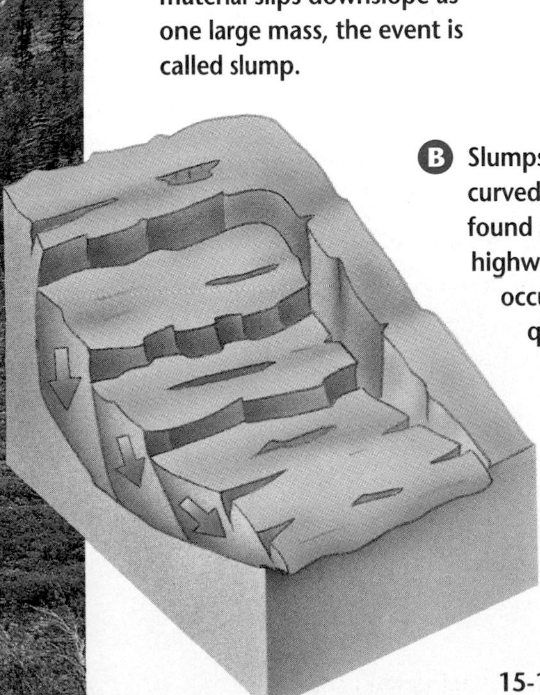

Figure 15-3

A When underlying material gives way and overlying material slips downslope as one large mass, the event is called slump.

B Slumps, which leave a curved scar, are frequently found along roads and highways and commonly occur after an earthquake or heavy rain.

Fast Erosion

On a really steep slope, large blocks of rock can break loose and tumble quickly to the bottom. As they fall, these rocks crash into other rocks, and they too break loose. The mass movement of falling rocks is called a **rockslide**.

Figure 15-4

Rockslides happen most often after heavy rains or during earthquakes, but they can happen on any steep rocky slope at any time without warning.

Where would you expect to find rockslides? Mountains are most likely to have steep, rocky slopes where this sudden mass movement could occur. If a heavy rain falls in a dry area with thick layers of sediments, the water mixes with the sediments and forms a thick, pasty substance. Masses of such wet, heavy material will easily slide downhill in a **mudflow**. The flowing mud can move anything in its path.

Controlling Soil Erosion

Farmers have developed methods to help them grow crops on land that otherwise might just erode away. Most of these methods are ways to keep water and soil from running downhill.

Terrace Farming

One method is to create terraces around steep inclines or mountains. As seen in the photo below, terraces are flat fields where crops can be grown. Steep inclines separate the terraces from each other. Rainwater runs down the inclines to soak the terraces below them. It's a good way to save water in dry climates.

A similar method is to create a terrace that coils around and up a mountain. In this case the fields are not flat, but gently rise, winding around and around the mountain.

Figure 15-5

As a mudflow reaches the bottom of a slope, it slows down, eventually comes to rest, and deposits all the sediment and debris it has been carrying. Why do you think mudflows are considered to be very destructive?

check your UNDERSTANDING

1. How is erosion related to weathering?
2. Where is the deposition of sediment most likely to occur?
3. How can you identify creep and slump?
4. Why can rockslides and mudflows be dangerous?
5. **Apply** How might cutting into hillsides to build houses or roads affect erosion?

Contour Plowing

On gentle slopes, farmers catch water by plowing across the slopes rather than up and down. This is called contour plowing. As the water travels downward, the plowed rows catch and slow it. Some of the water soaks in before the rest continues flowing downhill.

If land is prone to erosion, the use of good farming practices is especially important. Plowing a crop back into the ground helps it resist erosion. Leaving the crop residue as seen in the photo on the right, after the harvest also reduces erosion over the winter. In windy areas, sandy soil can be protected by planting coarse grasses to help hold the soil in place.

Unwise farming practices contributed to the dust bowl that occurred in the Central United States during the 1930's.

People cannot always control the causes of erosion, but they can do some things to keep erosion from destroying farm land.

What Do You Think?

Walk around your neighborhood or town, looking for examples of eroded land. How could that land be improved? Is there anything you can do to prevent further erosion?

15-2 Running Water

Section Objectives

- Explain how streams carry sediment.
- Explore the relationship between amount of sediment and rate of stream flow.
- Explain how streams and rivers shape the land.

Key Terms

floodplain
delta

Streams Erode

You know that the force of gravity can erode rock and soil material from slopes and deposit it at lower places. Can anything else erode and deposit sediments? What other factors cause loose material to travel down a slope?

Imagine following one small rock that landed in a creek at the bottom of a cliff after a rockslide. A heavy rain starts to fall. Soon the runoff begins to flow downhill, enters the creek, and picks up speed. The water in the creek in **Figure 15-6** is flowing quickly from a higher to a lower elevation. The small rock is lifted and carried along with the flowing water. This is one way that rock particles become eroded. Water moves them.

Figure 15-6

A This stream flows from a higher to a lower elevation. The water flows swiftly and carries a lot of sediment.

Explore! ACTIVITY

How can streams carry away rock and soil?

What To Do

1. Sprinkle some instant coffee grains, salt, and rice on a paper plate to represent loose soil and rock material. Squirt water from a spray bottle on one edge of the plate to act as rain.
2. Observe what happens to the material when the water droplets start to accumulate and flow in a stream. Record these observations *in your Journal.*
3. Now continue spraying as you tip the plate over a sink.
4. Can you explain what the stream of water has done to the different types of material? What do you observe about the color of the water?

B **The rock and other sediments in the water roll and scrape against the sides and bottom of the stream channel. As they travel, the sediments knock loose more soil and rocks, thus creating additional sediment.**

D **As it erodes rock and soil along its bottom and sides, the stream continually cuts a deeper and wider channel as it rushes forward.**

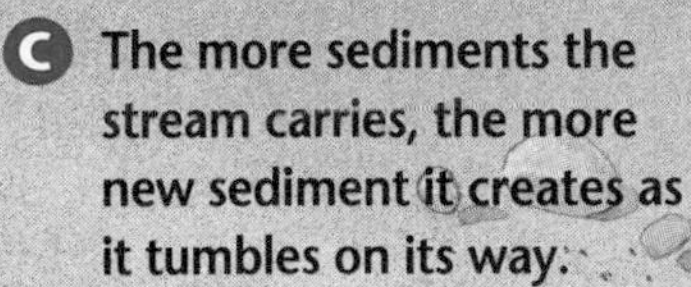

C **The more sediments the stream carries, the more new sediment it creates as it tumbles on its way.**

Figure 15-7

As the volume of a stream increases, its flow speeds up and the stream erodes at a faster rate. What evidence can you see in the photographs that tells you the fast stream is eroding more than the slow stream?

Water in a stream flows faster when the slope of the stream increases. It also flows faster when the volume of water increases. When more water is added to a stream as it combines with other streams, it speeds up. An increase in runoff from rainfall has the same effect.

Streams flowing swiftly down a steep hill eventually reach less sloping ground and flow less swiftly. As the rate of flow slows, it changes the way that a stream erodes.

Moving water on a gentle slope erodes the outside curves of a river instead of cutting downward into the streambed. If the river continues to meander in snakelike bends, it erodes its valley walls and widens the valley. If the volume of water in the river increases, the erosion increases.

Figure 15-8

A Mature rivers that have eroded their channels into broad valleys flow slowly in snakelike bends called meanders. Meanders result from erosion and sediment deposition.

B Because the water flows faster around the outside edge of a curve, the outer bank of a river is eroded more than the inner bank. Sediments are deposited along the inner bank by slower-moving water. This process of erosion and deposition builds slight bends in the river into wide meanders, and changes the course of the river.

Streams Deposit Sediment

What happens when a river floods? Runoff from heavy rains can cause a river to overflow its banks. During floods, a river carries a larger than normal amount of sediment. Bulky, heavy sediments drop along the banks of the river, forming ridges. Finer, lighter sediments travel out beyond the river channel and form a **floodplain**. Because these light sediments contain minerals and rich topsoil, they make floodplains a fertile area for planting.

Moving water deposits sediments even when the volume of water in the river is not increased. As a river starts to slow down, it can not flow fast enough to continue carrying heavier, bulkier sediments. The river begins to deposit the sediments. Slow-moving water is still able to carry fine, light sediments, however. Often sediments are deposited when the river empties into another body of water, such as a bay or lake. The deposited sediments may form a triangular-shaped land area called a **delta**.

Observing and Inferring

Imagine you are at the bottom of a canyon. You observe that its walls consist of reddish-brown sandstone. You also observe that the water in the river has a similar reddish brown color. How would you use your observations to explain the formation of this canyon? If you need help, refer to the **Skill Handbook** on page 659.

Figure 15-9

A Sediments of minerals and rich topsoil carried by the Mekong River and deposited into the South China Sea have formed the Mekong Delta in South Vietnam. Some sediments come from as far away as China.

B More than half of the people of Southern Vietnam live on the Mekong Delta, which is the chief agricultural area of Vietnam. Most Vietnamese are farmers and rice is their main crop.

DESIGN YOUR OWN
INVESTIGATION

Stream Erosion and Deposition

Streams are very effective movers of sediment. They can erode large quantities of sediment from an area and deposit them many miles away. But how do streams erode and deposit sediment, and where in the stream channel do these two processes take place?

Preparation

Problem
Which factors affect the way a stream erodes and deposits sediments?

Form a Hypothesis
As a group, list the factors that might influence stream erosion and deposition. Agree upon these factors, then form a hypothesis that can be tested in your experiment.

Objectives
- Design an experiment that tests the effects of different factors on stream erosion and deposition.
- Compare how different factors affect the way a stream erodes and deposits sediment.
- Determine where erosion and deposition occur in the stream channel.

Materials
stream table
sand, small pebbles, soil
plastic hose
screw clamps
pails with water
block of wood

Safety

DESIGN YOUR OWN
INVESTIGATION

Plan the Experiment

1. Examine the materials provided by your teacher. Determine how you will use these materials to create a stream channel.
2. Agree upon a way to test your hypothesis. Write down what you will do at each step.
3. Design a table for recording your data.

Check the Plan

1. How many factors will you test to observe stream erosion and deposition? Keep in mind that you should only test one factor or variable at a time.
2. If you are testing more than one variable, how will you ensure that the same conditions exist in the stream channel for each test?
3. Before you start the experiment, have your teacher approve your plan.
4. Carry out your experiment. Complete your data table *in your Science Journal.*

Analyze and Conclude

1. **Observe** Describe what happened to the stream channel in your tests. Where did most erosion take place? Where did deposition occur?
2. **Conclude** What happened to the eroded materials? Describe how they were deposited.
3. **Compare and Contrast** Compare the effects of different factors on stream erosion and deposition.
4. Explain how your results support or do not support your hypothesis.

Going Further

Based on your observations, infer where the greatest amount of sediment might be found along a river's course.

The Mighty Mississippi

Let's use the Mississippi River system to review how rivers erode Earth's surface. Thousands of smaller streams flow quickly from higher elevations into larger streams and rivers. These small, swift-moving streams erode sediments from the bottoms of their channels. As the larger streams and rivers reach gradually sloping ground, they slow down. When they finally reach the Mississippi River, they are flowing on flatter areas and beginning to meander.

The Mississippi River itself cuts into its banks, widens its valley, and picks up more sediment. The slow-moving Mississippi carries a great volume of water and large amounts of sediment. Eventually, at the Gulf of Mexico, it loses most of its sediment and forms a delta on the Louisiana coast.

Figure 15-10

A **The Mississippi River gets its water from thousands of small streams and rivers, which feed into larger and larger streams and finally into the Mississippi itself. One example is the Tennessee River, which feeds into the Ohio River.**

B **When the Ohio River joins the Mississippi at Cairo, Illinois, the volume of the Mississippi doubles. The Mississippi meanders through the valley, depositing sediments along the way.**

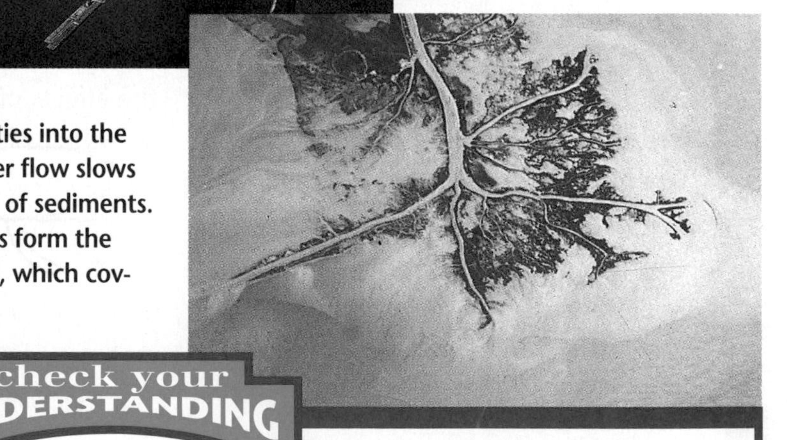

C **As the Mississippi empties into the Gulf of Mexico, the river flow slows and drops its final load of sediments. The dropped sediments form the fertile Mississippi Delta, which covers about 33 700 km^2.**

check your UNDERSTANDING

1. How do rivers cause erosion?
2. How does slope affect the amount of sediment the stream can carry?
3. How do rivers shape valleys and deltas?
4. **Apply** How could the construction of a dam upriver affect a delta?

15-3 Glaciers

What Are Glaciers?

What would it be like to live at a time when every winter is longer and colder than the one before? Every summer would be shorter and cooler—until eventually there would be almost no summer at all. This is what the climate was like over 16 000 years ago, during the last glaciation or glacial period. Then, ice covered much of the land.

A glacial period is a period of time when ice and snow cover much of Earth's surface. An ice age is a time during which many glacial periods occur. There have been a number of ice ages in Earth's history. The last glacial period ended about 10 000 years ago.

Yet huge masses of moving snow and ice called glaciers still cover parts of Earth. In fact, glaciers cover about one-tenth of Earth's land. Moving glaciers make enormous changes in Earth's surface. Melting glaciers provide much of the water that flows into rivers. Many people depend on this melted ice for their water supply. Citizens of Lima, Peru obtain their water from glaciers high in the Andes Mountains.

Section Objectives

- Describe how a glacier is formed.
- Differentiate between the two major types of glaciers.
- Describe how glaciers erode the land.

Key Terms

firn
continental glaciers
valley glaciers

Figure 15-11

A Ice sheets and glaciers, such as the Sawyer Glacier near Juneau, Alaska, hold 85 percent of all the fresh water on Earth.

B Melting glaciers provide much of the water that flows into rivers, which eventually erode and change the land.

Glacial Formation

Have you ever seen ice build up on the freezer walls of an old refrigerator? The same thing can happen in nature where snow remains on the ground year-round. If the snow doesn't melt during the summer, it begins to pile up just as frost can pile up in a freezer.

When snow falls and starts to accumulate, it is mostly air. Snow that doesn't melt after one year becomes a harder, denser material called **firn.** Firn has lost some of the air, and as it becomes more and more compressed by the snow on top of it, the firn will become glacial ice.

Some air is still in the glacial ice and is trapped in the ice. By analyzing this trapped air, we can learn what air was like when the ice was formed.

When gravity acts on the glacial ice it begins to move and is called a glacier. This movement depends on how thick the ice is, the steepness of the surface the glacier sits on, the weight of the ice, and air temperature surrounding the glacier.

Figure 15-12

Melting, evaporation, and refreezing gradually change delicate snowflakes into small, round, thick granules called firn. As the process continues and overlying layers of snow add pressure, snow becomes glacial ice. During the transformation, snow is changed from a loose sediment with plenty of air space around the individual ice crystals into a more solid mass of higher density.

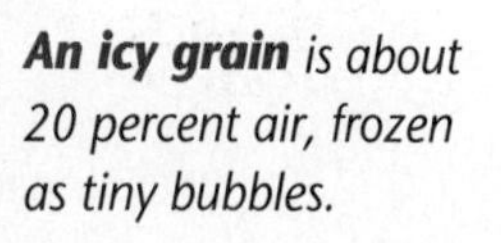

Figure 15-13

Glaciers exist as giant sheets of ice in polar regions such as Antarctica and parts of Greenland. Glaciers also exist as smaller ice caps and in mountain valleys found in such places as Iceland, Canada, and Alaska. Together glaciers cover about one-tenth of Earth's surface.

Types of Glaciers

Masses of ice and snow that cover large land masses near Earth's polar regions are called **continental glaciers**. They make up 96 percent of glacial ice. If you look at **Figure 15-13**, you'll see that continental glaciers are found in Greenland and in Antarctica.

Small glaciers are found at higher elevations in mountain regions. These glaciers usually occupy valleys in the mountains so they are called **valley glaciers**.

Glaciers contain up to 85 percent of the world's fresh water. If all of the glaciers were to melt as some have, world sea level would rise around 55 meters. What would happen to cities along the coast, such as Miami, New York, Bombay, or London? What would happen to the shapes of the continents?

Connect to... Life Science

As glaciers advance and retreat, plants and animals also migrate along with the glaciers. What adaptations might these plants and animals have to have to survive living near a glacier?

Figure 15-14

Continental glaciers, such as this one in northwest Greenland, cover large land areas near Earth's polar regions.

Figure 15-15

Valley glaciers like this one at Glacier Bay National Park, Alaska, occupy a single valley between mountains. The mass of ice and snow that makes up a valley glacier forms at and flows from higher elevations where snow stays year after year.

INVESTIGATE!

How Do Glaciers Change the Land?

Glaciers erode the land and can change it a great deal. In this activity, you'll observe how glaciers change the land as they erode Earth's surface.

Problem

How do valley glaciers affect Earth's surface?

Materials

ice block about 5 cm by 20 cm by 2 cm, containing sand, clay, and gravel
stream table with sand
lamp with reflector
metric ruler

Safety Precautions

You will be using electrical equipment near water in this investigate. Please keep these items apart from one another.

What To Do

1. Copy the data table *into your Journal.* Then set up the stream table and lamp as shown.
2. The ice block is made by mixing water with sand, gravel, and clay in a container and then freezing (see photo ***A***).
3. Make a V-shaped river channel. Measure and record its width and depth. Draw a sketch that includes these measurements (see photo ***B***).
4. Place the ice block, to act as a moving glacier, at the upper end of the stream table.

A

B

Data and Observations			
	Width	Depth	Observation
River			
Glacier			

5 Gently push the glacier along the river channel until it's under the light, halfway between the top and bottom of the stream table.

6 Turn on the light and allow the ice to melt. ***Observe*** and record what happens.

7 ***Measure*** and record the width and depth of the glacial channel. Draw a sketch of the channel and include these measurements *in your Journal.*

Analyzing

1. How can you ***infer*** the direction from which a glacier traveled?
2. How can you tell how far down the valley the glacier traveled?

Concluding and Applying

3. Determine the effect valley glaciers have on the surface over which they move.
4. **Going Further** How can you identify land that was once covered by a glacier?

Glacial Erosion

Glaciers covered large portions of land during the last ice age. As they move, glaciers cut through mountains, erode the land, and leave large deposits of ground-up rock. As glaciers melt, rivers and lakes form. Much of Earth's landscape has been shaped by glacial ice.

A glacier picks up loose materials as it moves over land. These eroded sediments are added to the mass of the glacier or pile up along its sides. Ridges form when a glacier recedes and deposits rocks and sediments. You can see hills or ridges like this in places that were once the sides or ends of a glacier.

Glaciers do more than just move sediments. They also erode rock and soil that aren't loose. Glacial ice melts, and the water flows down into cracks in rocks. Later, the water freezes in these cracks, then expands. The expanding, freezing water breaks the rock into pieces. The rock fragments then move along with the glacial ice. This process results in boulders, gravel, and sand being added to the bottom and sides of a glacier. Find out in the next activity how this matter frozen in glacial ice can cause further erosion.

Figure 15-16

A The brown streaks in this glacier are sediments that the glacier has picked up in its travels and is now depositing as it recedes.

B When rock fragments at the base of a glacier scrape bedrock, long parallel scars like these at Kelleys Island, Ohio, may be left behind.

Figure 15-17

A As glaciers push, break, and scrape their way over land, they displace tons of sediment, and leave behind many valleys and bowl-shaped depressions.

Find Out! ACTIVITY

How do glaciers make grooves in rocks?

What To Do

1. Mix sand and other small particles of soil, rocks, or gravel in a container of water.
2. Pour the mixture into an ice cube tray and place the tray in a freezer. Let each frozen cube represent a glacier.
3. Remove the cubes from the freezer. Leave the cubes at room temperature for a few moments, feel their texture, and record your observations *in your Journal.*
4. You should feel the grains of sand and small particles. Rub the cubes over a piece of wood.

Conclude and Apply

1. What do you observe in the wood's surface?
2. Explain how glaciers make similar patterns in rocks?

Materials at the base of a glacier scrape the soil and bedrock over which the glacier moves. The loose particles can cause even more erosion than the ice and snow alone. When bedrock is gouged by rock fragments, grooves may be left behind. Usually these scratches are long, parallel scars.

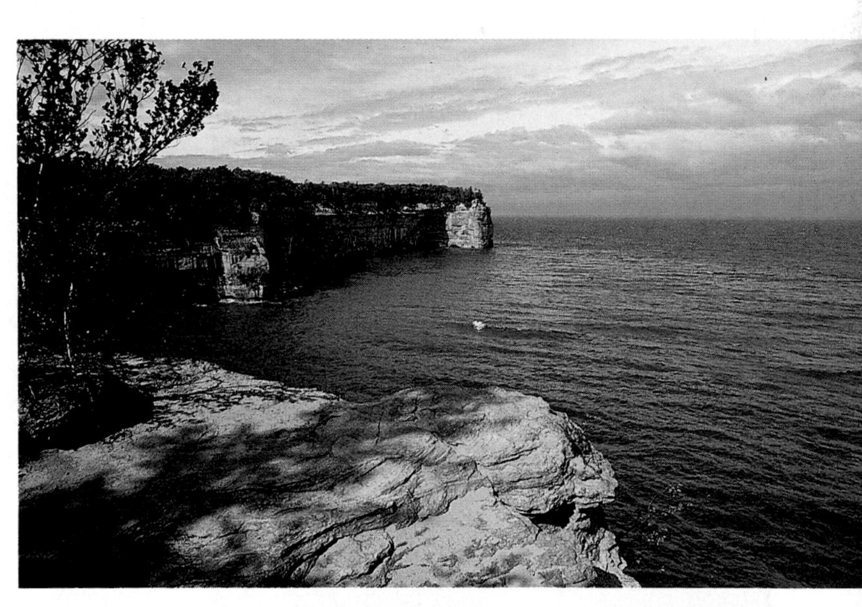

Figure 15-18

Lake Superior, shown here, and the other Great Lakes were formed by erosion of a river valley during the advancing and receding of glacial ice that covered the area during the last several glacial advances.

B **When the glaciers melt, a river might flow in the valleys and depressions which may fill with glacial melt-water and become lakes.**

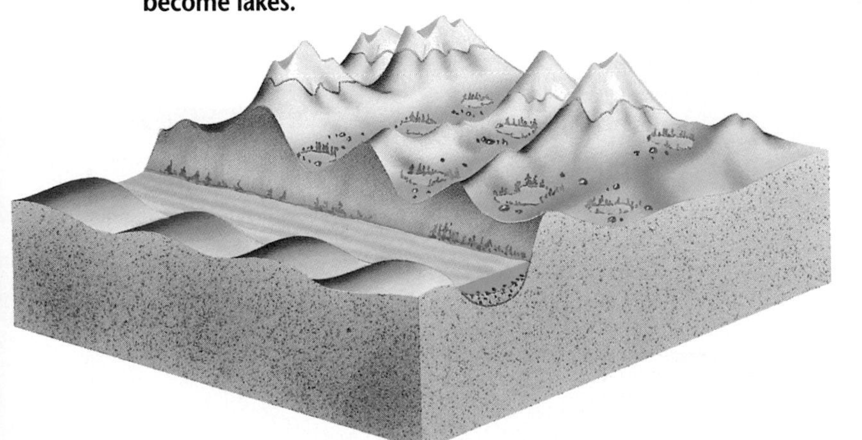

Glacial Valley

Valley glaciers erode land and deposit sediments as they move down mountain slopes. Valleys eroded by glaciers are a different shape from valleys eroded by streams.

You had to imagine what life on Earth was like long ago when much of it was covered by ice and snow, but you don't have to imagine the changes that were made. Many of the U-shaped valleys, rivers, and hills that were formed when ice age glaciers eroded the land and deposited sediments still exist today. The huge amounts of frozen snow and ice that remain in today's continental glaciers and valley glaciers provide us with a supply of fresh water.

Figure 15-19

A **Glacier-eroded valleys are usually U-shaped because glaciers pick up and drag soil and rock fragments along their sides as well as on their bottom. Glacier National Park, Montana, shown right, is one example.**

B **Stream-eroded valleys are normally V-shaped because the water in a stream erodes downward into its channel.**

check your UNDERSTANDING

1. How can snowfall lead to the formation of a glacier?
2. How can valley glaciers form in places where continental glaciers could not?
3. How do scientists know which areas were once covered by glaciers during the ice age?
4. **Apply** Explain how the Great Lakes could have been formed by a glacier.

15-4 Wind Erosion

Up, Up, and Away

Moving air can move loose particles. Particles that are too heavy to lift are dragged along the surface. Others are light enough to be picked up and carried by the air. Wind can move sand, clay, silt, and other loose sediments and when the wind dies down, the sediment is deposited.

Trying to eat a picnic lunch on the beach can be a challenge. Light items like napkins, plastic sandwich bags, paper cups, and potato chips blow away easily if the wind is strong. You may try to recover them as they bounce or roll away, only to find them useless because they are covered with sand. Can the same wind that blows your lunch away cause erosion? Explore in the next activity how these particles are carried by wind.

Section Objectives

- Describe how wind erodes and deposits sediment.
- Describe how a dune is formed and how it moves.
- Identify two factors that can decrease wind erosion.

Key Terms

dune

Explore! ACTIVITY

Which particles can be readily carried by the wind?

What To Do

1. Cut a sheet of aluminum foil into a variety of large and small sizes.
2. Then form the pieces into assorted shapes. Crumple some of the pieces of foil into loose balls, some into tight balls, and leave other pieces flat.
3. Put the assortment of aluminum shapes on a table and blow at them.
4. *In your Journal,* record which pieces move more readily. Do the size and shape of materials affect their ability to be transported by the moving air? Explain.

Wind Changes the Land

When wind erodes loose sediments by blowing them away, it eventually deposits the sediments when it stops blowing. This deposition can create new features on the land. For example, sand or loose sediment may be blown by the wind into a formation called a **dune**. You might find a dune on a beach or in a desert.

Dunes like the ones in **Figure 15-20**, are a result of erosion and deposition. The sand particles were eroded from one location and deposited here to form dunes. Not only can the sand particles in a dune move, but amazingly, the dune itself can move. Sand builds up a gentle slope on the side facing the wind. The sand continues to build up until it falls down a steeper slope on the other side.

Figure 15-20

Many sand dunes migrate because wind repeatedly picks up sand grains from one side of the dune and deposits them on the other side.

Eyes on the Planet

United States Landsat satellites are watching soil conditions and crops all over the world. These observation satellites are machines just a little bigger than a car. Landsat satellites orbit Earth 14 times a day at a height 400 miles above the ground.

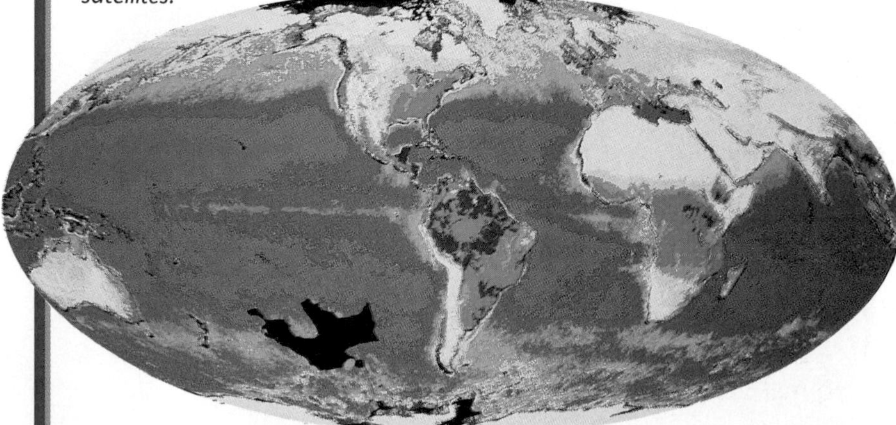

The distribution of Earth's vegetation, as seen by Landsat satellites.

Satellite Sensors

The Landsat satellites are filled with machines that gather information. Among them is the Landsat Thematic Mapper, which has 100 different detectors. As the satellite circles Earth, the machines take pictures of Earth. Their sensors can tell the difference between land and water, city and country, wheat and corn. They work even when Earth is covered with clouds, fog, storms, or darkness.

Scientists on Earth collect the Landsat information and pass it on to people who need it.

Find Out! ACTIVITY

How do dunes move?

What To Do

1. Get a covered shoe box and cut a 5-cm-square opening in one end.
2. Spoon flour into the box toward the open end to form a layer about 2.5 cm deep.
3. Cover the box and put it on a level surface.
4. Gently blow air into the box through the open end. Be sure to have a towel handy to wipe off any flour.
5. Occasionally lift the lid and observe what is happening.
6. Record these observations *in your Journal.*

Conclude and Apply

1. What happens to the flour on the side that you are blowing air into?
2. What happens on the other side?
3. What happens to the little piles of flour as you continue blowing air into the box?

Satellites Show Changes in the Land

For example, information from one Landsat orbit showed a massive erosion problem in Africa. Huge numbers of people in Africa were starving, but the exact reason had been unclear. Conditions there were similar to the dust bowl the United States experienced in the 1930s. Back then, there was no satellite information to show the problem.

But 50 years later, pictures from the Landsat satellites clearly identified the problem in Africa. Pictures showed that people had allowed animals to overgraze a large area of grassland. Years of overgrazing followed by no rain had created desert conditions. Wind blew the dry soil away. With no grasses to eat, the animals starved, leaving the people with no food.

Because of the Landsat satellite information, the African people can prevent future problems by changing their animals' grazing methods.

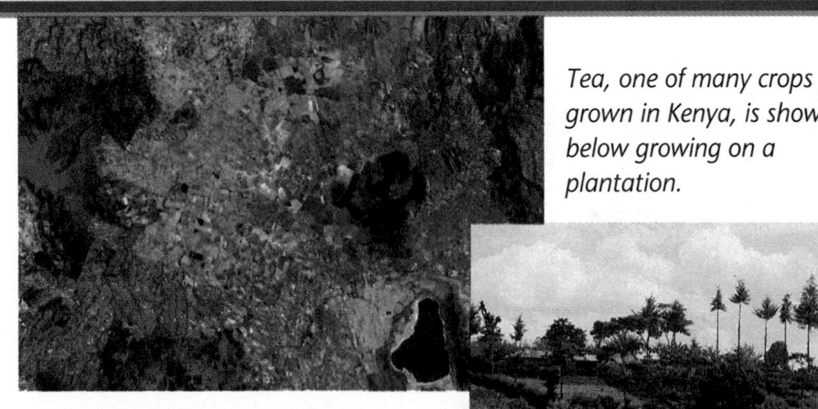

Tea, one of many crops grown in Kenya, is shown below growing on a plantation.

The Landsat photo above shows vegetation distribution in Nakuru, Kenya. Vegetation is shown in green.

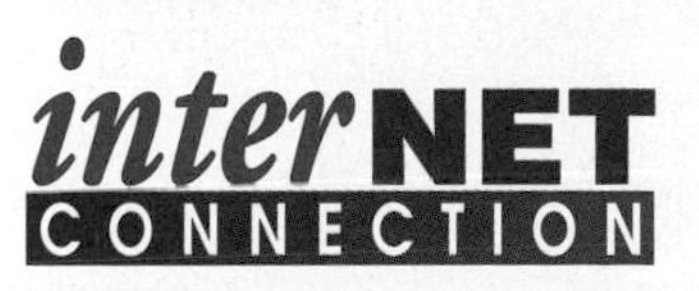

Find out what EROS Landsat data are available on the World Wide Web from the U.S. Geological Survey. How would these data be of use to people in your state?

Wind Erosion

Figure 15-21

The Sphinx has been influenced by Egypt's desert winds for thousands of years. Some of the damage to the Sphinx has been caused by windblown sediment. What type of sediment do you think causes the damage?

Not only does wind create deposits such as sand dunes, but it also erodes Earth's surface. It does this primarily by a process that is similar to sandblasting. Wind picks up small sand-sized particles and moves them. When these particles come in contact with objects such as the Sphinx, they erode them. Windblown materials like sand grind away whatever they hit.

Land can be eroded more easily during a drought. The soil gets very dry, and the plants in it dry up and die. Then wind can easily erode the soil. This happened in the central plains of the United States in the 1930s. The area became known as the Dust Bowl because as the soil was carried away by the wind, it created great swirling bowls of dust. Farmers today use planting and watering techniques that prevent this type of soil erosion.

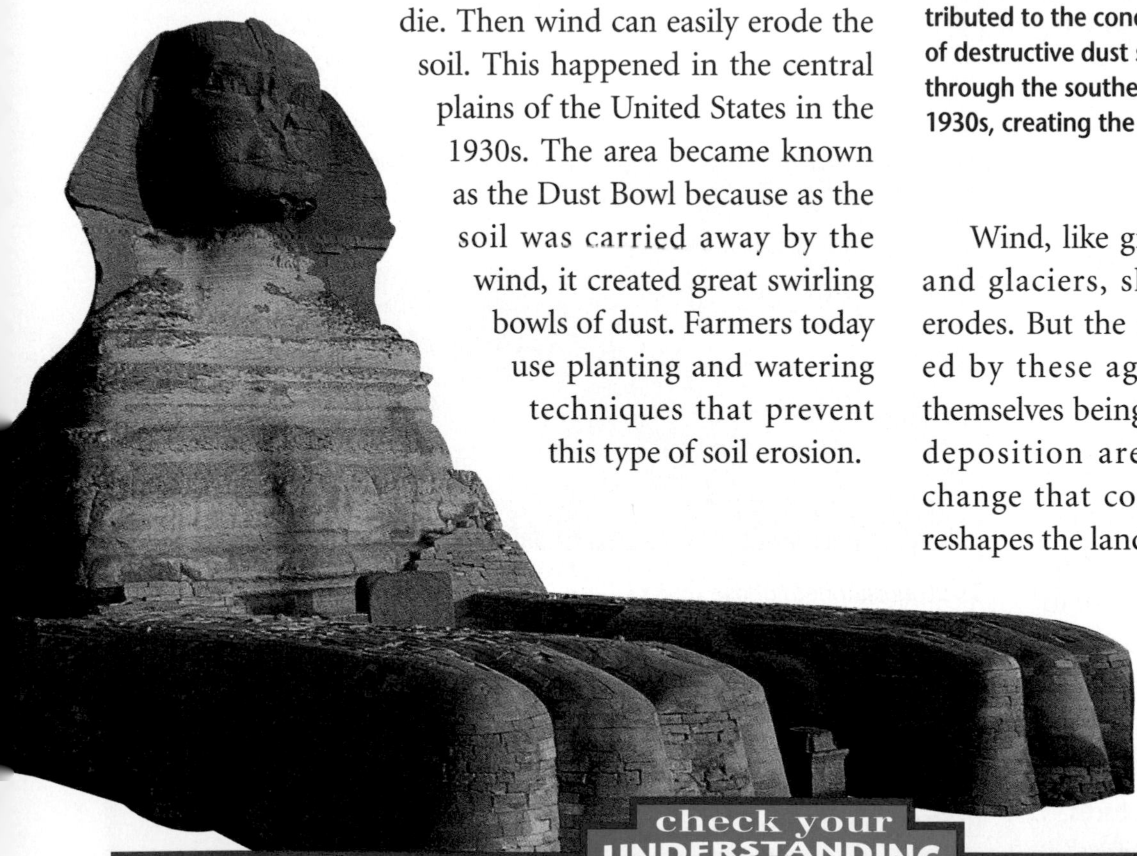

Figure 15-22

Overgrazing of natural grasslands contributed to the conditions that set off a series of destructive dust storms, which raged through the southern Great Plains in the 1930s, creating the Dust Bowl.

Wind, like gravity, running water, and glaciers, shapes the land as it erodes. But the new landforms created by these agents of erosion are themselves being eroded. Erosion and deposition are part of a cycle of change that constantly shapes and reshapes the land around you.

check your UNDERSTANDING

1. Explain how wind changes the landscape at beaches and in deserts.
2. Why are dunes constantly changing?
3. Describe at least two steps a farmer might take to decrease soil erosion.
4. **Apply** Explain how trees planted near the corners of a house can help keep the land from changing.

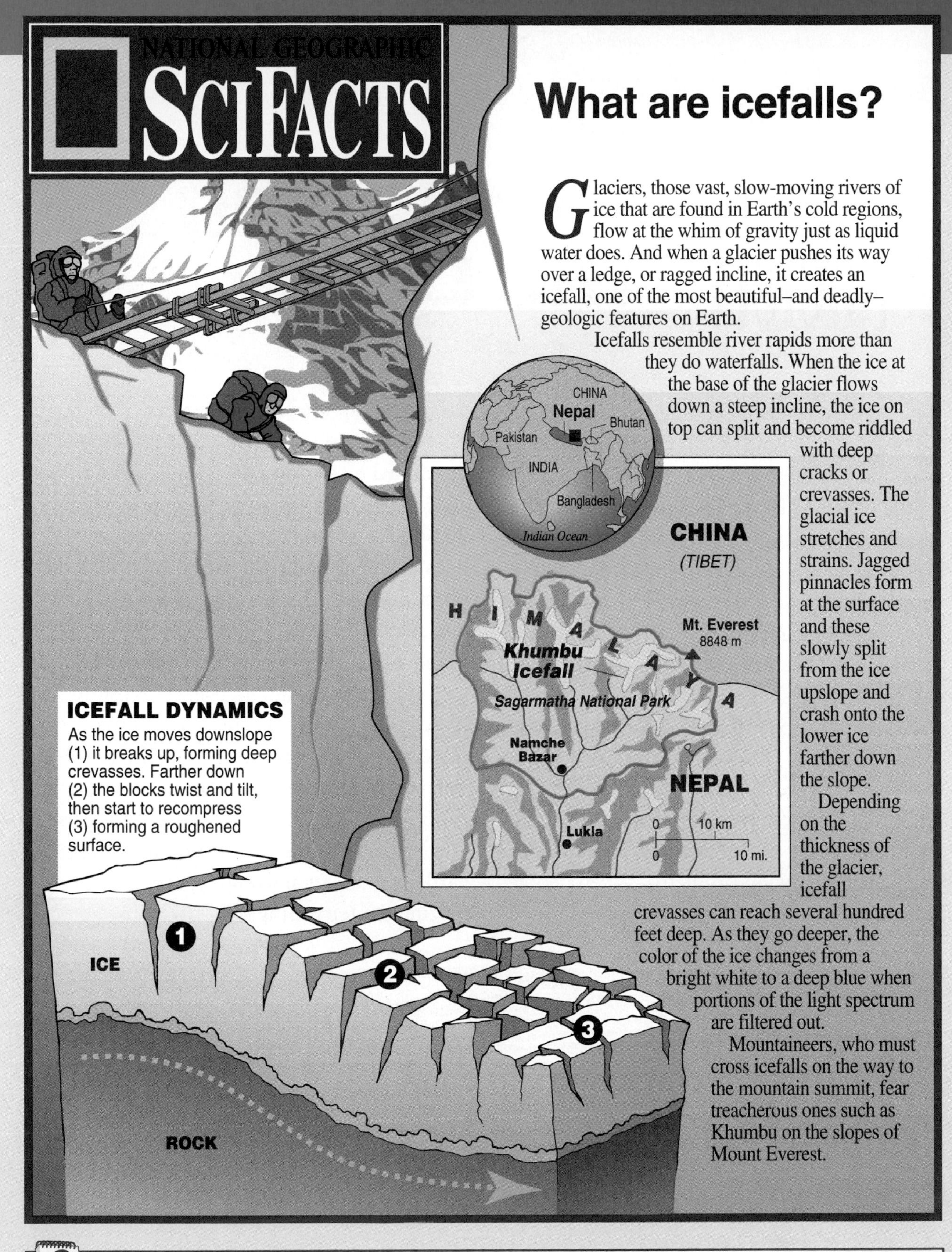

ICEFALL DYNAMICS

As the ice moves downslope (1) it breaks up, forming deep crevasses. Farther down (2) the blocks twist and tilt, then start to recompress (3) forming a roughened surface.

What are icefalls?

Glaciers, those vast, slow-moving rivers of ice that are found in Earth's cold regions, flow at the whim of gravity just as liquid water does. And when a glacier pushes its way over a ledge, or ragged incline, it creates an icefall, one of the most beautiful–and deadly–geologic features on Earth.

Icefalls resemble river rapids more than they do waterfalls. When the ice at the base of the glacier flows down a steep incline, the ice on top can split and become riddled with deep cracks or crevasses. The glacial ice stretches and strains. Jagged pinnacles form at the surface and these slowly split from the ice upslope and crash onto the lower ice farther down the slope.

Depending on the thickness of the glacier, icefall crevasses can reach several hundred feet deep. As they go deeper, the color of the ice changes from a bright white to a deep blue when portions of the light spectrum are filtered out.

Mountaineers, who must cross icefalls on the way to the mountain summit, fear treacherous ones such as Khumbu on the slopes of Mount Everest.

Science Journal

In your Science Journal, discuss why mountain climbers consider climbing on ice to be dangerous. What special precautions do they need to take?

Science and Society

Developing the Land

Have you noticed that many people live in houses and apartments beside rivers, lakes, and oceans, and on the sides of hills and mountains? If you ask real-estate agents, they'll tell you that people like to live where there's a good view. People like to look down on a valley or watch boats sail along a river. However, when you think of the effects of gravity and water, do you think steep slopes and river banks are good places for people to live? Perhaps not.

Creating Erosion Problems

When people settle in these locations, as seen below, they accept that they will constantly battle erosion problems. When people make a slope steeper or remove vegetation, they speed up the erosion process.

Once an area that has a natural slope is developed by clearing the land, building asphalt roads and parking lots, and putting up buildings, several effects may follow. Because there is less vegetation to absorb the water from heavy rainfalls, water runoff can increase in volume. This rapidly flowing water may sweep loose soil particles down the hill. The resulting increase in erosion may, over a period of time, actually make the slope of the hill more steep. And the more steep the slope, the more rapidly the water runoff flows, and the more erosion there is. Furthermore, the loss of topsoil may make it harder for any plants to grow and help in stabilizing the remaining soil.

Reducing Erosion

There are a variety of things that people can do to reduce erosion as seen in the photographs above. Planting vegetation is one of the best ways because not only do roots hold soil between them, but plant roots absorb a lot of water. A person living on a steep slope might also build terraces or retaining walls.

You already know that terraces are broad, steplike cuts made into the side of a slope. When water flows onto a terrace, it is slowed down, and is less likely to erode the slope.

Retaining walls are often made of concrete, stones, wood, or railroad ties. Their purpose is to keep soil and rocks from sliding downhill. These walls can also be built along stream channels, lakes, or ocean beaches to reduce erosion caused by flooding, running water, or waves.

People who live in areas with erosion problems spend time and money trying to preserve their land. Sometimes they're successful in slowing down erosion, but they can never eliminate it. Eventually, cliffs cave in, streams overflow their banks, and soil and rocks fall downhill.

Sediments constantly move, changing the shape of the land forever. Erosion is all part of Earth's natural dynamic processes.

What Do You Think?

Suppose you live beside a river. You love it there. It's beautiful, and there's so much to do. The only problem is that the river frequently floods. Several times your family has been evacuated to higher ground. One day, the mayor informs your family that you must move. She tells you that living along the river is not only dangerous, but it costs the city too much money each time you're evacuated. Do you think this is fair? Should communities control where people live?

Also, people often want to rebuild their homes in the same place after their original homes were destroyed by natural erosion. Do you think that federal disaster funds or insurance should be available for homeowners who choose to live in a region that is often threatened by mudslides or river floods?

HISTORY CONNECTION

Puzzle Solved!

Long ago, scientists had a problem—they couldn't figure out how the first people got from Africa and Europe to North and South America. Water separates these two continents from all other continents.

Bering Strait (Bering Land Bridge)
ASIA
Russia
NORTH AMERICA
Alaska
BERING SEA

Glaciers dominated much of Earth during the last glacial advance, which ended about 10 000 years ago.

When more glaciers were created, the level of water in the world's oceans dropped. As the oceans shrank, more land was exposed. It's like being at the beach and seeing the tide go out, giving you more beach to play on.

When the water level in the oceans went down, a land bridge was exposed near the Arctic Circle. Look at the map to see where Asia and North America nearly touch, north of the Bering Sea. Several times in the last two million years those pieces of land did connect with each other, and early human beings migrated—slowly—to North America. That piece of land, now under water, is called the Bering Land Bridge.

Scientists hypothesize early people migrated across this land bridge at different times 10 000 to 30 000 years ago. Marshes and forests supported animals such as reindeer, horses, mammoths, mastodons, birds, and fish. There was enough food for people to eat.

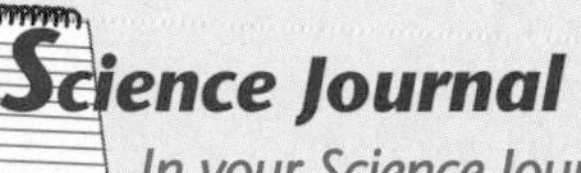

Science Journal

In your Science Journal, write about the following questions. What would life be like at the edge of a melting glacier? Would it be cold? Where would people get water? Can plants grow there? What would people eat?

chapter 15 REVIEWING MAIN IDEAS

Science Journal

Review the statements below about the big ideas presented in this chapter, and answer the questions. Then, re-read your answers to the Did You Ever Wonder questions at the beginning of the chapter. *In your Science Journal*, write a paragraph about how your understanding of the big ideas in the chapter has changed.

1. Erosion by gravity can be slow, or fast. ***Contrast slow erosion features with fast erosion features that are caused by gravity.***

2. Streams erode and deposit sediments. Fast streams erode more quickly than slow streams. As streams slow down, they deposit more sediments. ***What are some ways rivers act upon sediment?***

3. Glaciers form valleys as they push and carry loose materials and scrape against rock surfaces. ***Compare a valley formed by a glacier with one formed by a river.***

4. Wind can carry loose particles great distances, as well as erode rock surfaces. ***Describe how dunes are formed.***

chapter 15
CHAPTER REVIEW

Using Key Science Terms

continental glacier	firn
creep	floodplain
delta	mudflow
deposition	rockslide
dune	slump
erosion	valley glacier

For each set of terms below, choose the one term that does not belong and explain why it does not belong.

1. mudflow, creep, deposition
2. rockslide, creep, slump
3. erosion, dune, delta
4. continental glacier, valley glacier, firn

Understanding Ideas

Answer the following questions in your Journal *using complete sentences.*

1. List the four causes of erosion.
2. How is deposition related to erosion?
3. What three things affect a stream's rate of flow?
4. What can help decrease wind erosion?
5. How do glaciers change the land?

Developing Skills

Use your understanding of the concepts developed in this chapter to answer each of the following questions.

1. **Comparing and Contrasting** Repeat the Explore activity on page 479 varying the amount of water. Compare the results of this activity with those made in the original activity.
2. **Concept Mapping** Complete the erosion concept map.

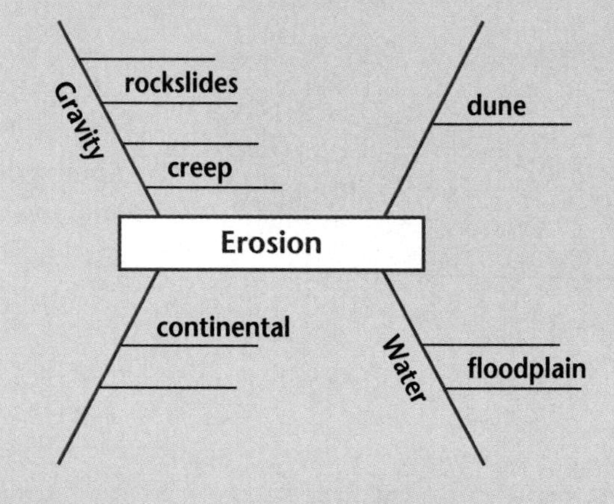

3. **Observing and Inferring** After doing the Find Out activity on page 495, use the box, flour, several small rocks, a crayon, and a lump of clay to create a structure to prevent wind erosion. Place the structure in the box and blow through the hole. What happened to the flour? Why might this kind of structure be helpful?
4. **Comparing and Contrasting** Using the materials from the Explore activity on page 493, repeat the activity using a fan or hair dryer with several different speed settings to move the aluminum foil materials. How does the speed of the wind affect the ability to transport the materials?

chapter 15
CHAPTER REVIEW

Critical Thinking

Use your understanding of the concepts developed in the chapter to answer each of the following questions.

1. What factors can increase the rate of erosion?
2. Study the photograph below. Then explain why farmland is common in river valleys. Do you think this river flows fairly quickly or fairly slowly? Why?

3. How does rainfall affect erosion by gravity on a steep slope? How does it affect erosion by wind on level land?
4. How do continental glaciers differ from valley glaciers?
5. How are the processes of erosion by gravity, wind, streams, and glaciers similar?

Problem Solving

Read the following problem and discuss your answers in a brief paragraph.

Imagine that you live in a hilly area. Your family is planning on building a new home.

1. What should they be concerned about when looking for a lot on which to build?
2. What steps should they take to prevent erosion if they build on the side of a slope?
3. How might landscaping with plants help prevent erosion?

CONNECTING IDEAS

Discuss each of the following in a brief paragraph.

1. **Theme—Stability and Change** Explain how rocks from an inland mountain might become sediments in the ocean.
2. **Theme—Stability and Change** How do glaciers affect stream erosion?
3. **Theme—Stability and Change** How can erosion explain the formation of various landforms on a map?
4. **A Closer Look** How does the building of terraces control soil erosion?
5. **Physics Connection** Explain how Landsat information helped explain the cause of dusty conditions in Africa.

CHAPTER 16

CHANGING ECOSYSTEMS

I n Chapter 11, you learned about ecosystems and the role of different organisms within ecosystems. What kind of ecosystem do you live in? Has your ecosystem changed during the time you've lived there? Are there more houses now or more cars on the streets?

What other changes are ahead? A new mall nearby? A park? An apartment complex? How will these changes affect you and the rest of your ecosystem?

Now think about a forest ecosystem. Do you think it changes? What about the ecosystem in a pond or under a rock? Do they change?

Did you ever wonder...

- How a forest can recover from a fire that destroys every living thing in it?
- Why some African animals allow birds to sit on their backs all day?
- Why some animals are threatened with extinction but others aren't?

Science Journal

Before you begin to study changes in ecosystems, think about these questions and answer them *in your Science Journal.* When you finish the chapter, compare your journal write-up with what you have learned.

In this chapter, you'll learn that most ecosystems change. The plants and animals in the ecosystems sometimes thrive on these changes—and sometimes die because of them. Let's explore some of these changes!

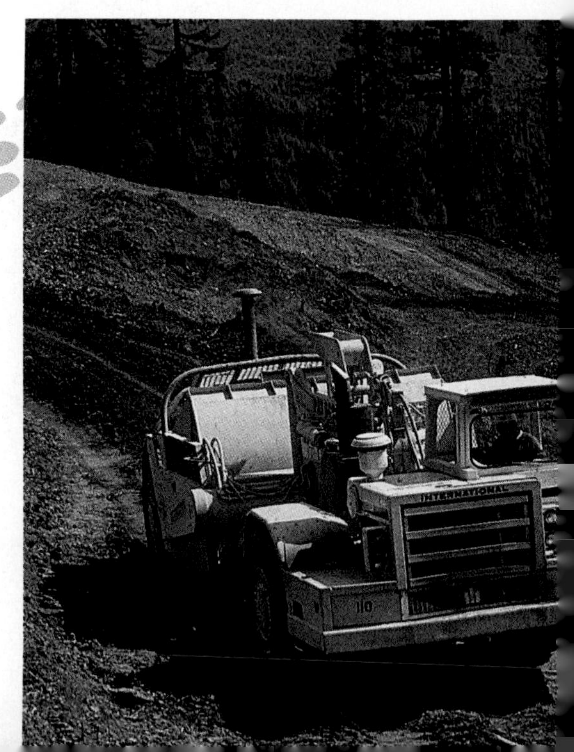

Explore! ACTIVITY

How can change affect an ecosystem?

Imagine that you're walking near a stream and see the animal tracks pictured on these pages.

What To Do

1. *In your Journal,* describe what animals you think caused the different sets of tracks.
2. What other organisms might you find in this ecosystem?
3. Why do you think these tracks are in this location? What is there to attract animals?
4. Think of ways this ecosystem could change. For example, the stream may become polluted. Describe another change that could affect this ecosystem.
5. Explain how the change that you thought of might affect the organisms in the ecosystem.

Succession—Building New Communities

Section Objectives
- Describe the process of succession.
- Explain the relationship between succession and diversity.

Key Terms

succession
pioneer species
climax community
diversity

Thinking About Change

Do you live in a place where some trees change with the seasons? Have you seen pictures of such places? If so, you know that these changes happen every year in many ecosystems.

Other changes in ecosystems don't depend on seasons. For example, have you ever seen a vacant lot or field after it has been cleared by a bulldozer? It's bare and brown, seemingly lifeless.

But then the "empty" lot starts changing. Tiny plants sprout from seeds brought by the wind or animals. In time, bushes and small trees will grow in the lot. Insects will be joined by mice and nesting birds. Under the right conditions, the lot could become a patch of forest, home to squirrels or even raccoons.

If a building is constructed on this lot, the ecosystem would be much different. Start exploring how ecosystems change by analyzing how one ecosystem might affect another.

Explore! ACTIVITY

How can one ecosystem affect another?

What To Do

1. *In your Journal,* describe the two main ecosystems in this photograph.
2. Explain ways in which each ecosystem affects the other.
3. If no one comes to live here, what would you expect this area to look like in 10 years?
4. Make a hypothesis to explain how one ecosystem can be transformed into another. Explain how you could test your hypothesis.

Ecosystems and Succession

When one community is slowly replaced by another, the process of change is called **succession**.

Succession is one way ecosystems recover from damage, such as fires. As you'll see in the next activity, succession is also a way for an ecosystem to begin where none had been before.

Find Out! ACTIVITY

How can an ecosystem start?

Do you think an ecosystem can develop in a cup of coffee?

What To Do

1. Carefully observe the hot coffee with a hand lens. *In your Journal,* describe what you see.
2. Label your cup and place it on a counter or shelf away from sunlight. Let the cup rest undisturbed for five days.
3. Observe the coffee each day, using a hand lens. Record any changes you see.

Conclude and Apply

1. Explain what you think happened in the cup.
2. Could the organisms have come from the boiling hot coffee? If not, what could have been their source?
3. Predict what might happen if the coffee sat for five more days.
4. Are the changes you observed examples of succession?

Pioneer Species

The organisms you saw in the coffee are called pioneer species. Much like the first settlers were pioneers, **pioneer species** are the first species to live in a new ecosystem. There are many kinds of pioneer species. The first plants that sprout after a forest fire are an example.

Once pioneers settle, does an ecosystem continue to change?

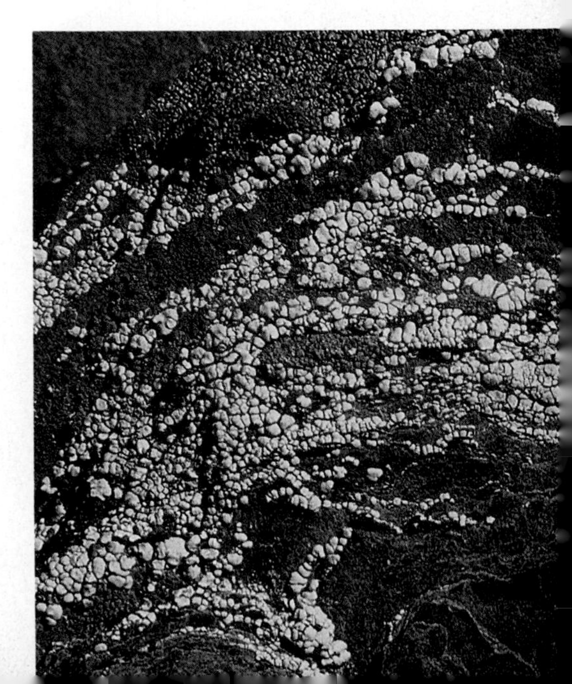

Figure 16-1

Lichens, organisms made up of an alga and a fungus living together, are an example of a pioneer species. Able to live in barren places, the fungus in the lichen makes acids that begin the breakdown of rock into soil.

DESIGN YOUR OWN
INVESTIGATION

Succession

How does a newly dug pond differ from one that has existed for years? In this investigation, you'll simulate a pond-water ecosystem to explore succession and to discover how new ponds fill with a variety of organisms.

Preparation

Problem

How does a pond-water ecosystem change?

Form a Hypothesis

As a group, write out a statement that predicts what will happen to the populations of organisms in a new pond-water ecosystem. Include in your hypothesis changes you might expect in color, smell, and other characteristics of the water.

Objectives

- Predict what happens in the succession of a pond-water ecosystem.
- Observe and explain changes in the ecosystem.

Materials

1 large, clean jar and lid
dried pond vegetation or pond water
distilled water
eyedroppers
microscope, slides, and coverslips

Safety Precautions

Wash your hands after handling the materials in this investigation.

DESIGN YOUR OWN INVESTIGATION

Plan the Experiment

1 Examine the materials provided. Decide how to use them to make a pond-water ecosystem.

2 How long will you conduct your investigation? How will you make observations? How often will you make observations?

3 What will you be observing? Some things to observe are water color, cloudiness, odor, sediment, and other factors that may change. Microscopically, look for organisms seen on page 509. Record how the number of organisms increases or decreases.

4 Design a data table in your Science Journal.

Check the Plan

1 How will you know when one organism increases and another decreases?

2 Make sure you have a variable and a control.

3 Make sure your teacher approves your plan before you proceed.

4 Carry out the investigation. Record your observations.

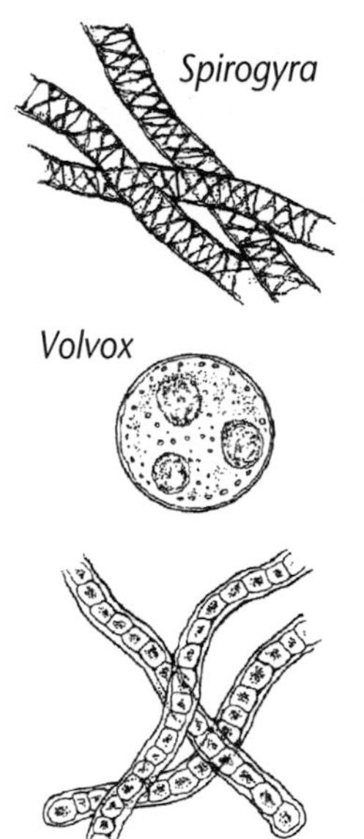

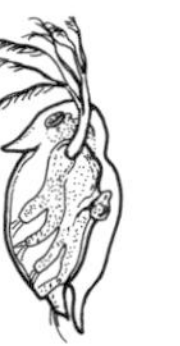

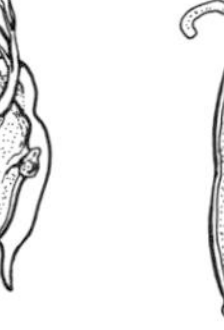

Daphnia *Hydra* *Euglena* *Paramecium* *Rotifer*

You may see organisms like these in your pond-water samples.

Analyze and Conclude

1. **Infer** What was the source of the organisms in the pond-water ecosystem?
2. **Observe** What changes occurred that were observable without a microscope?
3. **Observe** What changes occurred that were observable with a microscope?
4. **Observe** How many different organisms did you observe the first day? The last day?
5. **Compare and Contrast** Did any of the organisms increase in number? Decrease? Explain how this may have occurred by making a general statement about succession that explains what happened in your pond ecosystem.

Going Further

Have students work in small groups to produce rough graphs that reflect the relative changes in the populations of organisms that they observed. What kind of graph would be best to use?

Succession in Other Ecosystems

Figure 16-2

A Tallgrasses thrive in an abandoned field.

B Pine seedlings reduce the amount of sun reaching the ground and the tallgrasses. The tallgrasses begin to die out.

C Increasing shade keeps more pines from sprouting but provides the right amount of sun for oak seedlings.

D Hickory trees, which grow well in shade, join the oaks. The ecosystem no longer provides enough sunlight for the tallgrasses.

E This ecosystem has become a stable climax community of trees well-suited for the environment.

In the Investigate, you watched pond water fill with greater numbers and different types of living things. You may have noticed that some of the organisms you first saw in the water later disappeared. They may have served as food for other organisms. Thus, some kinds of organisms disappeared from the ecosystem, while others increased in numbers. This pond water was one example of succession. **Figure 16-2** shows another example of succession common in one type of forest in the eastern United States.

As an environment changes, new conditions make it possible for other species to grow, reproduce, and increase in number. As these species gradually take over the area, they cause even more changes in the environment, making it suitable for still different species.

As plant populations in the forest change, so do animal populations. Trees provide increasing amounts of food and shelter, becoming home to birds and small animals. As the number of small animals increases, they become numerous enough to support predators, which then enter the ecosystem.

Eventually, the ecosystem reaches the last stage of succession and becomes a climax community. In a **climax community**, plant and animal species living in the community are well adapted to the conditions. They make up an ecosystem that is in balance.

■ How Succession Can Repair Damage

Climax communities don't remain undisturbed forever, of course. A storm may knock over a tree. With the tree down, more sunlight reaches the ground. Succession begins again in this area, starting with the grasses that need full sunlight to grow.

The tree decays. As it does, the tree becomes a source of food and shelter for insects and animals. The decay of the tree releases nutrients which enter the soil. These nutrients will soon help feed pine seedlings, then oaks, then maybe hickories.

Sometimes an ecosystem suffers more damage than a fallen tree. The ecosystem on Mount Saint Helens was mostly destroyed by a volcanic eruption in 1980. A blast of superheated steam and rocks flashed down the mountain. The eruption flattened the forests and buried the slopes under tons of mud and ash.

Succession began on Mount Saint Helens once again as pioneer species started growing. Fireweed, named because it's one of the first plants to appear after a fire, pushed its way through the crust of ash.

Some plant roots had survived the blast underground, and from them new plants grew. Other organisms, including cottonwood seeds and tiny spiders, were carried to the slopes by the wind or birds and small animals.

Soon hardy plants created green islands of life in a sea of gray ash. The mountain was on its way to recovery. Study **Figure 16-3** to see succession on Mount Saint Helens.

Figure 16-3

A The eruption of Mount Saint Helens in 1980 destroyed the ecosystem around the mountain.

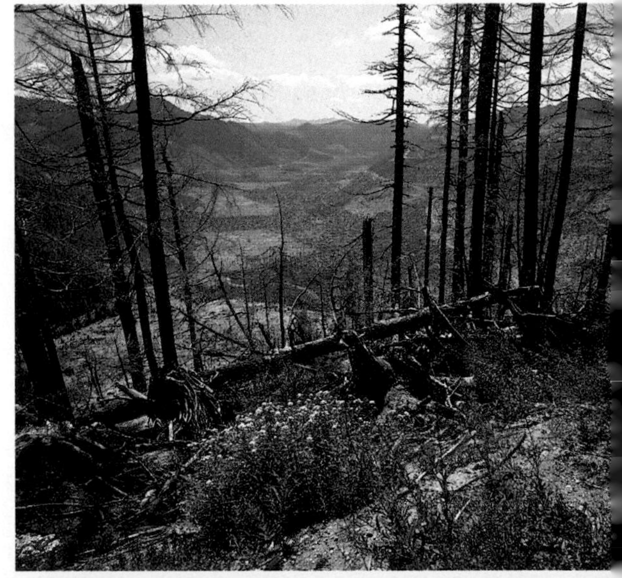

B The first evidence that Mount Saint Helens would recover appeared within thirty days when fireweed began pushing its way through the ash.

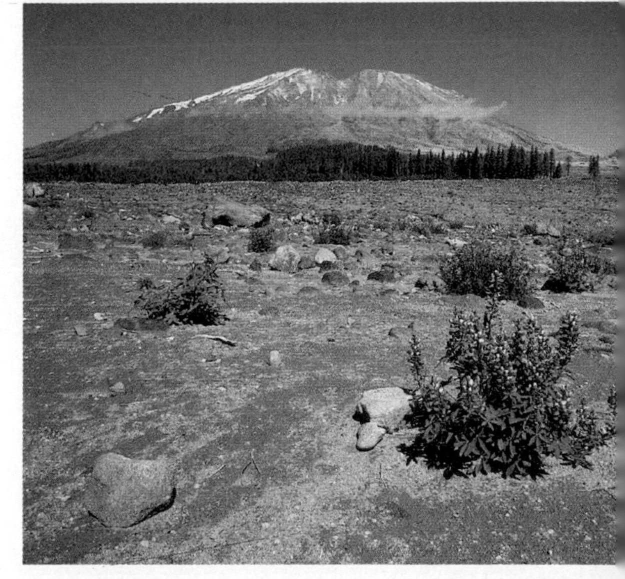

C Soon, hardy lupine plants created green islands of life in a sea of gray ash. Mount Saint Helens was on its way to recovery.

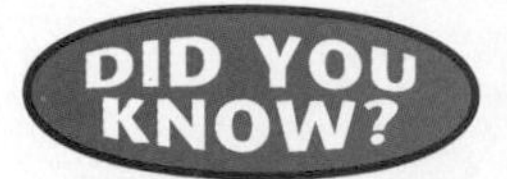

Succession in a rain forest is very slow. Part of one rain forest in Cambodia was cleared in 1431. It has had hundreds of years to recover, but the plants growing there now are still different from those in the typical, surrounding rain forest.

Diversity: The Key to Life on Earth

If ecosystems can recover by themselves, why should people worry about protecting forests or other environments?

The natural processes of succession can repair only a limited amount of damage. One of the most important elements in the recovery of an ecosystem is the diversity within an ecosystem. **Diversity** is the presence of many different species within a community. Diversity is one reason that succession can take place.

For example, on Mount Saint Helens, not many organisms appeared the first summer after the eruption. However, the organisms that did appear belonged to many different species. These plants and animals made it possible for other species to take root or to find food and shelter.

One example of recovery on Mount Saint Helens involves pocket gophers. These animals tunneled into the ground, bringing soil to the surface to mix with the nutrient-rich ash. In this soil, seeds and fungi sprouted. Without gophers to mix the old soil with nutrient-rich ash, fewer plants would have grown. The recovery of the whole ecosystem might have been much slower.

Succession and the recovery of ecosystems depends on diversity, or the many species that live in an area. Anything that is a threat to diversity is also a threat to the ability of an ecosystem to recover from disasters.

Figure 16-4

Pine seedlings, which thrive in sunlight, are essential to the growth of shade-loving oaks and hickories. If all the pine trees are cut for lumber, the forest will have a difficult time healing itself.

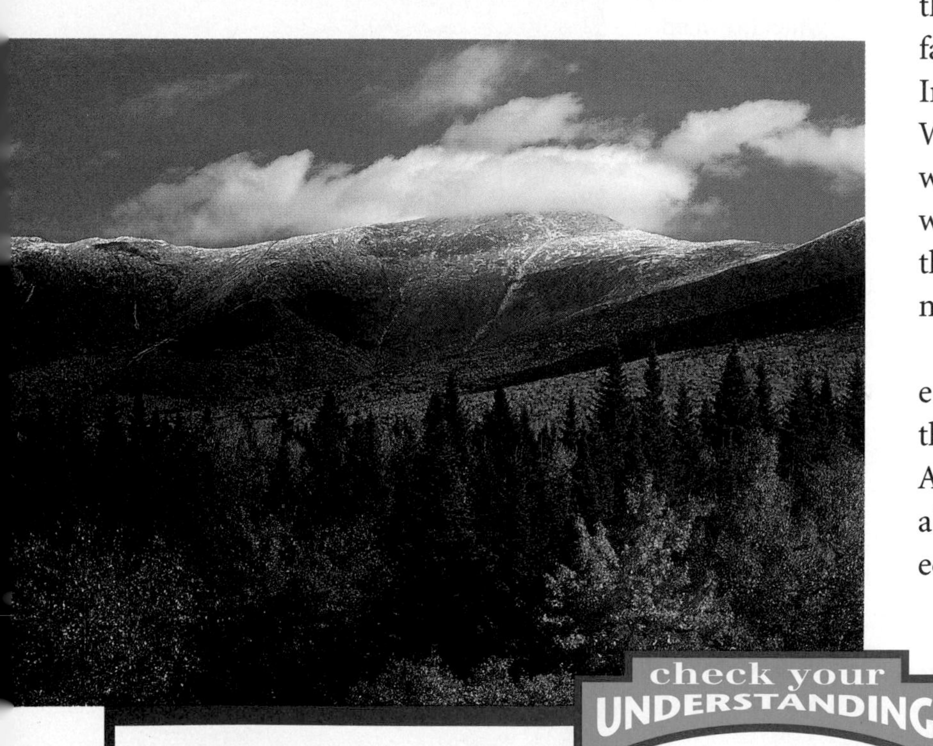

check your UNDERSTANDING

1. What is the relationship between succession and diversity?
2. Are oaks a pioneer species? Why or why not?
3. Does replanting a forest with one species of tree replace the forest? Why or why not?
4. **Apply** Are the species in your own ecosystem becoming more diverse or less diverse? Explain your answer.

Interactions in an Ecosystem

How Do Living Things Interact?

What do you know about the interactions among living things? In Chapter 11, you learned that organisms can be producers, consumers, or decomposers. All living things, including you, are parts of food chains.

But there are other types of interactions also. For example, why do certain kinds of mussels allow crabs to live in their shells?

These interactions can be as simple as a consumer eating a producer or a predator catching its prey or the interactions can be much more complex as seen in **Figure 16-5B**. In the Investigate on the following pages, you'll observe and record some complex interactions in an ecosystem.

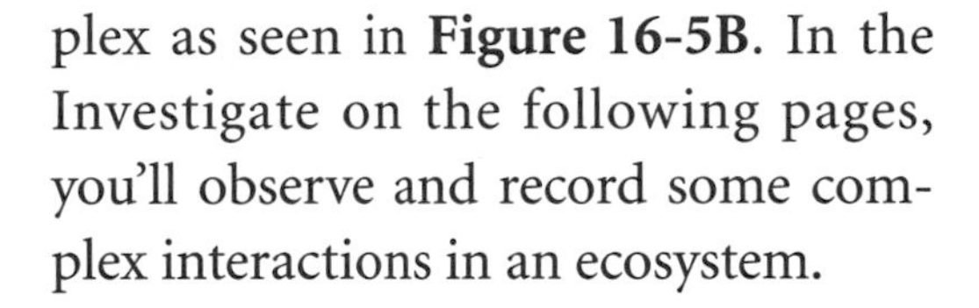

Section Objectives

- Classify and provide examples of the types of interactions that can occur within an ecosystem.
- Interpret how organisms and species interact with each other and with the environment.

Key Terms

symbiosis
mutualism
commensalism
parasitism

Figure 16-5

Organisms in an ecosystem can interact in many different ways.

A An owl eats a lizard.

B Fungi break down the dead log to obtain food. Some of the log will become part of the soil.

C Populations of gazelles, zebras, springbucks, and giraffes live and interact with one another at this waterhole in Namibia, Africa.

INVESTIGATE!

Getting Up-Close and Personal

Could you survive on a deserted island? Not without food! To get food you'd have to interact with other organisms in the ecosystem. In this activity, you'll find out more about how organisms in an ecosystem interact with one another.

Problem

How do certain organisms interact in an ecosystem?

Materials

Journal

hand lens or binoculars

What To Do

1. Choose an ecosystem near your school or home. It might be in a cluster of trees, a rotting log, a pond, a patch of weeds, or another setting.
2. Identify at least two organisms that are interacting within this ecosystem. You can include organisms that are not always present, but leave evidence of their interaction through tracks or feathers.
3. *In your Journal,* create a table to record and date your observations.

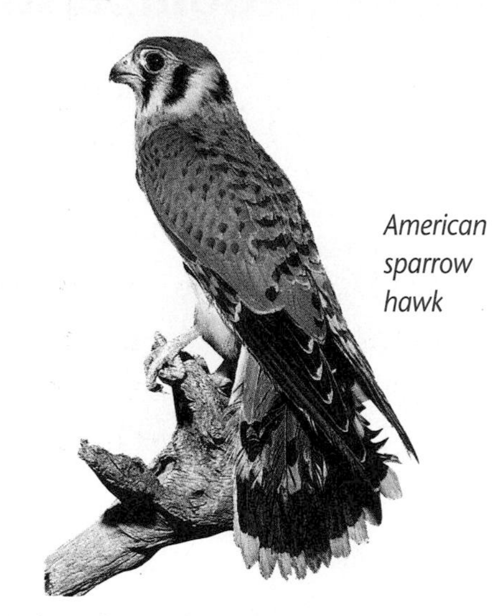

American sparrow hawk

Birdwatchers rely on binoculars to locate and observe both the American sparrow hawk and its tiny prey.

4 Over the next week, plan as many observations as possible. Schedule them for different times of the day.

5 Use a hand lens and/or binoculars to study the organisms you chose. Be sure to record *in your Journal* how these organisms interact with each other and with the environment.

Analyzing

1. Describe the environment of your ecosystem.
2. **Spreadsheet** List all the populations of organisms present in the ecosystem.
3. Which organisms did you study? Are they producers, consumers, or decomposers? Put these data in your spreadsheet.
4. What evidence did you find of competition within the ecosystem? Cooperation? Interaction between organisms and their environment?

Concluding and Applying

5. What did each organism you studied do that helped it survive?
6. What might happen if one or both of the organisms you studied disappeared from this ecosystem? In what ways would the ecosystem be affected?
7. **Going Further** Think of a change you could make in this ecosystem that would not deliberately damage it. ***Predict*** how the two organisms you studied would react to the change you suggest. Then, test your prediction.

Competition and Cooperation

Recall the discussion of competition in Chapter 11. In the Investigate you just did, you may have seen two or more species compete with one another for the limited resources of the environment. Plants and animals often compete for food, water, sunlight, and living space. If two species need a resource that is in limited supply, one species may eventually be forced out of the ecosystem.

Florida scrub jay

Individuals within a species may also compete with each other, especially for food, living space, and mates. The individuals within species that survive are those best adapted to the current conditions in the ecosystem. For example, giraffes with longer necks might be better adapted to conditions during which all the lower branches of their food trees have been stripped bare.

Animals of the same species also cooperate, often in family groups. One example is the Florida scrub jay. Pairs of these birds have "helpers," usually their offspring from the year before. The helpers watch for predators and feed the new chicks. Instead of competing with older jays for territory, the helpers stay "at home" and inherit their parents' feeding and living space.

Individuals of different species may also form cooperative relationships. For example, some species of barnacles will only settle and live on whales. A close association of two or more species is called **symbiosis**. In this section, you will learn about three types of symbiotic relationships—mutualism, commensalism, and parasitism.

Mutualism

How can two species cooperate? Take the example of the pea crab and

Figure 16-6

All of the pictures on these pages show mutualism. Mutualism often provides both of the organisms that are interacting with food, protection, or both.

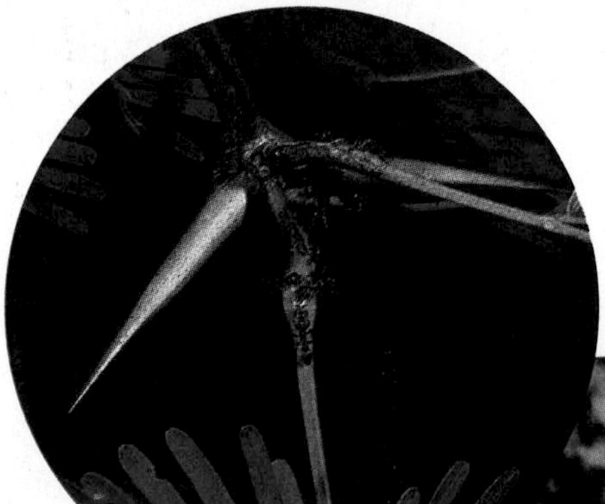

A Acacia ants eat a sweet substance produced by bull's horn acacia trees in Costa Rica, and live safely in the tree's large thorns. The ants protect their home and food source by biting animals that try to eat parts of the tree.

B The cleaner wrasse (next to the pectoral fin) eats organisms that live on the coral cod. Irritating pests are removed from the coral cod and the cleaner wrasse gets food.

the mussel. Tiny pea crabs live inside mussel shells. The crabs eat the young of organisms that would harm the mussels if they grew to adults inside the shell. In return, the mussels provide protection for the little crabs. In this relationship both species benefit. A relationship in which both species benefit is called **mutualism**.

Some fungi and plants have a mutualistic relationship. From 70 to 100 percent of all trees, grasses, shrubs, and flowers in any area grow well thanks to the fungi that grow on their roots.

Fungi, which can't make their own food, get food from the plant roots. In return, the fungi make huge, underground, threadlike nets that extend the plants' roots. With a larger root system, plants can get more nutrients from the soil.

Mutualistic relationships can help organisms get protection, food, additional nutrients, comfort and better health, free from pests.

Commensalism

You've read that certain fungi and plants have a mutual relationship. Some plants such as Spanish moss, orchids, and staghorn ferns grow high up in trees. These plants also have a relationship with the trees on which they grow. The host tree provides a safe growing place for the plants.

Connect to... Earth Science

Soils are extremely important to all life on Earth. Find out how soils form and how plants and animals contribute to soil formation.

C The oxpecker finds and eats ticks and blood-sucking flies from the rhinoceros's skin. The rhinoceros is rid of the irritating pests, and the oxpecker gets a good meal.

D An African honey guide bird locates a nest of honey bees and makes an effort to attract a honey badger's attention and lead it there. The badger breaks open the nest and eats the honey. The honey guide—too weak to break open the nest itself—eats the bees' grubs and wax.

At the same time, the plants get nutrients from rainwater and don't harm the host. However, the host tree doesn't benefit from the relationship. **Commensalism** is a relationship in which one organism benefits and the other neither benefits nor is harmed. See **Figure 16-7** for an example.

Some species of animals also live in commensal relationships. These animals rely on other animals in their search for food. For example, the remora fish, a weak swimmer, attaches itself to sharks and feeds on their leftovers. In a similar way, vultures follow lions and other predators and feed after they leave.

House sparrows can sometimes build their nests beside those of eagles. The sparrows are protected by the eagles' presence, while the eagles usually prey on rodents or birds larger than the sparrows.

In each commensal relationship, only one of the species benefits from having a host or protector, but the other species is not harmed.

■ Parasitism

You've already learned about two types of symbiosis—mutualism and commensalism. You may already know something about the third type—parasitism. Explore the effects of parasitism on different organisms with the activity on page 520.

a CLOSER LOOK

A Treasure in Danger

Coral reefs may not look like rain forests, but they're similar. Like rain forests, reefs cover a small part of Earth (0.17 percent of the ocean). Reefs are home to thousands of species—nearly a quarter of all the species in the ocean. Reefs, like rain forests, are also threatened with extinction.

What Is a Reef?

A reef consists of thousands of coral polyps. A coral polyp is an animal that makes a limestone cup around itself. The cup serves as the polyp's skeleton.

Algae live inside the coral polyp and have a mutualistic

Coral polyps

Algae that live in coral tissues

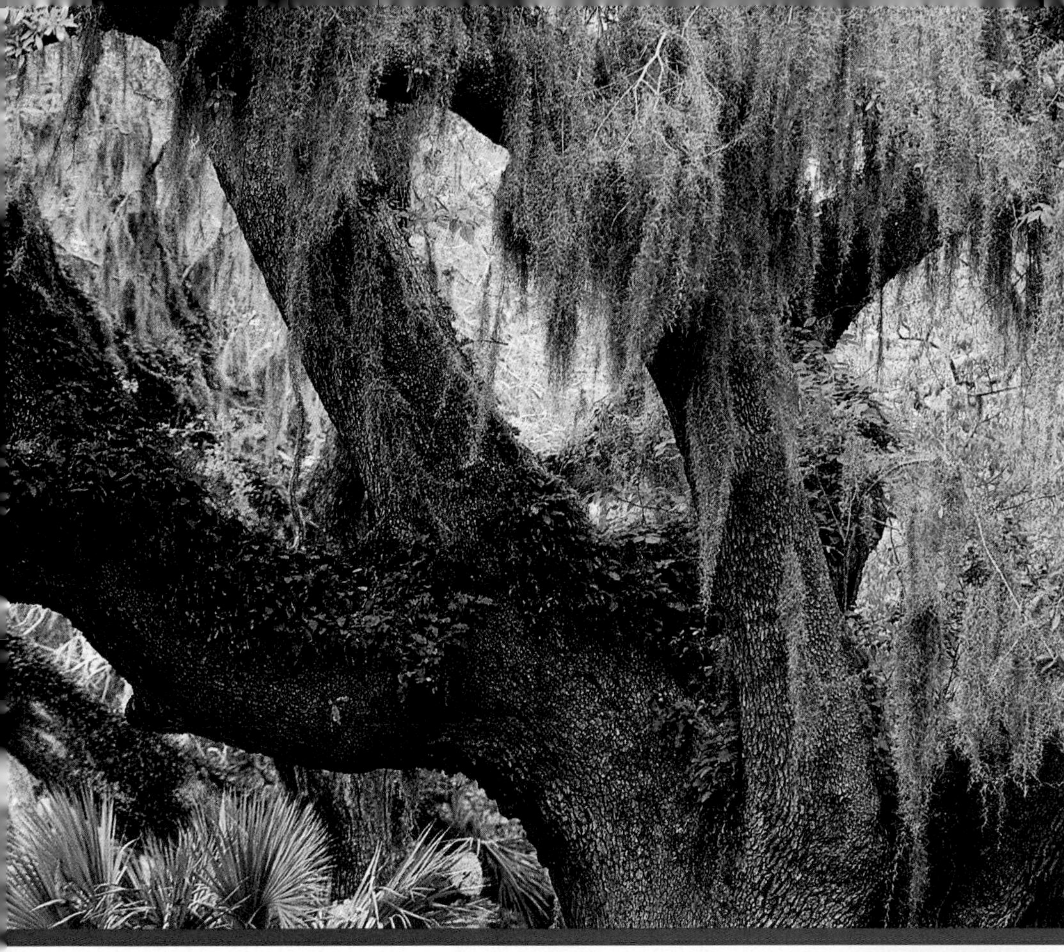

Figure 16-7

A Spanish moss, which is not really a moss, hangs on trees in the southeastern part of the U.S. and in tropical South America.

B Spanish moss uses its host only for support. The plant feeds on airborne dust, has no roots, and absorbs water directly from the air.

C The tree on which it lives is not harmed by the Spanish moss. This is an example of a commensal relationship.

relationship with the coral polyp. The algae produce food and oxygen which the coral polyp can use. In return, the polyp gives the algae a home and important nutrients.

Like other plantlike protists, these algae need sunlight to survive. That's one reason why coral live in clear, shallow water near coastlines.

Pollution and Reefs

Pollution and sediment from erosion can block sunlight, bringing about the death of the algae. Logging of mangroves that grow along coasts causes soil to erode into the ocean, and contributes to the death of the algae. In addition, when coral polyps are stressed by water conditions, they expel the algae.

Without the algae, the coral turns white or "bleaches" and can't grow or reproduce. After the polyps die, their limestone skeletons soon begin to erode.

Now that half of Earth's population lives along coasts, sewage increasingly pollutes the ocean. In addition, shipping leads to large and small oil spills. All of these problems contribute to the damage and death of coral reefs.

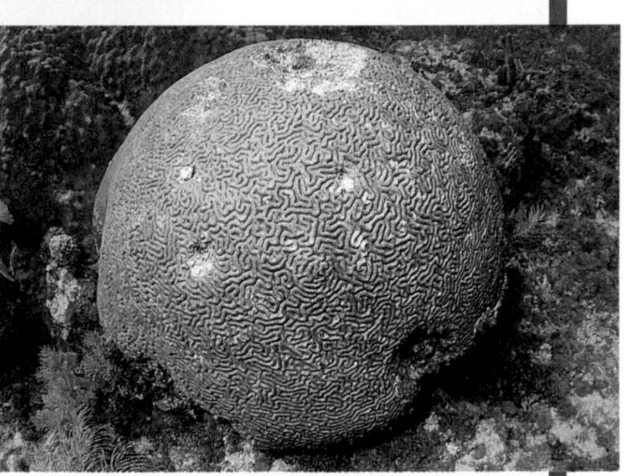

A coral head damaged by human activity

You Try It!

In what other ways could nations that currently dump sewage into the oceans treat sewage? Develop a suggestion for the treatment of sewage, and then develop a way to test whether your solution might work. Present your work in the form of a poster or display to the class.

Explore! ACTIVITY

How do parasites fit in?

What To Do

1. *In your Journal*, describe at least five parasitic relationships in nature. (Consult a reference book, if necessary.)
2. Explain how each relationship is harmful to one of the species involved.
3. Describe the role of each parasite in its own ecosystem.
4. Describe at least one parasite that is useful to humans.

In your list of parasites, did you include organisms like mosquitoes and bacteria? Both of these are examples of parasites.

In the relationship called **parasitism**, one of the species harms or kills the other one.

Many species of animals and plants, such as ticks, lice, tapeworms, and heartworms, feed on other animals and plants. Parasites feed on their hosts, slowly weakening them. Usually a parasite does not kill the organism it feeds on, but it does cause the host organism harm. In addition, mosquitoes and other blood-sucking parasites can give their hosts serious diseases, such as malaria.

When you did the Explore activity you may have thought of many examples of parasitism. Parasites always survive at the expense of the host organism.

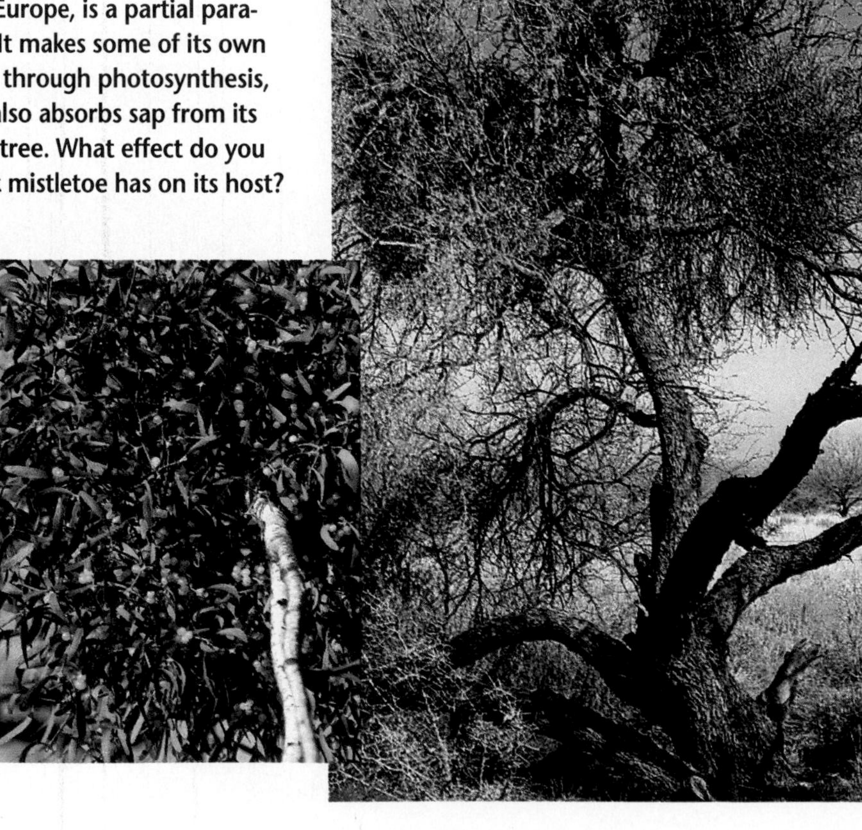

Figure 16-8

Mistletoe, a plant that grows on forest trees in both the U.S. and Europe, is a partial parasite. It makes some of its own food through photosynthesis, but also absorbs sap from its host tree. What effect do you think mistletoe has on its host?

Animals Interact with the Environment

Just as animals interact with other living things, they also interact with nonliving parts of their environments. Some animals are at the mercy of changing conditions in their environments. Others can alter their surroundings to better meet their needs, much as humans do. In the next activity, explore how people change their environments.

Explore! ACTIVITY

How do we change our environment?

What To Do

1. *In your Journal,* list at least three ways people change their environment to make it more suitable for them.
2. Describe how each of these changes affects the environment.
3. Research ways people could achieve the same results with less harm to the environment.
4. Explain what you have learned by creating a poster or making a class presentation.

Animals and plants change the environments in which they live simply by living there. Think back to the example of succession given in Section 16-1. When pines began to grow in a grassy field, they shaded the ground underneath. They changed the environment beneath them simply by growing. Animals often change the environment by creating or modifying shelters. For example, birds build nests, removing twigs and other things from the ground and placing them in trees. See **Figures 16-9** and **16-10** to learn about some other ways in which organisms alter their environment.

Sometimes the animals' changes to the environment conflict with

Figure 16-9

A In tropical countries, termites create their own complex environments by building huge mounds. One mound may be home to over ten million termites.

B A complex of rooms and passages, the mound is ventilated to bring in fresh air. The termites plaster the walls with a saliva mixture to control the temperature.

C Within the mound, the termites create a compost area where they grow fungus to eat. Gas from the decaying compost heats the mound.

Figure 16-10

A Beavers alter their ecosystem by cutting down trees and building dams. The dams turn rivers into small lakes, sometimes flooding farmers' fields.

B Beaver lodges, built upstream from the dam, are thick webs of branches plastered together with mud. Loose sticks on top allow air to circulate.

C Inside the lodge, accessible only from an underwater entrance, the beavers are safe, dry, and warm during the winter.

human needs or desires. For example, prairie dogs dig underground burrows for shelter from the sun and predators. In the winter, the tunnels are a warm place where young can be born and raised.

In the 1930s and 1940s, prairie dogs were shot and poisoned because they competed with livestock for grass. The livestock were also tripping over the burrows. The prairie dogs and their burrows interfered with human efforts to raise food.

The killing of prairie dogs had a bad effect on another type of animal. Black-footed ferrets eat only prairie dogs and live in their abandoned burrows. When prairie dogs were nearly wiped out, the ferrets starved. In 1983, because of conservation efforts, the prairie dog was on the way to recovery. However, black-footed ferrets did not recover and are now just one colony away from extinction.

Some changes organisms cause by living in an area may create problems for humans in that area. When this happens, people may "fight back." This can result in reducing the population of a species or in destroying a species entirely. You'll learn more about this in the next section.

check your UNDERSTANDING

1. Describe an example of a mutual relationship among humans.
2. Describe an example of a commensal relationship among humans.
3. **Apply** People often develop relationships with pets and farm animals. Explain how you could establish a mutual or a commensal relationship with a wild species.

16-3 Extinction—A Natural Process

Extinctions

You've probably heard about species that are threatened or endangered. You probably know that dinosaurs are extinct. But what is extinction? How could it happen? Make a model of one way in which single, small changes can build up to spell disaster!

Section Objectives

- Explain the common causes of local and global extinction.
- Provide examples of ways that human actions within an ecosystem can cause the extinction of species.

Key Terms

extinction

Find Out! ACTIVITY

Steps to Disaster!

Often a species can survive one or two threats to its well-being. In this activity, you'll find out what can happen as the threats accumulate.

What To Do

1. Work with a team of three other students. Take the tube your teacher gives you. Stretch the netting over the bottom of the tube. Attach it securely with a rubber band or tape so that there is no slipping.
2. Place 10-15 marbles inside the tube. Place the tube on a ring stand. Make sure the stand is high enough so that you can get to the bottom of the tube easily.
3. Place an aluminum pie pan under the tube.
4. Take turns cutting one thread of the netting at a time. Observe what happens. Record your observations *in your Journal*.
5. Record the total number of threads you were able to cut before the marbles started to fall. Did all of the marbles fall at that time?

Conclude and Apply

1. How did your tube-and-marble apparatus model an ecosystem? Describe what each part of the model stood for.
2. What did your model tell you about changes in ecosystems and their results? Was disaster immediate?
3. Imagine that your model is a specific ecosystem, such as a pond or forest. What kinds of changes might be represented by each thread you cut?

Figure 16-11

The Nile perch—introduced to Africa's Lake Victoria as a human food source—has eaten to extinction hundreds of species of fish unique to the lake.

In the Find Out activity you modeled the natural process of extinction. The crash of the marbles into the pan represented the extinction of a species or ecosystem.

Extinction means the disappearance of a species. Extinction is a natural process. Throughout Earth's history, millions of plants and animals have become extinct for natural reasons. See the Earth Science Connection for some notable examples.

Local extinction means that species disappear from a certain area. The cause could be a gradual change in the climate, such as a decrease in a region's rainfall. A plant species adapted to a swampy area will become extinct locally if the swamp dries up. Local extinctions often occur as part of succession.

Local extinction can lead to global extinction—the complete and permanent disappearance of a species. Species that are dependent on a certain habitat are vulnerable to global extinction.

The Human Side of Extinction

In the past, humans caused extinction of many species by killing them in large numbers—the dodo and the passenger pigeons are examples. Today, the most common way we cause extinction is by destroying

Earth Science CONNECTION

Ancient Extinctions

Millions of species became extinct long before people lived on Earth. In fact, our planet has experienced five natural mass extinctions. A mass extinction occurs when a large percentage of the existing species become extinct at once.

Five Mass Extinctions

During the first mass extinction, 440 million years ago, most species lived in the seas. Some survived this extinction, but many did not.

During the next mass extinction, 370 million years ago, many species of fish and

species' habitats. We eliminate these habitats directly by clearing the land and indirectly through pollution.

As we farm, log, and live on more and more of Earth, we interfere with succession's ability to repair damage. In the rain forest, one fallen tree is an opportunity for succession. But clear-cutting, or cutting down all of the trees in an area, leads to acres of sun-baked soil. With no protection from the sun, fragile rain-forest seeds dry out instead of sprouting.

Destruction of habitats is not the only way humans cause extinction. Species are also endangered by our introduction of competing species. See **Figure 16-11** for an example.

■ People vs. Plants

What difference does one species make? As an example, doctors discovered in 1984 that medicine made from the bark of the Pacific yew can help fight cancer. Before this was known, loggers burned or bulldozed about 90 percent of these trees. The Pacific yew grows slowly and mostly in climax communities called old-growth forests. A forest may take 1000 years to reach this stage.

SKILLBUILDER

Making Graphs

Use the figures below to make a line graph showing the number of species that became extinct between 1600 and 1900. Then, explain what the graph indicates. For help, refer to the ***Skill Handbook*** on page 657.

Year	Number of extinct species
1600	10
1700	11
1800	28
1900	70

about 70 percent of the marine invertebrates (animals without a backbone) became extinct.

The third extinction, 225 million years ago, was the most destructive. Between 80 and 96 percent of all species became extinct. Scientists estimate that of the 45 000 to 240 000 species existing at that time, only 1800 to 9600 species survived.

The next mass extinction, 200 million years ago, eliminated 75 percent of the sea-dwelling species and some land-dwellers. Dinosaurs, crocodiles, and mammals survived.

The last mass extinction, 65 million years ago, finished the dinosaurs off, along with about one-third of all species, mostly sea-dwellers.

After the death of the dinosaurs, mammals took over many of the land habitats and niches. Many new mammal and fish species emerged.

What Do You Think?

Research the hypotheses scientists have developed to explain dinosaur extinctions. What evidence do they use to support their ideas? Make a poster that shows one of the hypotheses for what caused the dinosaur mass extinction.

Taking Action

The dilemma of the Pacific yew illustrates why it's important to learn about how living things interact with each other. We need to preserve natural habitats and, with them, the diversity of life on Earth.

We know nothing about what valuable medicines or products may come from undiscovered species. If they become extinct before we ever find them, we may lose many valuable natural resources. But, there are some species we do know about that are on the brink of extinction. Explore these species and what you can do to save them.

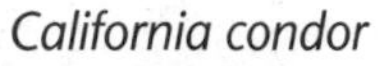

California condor

Giant panda

Orangutan

Florida panther

Tiger salamander

Explore! ACTIVITY

Which species should we save?

The government has chosen your team to decide which of the endangered species below to save first. You may not have time or money to save the rest, so choose carefully.

California condor
orangutan
giant panda
tiger salamander
Florida panther

What To Do

1. Work with your team to research the needs, the habitat, and the role of each of these endangered species in its ecosystem.
2. Discuss the pros and cons of saving each one. Decide which species your team would save.
3. Present your argument to the class. Try to convince them to join you in preserving the species you selected.

In the Explore activity, you thought of ways to save endangered species. What else can we do?

First, nations can help people in countries with rain forests find ways to make a living that help preserve the diversity of life.

Second, nations can support international treaties that protect wildlife. One is the Convention on International Trade in Endangered Species (CITES). Another is the U.S. Endangered Species Act, prohibiting anyone in the United States from killing, selling, or even chasing an endangered species.

Figure 16-12

There are several ways that you can help preserve diversity.

Refuse to buy or accept exotic pets or products, such as ivory, that come from endangered animals.

Reduce your use and recycle when you can. When we reduce the resources used, we reduce the number of habitats that will be destroyed to supply human needs and wants.

Learn about endangered species, such as the golden lion tamarin, and about the plants and animals that live in your own ecosystem.

Support conservation groups, zoos, seed banks, and other programs that protect endangered species.

Write to state and federal representatives. Urge them to support programs that protect both habitats and fragile species.

U.S. HOUSE OF REPRESENTATIVES

To see examples of things you can do to help preserve the diversity of life on Earth, see **Figure 16-12**.

You've learned about how organisms interact with other organisms and with the environment. Humans are an important part of nearly all ecosystems. As you become more aware of how your actions may affect the ecosystem around you, you'll be able to make choices that will help preserve the diversity of life on Earth.

1. Name two natural causes of local extinction.

2. Explain three specific ways humans directly or indirectly cause local or global extinction.

3. Apply Assume that the current rate of global extinction continues for another hundred years. What are at least three ways that the decreasing number of species will affect the people living a century from now?

EXPAND your view

Science and Society

Why All the Fuss over the Rain Forests?

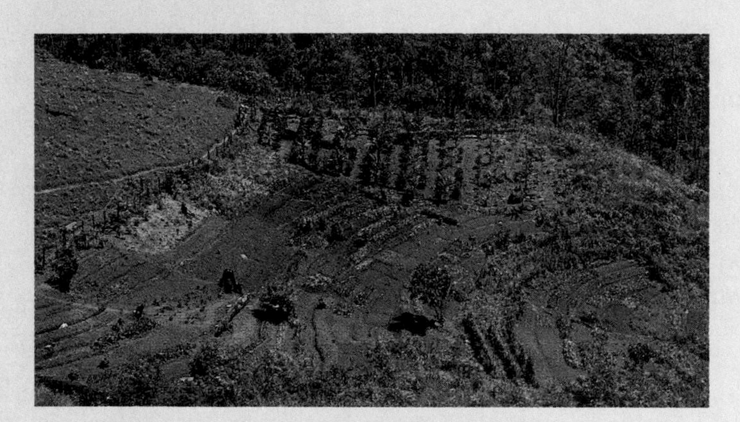

Do you live in a rain forest? Probably not, so why should you be concerned about the rain forest?

For one thing, the seven percent of Earth covered by rain forests supports at least half of all the species on Earth.

People who live near rain forests depend on farming, logging, or mining to support their families. As a result, they burn or clear-cut as many as 22 million acres of rain forest every year.

The Extent of the Damage

Rain forest occupying an area the size of 20 football fields is destroyed every minute of every day. In 1989, rain forests covered a region about as large as the continental United States. The amount of rain forest destroyed each year would cover an area the size of Florida.

The fires from the burning also send large amounts of carbon dioxide up into the atmosphere. Carbon dioxide traps the sun's heat in the atmosphere and may be causing gradual worldwide increases in temperature.

After clearing the land, farmers discover that the soil is too poor to support their crops or feed their cattle. Most of the nutrients in the rain forest are in the trees, not the soil.

Only a few plants grow in a shallow layer of humus on the forest floor. Under that layer is a claylike soil that bakes as hard as rock when exposed to sun.

The fires and logging destroy habitats found nowhere else on Earth. Scientists estimate that the loss of these habitats

destroys 4000 to 6000 species of plants and animals every year.

Does it seem as though, year after year, the numbers of songbirds where you live are decreasing? Songbirds migrate to the rain forests during the winter. As their habitats are destroyed, so are they. Between 1980 and 1990, the number of wood thrushes in the U.S. dropped 31 percent. The number of Baltimore orioles decreased 23 percent.

Valuable Products of the Rain Forests

The rain forest contains many valuable natural resources. For example, the sap of the copaiba tree is pure diesel fuel. In 1990, it supplied Brazil with 20 percent of its diesel fuel. Unlike our limited supply of fossil fuels, the copaiba produces fuel as long as it lives. The copaiba is a renewable source of fuel.

Scarlet macaw

You or your family may have used medicine made from rain forest plants. One-fourth of all medicines come from species found in the rain forest. For example, two chemicals in Madagascar's rosy periwinkle are used to treat cancer. Medicine made from the venom of the Brazilian pit viper helps lower blood pressure.

But only one percent of the rain forest plants have been checked for medicines that could be developed from them. Maybe a tiny plant growing there will cure cancer. But hundreds of unidentified species are being destroyed as you read this!

So we all need to be concerned about the destruction of the rain forests. The rain forests we preserve may hold the key to our own future!

You Try It!

Use the information in this article to construct a scale model of the amount of rain forest destroyed each day. Be sure to put in some recognizable object (at the same scale), such as a person, so that everyone will have an idea of how big the area is.

Health CONNECTION

Pets Are Good for You!

Did you know that many humans have a mutualistic relationship with animals? Do you know any of these people? You know that guide dogs and other animals can be trained to help people with physical disabilities. But now research shows that just spending time with animals helps people feel better.

Scientists have found that the presence of animals can help sick people recover, calm troubled children, and encourage withdrawn people to communicate.

Animals Help Hearts

Research shows that heart patients with pets had better chances of survival than patients without pets. And elderly people with pets visit the doctor less often than those without pets.

Organizations such as Pets for Life in Kansas City bring pets to nursing homes for monthly visits. The smiles and excitement show how pets boost morale.

In fact, 25 studies on elderly people in nursing homes have shown the benefits of having pets around. Residents who were exposed to pets smiled more and became more alert. The animals also helped angry and depressed residents feel more at ease and be more caring toward other people.

"Mutual" Love

These relationships between people and animals are examples of mutualism because both benefit. People take care of the pets, while the pets provide loving, undemanding companionship.

Pets are good for us, mentally and physically!

What Do You Think?

Why do you think pets have such an influence on people? If you have a pet, how do you feel about it? Write a paragraph describing how you think pets aid healing.

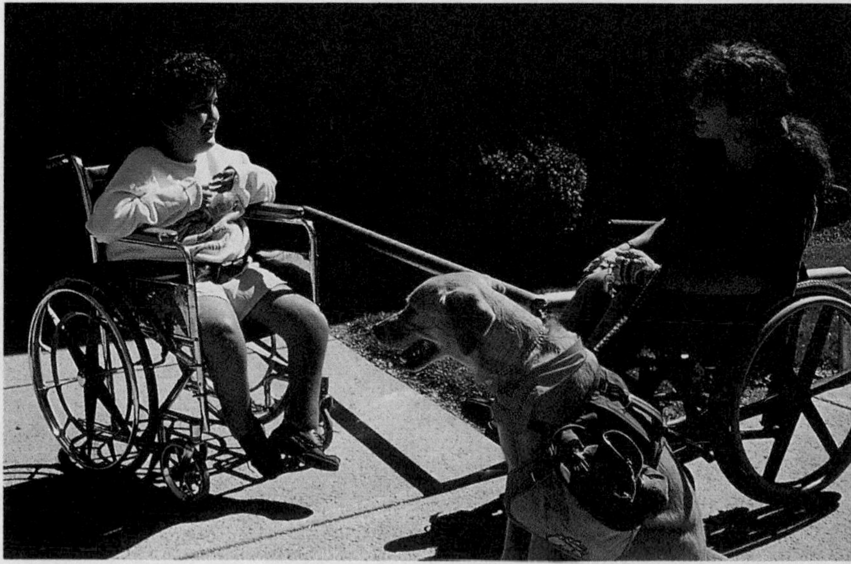

Technology Connection

Computers to the Rescue!

Often we don't know a species is endangered until it's almost too late to save it. New technology can help. Gap analysis uses computerized maps to indicate the diversity of plant and animal species in a specific ecosystem.

Gap Analysis

In gap analysis, three maps are stacked on top of each other, using computer graphics. One map shows the plant species. It can be programmed to show all plants in the ecosystem or just one, such as the endangered sage scrub.

Another map indicates all the animal species or just one group, such as reptiles. A third map outlines any protected wilderness areas within the region.

Locating Endangered Species

Sometimes when the maps are combined, they show a "gap" in the protected areas. Most of the endangered species are living outside the protected areas.

By pinpointing the location of these species, officials can better determine which areas should be protected. They can also decide whether a piece of land can be developed without threatening endangered species.

Information for the maps comes from aerial photographs, satellite images, and ground observations.

The Success of Gap Analysis

Twenty-two states are now using gap analysis. This new technology has already convinced the government not to use an "empty" Idaho field for testing bombs. The maps proved that the field was actually teeming with life.

Science Journal

In your Science Journal, make a gap analysis map of your school yard or neighborhood. Work with a partner or two to create a map of the area. Then go and record the plant and animal species in your area. Finally indicate any protected areas, such as city parks, and so on.

In the gap analysis below, Californian coastal sage scrub is shown growing outside protected reserve lands.

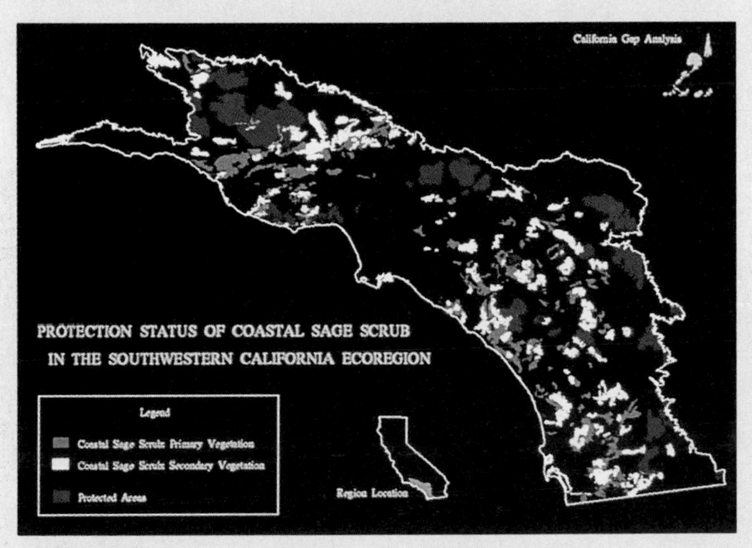

chapter 16
REVIEWING MAIN IDEAS

Science Journal

Review the statements below about the big ideas presented in this chapter, and answer the questions. Then, re-read your answers to the Did You Ever Wonder questions at the beginning of the chapter. *In your Science Journal,* write a paragraph about how your understanding of the big ideas in the chapter has changed.

1 Succession is the process by which new environments become inhabited or old ecosystems recover from damage. ***How do new ecosystems become established?***

2 There are three different ways in which species can form cooperative relationships—mutualism, commensalism, and parasitism. ***Compare and contrast mutualism and parasitism.***

3 Extinction is a natural process that has taken place throughout Earth history. However, human interactions with ecosystems have greatly increased the rate of extinctions. ***If human interference could be completely eliminated, would the extinction of species stop? Explain your answer.***

chapter 16 CHAPTER REVIEW

Using Key Science Terms

climax community	parasitism
commensalism	pioneer species
diversity	succession
extinction	symbiosis
mutualism	

Describe the relationship among the following words.

1. symbiosis, commensalism, parasitism, mutualism
2. succession, pioneer species, climax community
3. diversity, extinction

Understanding Ideas

Answer the following questions in your Journal *using complete sentences.*

1. What is one way that humans interfere with animal interactions with their environment?
2. What type of symbiotic relationship do a child and her goldfish have? Explain.
3. What is the main way humans now cause the extinction of other species?
4. What is the final stage of succession?

Developing Skills

Use your understanding of the concepts developed in this chapter to answer each of the following questions.

1. **Concept Mapping** Complete this concept map of symbiotic relationships.

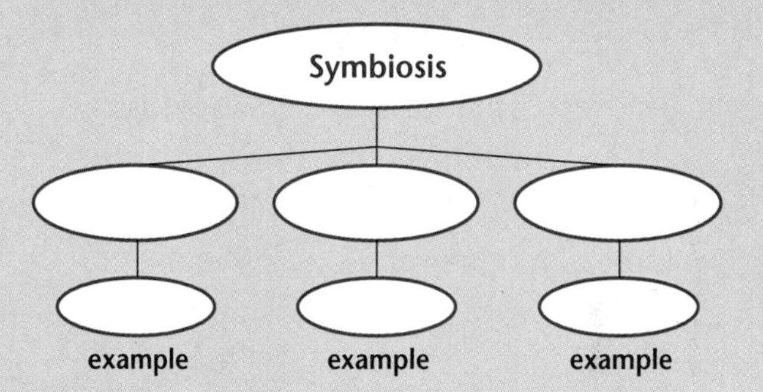

2. **Making Models** Repeat the Find Out activity on page 523, using a different kind of model. Explain how your model demonstrates the path to extinction.
3. **Comparing and Contrasting** Use water or milk instead of hot coffee for the Find Out activity on page 507. Compare and contrast the changes that occur in the water or milk with the results of the original activity.

Critical Thinking

In your Journal, *answer each of the following questions.*

1. Why is a pioneer species usually small in size?
2. How does farming interfere with natural succession?
3. The clownfish can hide within the tentacles of anemones, which are

chapter 16

CHAPTER REVIEW

deadly to other fish. When clownfish enter the tentacles, other fish sometimes follow. These fish may be killed and eaten by the anemone. What kind of symbiotic relationship do the clownfish and the anemone have? Explain.

4. Why do you think the ashy dogweed plant, which grows only in Texas, is on the brink of extinction, while the dandelion is not?
5. What kind of interaction is shown in the picture to the right? Explain.
6. Is a parasite ever useful? How can a parasite be useful if it is defined as something harmful?

Problem Solving

Read the following challenge and discuss your responses in a brief paragraph.

Design an animal that would not easily become extinct. Draw a picture of what it would look like, and write a paragraph to describe it.

1. Describe its physical characteristics.
2. Describe its habitat.
3. What would keep this animal from over-populating its habitat and depleting its food source?
4. How could you make sure its habitat would not be destroyed?

CONNECTING IDEAS

Discuss each of the following in a brief paragraph.

1. **Theme—Stability and Change** How could you tell whether a forest had stabilized into a climax community?
2. **Theme—Systems and Interactions** How does mutualism benefit the animals within an ecosystem?
3. **A Closer Look** Why do coral reefs depend on clear, clean water to survive?
4. **Earth Science Connection** Explain how you could predict a sixth natural mass extinction.
5. **Science and Society** What are four ways people who live thousands of miles from a rain forest can be affected by its destruction?

In this unit, you investigated motion and how it affected you, Earth, and objects near Earth.

You learned about velocity, acceleration, weight, and weightlessness. You saw how a projectile moves, and how satellites can remain in a stationary orbit over Earth. You learned that movement of water, wind, and ice on Earth's surface can change features of the land. You learned about how ecosystems grow and change, creating new conditions, and adapting to sudden alterations.

Try the exercises and activity that follow—they will challenge you to use and apply some of the ideas you learned in this unit.

CONNECTING IDEAS

1. As rocks on a cliff weather, fragments fall to the base of the cliff due to gravity. How does this motion caused by acceleration due to gravity affect weathering and erosion on Earth's surface?
2. Explain what happens to various sized particles of rock that are carried by a stream as the water in the stream empties into a larger body of water. What do these particles form?
3. Describe the changes in velocity and acceleration that occur on a daily trip from your home to school.

Exploring Further ACTIVITY

How Can You Help Increase the Diversity of Life in Your Environment?

What To Do

With three other classmates, develop a way to increase the diversity of organisms in your classroom. Some examples might be planting an indoor garden or setting up an aquarium. After your teacher approves your plan, try it. What will it need to be successful? What must you do to help maintain the new diversity you've established?

Wave Motion

Surf's up! Catch some waves . . . they're all around you! Water waves leave you wet. Sound waves bring you your favorite music. Seismic waves from an earthquake can knock you off your feet. Waves are formed when an object is set in motion. Learn more about the wonderful world of waves in this unit, and get some good vibrations!

NATIONAL GEOGRAPHIC

try it!

Mechanical waves are all around you. You see a mechanical wave when you watch a flag wave in the wind. You may have felt a mechanical wave while lying on a raft in a wave pool or in the ocean. You have even heard mechanical waves when your teacher tells you the next day's assignment. What causes a wave to form? Why does it move the way that it does? What happens to an object when a wave passes by it?

What To Do

1. Obtain a tuning fork from your teacher.
2. Gently tap the tuning fork against the edge of a book and observe the motion produced. If you have trouble seeing the vibrations, dip the tuning fork into a glass of water and observe the ripples caused by the vibrations.
3. Gently tap the tuning fork and hold it near your ear. What do you notice?
4. How do you think the tuning fork is affecting your eardrum?

CHAPTER 17

WAVES

Did you ever wonder...

- Why sometimes the waves in a swimming pool get so big?
- Why a horn on a train seems to change pitch as it passes you?
- How a radio speaker produces sound?

Science Journal

Before you begin your study of waves, think about these questions and answer them *in your Science Journal.* When you have finished the chapter, compare your journal write-up with what you have learned.

It's a beautiful day, and you're at the local pool. You are in the water with your friend Ladonna, who is basking on a float. Out of the corner of your eye you see Louie, the bodybuilder, launch himself off the diving board. SPLASH! Suddenly you are under the water, Ladonna bobs straight up, and water bursts over the sides of the pool. Louie has made a large wave in the pool.

After you get your hair out of your eyes, you think about what just happened. If someone had told you the wave were coming, you might have assumed it would knock you down. But the wave just flowed over and around you. Ladonna simply bobbed up and down and ended up right back beside you. Later in this chapter, you will think back to these observations and be able to explain them.

In the activity on the next page, explore some of the characteristics of waves on a rope.

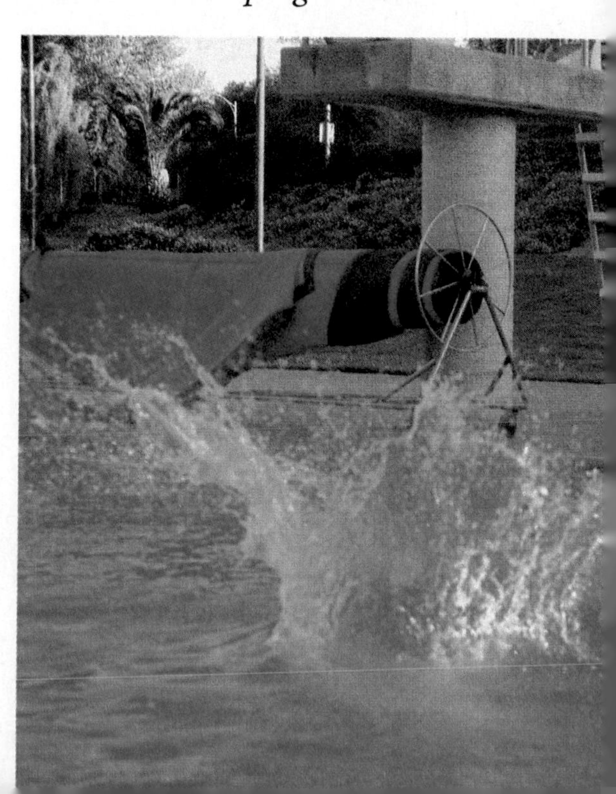

Explore! ACTIVITY

Can you make a wave on a rope?

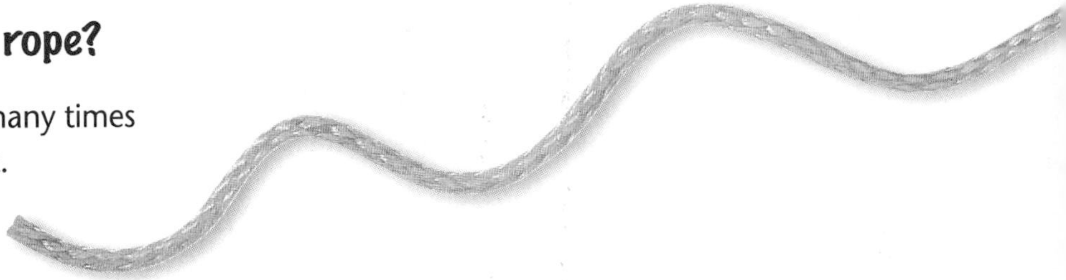

You have probably shaken a rope many times and watched waves travel down it. Now do it again and really observe what happens.

What To Do

1. Tie one end of a heavy 4-m rope to a desk or a doorknob.
2. Holding onto the other end of the rope with your hand, shake the rope up and down once.
3. Observe the pulse as it travels away from your hand.
4. Shake the rope up and down slowly and at a steady rate.
5. Describe the motion of the wave on the rope *in your Journal.*
6. Does the wave seem to move from one end of the rope to the other?
7. In what direction does the rope move?

17-1 Waves and Vibrations

Section Objectives
- Describe how waves are produced.
- Identify transverse and longitudinal waves.

Key Terms
transverse waves
longitudinal waves

Waves Around You

What do you think of when you hear the word wave? Perhaps you think of a friendly greeting, the ocean, the beach, or people in a stadium performing a "wave."

What exactly is a wave? Think about Louie's wave. His dive caused a large disturbance when he pushed the water aside. That disturbance traveled out across the pool in the form of a wave.

Louie's wave certainly disturbed Ladonna and you, to say nothing of the water in the pool. Now, try to think of some more everyday experiences you've had with waves.

Think back to the Explore activity. Do you remember how you made the rope wave? You disturbed the rope by shaking it. The rope in your hand had an up-and-down movement. But the wave you created didn't stay in one place. It moved along the rope, hit the doorknob, and came back. Thus the wave was a disturbance traveling along the rope. Just like Louie's wave, this wave can move things it hits. A wave can carry energy.

Figure 17-1

A The energy released by undersea earthquakes cause giant waves called tsunamis.

B Although difficult to detect in open water, tsunamis sometimes build to a wall of water more than 30 m high when they reach shallow waters.

C When the tremendous energy that tsunamis carry is released against the shoreline, everything in the wave's path is swept away.

D The northern Japanese island town of Aonae was hit by a tsunami in July 1993, causing extensive damage.

Types of Waves

In this chapter we will talk about mechanical waves. A mechanical wave is a wave that travels through matter. For now, think of matter as anything that takes up space. You saw one example of a mechanical wave when Louie landed in the water. Waves in the rope and sound waves in the air are also mechanical waves. In Chapter 3, you learned that air was the medium that carried sound from the source to your ear. In any mechanical wave, the matter through which the waves move is called the medium. A mechanical wave can be described as a periodic disturbance in a medium.

Transverse Waves

Once again, think back to the opening Explore activity. In the wave you made on the rope, the rope was the medium. The rope moved up and down or side to side. This was at right angles to the direction of the wave itself, which moved away from the source of the disturbance—in this case, you. The wave you produced with the rope was a transverse wave. As shown in **Figure 17-2**, **transverse waves** are waves in which the wave disturbance moves at right angles to the direction of the wave itself.

Figure 17-2

A When a drop of water falls into a pool, the drop transfers energy and causes the surrounding particles of pool water to move in tiny down-and-up circles.

B Their movement causes nearby particles to also move down-and-up. This disturbance, seen as waves moving across the surface of the water, passes from particle to particle and travels outward from the place the drop entered the pool. In what way are these waves transverse waves?

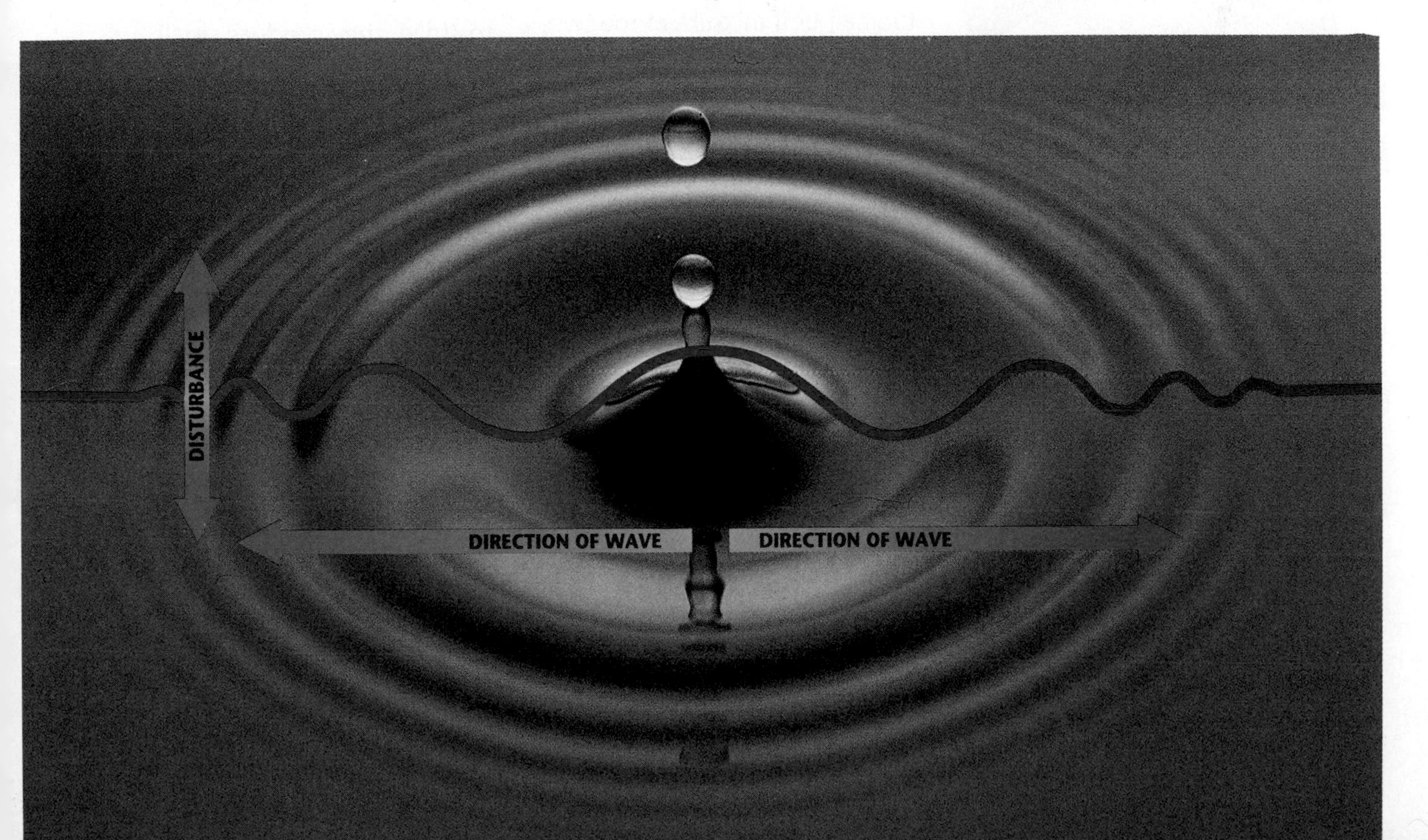

Figure 17-3

Certain sound waves produced by a singer's voice may shatter glass. Longitudinal waves travel in the same direction as the disturbance. Sound waves are a type of longitudinal wave that travels through the air in a series of compressions and rarefactions. The drawing below shows a longitudinal wave on a spring.

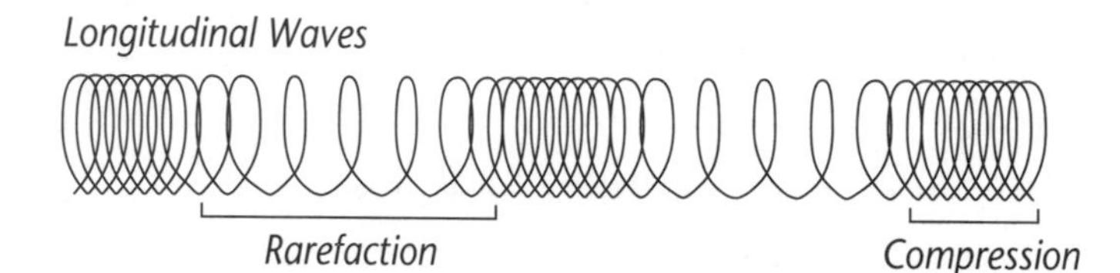

Longitudinal Waves

In Chapter 3, you learned that sound traveled through the air in a series of compressions and rarefactions—a bunching up and spreading out of the air that carried the sound from the source to you. This type of wave is called a longitudinal wave. In a **longitudinal wave**, as shown in **Figure 17-3**, the medium vibrates in the same direction as the wave itself travels. You can't directly observe longitudinal waves in air. However, you can find out more about them by seeing how they affect other substances.

Earth Science CONNECTION

Seismic Prospecting

Seismic waves are waves produced by an earthquake. They may be transverse, longitudinal, or a mixture of the two, like a water wave. Scientists study seismic waves in order to understand earthquakes and the structure of Earth. They can also be used in the search for mineral deposits such as oil, natural gas, and sulfur.

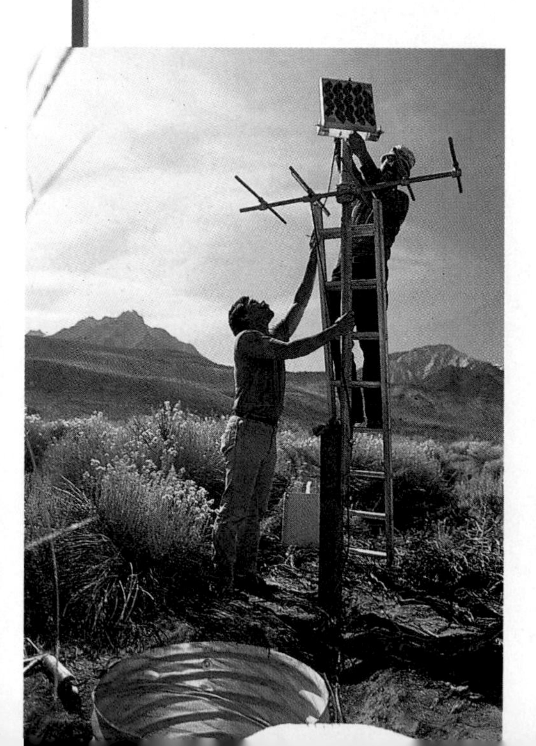

These scientists are setting up instruments to record seismic disturbances.

Artificial Earthquakes

In this case, however, scientists don't wait for an earthquake to strike, they produce small artificial quakes. These are created by setting off explosives in a small hole in the ground or by using vibrator trucks that can violently shake the ground. The artificial earthquake sends seismic waves thousands of feet into the ground. Waves then bounce off the rock formations and are reflected back. Acoustic receivers, called geophones, placed at different distances from the explosion, pick up the seismic waves and

Find Out! ACTIVITY

Can you observe the effects of a longitudinal wave?

Sound causes your eardrum to vibrate. If you made a model of the ear with a large "eardrum" could you feel and see it vibrate?

What To Do

1. Get a portable radio with a round speaker. Find a can or other container with the same or slightly larger diameter than that of the speaker.
2. Cut out the bottom of the can so that both ends are open.
3. Stretch a piece of plastic wrap across one end of the can and secure it with a rubber band.
4. Place the open end of the can over the speaker, facing up, and sprinkle some dry rice on the plastic.
5. Tune the radio to a song with a heavy beat and observe.
6. Put your fingertips lightly on the plastic. What do you feel?
7. Turn up the volume.

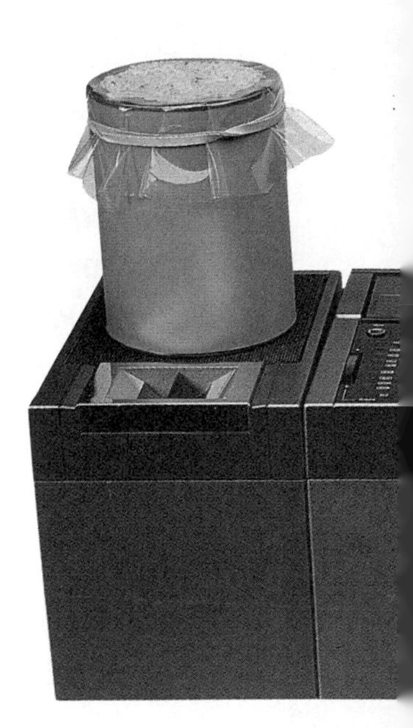

Conclude and Apply

1. Is the can necessary? How could you find out?
2. What happens to the vibrations of the plastic when you turn up the volume?

send signals to a truck outfitted with recording equipment. There, the seismic waves are amplified and recorded on tape.

Interpreting the Earthquake

The tapes are processed on a computer, and a printout is produced. This process is called seismic mapping. By analyzing the amplitudes of the seismic waves, and the time it takes them to bounce off rocks, scientists can get an idea of the nature of rock layers, and the depths and locations of mineral deposits. This is a much less expensive way of deciding where to drill for mineral deposits than prospecting by drilling a number of deep holes.

What do you think?

Seismic prospecting is not only cheaper than drilling a number of deep holes, but damages the environment much less than drilling. How do you think drilling can harm the environment?

DESIGN YOUR OWN
INVESTIGATION

Waves on a Coiled Spring

You have learned about longitudinal and transverse waves. How do waves travel on a coiled spring? Are they transverse waves or longitudinal waves?

Preparation

Problem
How many types of waves can you create with a coiled spring?

Form a Hypothesis
As a group, decide on a hypothesis that predicts how waves can travel on a coiled spring. Write it down.

Safety Precautions

Objectives
- Observe how waves travel along a coiled spring.
- Operationally define types of waves.

Materials
coiled metal spring
piece of colored yarn

DESIGN YOUR OWN INVESTIGATION

Plan the Experiment

1. Examine the materials and decide how you will test your hypothesis. Write down your plan.
2. *In your Science Journal,* prepare a place to draw diagrams of the wave types your group creates with the coiled spring. Plan to use arrows on the diagrams to show direction of movement.

Check the Plan

1. Determine if two people will hold the spring or if you will let the spring hang down.
2. Before you begin, check your plan with your teacher.
3. Do the experiment. Make certain that you observe closely to see what kinds of waves you can make and to see what happens to the waves when they reach the end of the coil. Do they come back? Observe closely and *in your Science Journal,* draw diagrams of what occurs.

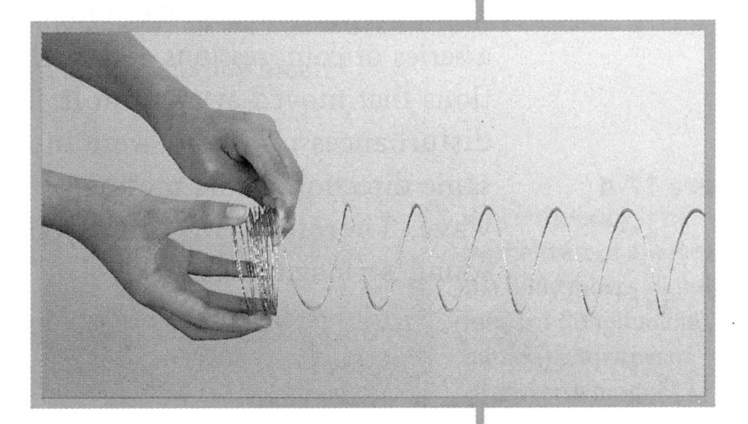

Analyze and Conclude

1. **Observe** What types of wave pulses did you create?
2. **Interpret Data** Draw a diagram of each type of wave that occurred in the spring. Label your diagrams. Show direction of the movement.
3. **Observe** Did the waves move in the same direction as the source of the disturbance? Explain.
4. **Observe** What happened when the waves reached the end of the spring?
5. **Infer** Compare the motion of a radio speaker tested in the Find Out! activity to the waves you created with the spring. Is a sound wave a transverse or longitudinal wave? Is an ocean wave a transverse or longitudinal wave?

Going Further

Observe how fast transverse and longitudinal waves move along the spring. Is there a set speed?

17-2 Wave Characteristics

Section Objectives
- Draw a wave.
- Identify the wavelength, amplitude, crest, and trough of a wave.
- Explain the relationship among frequency, wavelength, and speed in a wave.

Key Terms
crest, trough, amplitude, wavelength

Properties of Waves

The wave you produced earlier with the rope can be described by its properties. When you quickly moved the rope up and down, you may have noticed high and low points—hills and valleys. These low points, the valleys, are called **troughs**. The high points, the hills, are called **crests**. In the following Find Out activity, you will observe these parts of a wave again.

Figure 17-6

A This boat is sailing across the waves, through troughs and crests in the ocean.

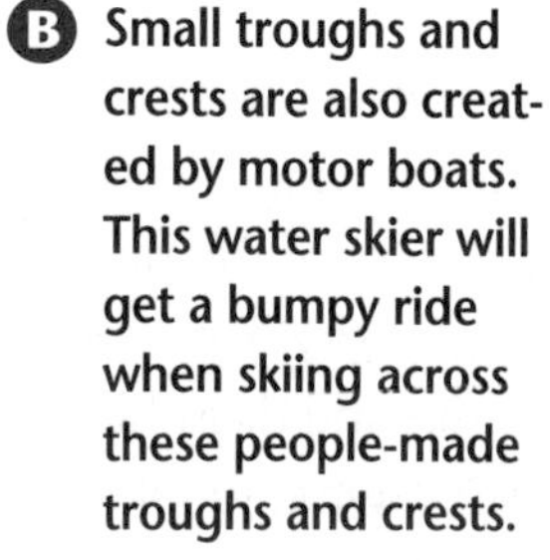

B Small troughs and crests are also created by motor boats. This water skier will get a bumpy ride when skiing across these people-made troughs and crests.

Find Out! ACTIVITY

What are some wave characteristics?

You may have seen excited fans in the stands of a sporting event make a human wave. Now, you will make a wave in class and study its characteristics.

What To Do

1. Your class will sit or stand in a large circle. One student will raise and lower his or her hands to start a wave moving around the circle. The raised hands are like a wave pulse on a rope.
2. Practice "doing the wave" until the pulse moves at a constant speed around the circle.
3. Measure the distance around the circle and the time (in seconds) it takes for a pulse to travel around the circle.
4. While a wave is moving around, the first student starts a second pulse when the original pulse reaches the student exactly opposite him or her.
5. If the class is large enough, try having three or four pulses moving around the circle at the same time.
6. Try to have enough pulses moving around the circle so that each student has his or her hands up as long as they are down.
7. Make a drawing of the people wave when it had the largest number of pulses traveling around.

Conclude and Apply

1. What was the speed of your wave, that is, the distance around the circle divided by the time the wave took to go around the circle?
2. How many times did the first student raise his or her hands each minute when one pulse was moving around? To find out, divide the number of seconds in one minute, 60, by the time it took the pulse to travel the circle in seconds.
3. How many times did the first student raise his or her hands each minute when two pulses were moving around? When three pulses were moving?

The largest wind-driven wave ever measured had an amplitude of over 17 meters. It was created by winds of over 100 kilometers per hour blowing across the ocean for thousands of kilometers.

Amplitude

Suppose you want to know the amplitude of Louie's wave in the swimming pool. The normal level at the shallow end of the pool is 1 m. But, when Louie jumped in, the wave made the level rise 30 centimeters. Thus, the crest of Louie's wave was 30 centimeters higher than the normal level of the pool. This was the amplitude of his wave. As shown in **Figure 17-7**, the **amplitude** is the distance from the crest or trough of the wave to the middle level. What changed the amplitude of your people wave? The higher a person raised his or her hands, the larger the amplitude.

Have you ever seen waves on the ocean? On a calm day they can gently lap at the beach. Their amplitudes are small. But, when there is a storm off shore, their amplitudes can be meters high. Then they can be very dangerous. The energy they carry can do much damage. The energy carried by a mechanical wave depends on its amplitude.

Speed

You learned in Chapter 12 that the speed of a ball, auto, or person is the distance traveled divided by the time it takes to go that far. Did anyone in the wave circle move in a direction around the circle? No, but the wave did, didn't it? The speed of a wave is found the same way the speed of a ball is found. You measure the distance the wave travels and the time it takes and then divide the distance by the time. The speed of the people wave didn't depend on the number of

Figure 17-7

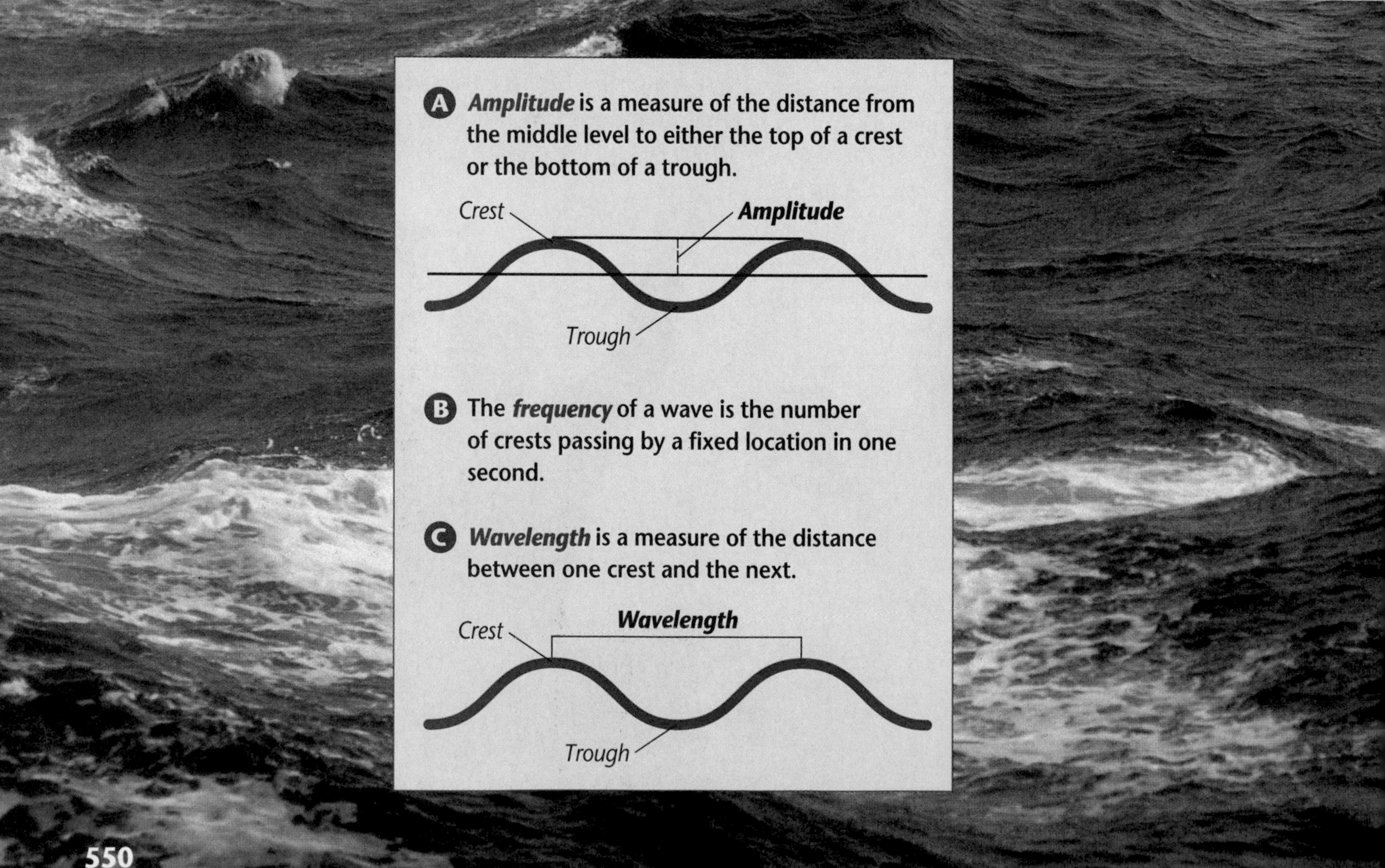

waves, just on how fast people could raise their hands. That is, the speed depended only on the medium—the people through which the wave moved.

Frequency

What changed when you added more pulses in your people wave? Not the speed; each pulse moved around the circle at the same rate. When only one pulse went around the circle you didn't have to raise your hands very often, but when many pulses were moving around, you had to raise your hands more frequently. The frequency of a people wave is the number of times you had to raise your hand each second. The frequency of a wave is the number of crests passing by a fixed location in one second.

Wavelength

How far apart were the pulses in your people wave? When there was only one pulse going around, the distance was the circumference of the circle. What was it when two pulses went around? What about three? The distance was first half the circumference, then one third the distance around the circle.

When you measured the distance between the pulses of your people wave you measured a property called wavelength. **Wavelength** is the distance between the crest of one wave and the crest of the next. As the wavelength decreased, how did the frequency change? In the following activity you will study the relationship between wavelength and frequency in a different type of wave.

INVESTIGATE!

Ripples

Do water waves behave the same as people waves and spring waves? How are their speed, frequency, and wavelength related? In this activity you will use the patterns produced by light shining through the crests and troughs of waves in a shallow dish to investigate water waves.

Problem

How are a wave's frequency and wavelength related?

Safety Precautions

Materials

clear glass dish approximately 30-cm square
pencil or pen
1 piece of blank white paper
strips of plastic foam
tape
water
overhead light
ruler

What To Do

1. Tape strips of plastic foam to the inner edges of the dish (see photo ***A***). Then, fill the clear glass dish with about 3 cm of water (see photo ***B***). Set it on a piece of blank white paper under an overhead light source.
2. Tap the water with the end of your pencil or pen. Observe the wave by looking at the paper. *In your Journal*, draw the shape of the wave. Compare the speed of the wave in all directions. How fast does the wave travel? Estimate how long it takes to travel the length of the dish.

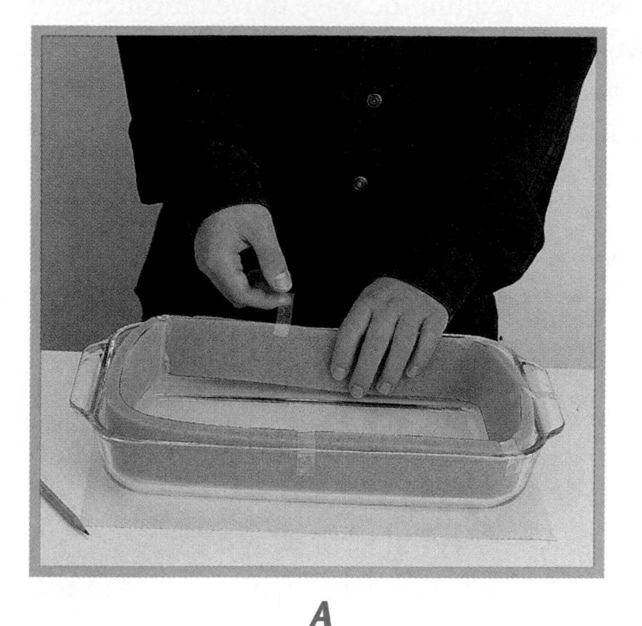

A

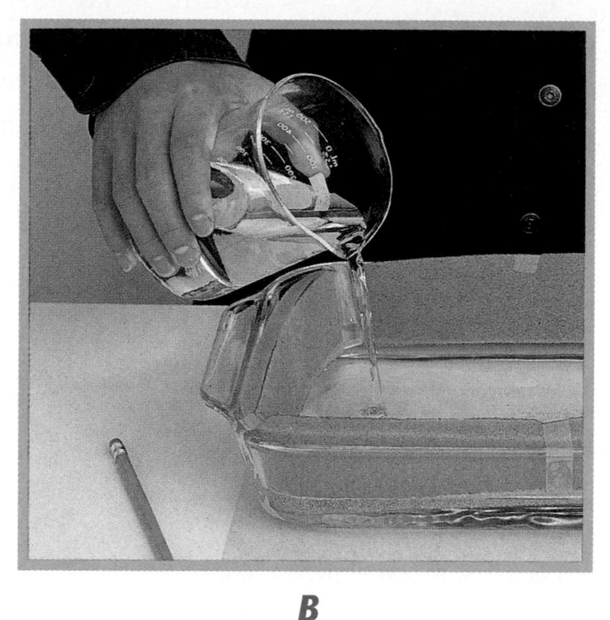

B

3 Now, tap the water again, producing a series of waves. Increase the frequency by tapping the water faster and observe the change in wavelength. Draw an example of low- and high-frequency waves being produced.

Analyzing

1. What effect does increasing the frequency have on the wavelength of the waves produced in Step 3?
2. What would happen to the wavelength if you decreased the frequency?

Concluding and Applying

3. What is the relationship between wavelength and frequency in water waves?
4. **Going Further** Predict whether the wave speed depends on the water depth. In your Journal write a plan about how you could make different depths of water in the same dish and find out.

Forming a Hypothesis

Sound travels slower in air at high altitudes than at low altitudes. State a hypothesis to explain this observation. If you need help, refer to the **Skill Handbook** on page 663.

Just as in the case of people waves, you found that as you increased the frequency of the water wave, the wavelength got smaller. The speed, however, didn't depend on the frequency or the wavelength, just the depth of the water. That is, the speed depended on the medium the wave moved through.

The wavelength of a wave is the distance between the crests or troughs, and the frequency is how many crests or troughs flow by you in one second. What happens when waves run into one another? You'll find out in the next section.

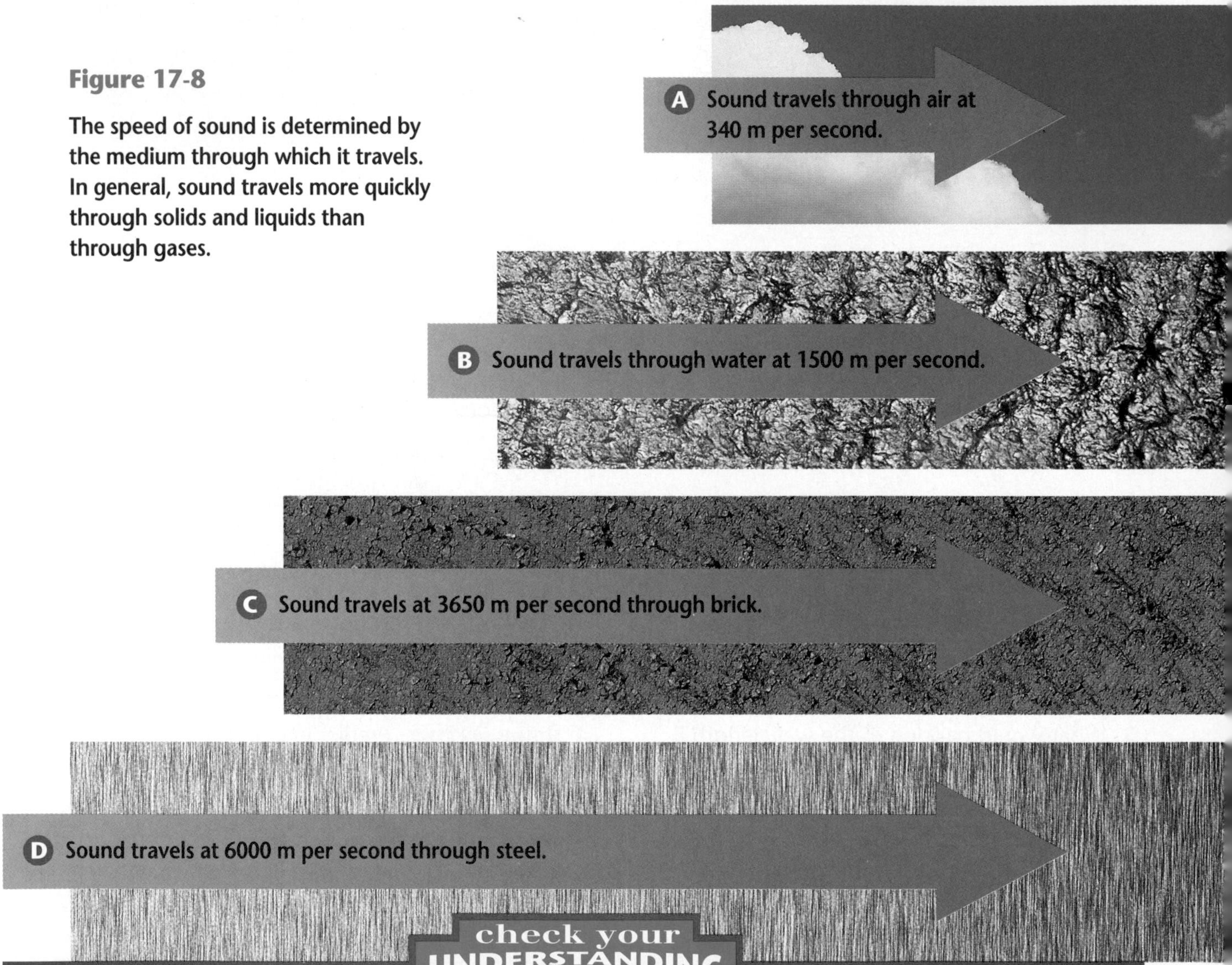

Figure 17-8

The speed of sound is determined by the medium through which it travels. In general, sound travels more quickly through solids and liquids than through gases.

A Sound travels through air at 340 m per second.

B Sound travels through water at 1500 m per second.

C Sound travels at 3650 m per second through brick.

D Sound travels at 6000 m per second through steel.

check your UNDERSTANDING

1. Sketch a transverse wave. Label a crest, a trough, a wavelength, and the amplitude.
2. What is the relationship among the frequency, wavelength and speed of a wave?
3. **Apply** What characteristic of a wave would be most important to a surfer?

17-3 Adding Waves

Interference

Imagine you are on the edge of a pond or pool. Now suppose you drop two rocks into the water about 100 centimeters apart. The ripples created by each rock move out in circles, and quickly run into each other.

If you have seen two wave patterns created in this way, you know that the waves don't bounce off each other. Instead, they appear to pass right through each other. Thus, it appears as if the waves from both rocks are able to exist in the same place at the same time.

Section Objectives

- Explain how waves add together.
- Describe two examples of wave interference.

Key Terms

interference

Find Out! ACTIVITY

What happens when waves pass?

You've studied the characteristics of a single water wave. Now you will investigate how two waves behave when they meet.

What To Do

1. Using the clear dish, water, and light from the last Investigate, tap the surface of the water with the tip of one pencil. Can you find the crests and troughs of the spreading wave?
2. Now, tap the surface with the tips of two pencils about 10 cm apart. Observe the waves carefully.
3. Try alternating the pencils so one hits the water while the other is raised. Observe the result.

Conclude and Apply

1. Describe what happens when the wave from one pencil meets a wave from the other.
2. Did anything change when the two pencils didn't hit the water at the same time?

As the waves pass through each other, they interact in one of two ways. If two crests pass through each other, they briefly form a new wave that is equal to the sum of the amplitudes of the two waves, as shown in **Figure 17-9 A, B,** and **C.**

Because the waves in **Figure 17-9** "interfere" with each other, this situation is called interference. **Interference** is the interaction of two or more waves at one point. When two or more waves add together, it is called constructive interference.

But what would happen if a trough of one wave passed through the crest of another? Look at **Figure 17-9 D, E,** and **F.** What happened?

You might say that one wave destroyed the other. What you just saw is called destructive interference. The waves, however, are not really destroyed because they will emerge on the other side unchanged.

Figure 17-9

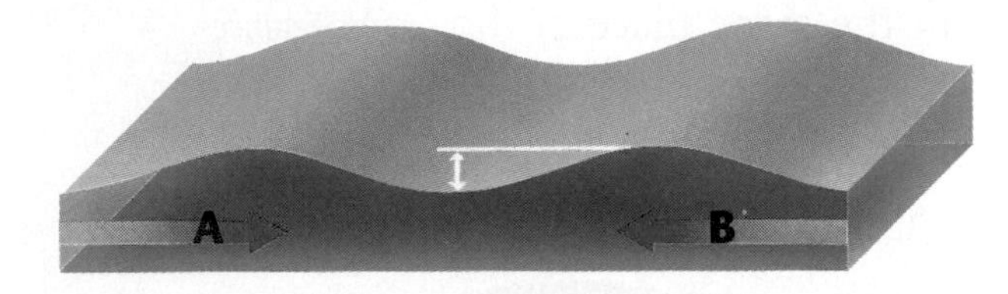

Constructive Wave Interference

A Two crests of equal amplitude—A and B—approach each other from different directions.

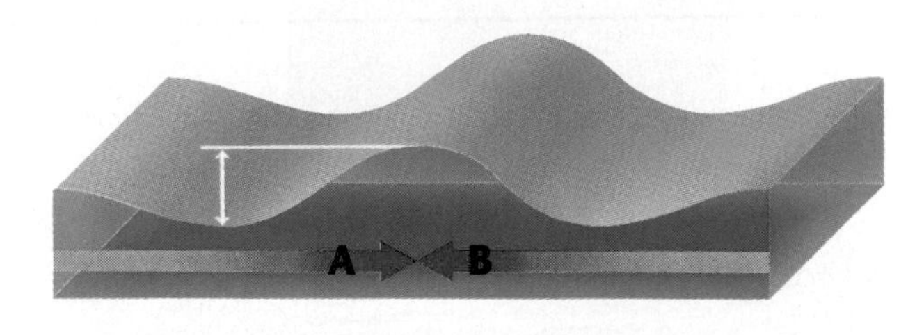

B When waves A and B meet, they briefly form a new wave, A + B, which has an amplitude equal to the sum of the amplitudes of both waves.

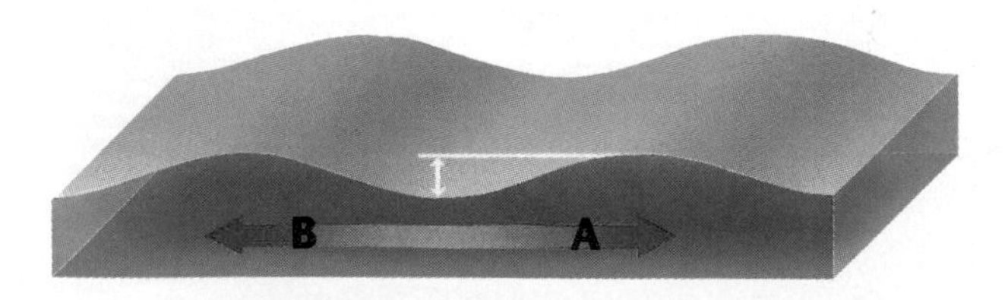

C Once the waves pass through each other, they are unchanged and each retains the amplitude it had before the meeting.

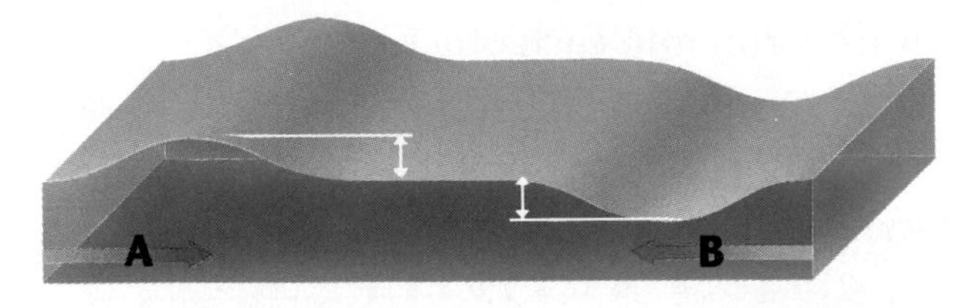

Destructive Wave Interference

D The Crest of wave A and trough of wave B- approach each other from different directions. The amplitude of A is equal to the amplitude of B-.

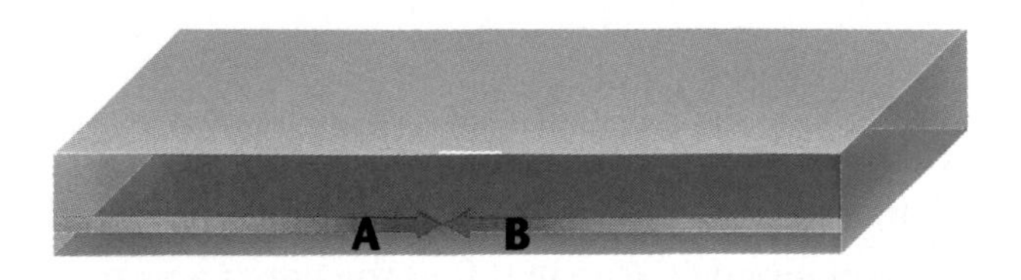

E When A and B- meet, they briefly form a new wave, A + B-, which has an amplitude equal to the sum of the amplitudes of the crest A and the trough B-. The result is that for an instant, the amplitude of the new wave is zero and the water shows no disturbance.

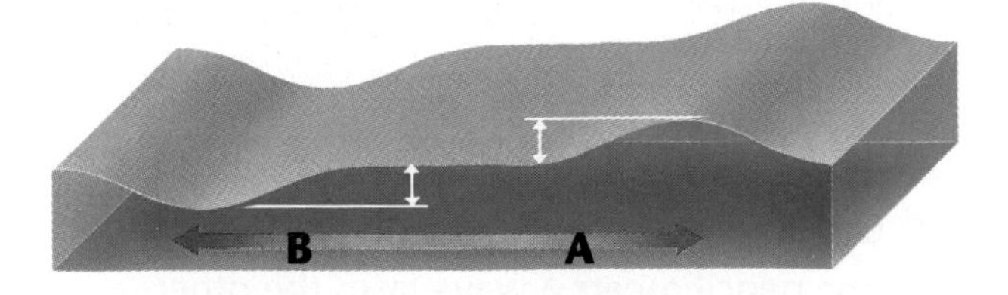

F Once the crest and the trough pass through each other, they are unchanged and each retains the amplitude it had before the meeting. How are constructive and destructive wave interference alike? How are they different?

Patterns of Interference

In **Figure 17-11**, you see a display from a ripple tank. It is a more sophisticated version of what you used in the Investigate. Notice that two overlapping water waves have been produced by two sources hitting the water at the same time. Locate a crest and a trough close to a source. How did you identify each of them?

Now locate the areas where two wave crests have added, producing a larger crest. Look for very bright bands of light. How can you tell that constructive interference is going on? Now find areas where destructive interference is going on. How can you tell that waves are canceling each other?

Figure 17-11

Scientists create various wave patterns in ripple tanks to observe the way waves interact. You can model many wave behaviors with a homemade tank.

Figure 17-10

A When you look at a bubble or a CD and see a spectrum, you are witnessing wave interference. When white light strikes the tiny pits of a CD disk, it is diffracted in many directions.

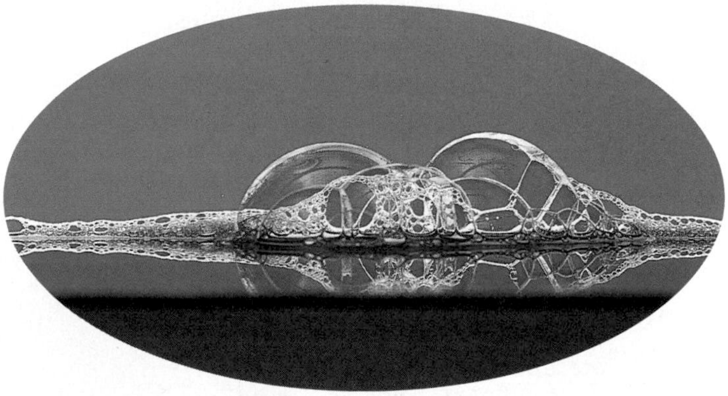

B When light strikes a bubble, some light is reflected by the bubble's outer surface and some by its inner surface.

C When two or more light waves from a bubble or from a CD meet, interference occurs. If waves of one color interfere constructively, you see that color.

Useful Interference

Recently, interference has been put to use protecting human hearing. In the past, people working in noisy environments have damaged their hearing. One example is pilots of small planes. The pilots could not shut out all noise. They had to be able to hear the instructions from the air traffic controllers. Now pilots can wear special ear protection that not only protects their hearing, but allows them to hear normal conversation.

These special earphones have circuits in them that produce sound that destructively interferes with the damaging engine noise but allows conversation to be heard and understood. **Figure 17-12** shows an example of these new earphones.

In this section, you learned how waves interact. If you were really lucky, you could do the same thing with Louie's wave. If Louie's identical twin, Roberto, dived into the other end of the pool a little later than Louie, Louie's and Roberto's waves would be opposite in terms of where their crests and troughs were located. Then the two waves would meet in the center, and destructive interference would produce a calm area. However, if Ladonna were floating at the center of the pool and Roberto jumped at the same time as Louie, constructive interference would give her a real ride. What other effects can waves have on you? You'll find out in the next section.

Figure 17-12

A Loud noises, like those produced by a chainsaw, can damage the human eardrum and result in hearing loss. Engineers have applied what they know about wave interference to design ear protection for people who work in noisy environments.

B Ear protectors used by some pilots muffle noises by reflecting and absorbing them.

check your UNDERSTANDING

1. Compare and contrast constructive and destructive interference.
2. Explain how it is possible for one wave to cancel another with a resulting amplitude of zero. Use a diagram in your answer if you like.
3. **Apply** In some theaters, you may find that there are certain areas where the sound is either much softer or muffled in some way. What do you think causes this?

17-4 Sound as Waves

Looking at Sound

Have you ever felt a vibrating loudspeaker on your stereo? If you are able to touch the cone of the speaker, you will feel it move in and out in time with the music. This in-and-out movement creates the compressions and rarefactions in the air that are characteristic of longitudinal waves. Under normal conditions you can't see sound. However, the following Find Out activity will allow you to see some of its effects.

Section Objectives

- Demonstrate sound as a wave.
- Explain the Doppler effect.

Key Terms

Doppler effect

Find Out! ACTIVITY

Can you see sound?

You saw how sound waves could make rice grains jump. How could you see the vibrations in the rubber sheet? With light, of course!

What To Do

Use the same container that you used in the Find Out activity on page 543. Make sure both ends are open.

1. Now, cut a piece of balloon large enough to fit over one end. Stretch the balloon over the end and hold it in place with a rubber band.
2. Next, glue a small mirror slightly off the center of the balloon.
3. After the glue has dried, hold the open end of the container to your mouth or a loudspeaker.
4. Have a classmate reflect a flashlight beam off the mirror to a flat surface.
5. Explore the effect of sounds on the patterns .

Conclude and Apply

1. Draw the patterns and label them. What happened to the reflected spot on the wall when a loud sound went into the container?
2. How did the reflections change as you changed the sounds?

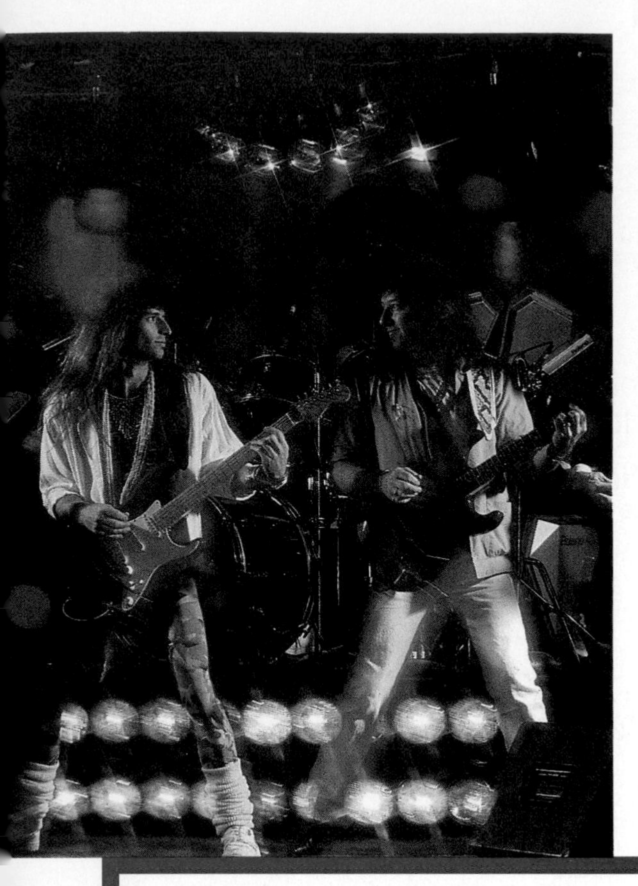

Figure 17-13

If you listen to music at high levels of volume for long periods of time, you could damage your hearing. Many rock musicians have some hearing loss as a result of their exposure to loud music. Many musicians wear some form of ear protection while on stage.

The patterns you observed were produced by the compressions and rarefactions of air moving the balloon. As the compressions caused the balloon to bulge, the mirror was tilted, and the light reflected in one direction. Then, when the rarefactions were behind the balloon, the mirror was tilted the other way, and the reflection moved in another direction. Thus, the pattern traced on the wall was a rough picture of the balloon's vibration and the sound waves that caused it.

Imagine that you could do the Find Out activity on page 559 at a rock concert like the one in **Figure 17-13.** What would the pattern be like?

Filling a Room with Sound

Symphony Hall in Boston, built in 1898, was designed by a professor of physics who had studied acoustics. It is considered one of the greatest music halls of all time.

Symphony Hall

Acoustics, the science of sound, is used in designing buildings such as concert halls and recording studios. Imagine sound waves coming out of your stereo speaker, like rings in the water where you've tossed in a pebble. When sound waves strike a surface such as a wall, floor, or ceiling, some of the sound is absorbed, and some is reflected. A hard surface reflects more sound. Soft materials, such as drapes or a carpet, absorb more sound.

A room that absorbs too much sound is acoustically dead. The sound in a room with some reflections is more pleasing to the ear. As people also

Properties of Sound Waves

For humans, a low sound will have a frequency from about 20 to about 200 hertz whereas the highest sounds you can hear are about 15 000 to 20 000 hertz. You would hear 20 hertz as a low rumble, such as thunder.

The highest note on the piano is less than 4000 hertz. Rich musical sounds, however, do not have only one frequency, but contain frequencies that are much higher than 4000 hertz. Elephants can hear frequencies much lower than 20 hertz. Bats, on the other hand, locate their prey with frequencies as high as 120 000 hertz.

Figure 17-14

People and various animals have limits to the sound frequencies they can detect. Dog whistles generate sounds at such a high frequency that dogs can hear them but people cannot.

absorb sound, a large audience reduces reflections.

Reverberation

Have you ever shouted when you were in a tunnel? You hear many echoes or sound reflections. Sometimes the echoes last for almost a second. The echoing sound is called reverberation. The time it takes for the sound to die out is called reverberation time.

An auditorium or concert hall must be carefully designed to have the proper reverberation time. Many concert halls built in the 19th century have better acoustics than modern halls. The halls were usually long and narrow. In a narrow hall, you hear the sound coming from the source first, and then reflected off the walls. The reverberation was correct for music played by an orchestra. The halls were smaller, too. With a smaller audience, less sound was absorbed.

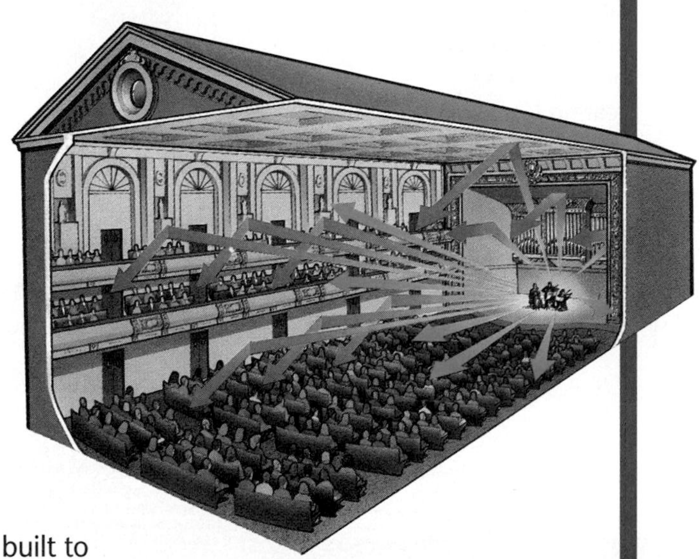

Modern halls are built to hold more people. They are usually built wide to provide more emergency exits. Ceilings are lower, which also affects the sound. In the older halls, the reverberation makes you feel surrounded by sound. Acoustic experts today are taking their cues from the older builders.

You Try It!

Turn stereo speakers so that the sound reflects off the ceiling, then off the opposing walls. Describe the differences.

Dangerous Sounds

The louder the sound, the greater the amplitude of the wave. In fact, some sounds can hurt you. Some rock concerts are so loud that the musicians have damaged their hearing. Even the spectators should be careful, as over-exposure to loud noise can destroy their hearing. Sometimes people doubt this because the loss of hearing may not show up for many years.

High amplitude compressions can cause your eardrum to rupture. When scar tissue grows over the split, the eardrum can no longer reproduce sound accurately. It is like mending a drumhead with tape.

Secondly, inside your ear are tiny nerve fibers surrounded by fluid. When a compression caused by a loud sound travels through the fluid in your ear, it can damage or destroy the nerve fibers. If enough fibers are destroyed, hearing is permanently damaged because the nerves do not grow back.

Some machines, such as air compressors and jet engines, are also very loud, and it is important that workers using them wear ear protection. It is the loudness or amplitude that creates the large compressions. Sounds of low or high frequency are equally damaging.

Figure 17-15

When you play a personal stereo or radio, the sound goes in all directions, including your ears. When you wear earphones, nearly all the sound goes directly into your ears. The sound levels inside your ears can be very high. Listening to loud music too long can cause hearing loss.

The Doppler Effect

You've probably been at a railroad crossing when a train passed by. Did you notice that the train's horn seemed to be higher in pitch as it approached and then was lower as it went away? The apparent change in pitch of a sound as the source moves with respect to the observer is called the **Doppler effect.** It applies to all waves, including light and sound.

If you were on the train, you wouldn't hear the Doppler effect. To people on the train, the horn would seem to have the same frequency at all times. How can two people listening to the same horn hear different frequencies?

The motion of the train as it moves toward you causes the sound waves to be squeezed together. As each compression is sent out, the train moves closer, and the next compression gets a head start. Thus, the compressions in front of the train are closer together, as shown in **Figure 17-16.** This causes a higher frequency to reach your ear. What do you think happens as the train passes you? Think about it. Imagine that the frequency of the sound is 100 hertz or 100 vibrations per second. Now imagine that the train is moving at 20 meters per second. That means that 5 compressions are sent out from the horn every meter that the train moves.

What about the operator and passengers on the train? Do they hear the Doppler effect? No, they hear the same frequency all the time because they and the sound are moving together.

The Doppler effect is more than just an interesting phenomenon.

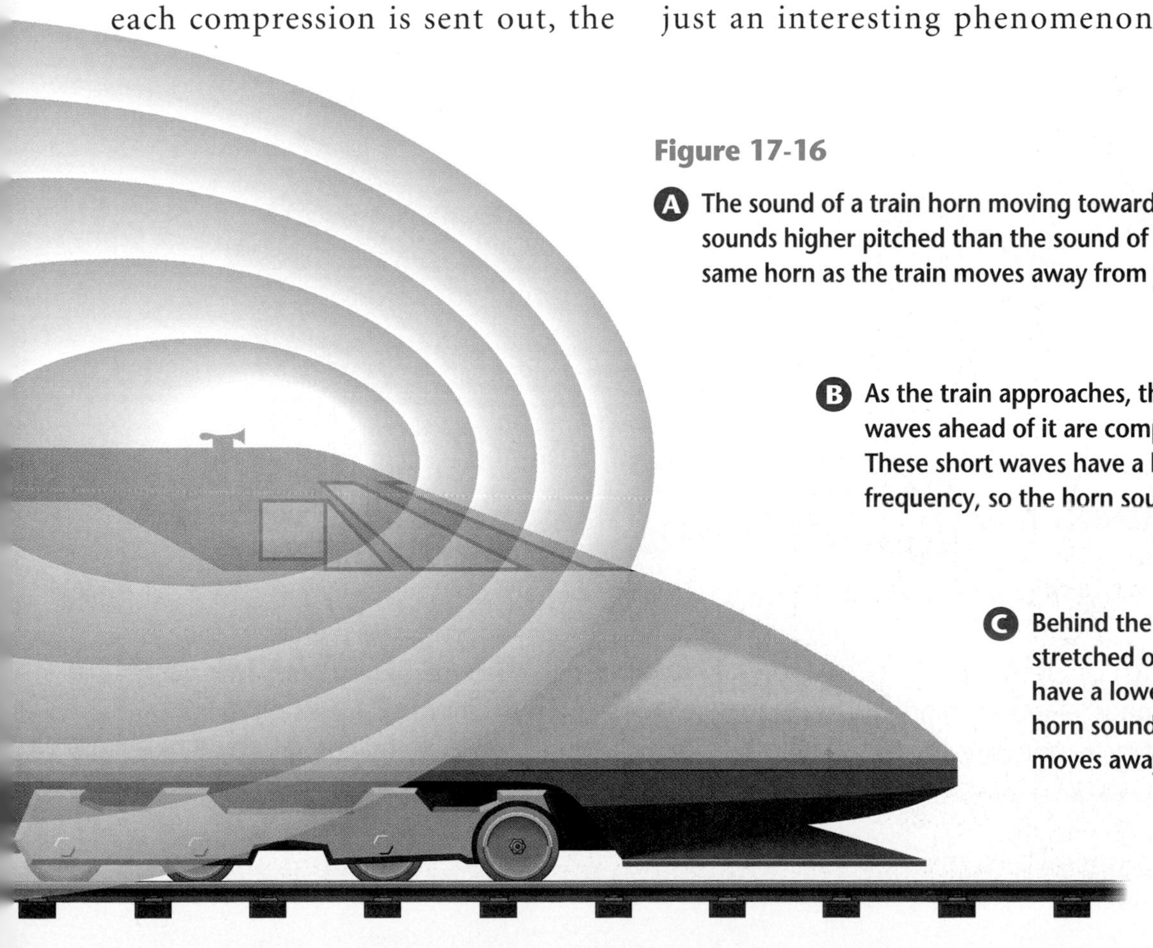

Figure 17-16

A The sound of a train horn moving toward you sounds higher pitched than the sound of the same horn as the train moves away from you.

B As the train approaches, the sound waves ahead of it are compressed. These short waves have a high frequency, so the horn sounds high.

C Behind the train, the waves are stretched out. These longer waves have a lower frequency, so the horn sounds lower as the train moves away from you.

Some radars (radio detection and ranging) use the effect to find the speed of objects. One use you are probably familiar with is the Doppler radar that police use to identify speeding motorists.

As you've seen in this chapter, there's a lot more to waves than water splashing up on the beach. As you go to school or just walk around the neighborhood, identify the waves you observe and how they affect your life.

Figure 17-17

A If a police officer using Doppler radar equipment beams a radio wave of a specific frequency at a stationary automobile, a wave of the same frequency bounces back.

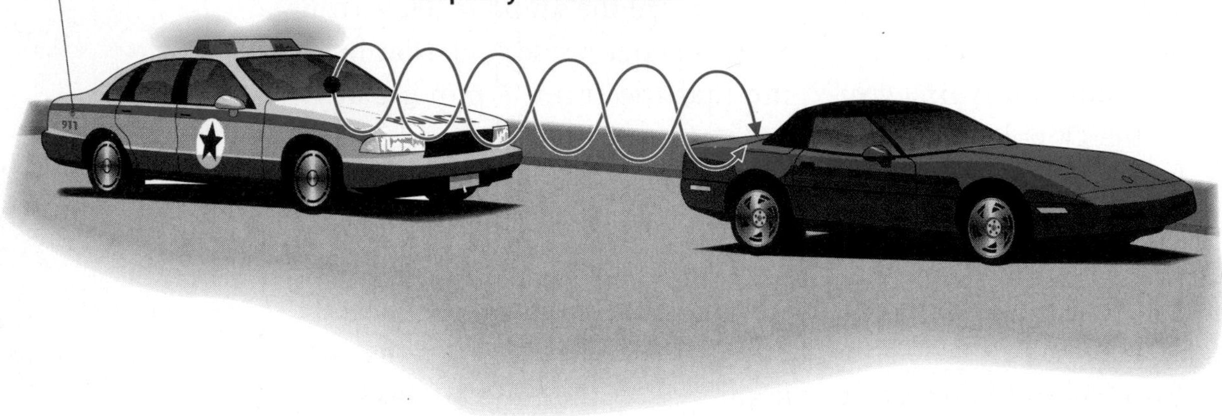

B If the officer beams the wave at a moving automobile, the wave that returns to the equipment will be of a different frequency. The greater the difference in frequency between outgoing and incoming waves, the greater the speed of the automobile.

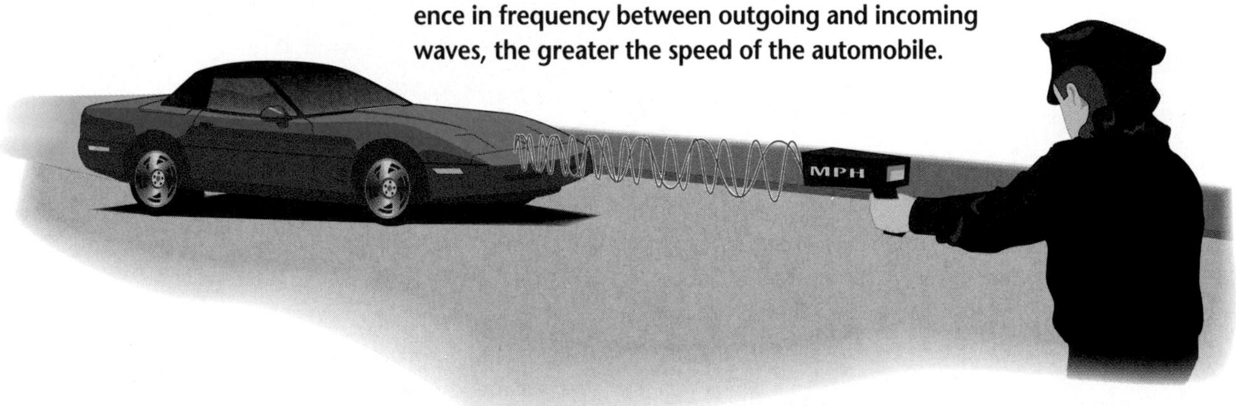

check your UNDERSTANDING

1. How can you demonstrate that sound is a wave?
2. When will the pitch of a racing car engine be the highest—approaching you, going away, or directly opposite you? Explain your answer.
3. **Apply** Weather forecasters use Doppler radar to detect storms. How would a violent thunderstorm reflect radar waves differently than from rain when the winds are calm?

Technology Connection: Wave Energy

The first wave-powered electricity generating station powered by the ocean was opened in the mid-1980s on the coast of Norway. Since then, other power stations have opened in England and Scotland.

The amplitude of a wave determines how much energy it can carry. The energy contained in waves comes from the wind. How hard the wind blows, how long the wind blows, and the distance it blows across the water all help determine wave amplitude. Waves grow taller as they absorb more of the wind's energy. Every time waves double in height, their energy is quadrupled.

The Salter Duck

One well-known wave-powered device is called the Salter duck, named for its inventor, Dr. Stephen Salter of Scotland. The device looks like a duck bobbing on the water. It uses a hydraulic pump that moves on the action of the waves, pumping fluid into a turbine-driven generator that produces electricity. Salter has built duck models, but estimates indicate that at least five million pounds of concrete would have to be poured for a full-scale generating plant. Salter is working on the problem of size.

The oscillating water column (OWC) also uses wave power. The device traps a column of water inside a chamber that is moved up and down by wave action. It compresses air at the top of the chamber and forces the air into a turbine, which turns a generator. The OWC must be built on a huge scale to produce a substantial amount of electricity.

Scientists estimate that wave-powered stations could provide at least ten percent of the world's energy needs. Inventors and investors will continue to pursue the power of the ocean wave.

Science Journal

How do you think this emerging technology will change the world? *In your Science Journal,* tell what you think are the advantages and disadvantages.

Dangerous To Your Ears

You get up in the morning and turn on the radio. You travel in busy traffic. At school, the halls are noisy, and loud bells ring. After school, you play your stereo or mix a milkshake in the blender. It's just an average day for your eardrums. Noise pollution is so much a part of our everyday lives, we hardly notice it's there.

When sound waves reach the ear, the air pressure pushes against the eardrum. The vibration is passed to microscopic nerve cells, and then to the brain where it is interpreted as sound. The loudness of sound depends on the size of the pressure vibrations. The loudness is measured in decibels. The louder the sound, the higher the decibel level. For example, the sound level of a quiet library is 30 decibels, while that of loud rock music might be 110 decibels.

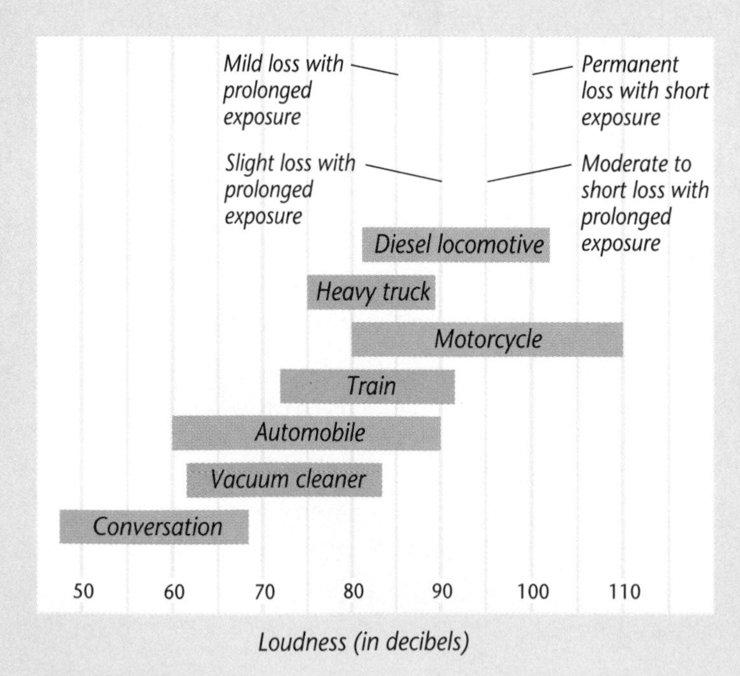

Noise All Around Us

Many people become deaf from long exposure to loud noise. The graph on the left shows the average sound levels for several common items. The graph also shows what kind of hearing damage is caused by exposure to high sound levels.

The way noise affects people's behavior may be as important as the damage it does to hearing. Acoustical sociologists and other experts who specialize in hearing study noise to see how it influences physical and mental health. Noise pollution is all around us. We may adapt, but our bodies and minds still experience stress from the extreme noise.

People often may react physically to noise pollution. The Acoustical Society of America released a study that said people who live near airports are more likely to suffer from physical problems such as heart disease or high blood pressure. People who live in noisy neighborhoods complain of increased anxiety and sleeplessness. When too many sound waves assault the eardrums, the brain cannot process all the information at once. This may

explain why people in noisy environments say they are unable to think. Studies on noise pollution have shown that in noisy neighborhoods, people feel more isolated and afraid. A person's appetite may be lowered when there is a lot of noise, which may be why it is harder to enjoy a meal in the school cafeteria. There are also more traffic accidents at very noisy intersections.

Noise Control

The Environmental Protection Agency (EPA) established the Office of Noise Abatement and granted it powers to regulate sources of noise pollution by passing the Noise Control Act in 1972. However, the Office of Noise Abatement was closed in 1982 due to government budget cuts. Most experts agree that passing laws on noise control is the most important step toward controlling noise pollution. In recent years, most noise laws have been passed at the local level of government. But that may be changing.

The U.S. Department of Transportation and the Federal Aviation Administration recently released new policy guidelines to control airport noise. The policy requires airlines to replace older aircraft with newer, quieter models. The policy also restricts local communities from imposing their own noise control laws. The airlines have until the year 2001 to comply with the new regulations, so local areas may have to live with the noisier aircraft until then.

Noise pollution activists are not happy with the new policy. With government offices getting involved in noise pollution again, noise control may be the next big wave for environmentalists.

Acoustical physicists study the production, reflection, and absorption of sound. Many are employed by the auto industries and other transportation companies. They study ways to improve or control noise, sounds, and vibration.

You Try It!

Are you breaking any local laws against noise pollution? Is there a local law in your area about playing music in public, such as on a bus or on the beach? Find out by writing to your local health department or the mayor's office and ask about local ordinances against noise.

Teens in SCIENCE

Riding a Musical Wave

Jason Cobb always loved computers. In the seventh grade, he had his first science lesson on sound. For his class project, Jason wrote a computer program about how sound works. Thus began his adventure as a computer music composer.

Programming Sound

After his first sound project, Jason studied programming languages on his own. Now he is an intense young man whose conversation is peppered with computer music lingo. Jason composes music on a personal computer with a keyboard, mouse, synthesizer, and stereo system.

Jason writes music in the language of sound waves. Each key he presses on the keyboard represents a different musical sound. The sounds appear as graphic pictures, called waveforms, on his computer screen. The waveforms let him "see what the music looks like." Jason edits sounds and puts together simple waveforms into complex compositions. He stores his compositions on a disc until he's ready to convert them to audio tape.

The technical wizardry is in the synthesizer, a musical instrument that produces sounds electronically.

MIDI

Playing the synthesizer allows Jason to determine the loudness, pitch, and tone of the sounds. The synthesizer uses Musical Instrument Digital Interface (MIDI). MIDI is a standard language that connects computers to electronic instruments. MIDI converts the numbers in the computer into forms that the instruments can use to produce sound. With MIDI and a synthesizer, Jason can change the pitch, tempo, or tone of a variety of musical sounds.

For all his technical mastery, what Jason produces is melodic music. His dream is to be an electronic musician, creating computerized compositions that the public and other electronic artists will appreciate. Does he have an equipment wish list? "Are you kidding?" he asks. "Of course, but what I really want costs a million dollars, so I'll have to wait awhile to buy it."

You Try It!

Can you tell the difference between music that is computer-generated and music from traditional instruments? Next time you're listening to the radio, see if you can identify each type of music.

chapter 17 REVIEWING MAIN IDEAS

Science Journal

Review the statements below about the big ideas presented in this chapter, and answer the questions. Then, re-read your answers to the Did You Ever Wonder questions at the beginning of the chapter. *In your Science Journal,* write a paragraph about how your understanding of the big ideas in the chapter has changed.

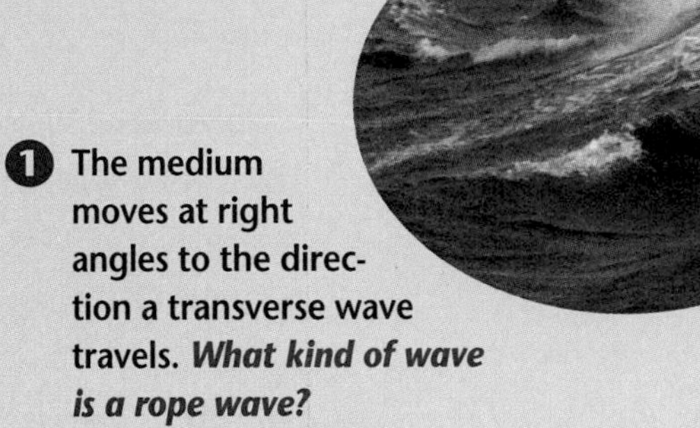

1 The medium moves at right angles to the direction a transverse wave travels. ***What kind of wave is a rope wave?***

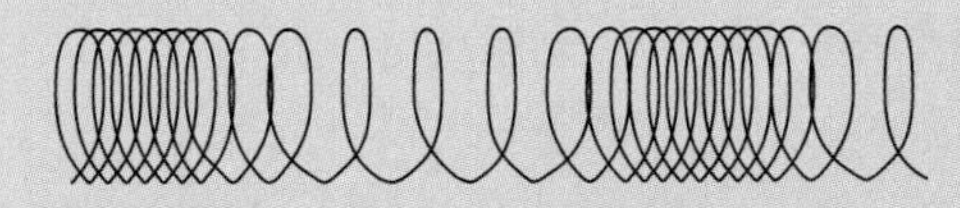

2 The medium moves in the direction of a longitudinal wave. ***What are the parts of a longitudinal wave?***

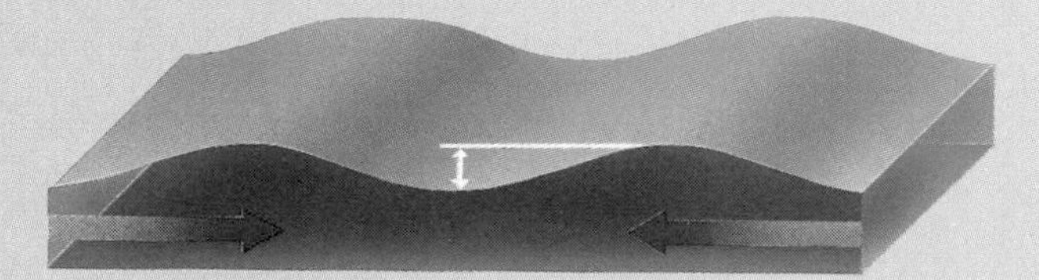

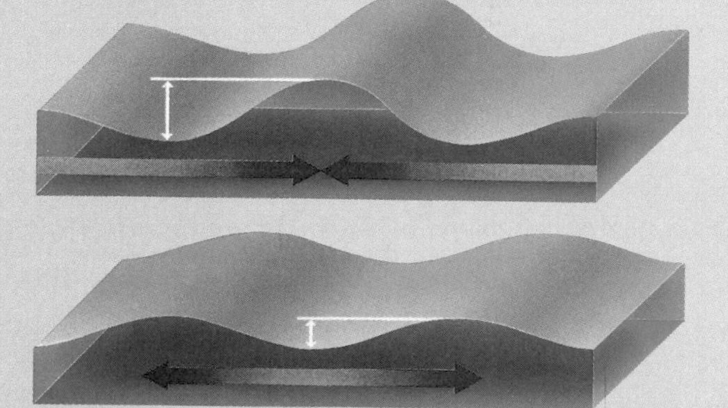

3 In the same medium, as frequency increases, wavelength decreases. ***Arrange in order of decreasing speed of transmission: plastic foam, air, wood.***

4 As waves cross, their crests and troughs add and subtract to form constructive and destructive interference patterns. ***What do the waves look like at the point where they interact?***

5 The Doppler effect is an apparent change of frequency and pitch of a sound as an object moves with respect to another. ***Why is the sound of an approaching train higher than when the train is actually passing you?***

chapter 17
CHAPTER REVIEW

Using Key Science Terms

amplitude	longitudinal waves
crest	transverse waves
Doppler effect	trough
interference	wavelength

For each set of terms below, choose the one term that does not belong and explain why it does not belong.

1. amplitude, frequency, wavelength, crest
2. crests, troughs, speed, interference
3. rarefaction, transverse waves, compression, longitudinal waves
4. trough, transverse waves, longitudinal waves, crests

Understanding Ideas

Answer the following questions in your Journal *using complete sentences.*

1. The highest wave ever measured on the open ocean was over 34 meters from trough to crest. What characteristic of the wave could this give you a measure of? Explain.
2. Lying in your room at night you hear a large truck out on the freeway. It approaches from a distance, passes your home, and goes on. The changing pitch of the truck's sound is an example of what?
3. Crests and troughs are properties of transverse waves. What are the corresponding properties of longitudinal waves?
4. Does a surfer move in the same direction as the wave disturbance? Explain.

Developing Skills

Use your understanding of the concepts developed in this chapter to answer each of the following questions.

1. **Concept Mapping** Make a cycle concept map showing how the water level changes as a wave passes a certain point. Use the following terms: *crest, trough, rest position, rest position.*
2. **Making and Using Graphs** The graph shows the noise level of several common situations. Hearing damage is caused by extended exposure to sound over 85 decibels. Which of the sounds on the graph could damage your hearing?

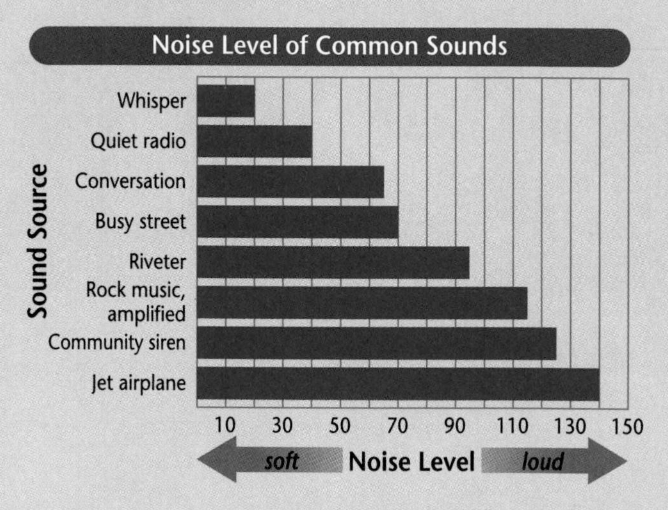

3. **Interpreting Data** Destructive interference occurs when the crest of a wave of amplitude 2.5 m meets the trough of a wave of amplitude 1.7 m. What is the resulting displacement at the point where the interference occurs?

chapter 17

CHAPTER REVIEW

Critical Thinking

In your Journal, *answer each of the following questions.*

1. Write a brief paragraph that explains how your knowledge of waves might make you a better musician.
2. Suppose that as sound waves move from one medium to another, their velocity doubles, but their frequency remains the same. What happens to the wavelength?
3. A bus driver is rounding a curve approaching a railroad crossing. She hears a train's whistle and then hears the whistle's pitch become lower. What assumption can she make about what she will see when she rounds the curve and looks at the crossing?

Problem Solving

Read the following problem and discuss your answer in a brief paragraph.

You've just been given a new stereo system for your birthday, and you want to set it up in your room to get the best possible sound.

1. Draw and discuss three separate setups for the speakers, showing the direction of the sound from each speaker, how to get the best stereo effect, and possibilities for destructive interference—dead spots. Keep in mind that sound will also be reflected from the walls.
2. Your baby sister's crib is against the wall in the room next to yours. How would that affect the placement of your speakers?

CONNECTING IDEAS

Discuss each of the following in a brief paragraph.

1. **Theme—Systems and Interactions** People living near airports sometimes report that their windows rattle as a plane passes overhead. Explain what is happening in these cases.
2. **Theme—Energy** Explain why waves on a lake are larger on a windy day than on a calm day.
3. **Science and Society** There are tapes available of sounds such as babbling brooks, gentle rain, and bird calls. Why could these tapes help calm people who live in urban areas?
4. **A Closer Look** You're in charge of converting a gymnasium to a lecture hall. What can you do to be sure the audience noises do not drown out the lecturer?
5. **Earth Science Connection** If a seismic wave in one area is reflected back in less time than in another area, what might be true of the density in the first area compared to the second?

CHAPTER 18

Earthquakes and Volcanoes

Did you ever wonder...

- **What happens when an earthquake strikes underwater?**
- **How volcanoes form?**
- **Why some buildings crumble in an earthquake while others remain standing?**

Science Journal

Before you begin to study about earthquakes and volcanoes, think about the answers to these questions and answer them *in your Science Journal.* When you finish the chapter, compare your write-up with what you have learned.

Change is always taking place on Earth. The sun appears to change position in the sky. Seasons change. The weather changes. Some changes, such as the carving of a canyon by a river, take place so slowly that you may not notice the change in your lifetime. Other changes, however, are sudden and dramatic, catching everyone's attention.

Among the most powerful and frightening types of change that take place on Earth are earthquakes and volcanic eruptions. Earthquakes move the very ground you walk on. Volcanoes can blast tons of rock and smoke into the air. This chapter will explain why these fascinating and destructive changes occur.

▶ ***In the activity on the next page, you will explore what an earthquake feels like.***

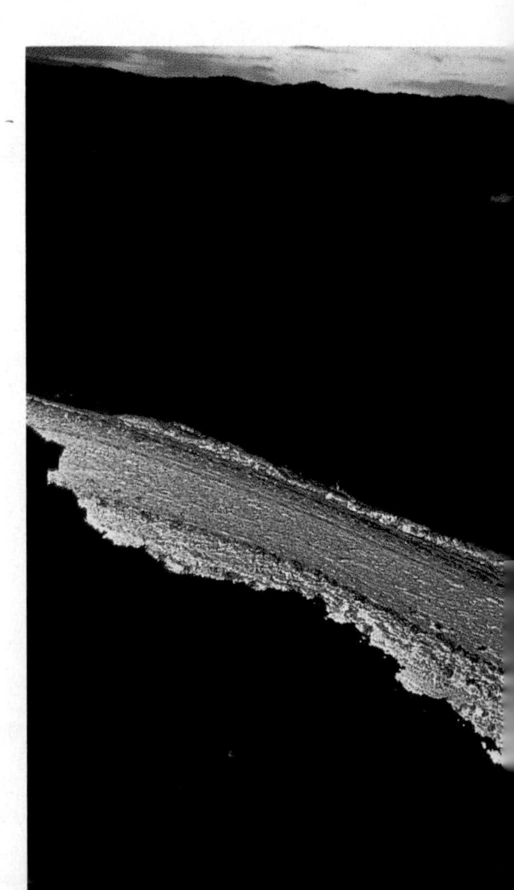

Kilauea Volcanoes National Park in Hawaii

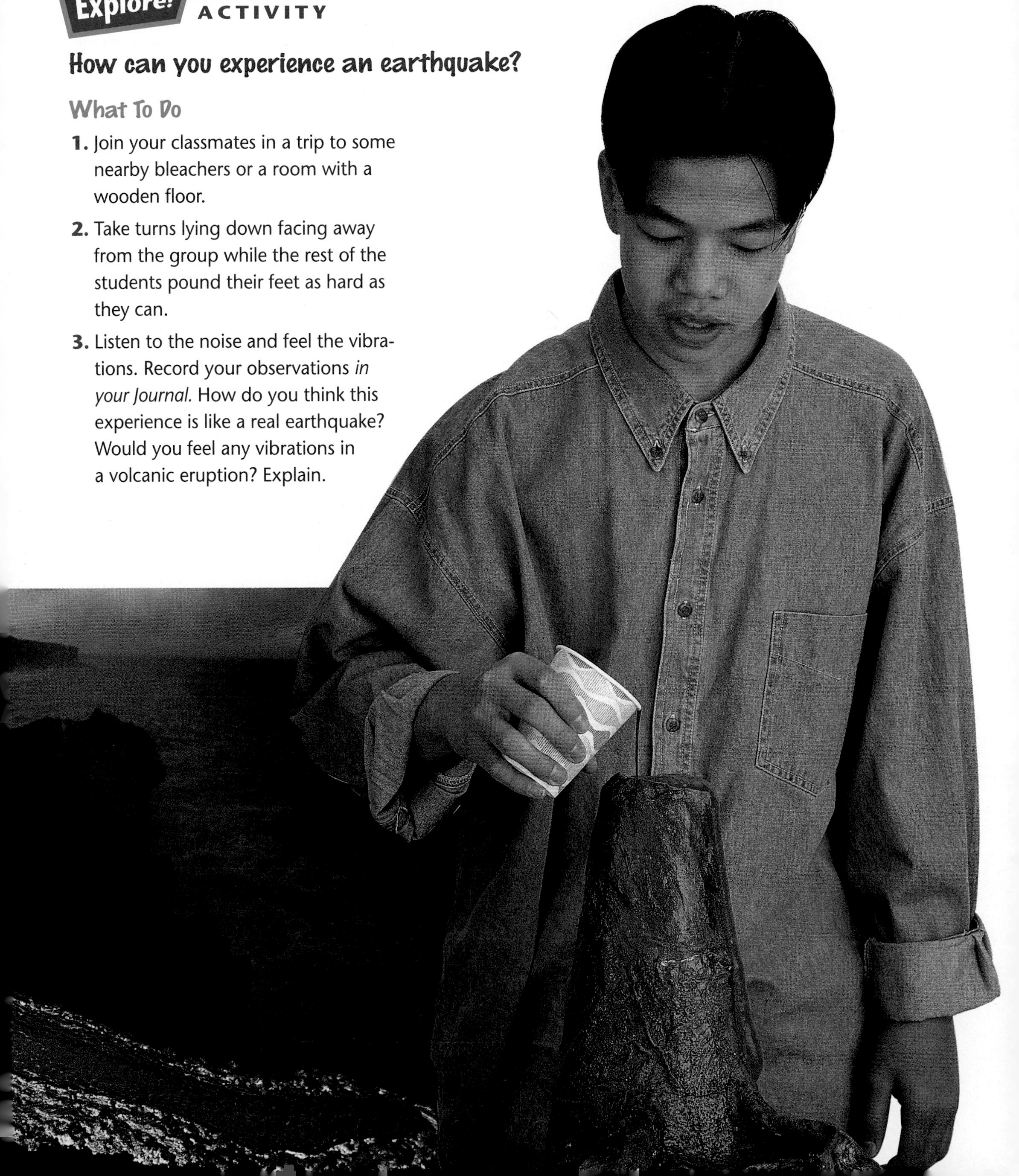

Explore! ACTIVITY

How can you experience an earthquake?

What To Do

1. Join your classmates in a trip to some nearby bleachers or a room with a wooden floor.
2. Take turns lying down facing away from the group while the rest of the students pound their feet as hard as they can.
3. Listen to the noise and feel the vibrations. Record your observations *in your Journal.* How do you think this experience is like a real earthquake? Would you feel any vibrations in a volcanic eruption? Explain.

Earthquakes, Volcanoes, and You

Section Objectives

- Explain how waves at Earth's surface generated by earthquakes cause structures to collapse.
- Make models of volcanic cones and describe the types of eruptions that produce them.

Key Terms

magma
lava

Vibrations in Earth

Have you ever felt the ground quake beneath your feet? Or seen the fiery eruption of a volcano? You've probably seen pictures of the destruction caused by earthquakes in magazines or watched volcanic eruptions on television.

People have long wondered about earthquakes and volcanoes. What happens when unseen events inside Earth unleash such tremendous amounts of energy that the very ground vibrates? In the following activity, you will construct a model and observe material when it vibrates.

Explore! ACTIVITY

How do vibrations travel through a material?

What To Do

1. Pour water into a rectangular pan until it is about three-quarters full. Place a table tennis ball on the surface of the water near the middle of the pan.
2. Near one end of the pan, place a pencil in the water and move it up and down, disturbing the water. The waves you create are vibrations moving through the water.
3. Observe the motion of the ball. Does the ball move toward either end of the pan?

The waves you produced in the Explore activity above are similar to one type of wave generated at Earth's surface by an earthquake. However, earthquake waves move through the solid earth.

What would happen to a building if the ground beneath it moved in a way similar to the water? Keep this picture in your mind as you learn what it is like to experience an earthquake.

Figure 18-1
The large arrow in this diagram indicates the direction of waves generated by an earthquake. The small elliptical arrows and the small side-to-side arrow indicate the motion of particles in Earth's surface as waves pass through.

A When the first surface wave arrives at a building, the wave lifts first one side of the building, and then the other side. The building is put into motion similar to that of the table tennis ball in the Explore activity.

B When surface waves pass through them, the structures vibrate. This vibration can cause buildings to crumble and fall.

■ Experiencing an Earthquake

An earthquake occurs when part of the solid earth below the surface suddenly shifts. This action produces waves like the ones you caused when you made waves in the pan of water. The sudden shifting in Earth causes rocks and soil at the surface to vibrate. These vibrations travel out in all directions from this surface spot. They create movement similar to that caused by the water waves. Buildings and other structures on Earth then move as in **Figure 18-1**. When the waves pass through them, the structures vibrate. This movement can cause buildings to collapse.

Earthquakes can cause a great deal of destruction. Northridge, California, was dramatically rocked by an earthquake in 1994. When the earthquake hit, vibrations moved through the city in a series of waves that threw people from their beds as they slept and could be seen moving up and down, much like waves in the ocean. Standing in a building in Northridge during the quake would have been like standing in a rowboat on a stormy sea. If you had been there, you would have heard a sound like hundreds of locomotives rushing through the city. Many buildings and other structures could not withstand the strain, and they crumbled. Although 61 people died, this is fewer than expected for an earthquake of its strength.

Think about what would happen to your school if an earthquake similar to the Northridge quake struck nearby. What would happen to books and other objects on shelves inside the building? What would happen to the building itself?

Although earthquakes tend to occur in specific areas, they can happen almost anywhere. Some of the most powerful earthquakes ever to occur in the United States took place in New Madrid, Missouri, in late 1811 and early 1812.

Observing Volcanoes

Are there any volcanoes near where you live? If not, how would you feel if one suddenly began forming in your neighborhood? Probably like the farmer in Mexico who went out to work in his cornfield one day in 1943. He discovered hot smoke and ash rising from an opening in the ground that had formed in his field.

The farmer was witnessing the birth of a volcano. In less than 24 hours, a hill 40 meters high stood where the land had once been flat. By the end of a week, the hill was more than 160 meters high and still forming. The volcano, called Parícutin, eventually reached a height of 412 meters, and its base covered an area larger than 16 000 football fields.

Figure 18-2

A **Magma is forced slowly upward to Earth's surface through cracks in rock or by melting through rock.**

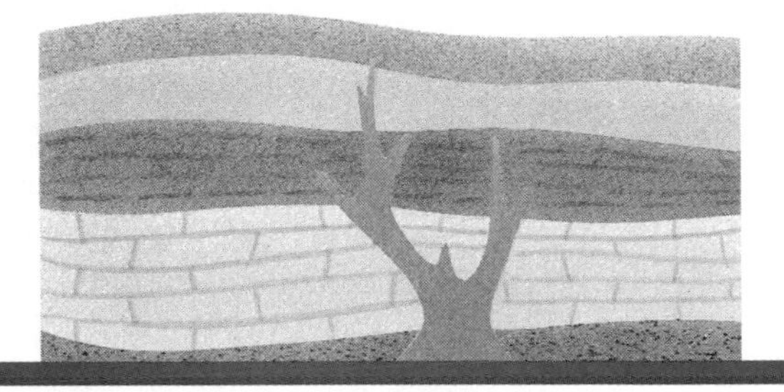

The Great San Francisco Earthquake and Fire

When powerful earthquakes strike, they can break gas lines, short-circuit electrical wires, overturn stoves, and crack chimneys. Any of these problems may lead to a fire. When a gas line is broken, all it takes is a spark to start a fire.

One of the worst earthquakes of the twentieth century struck San Francisco on April 18, 1906. About 80 percent of the damage was caused by the

The earthquake destroyed the San Francisco City Hall, pictured here on the left.

But almost nine years from that day in 1943, Parícutin stopped erupting. The volcano, pictured in **Figure 18-4B** on page 581, has been inactive ever since.

Like Parícutin, all volcanoes originate when hot, melted rock material is forced upward to Earth's surface by denser surrounding rock. This molten rock material beneath Earth's surface is called **magma**. Once it reaches the surface, it is called **lava**. **Figure 18-2** shows how magma from Earth's interior forms a volcano near its surface. What conditions deep inside Earth might cause this rock material to become melted in the first place?

B At the surface, the eruption of magma—now called lava— ash, and volcanic rocks can build to form a cone-shaped mountain.

C As the lava and other volcanic materials continue to flow from the opening, the volcanic cone grows.

fires that followed the earthquake, and only 20 percent by the earthquake itself.

The violent tremors that had shifted the ground—as much as 20 feet in places—had broken many water mains (huge pipes) for the city's 80-million-gallon reservoir system. This left fire fighters nearly powerless to stop the blaze that roared through the city for three days and nights.

After trying one fire hydrant after another, the city's desperate fire fighters finally found just enough water to help tame the leaping flames—but not until several hundred people had lost their lives.

The 1906 earthquake and fire destroyed most of the city's business district and a number of residential areas.

Many businesses and homes collapsed during the earthquake, like the hotel in the photo at left. Many more buildings were destroyed later by fire. The photo above shows just a small portion of the destruction.

What Do You Think?

If you were in an earthquake in which the water mains were broken, where might you look for safe water to use until the pipes could be repaired?

DESIGN YOUR OWN
INVESTIGATION

Locating Active Volcanoes

Volcanoes form when hot, melted rock material is forced upward to Earth's surface. As the melted rock moves inside Earth, vibrations occur, which are felt as earthquakes. How would you determine whether active volcanoes are located near earthquake epicenters?

Preparation

Problem

Is there a connection between the locations of active volcanoes and the locations of recent earthquakes?

Form a Hypothesis

As a group, discuss the areas where earthquakes and volcanoes are commonly located. Then form a hypothesis about whether you expect to see a relationship between the locations of active volcanoes and the locations of earthquake epicenters.

Objectives

- Plot the locations of several active volcanoes.
- Describe patterns of distribution for volcanoes and earthquake epicenters.
- Relate the locations of active volcanoes to the locations of recent earthquakes.

Materials

world map (Appendix H)
tracing paper

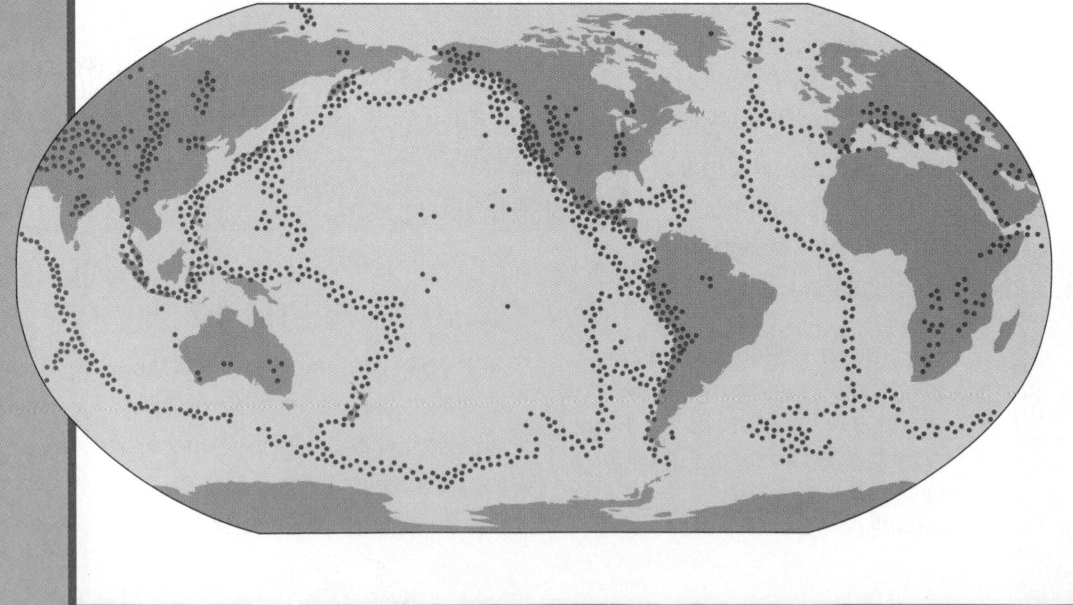

Each dot on this diagram represents an earthquake. Eighty percent of earthquakes occur along the "Ring of Fire," a band of volcanic activity that circles the Pacific Ocean.

DESIGN YOUR OWN INVESTIGATION

Plan the Experiment

1 As a group, agree upon a way to test your hypothesis. Write down what you will do at each step of your test.

2 Examine the volcano latitude and longitude chart. What is the best way to plot the data on a tracing of Earth's surface?

3 Examine the map of earthquake epicenters on page 578. How will you compare your data with this map?

Check the Plan

Discuss and decide upon the following points and write them down.

1 As a group, decide how you will summarize your data.

2 How will you determine whether certain facts or conditions indicate a correlation between the locations of active volcanoes and earthquake epicenters?

3 Make sure your teacher approves your experiment before you proceed.

4 Carry our your experiment. Record your observations.

Volcano	Latitude	Longitude
#1	64° N	19° W
#2	28° N	34° E
#3	43° S	172° E
#4	35° N	136° E
#5	18° S	68° W
#6	25° S	114° W
#7	20° N	155° W
#8	54° N	167° W
#9	16° N	122° E
#10	28° N	17° W
#11	15° N	43° E
#12	6° N	75° W
#13	64° S	158° E
#14	38° S	78° E
#15	21° S	56° E
#16	38° N	26° E
#17	7° S	13° W
#18	2° S	102° E
#19	38° N	30° W
#20	54° N	159° E

Analyze and Conclude

1. **Interpret Scientific Illustrations** Describe any patterns of distribution formed by active volcanoes.
2. **Interpret Scientific Illustrations** Describe any patterns of distribution formed by earthquake epicenters.
3. **Compare and Contrast** How did the patterns that you observed in the distribution of volcanoes compare with the locations of earthquake epicenters?

Going Further

How are the locations of volcanoes and earthquake epicenters related to Earth's geographic features?

Eruptions

Figure 18-3

A In the quiet eruption shown on the left, lava oozes onto the surface of Earth and flows downhill, often quite slowly.

B In the more explosive eruption shown on the right, lava, gas, dust, ash, and volcanic rocks may be sent forcefully into the air.

Any time volcanic material reaches the surface of Earth, we call the event an eruption. However, not all volcanic eruptions are the same. They range from quiet lava flows to violent explosions that send lava, gases, rock, ash, and dust several kilometers into the atmosphere. The figure on the left in **Figure 18-3A** shows a quiet eruption in which lava is flowing slowly onto Earth's surface and downhill. The figure on the right in **Figure 18-3B** shows the explosive eruption of a volcano.

Different kinds of eruptions produce differently shaped volcanoes. Do the following Find Out activity to discover two of these shapes.

Find Out! ACTIVITY

What are two types of volcanic shapes?

What To Do

1. Create models of two volcanoes. First, pour 1 cup of a substance like sand or sugar into the center of a paper plate from a height of about 50 cm.
2. Then, prepare a thick mixture of plaster of paris and water and pour it into the center of a second paper plate from a height of about 20 cm.
3. Compare the shapes of your volcano models. Use a protractor to measure the slope angles of the sides of the two models. What differences have you discovered in the two forms of models produced?

Conclude and Apply

1. Of the materials that erupt from volcanoes—lava, gases, dust, ash, and rock—which do you think form volcanoes with gentle slopes?
2. Which materials probably form volcanoes with steep slopes?

Although no two volcanoes are exactly the same shape, there are three basic shapes of volcanoes. You discovered two of the shapes in the Find Out activity. The third shape forms from a combination of quiet

Figure 18-4

A Shield volcanoes are broad with gently sloping sides. In a quiet eruption, dense lava flows onto Earth's surface and spreads out over a large area in fairly flat layers. Over time, these layers build up to form a shield volcano. Kilauea in Hawaii is the largest active shield volcano in the world.

B Cinder cone volcanoes, like this one in Mexico called Parícutin, form in explosive eruptions. In an explosive eruption, gases and rock fragments may be hurled many kilometers into the air. These rock fragments which range in size from powdery volcanic dust to large lumps of lava called bombs, fall to the ground and form a steep-sided, loosely packed mountain.

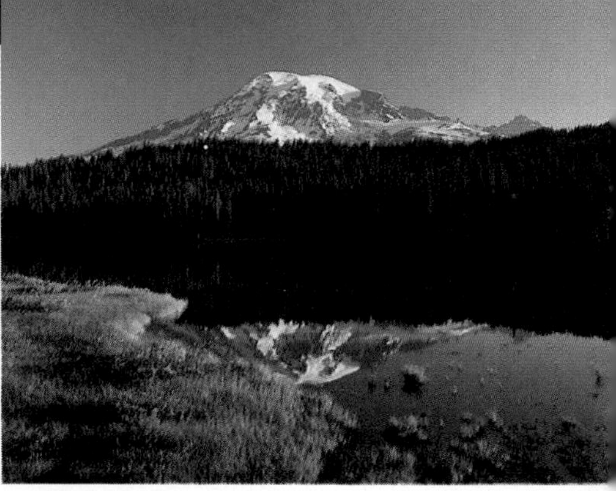

C Composite volcanoes, such as Mount Ranier, are produced by alternating quiet and explosive eruptions. Their sides are formed of layers of lava alternated with layers of cinders and ash. How does a composite volcano's shape compare to those of the other volcanoes?

and explosive eruptions. These are common in the northwestern United States. Study **Figures 18-4 A-C** to find out how the shapes are made.

Powerful and potentially dangerous earthquakes and volcanic eruptions originate deep below Earth's surface. In the next section, you'll discover some of the effects they have on us at the surface.

1. Explain why buildings and other structures crumble during earthquakes.
2. Name and describe the three forms of volcanoes and the type of eruption associated with each.
3. **Apply** Why might a building that is made of flexible material like wood withstand the effects of an earthquake better than a building that is made of a rigid material like brick?

Earthquake and Volcano Destruction

Section Objectives

- Determine four factors that influence the amount of damage caused by an earthquake.
- Describe the types of damage caused by earthquakes.
- Describe the types of damage caused by volcanoes.

Key Terms

tsunami

Earthquake Damage

How would you feel if your home collapsed during an earthquake? Your first concern would probably be your family's safety. Once you knew everyone was safe, you'd survey your home. Your clothes, furniture, television, and other belongings—all would be buried under rubble. Fire would be a possible hazard because natural gas lines are often split open by a quake, and sparks may ignite the escaping gas.

From time to time, people face this kind of damage after an earthquake has hit. Actually, very few earthquakes are destructive. Earthquakes vary in strength, and most quakes are so weak that people don't even notice them. This next activity will show you how the strength of an earthquake, plus one other earthquake characteristic, can determine the amount of damage it will cause.

Explore! ACTIVITY

What makes an earthquake destructive?

What To Do

1. Take a rectangular pan and fill it halfway with sand or fine soil. Place its ends on two large books so that you can reach your hand underneath.
2. Pound lightly on the underside of the pan. Observe how much sand or soil moves in the pan.
3. Now pound harder, then harder still. Note how much more sand or soil shifts the harder you hit the bottom of the pan.
4. Now vary the place where you strike the pan. First pound in the middle and note where most of the sand or soil shifts. Is it directly over the spot where you strike the pan, or off to the side?
5. Move the pan so that one side extends over the edge of the table and pound under this side. Where does most of the sand or soil shift? What could happen to a building directly above such an underground disturbance? What would happen to a building on the other side of the pan?

When considering the threat of an earthquake, you must consider four factors—the strength of the earthquake, its location relative to populated areas, the design of buildings, and the type of ground on which these structures are built. While people can't do anything about the first two factors, they do have some control over the other two. They can design and construct buildings that will withstand many earthquakes, and they can build these structures on solid ground.

To gain a better understanding of how these other factors can influence the damaging effects of earthquakes, look at the examples below.

Figure 18-5

A Structures unable to withstand the vibrations of earthquake waves were a major cause of damage to buildings during the San Francisco earthquake of 1906, as seen in the photo on the right. Modern San Francisco buildings have the strength and flexibility to better withstand strong vibrations. Considering their structure, how well do you think buildings in your area could withstand an earthquake?

B Bridges are easily damaged by earthquakes. The freeway overpass below collapsed when an earthquake struck Northridge, California, on January 17, 1994.

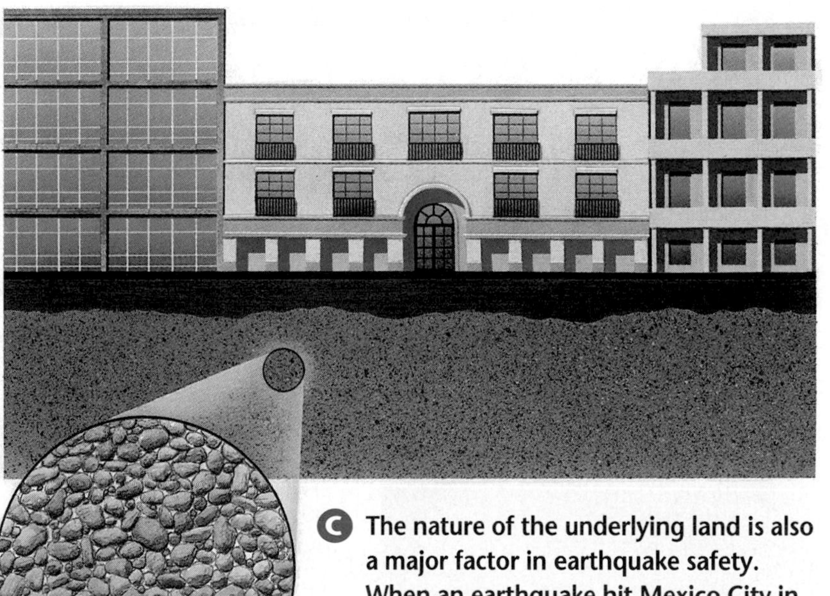

C The nature of the underlying land is also a major factor in earthquake safety. When an earthquake hit Mexico City in 1985, the quake shifted and vibrated the loose land materials on which most of the city was built. About 250 structures collapsed, killing more than 9000 people.

Tsunamis

If you lived at the seashore in an area where earthquakes occurred fairly often, what major concerns would you have? You might worry about the sandy soil on which your house is built. You know from the Mexico City example and from your own Explore activity that loose material like sand becomes unstable when earthquake waves travel through it. But there is another problem that may occur at seashore homes.

Find Out! ACTIVITY

What may happen when an earthquake strikes offshore?

What To Do

1. Use one or two books to tilt a cake pan at a 20-degree angle. Pour water into the lower end of the pan. Leave about one-third of the pan at the upper end dry.

Physics CONNECTION

Almost all of the two hundred houses in El Tranisto, Nicaragua, were destroyed by a tsunami in September of 1992.

The Terror of the Tsunami

Earlier you read about tsunamis—giant waves caused by earthquakes beneath the ocean floor or by underwater landslides or volcanic eruptions in the sea. How do the characteristics of tsunamis compare with the waves you studied in Chapter 17?

When an earthquake occurs under the ocean, the movement of the ocean floor pushes against the water, creating a powerful wave that reaches all the way to the ocean surface. These enormous water waves may travel thousands of kilometers in all directions. Far from shore, where the water is deep, the wavelengths of earthquake-related waves can be hundreds of kilometers long. But when one of these waves nears a coastline, the water piles up and forms a towering wave crest that can exceed 30 meters in height.

Just like other waves, tsunamis have a frequency. You know that an earthquake produces a series of vibrations in Earth's crust. The frequency of the tsunami is dependent on the frequency of the earthquake vibrations.

The powerful wave of a tsunami can travel as rapidly as a jet plane. As the wave moves away from the spot of its origin, it may travel at a speed of more

2. Create a coastline by packing a layer of damp sand 2-3 cm thick at the dry end of the pan. Use your hands to build dunes and low areas.
3. Punch a hole near the rim of a plastic lid and thread a piece of string about 20 cm long through the hole.
4. Tie a knot near the end of the string to keep it from slipping back out. Carefully place the lid on the bottom of the pan at the low end.
5. Use your fingers to hold the edge of the plastic lid firmly against the bottom near the upper end of the pan. While holding this edge of the lid down, pull the string straight up with one rapid movement. This action simulates an underwater earthquake. Observe what happens.

Conclude and Apply

1. What happens to land near the water when an earthquake strikes under the ocean?

As you learned in the Find Out activity, an underwater earthquake can send a huge, rapidly moving water wave crashing onto the shore.

Such a tremendous ocean wave generated by an earthquake is called a **tsunami**. You can find out more about tsunamis in the "Physics Connection" feature below.

---

than 700 kilometers per hour. At this rate, a tsunami produced near the Hawaiian Islands could reach Seattle, Washington, in less than six hours.

As the diagram below shows, the amplitude of a tsunami may not look any greater than a normal ocean wave when it is in deep water. As it reaches shallower depths, however, the water begins to pile up, dramatically forming a wall of water by the time the tsunami reaches the shallow waters near the shore. The shallower the water, the taller the wave becomes. Tons of water crash onto coastal areas, tossing boats around like bath toys and doing tremendous damage to buildings.

What Do You Think?

Why might the damage to a coastal town on a U- or V-shaped inlet be greater than to a coastal town on a straight shoreline?

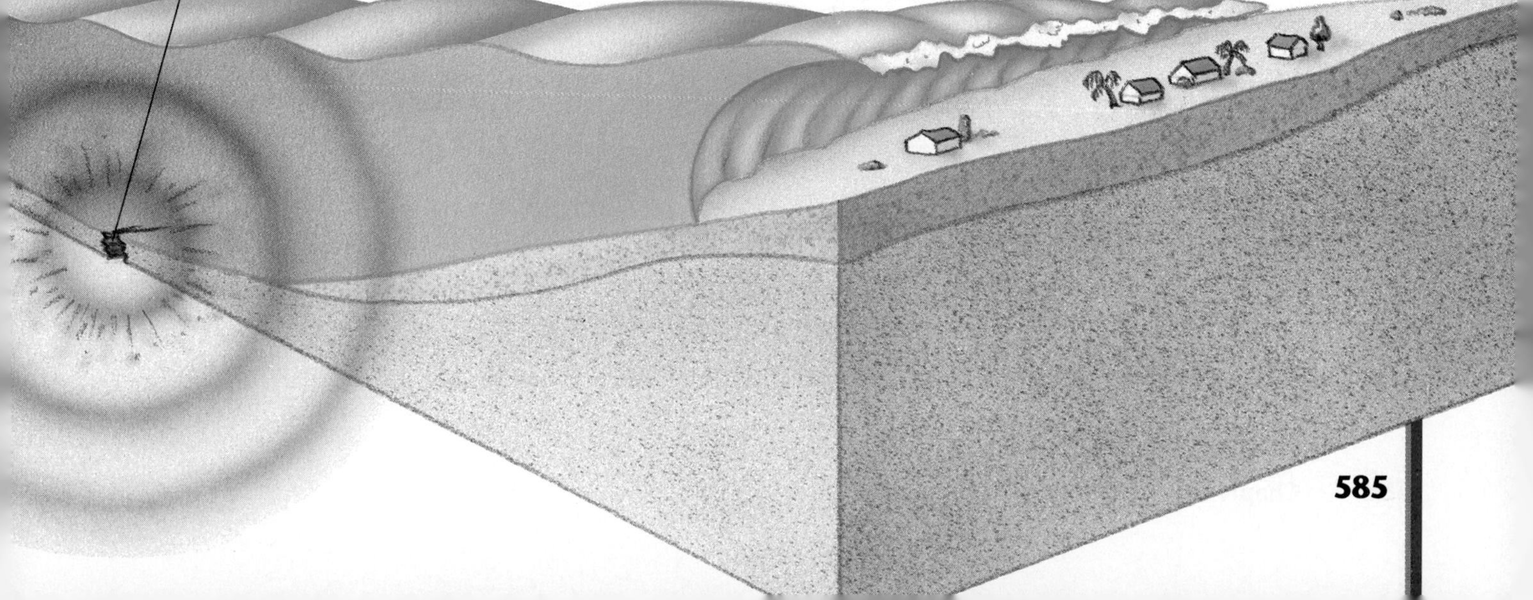

Volcano Damage

Connect to...

Chemistry

Volcanoes can give off large quantities of different gases. Some of the gases are greenhouse gases. Make a table that includes the gases given off by volcanoes and identify which of those are greenhouse gases.

Can you imagine red-hot lava oozing toward your home? People in Hawaii—and elsewhere on Earth—have had to watch just such a scene.

Early in Earth's history, volcanic activity was more widespread than it is today. Most of the volcanoes on Earth today are dormant, which means that they are not currently active. An active volcano is one that shows evidence of releasing materials, ranging from occasional smoke and gases to constant spewing of dust, ash, cinders, and lava. Currently, more than 600 volcanoes on Earth are classified as active.

The recent eruptions of volcanoes in the Philippines, Japan, the state of Washington, and Hawaii are evidence that volcanoes can do tremendous damage. Look at the figures on these two pages to see how destructive volcanoes can be.

Figure 18-7

On May 18, 1980, Mount Saint Helens, in the state of Washington, hurled over 275 trillion tons of ash and rock into the air, killing nearly every living thing in a fan-shaped area extending as far as 90 kilometers from the mountain.

Figure 18-6

Kilauea, the most active volcano in the world, has been quietly erupting off and on for centuries. The most recent series of eruptions began in January 1983 and continued into the 1990s.

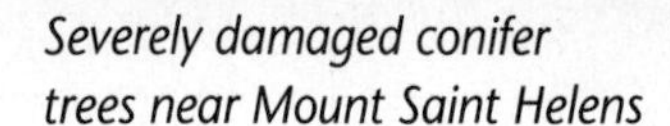

Severely damaged conifer trees near Mount Saint Helens

Home surrounded by lava in Kalapana Gardens, Hawaii

Figure 18-8

Perhaps the best-known volcanic eruption in the world is that of Italy's Mount Vesuvius, shown above, in the year 79. Ash and cinders from the eruption buried the nearby cities of Pompeii and Herculaneum.

Figure 18-9

A **In 1815, Indonesia's Mount Tambora violently erupted, releasing 6 million times more energy than an atomic bomb. Volcanic dust circled the globe for months.**

B **This diagram illustrates why the year following Tambora's eruption was called "the year without a summer."**

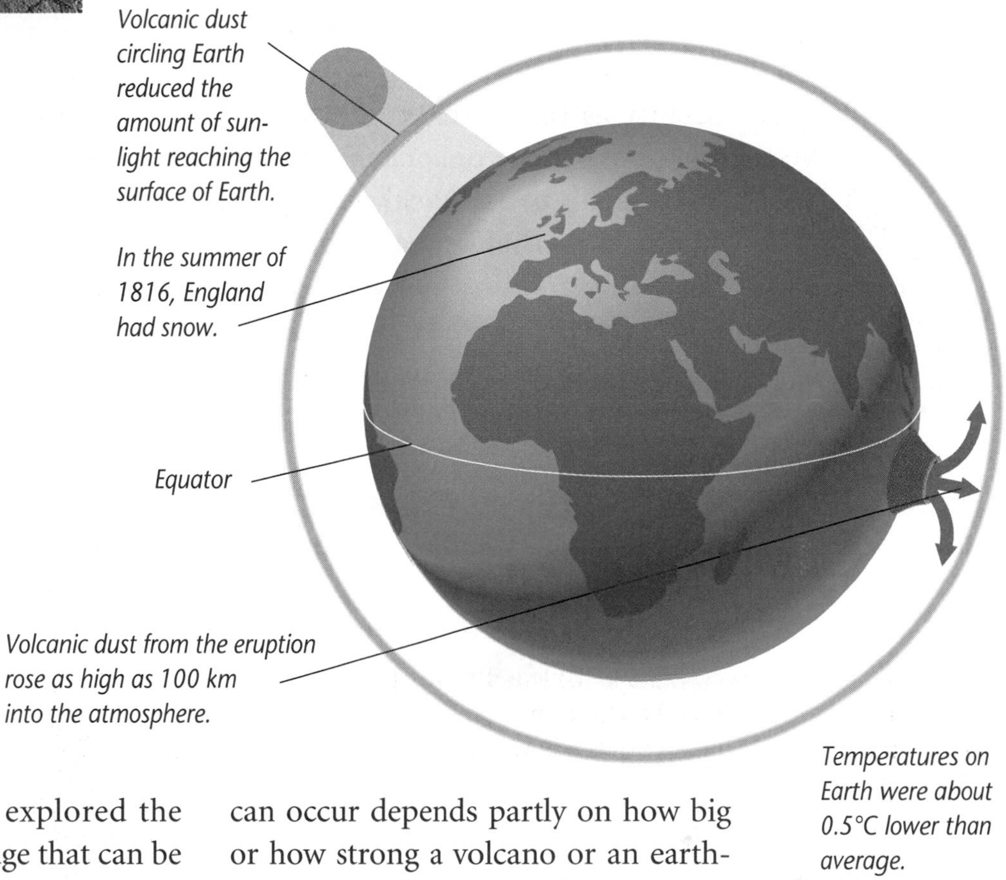

Volcanic dust circling Earth reduced the amount of sunlight reaching the surface of Earth.

In the summer of 1816, England had snow.

Equator

Volcanic dust from the eruption rose as high as 100 km into the atmosphere.

Temperatures on Earth were about 0.5°C lower than average.

You have explored the types of damage that can be caused by earthquakes and volcanoes. You know that the amount of damage that can occur depends partly on how big or how strong a volcano or an earthquake is. In the next section, you will discover how the strength of an earthquake is measured.

check your UNDERSTANDING

1. List four factors that affect the amount of damage caused by an earthquake.
2. What kind of damage occurs when an earthquake strikes on land? When an earthquake strikes the ocean floor?
3. What are some of the dangers faced by people living near an active volcano?
4. **Apply** Some scientists have hypothesized that high levels of volcanic activity may have occurred about 66 million years ago. This time is the same period during which the dinosaurs became extinct. If many volcanoes were spewing ash and dust into the atmosphere, how might the climate of Earth have changed? How would a climate change have affected plant and animal life at that time?

18-3 Measuring Earthquakes

Section Objectives

- Demonstrate how a seismograph measures an earthquake's strength.
- Explain how the Richter scale is used to indicate earthquake magnitude.

Key Terms

seismograph
magnitude

Recording Vibrations

Just as the severity of volcanic eruptions varies from one to the next, the strength of earthquakes varies as well. Recall that an earthquake is caused by a shifting of rock in the solid earth below the surface. Many earthquakes are not even felt at the surface. Earthquakes that are felt range in strength. At one end, they may be only a mild shaking of the ground, similar to the vibrations you felt when your classmates pounded the floor or bleacher in the Explore activity at the beginning of this chapter. At the other end, they may be a violent trembling.

Whether or not they are felt at Earth's surface, earthquakes produce vibrations in rocks and soil. The strength of an earthquake is determined by recording and measuring its vibrations.

A scientist who studies earthquakes is called a seismologist. Seismologists use an instrument called a **seismograph** to record earthquake vibrations. **Figure 18-10** describes how a seismograph works. The vibrations of Earth are recorded as a wavy line. The height of the peaks of the wavy line indicates the earthquake's magnitude. The **magnitude** of an earthquake is a measure of the earthquake's strength.

Figure 18-10

The roll of paper is held firmly in the frame of the seismograph, while the pen moves freely. When the ground vibrates, the roll of paper also vibrates, but the pen does not. As the roll of paper turns, the pen traces a record of the vibrations on the paper. This record appears as a wavy line.

Seismologists use a special scale called the Richter scale to describe the earthquake magnitudes they measure. The numbers on the scale relate to the amounts of energy released by the earthquakes. Each number on the scale represents an earthquake about 32 times stronger than the previous lower number on the scale.

For example, an earthquake measuring 6.5 on the Richter scale is 32 times stronger than an earthquake that measures 5.5 on the scale. How much stronger would an earthquake measuring 7.5 on the Richter scale be than one measuring 5.5? Because there is a difference of 2.0 on the scale, you would multiply 32 times 32. The stronger earthquake would be 1000 times stronger than the weaker one.

Earthquake Occurrences

Richter Magnitude	Number Expected Per Year
1.0 to 3.9	949 000
4.0 to 4.9	6200
5.0 to 5.9	800
6.0 to 6.9	226
7.0 to 7.9	18
8.0 to 8.9	<2

Table 18-1

Study **Table 18-1** to see how many earthquakes at each magnitude are expected each year. What happens to the number of occurrences as the magnitude increases? How many earthquakes are predicted to occur with a Richter value between 1.0 and 3.9? How would you account for the fact that you hear about only a few earthquakes each year?

Which do you think is more destructive—an earthquake measuring 8.5 that occurs in a desolate, unpopulated part of the world or one measuring 6.5 that occurs near a densely populated area? Although the stronger quake releases much more energy, the second quake may cause much more damage. The magnitude of an earthquake does not tell you all you need to know about an earthquake.

Figure 18-11

A Zhang Heng, a Chinese scientist living in the second century A.D. built the first instrument for recording the occurrence and direction of earthquakes too slight to be felt. The bronze device was about 2 m across.

B During a tremor, the vessel would move more than the heavy pendulum, which hung inside. The motion would open the jaws of one or more of the dragons. The open jaw released a ball which fell into the mouth of the toad below.

INVESTIGATE!

Making a Model Seismograph

In this activity, you will make a model seismograph and record some vibrations.

Problem

How can you measure the magnitude of vibrations?

Materials

- ring stand with ring
- wire hook from coat hanger
- masking tape
- sheet of paper
- piece of string
- 2 rubber bands
- fine-tip marker
- metric ruler

What To Do

1. Copy the data table *into your Journal.*
2. Set up your seismograph using the illustration as a guide.
3. Place a sheet of paper under the ring. Adjust the position of the marker so that its tip just touches near the end of the paper.

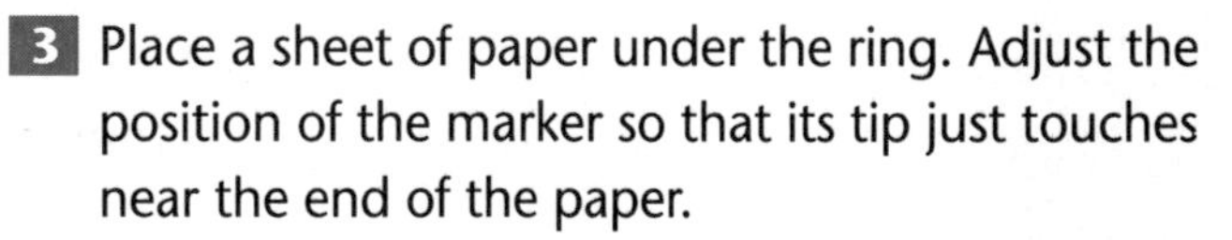

4. Work with a partner. While one person strikes the table several times with equal strength, the other one should slowly pull the paper under the marker.
5. Recall from Chapter 17 that amplitude is half the height of a wave from crest to trough. ***Measure*** the amplitude marked on your paper. Record your measurements and observations as Trial 1.

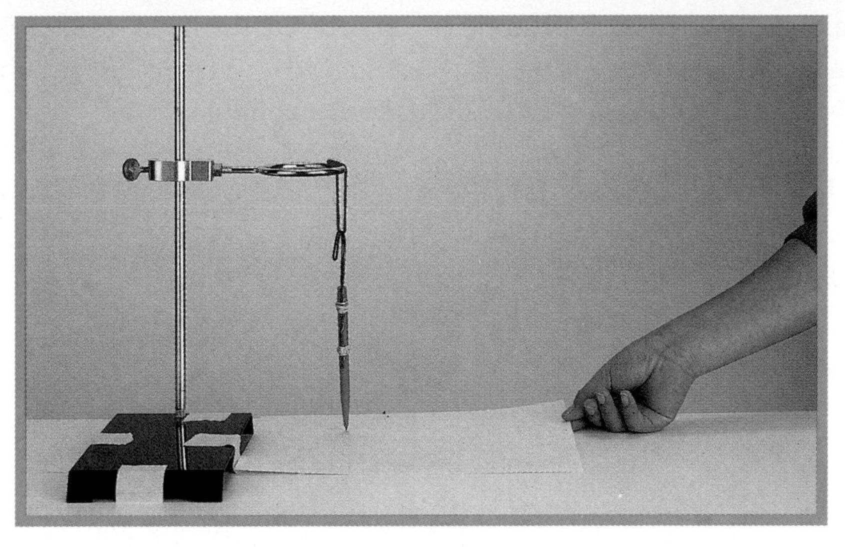

A

Data and Observations		
Trial Number	Amplitude (Height of Marks)	Observations
1		
2		
3		

6 ***Hypothesize*** about the effect of the magnitude of the vibrations on the amplitude of the peaks.

7 Repeat Steps 3 and 4, hitting the table with less strength for Trial 2 and more strength for Trial 3. Record your measurements and observations.

Analyzing

1. Which trial resulted in the greatest amplitudes recorded on the wavy line?

2. How did the movement of the marker compare with the movement of the frame of the seismograph?

Concluding and Applying

3. How does your hypothesis ***compare*** with the results of the activity?

4. Determine the effect the magnitude of vibrations had on the amplitude of the wave peaks.

5. **Going Further** What difference would you ***predict*** between the amplitudes generated by a strong earthquake and those generated by a weaker one?

Table 18-2 shows some strong earthquakes that have occurred in the past 400 years. Study the table and determine whether loss of life is always related directly to earthquake magnitude. Do you live in an area where earthquakes are common? Can you think of some ways to reduce your risk of being injured in an earthquake?

Table 18-2

Strong Earthquakes

Year	Location	Richter Value	Deaths
1556	Shensi, China	?	830 000
1737	Calcutta, India	?	300 000
1755	Lisbon, Portugal	8.8	70 000
1811-12	New Madrid, MO	8.3	few
1886	Charleston, SC	?	60
1906	San Francisco, CA	8.3	1 500
1920	Kansu, China	8.5	180 000
1923	Tokyo, Japan	8.3	143 000
1939	Concepcíon, Chile	8.3	30 000
1964	Prince William Sound, AK	8.5	131
1970	Peru	7.8	66 800
1975	Liaoning Province, China	7.5	300
1976	Tangshan, China	7.6	240 000
1985	Mexico City, Mexico	8.1	9 500
1988	Armenia	6.9	28 000
1989	Loma Prieta, CA	7.1	62
1990	Iran	7.7	50 000
1993	Maharashtra, India	6.4	30 000
1994	Northridge, CA	6.7	61

Making and Using Tables

Use **Table 18-2** to answer the following questions:

1. Which earthquake resulted in the greatest number of deaths? The fewest?
2. Which quake had the greatest magnitude?
3. Hypothesize why the 1975 China quake resulted in fewer deaths than the 1976 quake.

If you need help, refer to the **Skill Handbook** on page 656.

check your UNDERSTANDING

1. How is earthquake magnitude measured?
2. Using Table 18-2, what would be the magnitude of an earthquake that is 32 times stronger than the 1988 quake in Armenia?
3. **Apply** Suppose you studied seismograph readings from two earthquakes, A and B. What would you infer from the fact that the amplitude of the peaks produced by quake B were much higher than those produced by quake A?

Technology Connection

Earthquake-Proof Construction

What makes some structures withstand earthquakes, while others are damaged or destroyed?

The geological foundation is perhaps the most important factor. Buildings built on solid rock near an earthquake's center—where vibrations are the strongest—may hold up better than buildings built on softer ground farther away.

Heavy-Duty Buildings

Extending a building's foundation well below ground level can help a building withstand an earthquake because the building will be less likely to lean or tip. Buildings may be reinforced by beams that cross at different angles or with steel embedded in concrete.

Because buildings with a lot of glass often lack support, steel-framed buildings and concrete buildings with few doors or windows hold up better than some other types of structures. Brick buildings tend to buckle during earthquakes.

Go with the Flow

The objective in earthquake-proof construction is to build structures that will move as a unit rather than as individual, unrelated parts. Engineers accomplish this by placing rollers, jacks, springs, bearings, or plastic sheets under the bases of buildings. Architects are also experimenting with shock absorbers for buildings and bridges.

Safety Is No Accident!

Even if you are in a building with earthquake-proof construction, during an earthquake follow these safety measures:

Keep away from windows.

Avoid standing where objects might fall on you.

Avoid fallen power lines.

Stay clear of rubble with sharp edges and broken gas lines.

Science Journal

Start with photos or drawings of three different structures. For each structure, describe *in your Science Journal* three areas where damage from an earthquake is most likely to occur. Explain why. Next, indicate how and where these structures might be reinforced to minimize earthquake damage. Explain why.

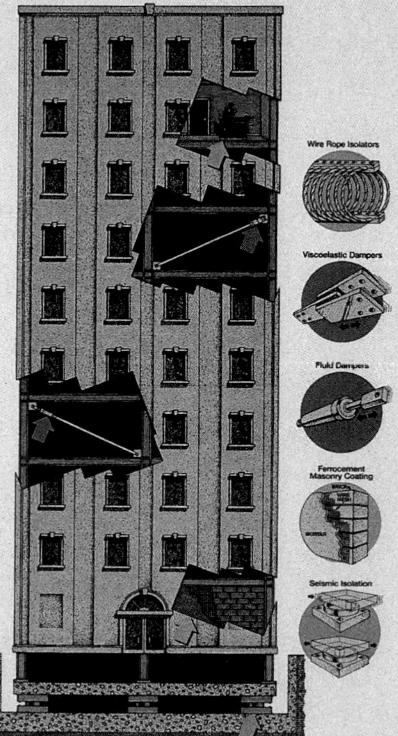

Artist's rendering of a building's earthquake-proofing features

Science and Society Earthquake Prediction

Earthquakes rarely strike without warning. Often, the ground will vibrate days or even months before a major earthquake hits. Measuring even the slightest shifts in Earth can therefore help scientists predict an impending earthquake. Seismologists obtain data about movements within Earth from instruments that register changes in Earth's crust. You already know about seismographs. Let's examine some other seismic measurement devices.

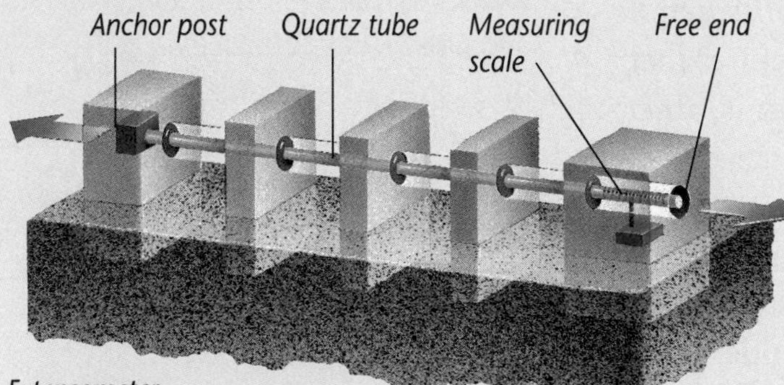

Extensometer

Stretch-O-Meter

An extensometer has a long quartz tube threaded through a row of posts in the ground. Look at the picture of the extensometer. One end of the tube is anchored firmly inside the first post. The other end of the tube moves freely inside the last post. The additional posts help support the quartz tube. Extensometers can be more than 300 feet long.

When an earthquake occurs, the free end of the tube moves farther into or out of the last post. By reading a scale on the free end of the tube, scientists can measure the tremors.

Tipping the Scale

Tiltmeters set up near faults in Earth's surface help detect changes in the slope of the ground. A change in the tilt of the ground may indicate that one side of a fault is being forced upward or downward in relation to the other side of the fault.

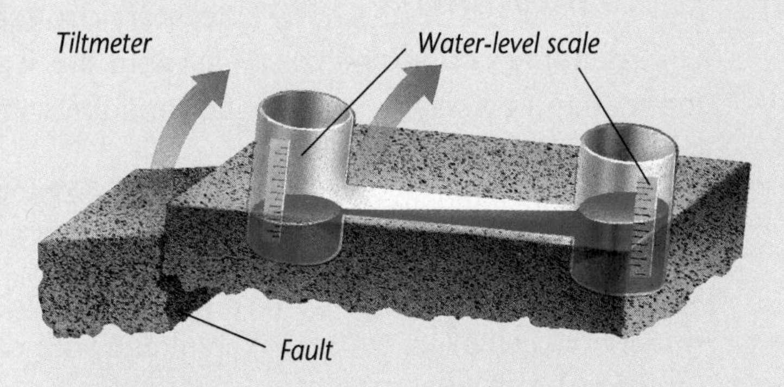

Tiltmeter

Have you ever seen a carpenter's level? A tiltmeter works the same way. It has a tube connected to two water-filled containers. When the ground near one of the containers shifts upward, the water level in that container drops, while the water level in the other, lower container rises. Tiltmeters are usually about 30 feet long.

Faster than a Speeding Bullet

Seismologists use laser distance-ranging devices to help detect small horizontal shifts in Earth's surface along fault lines. As shown in the picture, these devices aim a narrow laser beam from one side of a fault toward a reflector on the other side of the fault, and time how long the beam takes to return.

Because we know the speed at which light travels, if the beam takes less time or more time to return, we know that the distance it is traveling has changed. This change in distance may indicate a shift in Earth's crust—a sign that an earthquake may be on its way.

Seismologists study faults and earthquakes to learn more about Earth's interior, to predict earthquakes, and to provide advice about construction sites and building materials in earthquake-prone areas.

Warning!

We may not be able to prevent earthquakes, but if we learn to predict them accurately and if we're prepared, we may save many lives. To demonstrate the difference a warning can make, let's compare two earthquakes that occurred in China and were of approximately the same magnitude.

The earthquake in the Liaoning Province of China in February 1975 took very few lives because people knew it was coming. Days before, the ground had shifted, and minor tremors had been felt. Government officials told people to stay outside their homes so they would not be crushed if their homes collapsed. Even with the warning, 300 lives were lost. Had the people not been warned, 10 000 more might have died!

The following year, an earthquake hit Tangshan, China. The people had no warning. As many as 240 000 people were killed—about one-sixth of Tangshan's population at the time! Little was left of the city except piles of bricks and twisted steel.

What Do You Think?

It's hard to pinpoint precisely when an earthquake will hit. What problems might occur if officials warn people about an earthquake too early? Should officials wait to inform people until they are more certain about when an earthquake will strike? Why?

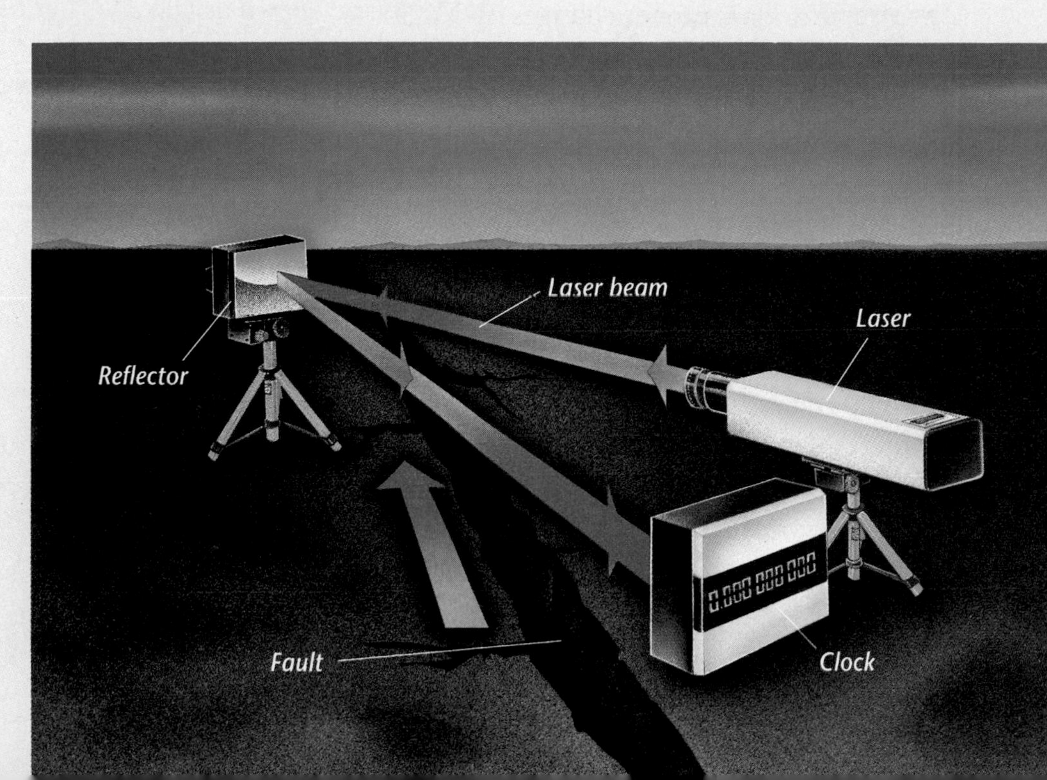

Teens in SCIENCE

Shake, Rattle, and Roll

The floor is moving under your feet. A lamp swings from side to side over your head. Can you guess why? It's an earthquake!

Seventeen-year-old Deena Stroham knows a lot about earthquakes. As part of a 4-H project, Deena teaches younger students what she has learned. "I try to help kids know what to expect. But the lessons are fun."

Although Deena lives in earthquake-prone California, she has never actually felt one.

You Try It!

Deena uses this experiment to show how earthquakes affect houses built on two different types of earth. The gelatin dessert represents landfill. The clay represents bedrock.

Materials

1 package of gelatin dessert
1 package unflavored gelatin
boiling water
firm clay
48 toothpicks
24 marshmallows
6-in by 6-in by 1-in container

What To Do

1. Mix the powdered gelatin dessert and unflavored gelatin together. Follow the directions on the back of the dessert package. Pour the mixture into a container that is at least 6 inches by 6 inches and 1 inch deep. Refrigerate. When firm, cut the gelatin dessert into a 6-inch by 6-inch square.
2. Make a 6-inch by 6-inch square at least 1 inch thick out of clay.
3. Now build a house from the toothpicks and marshmallows. Make the vertical corners first. Press a marshmallow on the end of a toothpick. Push the other end of the toothpick into the gelatin square. Space each of the four corners a toothpick's length apart. Next, connect the four marshmallows with horizontal toothpicks. This is the first story of your house. Add two more. Follow the same steps with the clay square.
4. Shake each square to simulate an earthquake. Which house stood longer? Is it safer to build on landfill or bedrock?

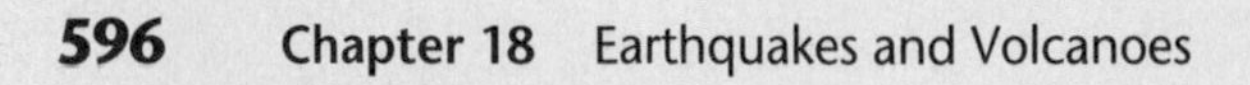

chapter 18
REVIEWING MAIN IDEAS

Science Journal

Review the statements below about the big ideas presented in this chapter, and answer the questions. Then, re-read your answers to the Did You Ever Wonder questions at the beginning of the chapter. *In your Science Journal*, write a paragraph about how your understanding of the big ideas in the chapter has changed.

1 An earthquake is caused by vibrations set in motion when part of the solid earth below the surface suddenly shifts. ***How does energy from earthquakes travel?***

2 A volcano builds as magma reaches Earth's surface and material from eruptions accumulates over time. ***Why aren't volcanoes found everywhere on Earth?***

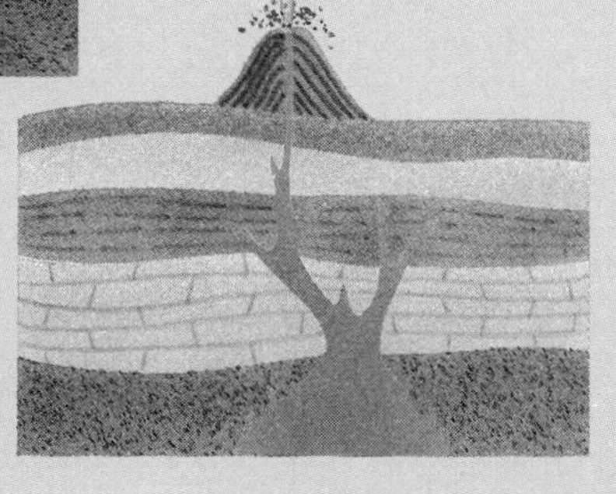

3 The shape of a volcano depends on the material it's made of and whether the eruptions are quiet or explosive. ***Compare and contrast the shapes of volcanoes and the types of eruptions.***

4 The amount of damage caused by an earthquake depends on the strength of the quake, its distance from inhabited areas, the design of buildings, and the type of ground on which the buildings are found. ***Describe how people can use these factors to make a city as safe as possible from an earthquake.***

chapter 18

CHAPTER REVIEW

Using Key Science Terms

lava
magma
magnitude
seismograph
tsunami

An analogy is a relationship between two pairs of words generally written in the following manner: a:b::c:d. The symbol : is read "is to," and the symbol :: is read "as." For example, cat:animal::rose:plant is read "cat is to animal as rose is to plant." In the analogies that follow, a word is missing. Complete each analogy by providing the missing word from the list above.

1. air temperature:thermometer::earthquake magnitude: ______________
2. geyser:groundwater::volcano:__________
3. air:sound::ocean water: ______________
4. ice cream:chocolate syrup::Earth's surface:______________

Understanding Ideas

Answer the following questions in your Journal *using complete sentences.*

1. Explain what causes earthquakes.
2. Describe how people can control the damage caused by earthquakes.
3. How is the strength of an earthquake determined?
4. Describe two kinds of volcanic eruptions.
5. What types of damage may be caused by an erupting volcano?

Developing Skills

Use your understanding of the concepts developed in this chapter to answer each of the following questons.

1. **Concept Mapping** Complete the following events chain concept map of earthquakes.

Initiating event

Part of the solid earth below the surface shifts.

Event 1

Event 2

Final outcome

Buildings and other structures on Earth move. Some may even crumble and fall.

2. **Comparing and Contrasting** Repeat the Explore activity on page 574 using unflavored gelatin instead of water. Compare the results of this activity with those made in the original activity.
3. **Making and Using Graphs** After doing the Find Out activity on page 580, use the information below and make a graph to compare the shapes of the volcanoes. What type of volcano is X? What type of volcano is Y?

Volcano	Points
X	1-1, 5-5, 10-11, 11-17, 10-25, 5-33
Y	1-8, 9-17, 1-26

4. **Comparing and Contrasting** After doing the Find Out activity on pages 584-585, repeat the activity changing the shape of the shoreline to see how different shorelines are affected by tsunamis.

chapter 18

CHAPTER REVIEW

Critical Thinking

Use your understanding of the concepts developed in this chapter to answer each of the following questions.

1. The table shows the chances that an earthquake of a specified magnitude will strike five selected locations in California within the next 30 years. Which location is most likely to be struck by an earthquake? Which location is likely to experience the strongest earthquake?

Location	Richter Scale Magnitude		
	8^{+}	7-7.9	6-6.9
North Coast	10%		
San Francisco		20%	
Parkfield			90%
Mojave		30%	
Coachella Valley		40%	

2. Why is flexibility an important factor in designing an earthquake-safe structure?
3. On land, the closer a spot is to the source of an earthquake, the more damage may occur. How does this situation compare with what happens when an earthquake occurs below the ocean?

Problem Solving

Read the following problem and discuss your answers in a brief paragraph.

Suppose you live in an area where earthquakes are common, and you want to set up a seismograph at home.

1. Describe how a seismograph that uses a beam of light and photographic film might work.
2. Can you think of another way to set up a seismograph using common objects? Explain.

CONNECTING IDEAS

Discuss each of the following in a brief paragraph.

1. **Theme—Energy** Name two ways in which earthquake waves are similar to sound waves.
2. **Theme—Stability and Change** How does gravity affect the motion of lava?
3. **Theme—Energy** How are earthquakes and volcanoes alike? How are they different?
4. **Technology Connection** What areas of interest do seismologists and building engineers have in common?
5. **Physics Connection** Suppose a tsunami strikes two towns the same distance from the site of an underwater earthquake. Which town would probably have more damage—the one along a straight coastline or the one at the inland end of a narrow bay? Explain your answer.

CHAPTER 19

The Earth-Moon System

Did you ever wonder...

- Why it's cooler in winter and warmer in summer?
- What the far side of the moon looks like?
- Why sometimes a beach is narrower than it was just a few hours earlier?

Science Journal

Before you begin to study about the moon and Earth, think about these questions and answer them *in your Science Journal.* When you finish the chapter, compare your journal write-up with what you have learned.

Do you like to travel? Let's hope so, because you're on a journey right now—around the sun. You'll travel 940 million kilometers and never leave town. You'll complete your trip in one year without missing school. You'll need nothing special, but you'll take everything you own. Your vehicle? You'll be riding planet Earth, and the moon will be coming right along on this trip.

In this chapter you'll explore the relationship between Earth and the moon. Let's begin our trip. We'll be traveling through space at more than 107 000 kilometers per hour!

In the activity on the next page, explore the shape of the vehicle that's taking you on your journey through space.

Explore! ACTIVITY

What if Earth were shaped like a pizza box?

What To Do

1. Using an atlas, trace the continents on a sheet of paper.
2. Then, glue the sheet onto the top of a small pizza delivery box.
3. Fold the map around the edges of the box. What places are now at the "edge of the world"? *In your Journal*, describe how people's lives might be different if Earth were shaped like a box.

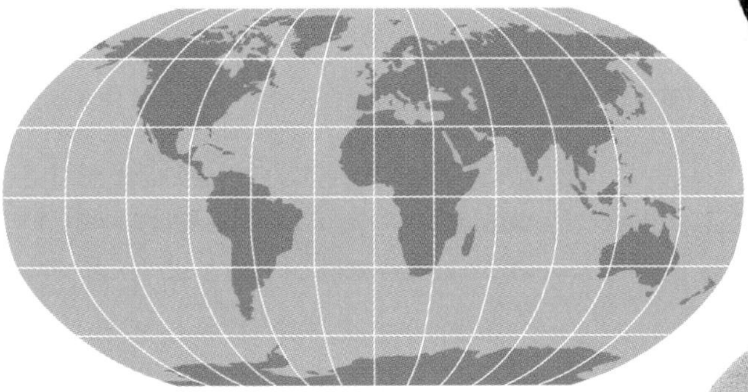

19-1 Earth's Shape and Movements

Section Objectives

- Demonstrate evidence that shows Earth's shape.
- Describe the cause of day and night.
- Explain what causes the seasons on Earth.

Key Terms

sphere
rotation
revolution
equinox
solstice

Evidence of Earth's Shape

In the very first Explore activity in this book, you looked all about you and drew what you observed. How far away could you see? On a clear day, across open country, you can see about 32 kilometers. If you turn full circle, the world you can actually see is about 64 kilometers from edge to edge. If this was all you could observe, Earth might as well be a flat circle 64 kilometers in diameter. In the following Find Out activity, you will observe the type of evidence that suggested to many people that Earth was not flat but that it had a very different shape.

Find Out! ACTIVITY

How does Earth's shape affect what you see?

What To Do

1. Cut a strip of cardboard in the shape of a mountain about 8 cm tall, and decorate it. Fold about 2 cm of the mountain's base. Tape the 2-cm section to a basketball so that the remaining 6 cm are sticking straight up from the surface of the ball.
2. Now set the basketball on a table so that the mountain is sticking out horizontally, parallel to the table.
3. Kneel down on the other side of the ball so that you are eye level with it. Look at the top of the ball; think of this curve as a horizon.
4. Now, roll the ball toward you very slowly so that the stripes come into view over the top curve of the ball. Stop when you can see the entire length of the paper.

Conclude and Apply

1. What effect did the shape of the basketball have on your view of the approaching cardboard mountain?

Ancient Greek scientists suggested that Earth was shaped like a ball. Sailors noticed that as they approached an island, it seemed to rise from the horizon.

Figure 19-1 shows what these sailors were seeing. They also noticed that as another ship approached, they would first see the top of its mast, then the sails, and finally the hull. This experience is similar to yours as you observed the strip of paper coming toward you with the roll of the basketball. The sequence of mast-sail-hull suggested to the sailors that the ship was approaching over a curved surface.

Earth's Shape

Earth is sphere-shaped. A **sphere** is a round, three-dimensional object whose surface at all points is the same distance from its center. You have probably played with a basketball, beachball, or volleyball. These balls are all spheres. In reality, however, Earth bulges slightly at the equator and is somewhat flattened at the poles, as shown in **Figure 19-2**. You could make this shape by sitting on a basketball.

Figure 19-1

A As the ship approaches the island, the crew's first view of land is only the top of the island.

B As the ship draws closer, the island appears to rise from the horizon. The closer the ship gets, the more island is visible.

C Finally, the shoreline of the island is visible. The increasing visibility from the top down suggests that the ship was approaching the island over a curved surface.

Figure 19-2

The red line in this diagram shows the shape of a perfect sphere. How does Earth's shape compare with the sphere?

Earth's Motions

Connect to...
Life Science

Plants have regular daily movements or cycles. These are called circadian rhythms. Prepare a report that describes circadian rhythms and give two examples for plants.

Picture yourself on an average day. You wake up after sunrise. During breakfast and into the morning, you begin to notice the sun's movement across the sky. But is the sun really moving? Or are you?

Rotation

People have always talked about the sun moving across the sky. However, the change in its position is actually caused by the motion of Earth, not the sun. Earth spins in space. This spinning motion is called **rotation.**

As Earth rotates around its axis, the sun comes into view as a location begins to face the sun.

As Earth continues to rotate, the sun appears to move across the sky until it goes below Earth's horizon.

During the next several hours, you experience the growing darkness of night, and then the sunrise-sunset cycle begins again. In reality, a spot on Earth spins toward the sun and away from the sun as seen in **Figure 19-3.**

Revolution

Earth is also in motion on a yearly trip around the sun. A complete **revolution,** or trip, takes about 365 1/4 days, or one year. It's during the course of one revolution that we experience the change of seasons.

Earth's revolution around the sun is in the shape of an ellipse, which looks somewhat like a flattened circle. The sun is a bit off-center of the ellipse, as you can see in **Figure 19-4.**

Is this elliptical path causing the changing temperatures and changing seasons on Earth? If it were, you would expect the warmest days to occur in January. But you know from experience that this isn't the case in the Northern Hemisphere. The following Find Out activity will show you the cause.

Figure 19-3

A **Earth rotates around an imaginary line running through its poles. This line is called Earth's axis. It takes 24 hours for Earth to complete one rotation.**

Sun

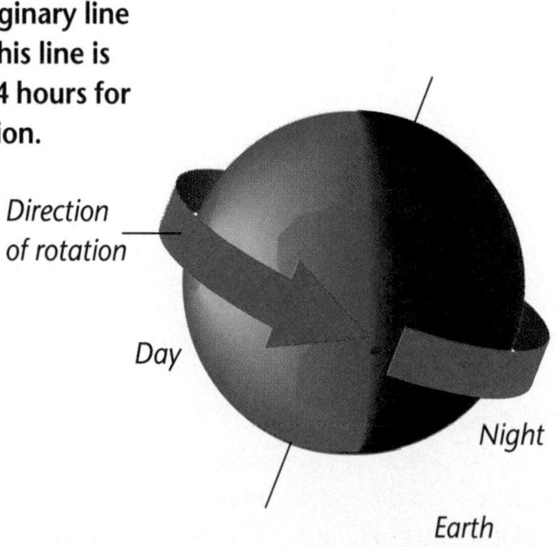

B **You see evidence of Earth's rotation by observing the sun. As Earth rotates, the sun appears to rise from the horizon at dawn, move across the sky as the day progresses, and drop below the horizon at night.**

Find Out! ACTIVITY

What causes the changing seasons?

What To Do

1. Use a lamp without a shade to represent the sun and use a globe to represent Earth. With the lamp on, hold the globe about 2 m away. Tilt the globe slightly so that the northern half points toward the lamp. Where on the globe is the light striking most directly?
2. Now, walk the globe around the lamp, keeping it tilted at the same angle and pointed in the same direction as when you started. What do you notice about the area receiving the most direct light?

Conclude and Apply

1. At what point in your walk around the lamp do you think winter would occur in the northern half of this globe?

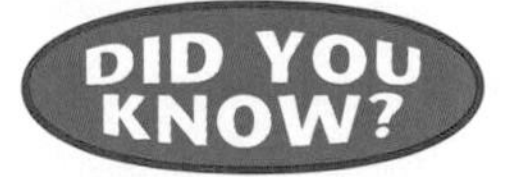

A stationary object at Earth's equator is actually traveling about 1670 kilometers per hour as it spins with its location.

In the activity, you tilted the globe because Earth's axis is tilted at a 23 1/2° angle. You demonstrated how the amount of direct sunlight striking Earth varies from one hemisphere to the other because of this tilt. In the next Investigate, you'll explore more about how Earth's tilt causes the seasons.

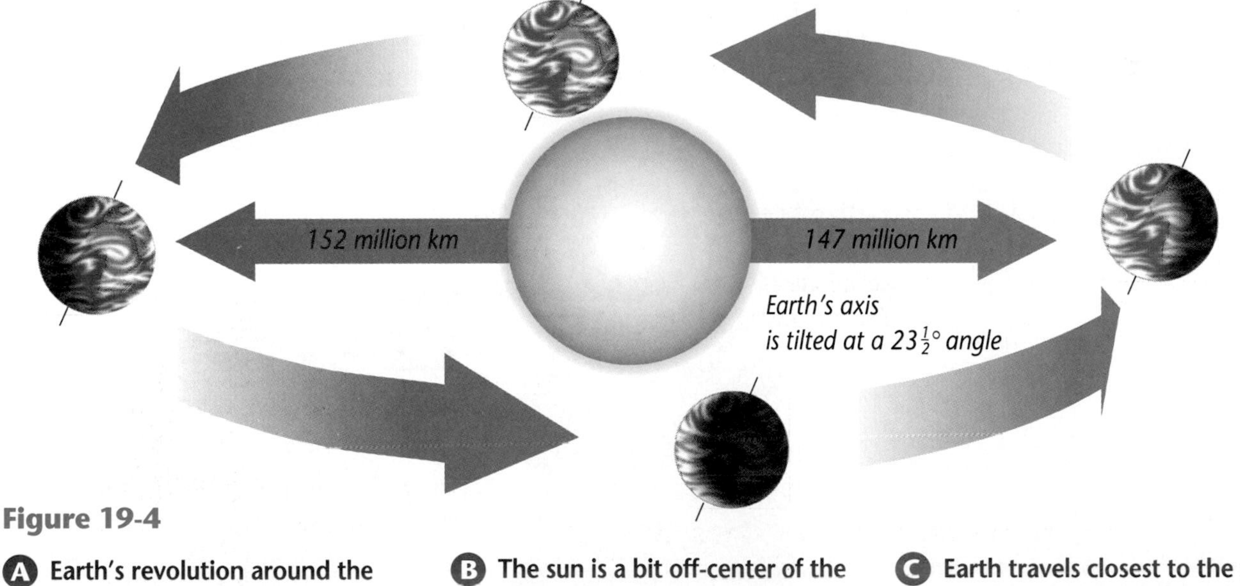

Figure 19-4

A **Earth's revolution around the sun is in the shape of an ellipse, a closed curve that looks somewhat like a flattened circle.**

B **The sun is a bit off-center of the ellipse, therefore, the distance between Earth and the sun changes during Earth's year-long-journey.**

C **Earth travels closest to the sun—about 147 million km away—in January. Earth is farthest from the sun—about 152 million km away—in July.**

DESIGN YOUR OWN
INVESTIGATION

Tilt and Temperature

Earth's tilt causes the amount of direct sunlight that strikes Earth to vary from one hemisphere to the other. How might this affect the amount of heat from the sun received by an area?

Preparation

Problem

How is the angle at which light strikes an area related to the amount of heat energy received by that area?

Form a Hypothesis

As a group, discuss the effects of light striking an area from several different angles. At what angle would the area receive the most heat? Agree upon a hypothesis that can be tested in your experiment.

Objectives

- Use a model to measure the amount of heat received by an area from light striking the area at different angles.
- Describe how the angle at which light strikes an area is related to Earth's changing seasons.

Possible Materials

black construction paper
protractor
Celsius thermometer
watch
tape
gooseneck lamp with 75-watt bulb

Safety

Do not touch the lamp. The lightbulb and shade can be hot even when the lamp has been turned off. Handle the thermometer carefully. If it breaks, do not touch anything. Inform your teacher immediately.

DESIGN YOUR OWN
INVESTIGATION

Plan the Experiment

1. As a group, agree upon how you will use the materials provided to test your hypothesis.
2. Write down exactly what you will do during each step of your test.
3. Make a list of any special properties you expect to observe or test.
4. Identify any constants, variables, and controls in your experiment.

Check the Plan

1. How will you determine whether the length of time the light is turned on affects heat energy?
2. How will you determine whether the angle at which light strikes an area causes changes in heat and energy?
3. Make sure your teacher approves your experiment before you proceed.
3. Carry out your experiment. Record your observations.

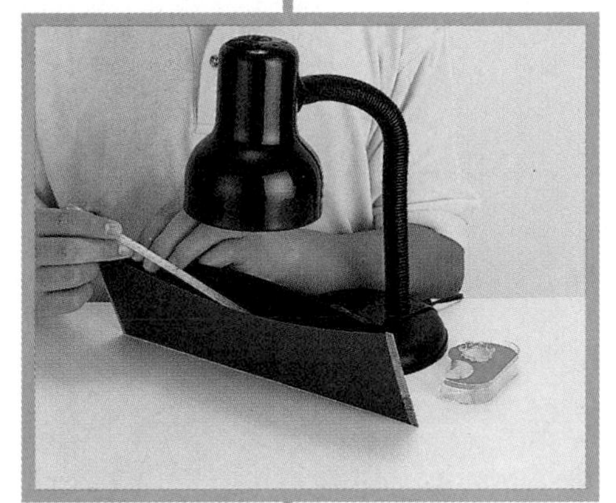

Analyze and Conclude

1. **Observe** Did the temperature in the envelope continue to rise at the same rate every three minutes?
2. **Interpret Data** How does the angle of light affect temperature? How might this be related to Earth's changing seasons?
3. **Design an Experiment** Did your experiment support your hypothesis? If not, determine how you might change the experiment in order to retest your hypothesis.

Going Further

Predict how the absorption of heat would be affected by changing your independent variables. Try your experiment with different values for your independent variables.

Equinoxes and Solstices

You now know that the tilt of Earth as it revolves around the sun causes the change in seasons. Because of this tilt, the sun's position relative to Earth's equator changes, too. Most of the time, the sun's most direct rays fall north or south of the equator. Two times during the year, however, the sun is directly over the equator. Each of these times is called an **equinox**.

When the sun reaches an equinox, night and day are the same length all over the world. Neither the Northern nor the Southern Hemisphere is tilted toward the sun. **Figure 19-5** shows you how this can happen.

A solstice also occurs two times each year. At the time of a **solstice,** the sun is directly over the north or the south edge of the tropics. If you measured the number of daylight hours each day for one year, you would find that the day of the winter solstice has the fewest daylight hours. This fact

Figure 19-5

During summer solstice in the Northern Hemisphere, the sun's rays directly strike the Tropic of Cancer. During winter solstice, the sun is directly over the Tropic of Capricorn. During both fall and spring equinoxes, the sun is directly over the equator.

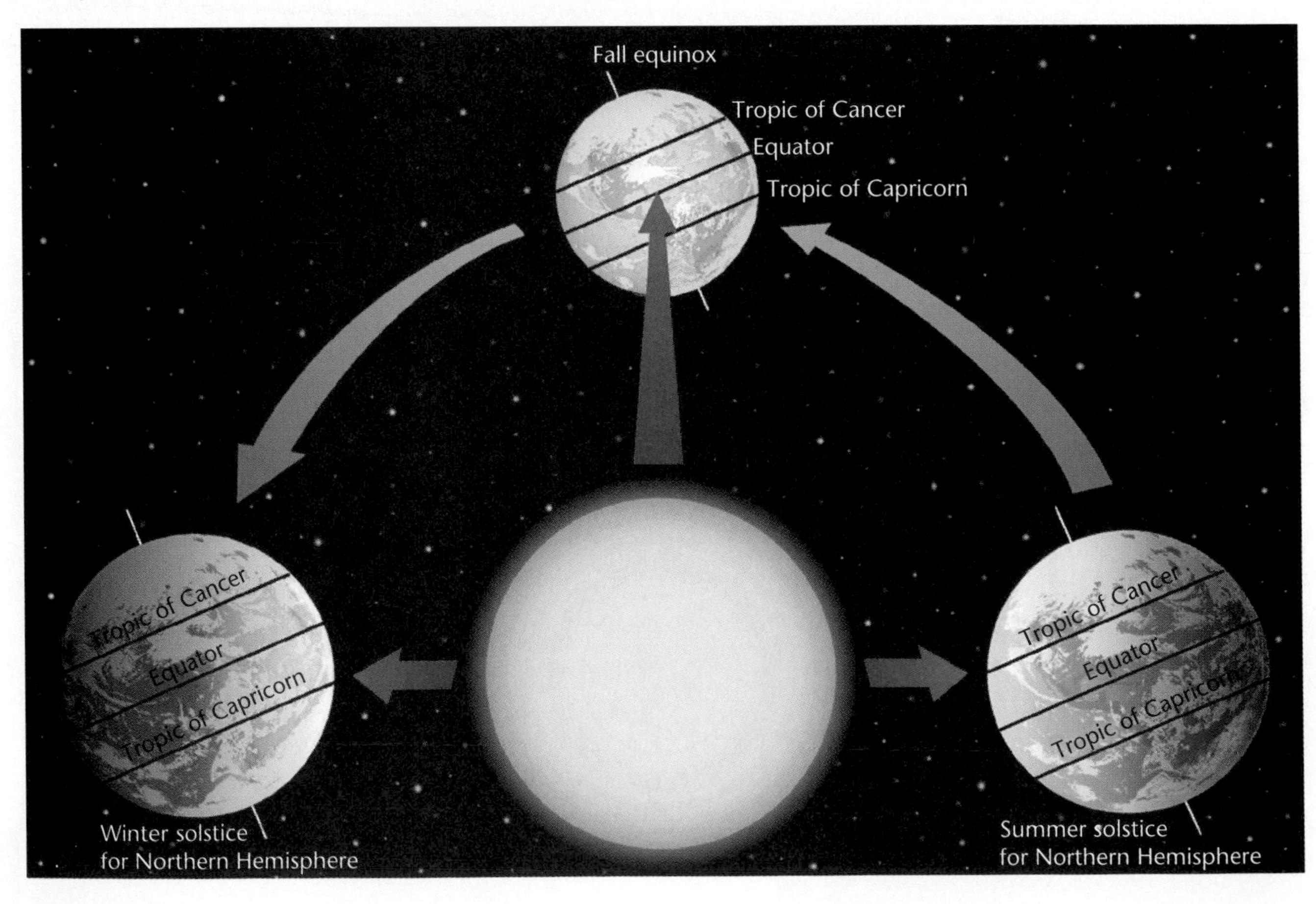

demonstrates what you've already learned: when sunlight is at a less direct angle for less time, the temperature will be lower than if the sunlight is direct and shines for a longer time. **Figure 19-6** shows the difference between hemispheres on a June day.

As you've seen, the motions of Earth affect you a great deal. The rotation of Earth causes day and night, and the revolution of Earth around the sun on a tilted axis is responsible for the changes in seasons. However, Earth is just one of the many bodies traveling around the sun. In the next section, you will learn how Earth's neighbor, the moon, is also moving through space. You will learn the effects of this movement and observe its consequences.

Figure 19-6

These two photographs—one of the Northern and one of the Southern Hemispheres—were both taken on the same day in June.

A The Northern Hemisphere is receiving sunlight at its most direct or highest angle. The Southern Hemisphere is receiving sunlight at its most indirect or lowest angle.

The Umpqua National Forest in Oregon is located in the Northern Hemisphere.

B On this day, which hemisphere is pointing toward the sun? Is Earth at its closest or farthest point from the sun?

New Zealand is located in the Southern Hemisphere.

check your UNDERSTANDING

1. What observable evidence do we have of Earth's shape?
2. There is not truly a sunrise or sunset in the usual sense of the terms rise and set. How can you explain the apparent movement of the sun across the sky?
3. Based on what you've learned about Earth's tilt and the effect of direct sunlight, explain why Chicago experiences seasons.
4. **Apply** Consider yourself manager of an Olympic ski team. The team needs year-round practice to be the best. Around the time of the summer solstice in the United States, to what region of the world would you take the team for practice? What factors influenced your decision?

Measuring in SI

The moon's diameter is about 3476 kilometers. This measure is about a fourth of the diameter of Earth and about 400 times smaller than the diameter of the sun. Calculate the diameters of Earth and the sun. If you need help, refer to the **Skill Handbook** on page 661.

moon is revolving around Earth. The phase you see depends on the position of the moon in relation to both Earth and the sun.

Look at **Figure 19-9**. A new moon occurs when the moon is between Earth and the sun. During the *new moon* phase, the far side of the moon, the side facing away from Earth, is lighted. As the moon continues to revolve around Earth, part of the side facing Earth is lighted and becomes visible. Approximately 24 hours after a new moon, a thin slice of the side facing Earth is lighted. This phase is called a *waxing crescent.* About a week later, one half of the side facing Earth is lighted. This phase is called *first quarter.*

Over the next few days, more and more of the side of the moon facing Earth becomes lighted. When more than half, but less than all of the side facing Earth is lighted, the moon is in its *waxing gibbous* phase. *Full moon* occurs when the whole side facing Earth is lighted. After becoming full, less and less of the side facing Earth is lighted, the phases are waning, and the portion of the visible moon shrinks.

The Moon's Surface

Scientists studying the 380 kilograms of moon rock brought back by *Apollo* astronauts have concluded that the moon is about the same age as Earth—about 4.6 billion years old. For the first 1.5 billion years, the moon was struck by thousands of huge, rocky objects called meteorites. Also, during these early years, erupting volcanoes flooded the moon basins with lava.

In Chapter 1, you learned that the moon has large, flat areas called maria, which means seas. Although there is no water on the moon, observers in the 1600s thought they might have been seas. Scientists hypothesize that maria were formed during the lava flows mentioned earlier.

The low-lying maria have fewer craters than other areas. The indentations in the maria (visible through a telescope) were formed by the impact of interplanetary rocks since the

This rock was collected from the moon on the Apollo 16 *mission.*

Figure 19-9

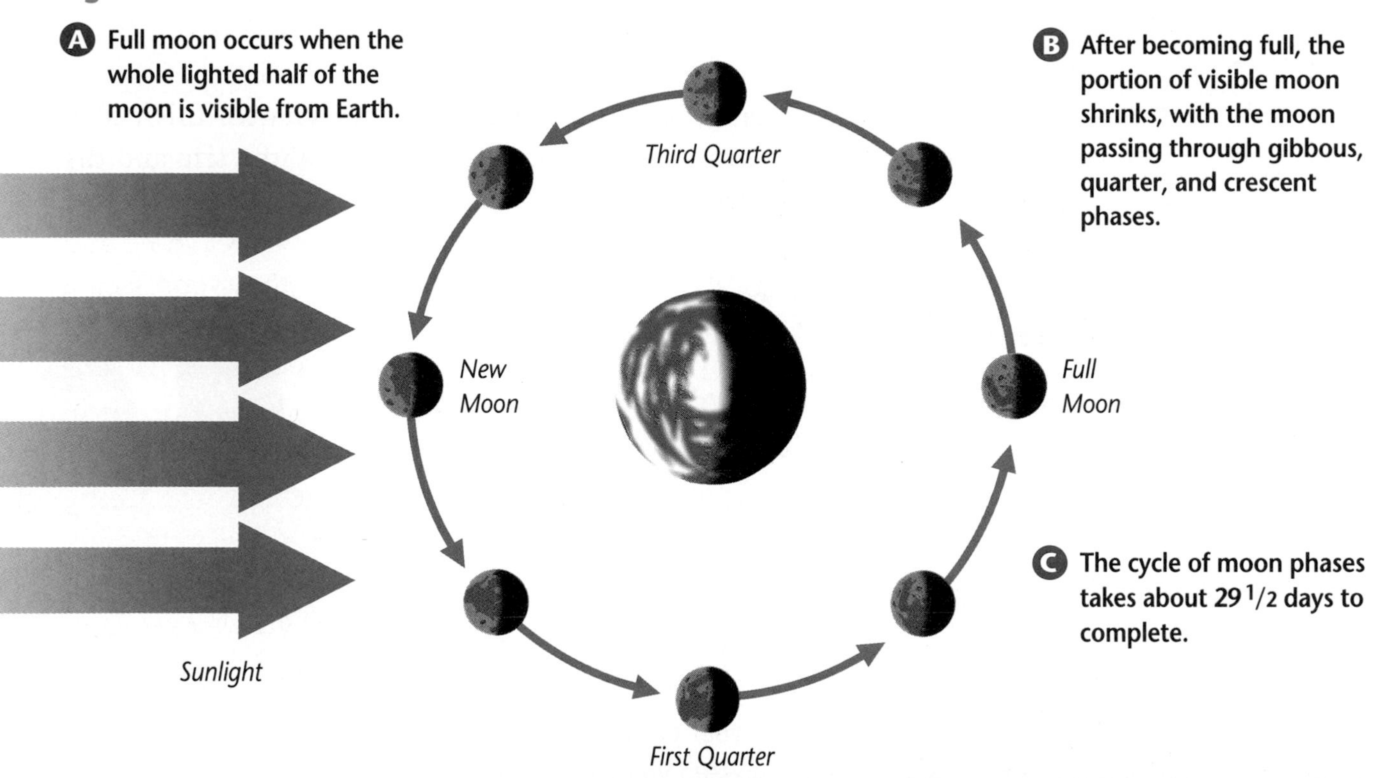

A Full moon occurs when the whole lighted half of the moon is visible from Earth.

B After becoming full, the portion of visible moon shrinks, with the moon passing through gibbous, quarter, and crescent phases.

C The cycle of moon phases takes about 29 1/2 days to complete.

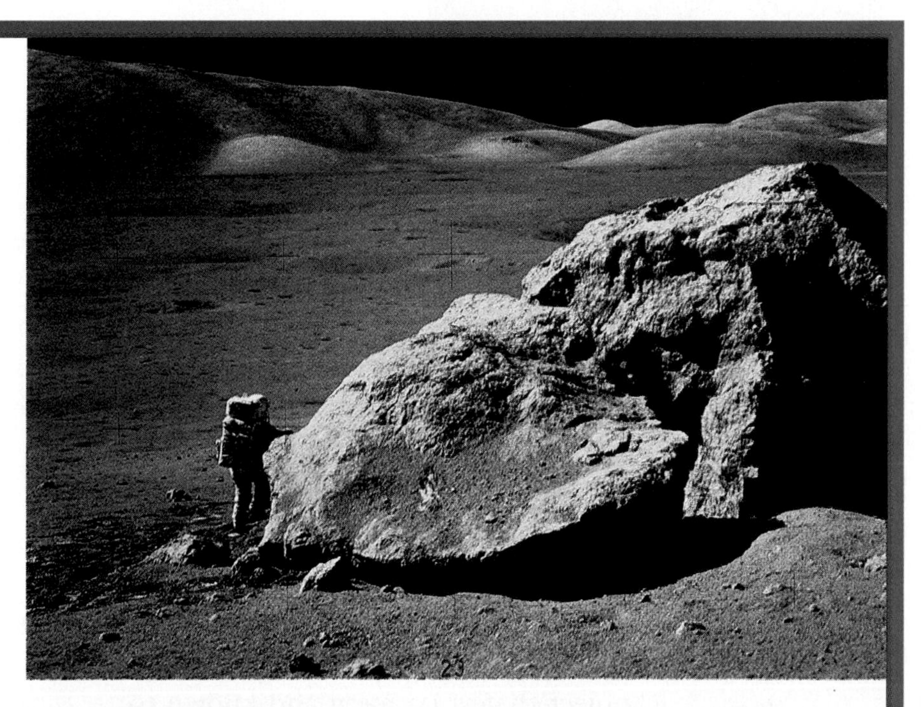

time of the lava flows. The largest of the moon's maria is called Mare Imbrium. Some of the other moon features have been named lacus (lake) and palus (marsh), while edge inlets are called sinus (bays), all despite the fact that—once again—there is no liquid water on the moon.

Other regions, called highlands, are covered with craters. Some of these craters, measuring hundreds of kilometers across, have central peaks. Explosive bombardment of meteorites formed the round craters. Their peaks, too, were a result of these crashes.

The moon has mountain ranges and smaller rows or peaks known simply as ridges. Some valleys, called rilles, curve and wind great distances across the moon's surface.

You Try It!

Make a model of a portion of the moon's surface, using photographs from a book on the *Apollo* missions. Write a description of your creation, explaining how the formations occurred.

Eclipses

What do you think can happen when one member of the sun-moon-Earth system moves between the other two? Your view of this occurrence is affected by the size and distance of the sun and moon.

Explore! ACTIVITY

How is your perception of an object's size affected by its distance from you?

What To Do

1. With a partner, choose an object in the distance that you know is larger than you are, for example, a car or a house.
2. Have your partner stand directly between you and this object. Stand far enough apart so that your view of the object is partially blocked. Describe *in your Journal* what you can see.
3. Next, ask your partner to move closer. Can you still see the object?
4. Finally, ask your partner to stand as close as 0.5 m from you. Now what part of the object can you still see?

In this simple demonstration, you observed how a small, close object can appear to be as big or bigger than an object that is far away and known to be much bigger. This same principle causes the sun and the moon to appear equal in size. Even though the sun's diameter is 400 times greater than the moon's, the moon is about 400 times closer to Earth than the sun. Therefore, the sun and the moon appear to us to be about the same size.

The Explore activity also showed how a smaller object can totally block your view of a larger object. When the moon blocks our view of the sun, as your partner blocked your view of a distant object, we call the event a solar eclipse.

■ Solar Eclipses

Around 600 B.C.E., warriors from ancient Media, in what is now northern Iran, launched an early-morning attack on the neighboring country of Lydia, in present-day Turkey. After several hours of battle, the clear, blue sky darkened, and all color seemed to drain from the landscape. The air became cool, and within minutes the day was as black as night. The planets and stars were visible. The soldiers were stunned. But after several minutes, the stars began to fade, daylight replaced darkness, and the sun reappeared. The soldiers were so frightened that they dropped their weapons and fled the battlefield. They were certain that the end of the world was near.

The soldiers had experienced a solar eclipse. You can see what a total solar eclipse looks like in **Figure 19-10**. It is a rare but natural event that leaves observers standing in the shadow of the moon. Recall from Chapter 2 how shadows are formed. A **solar eclipse** occurs when the moon passes directly between Earth and the sun. The moon blocks out some of the sun's light, casting a shadow on Earth.

Look at **Figure 19-11** to help you understand how a solar eclipse occurs. In areas of total solar eclipse, the only portion of the sun that is visible is part of its atmosphere. This appears as a white glow around the edge of the eclipsing moon.

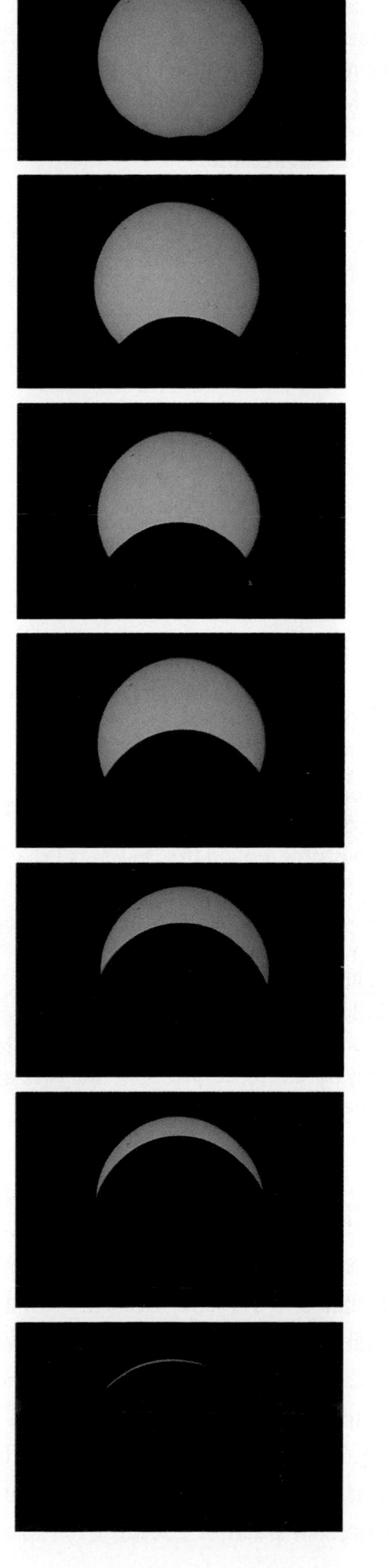

Figure 19-10

During a solar eclipse, the moon passes directly between Earth and the sun.

Figure 19-11

A **A solar eclipse occurs when Earth passes into the moon's shadow. The moon's shadow is only about 270 km to 300 km wide, so only people standing in the shadow's path see the eclipse.**

B **The moon casts a dark inner shadow called the umbra. The umbra is the center of the moon's shadow where the sun's light is completely blocked from view on Earth.**

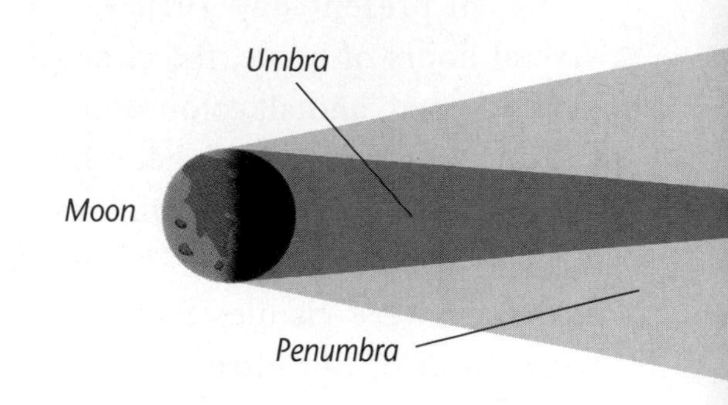

Sun

C **In the outer part of the moon's shadow, called the penumbra, sunlight is only partially blocked.**

Figure 19-12

Jumbo, a forty-foot solar telescope, was hauled to various sites around the world to view solar eclipses. Jumbo recorded almost every total solar eclipse worldwide between 1892 and 1931. Here, astronomers get Jumbo ready for a total eclipse of the sun in Jeur, India, on January 22, 1898.

Earth and Moon Shadows

Because the sun is so large and its rays spread out, the moon's and Earth's shadows have two parts. They cast a dark, cone-shaped shadow called the *umbra* inside a larger, lighter shadow called the *penumbra.* A total eclipse is only experienced by people in the narrow path of the umbra. You can see the two different shadows in **Figure 19-11**.

A partial eclipse occurs on Earth when the moon covers only part of the sun. This is what observers within the penumbra see. As the moon slides in front of the sun, it may look as though a sliver has been cut out of the edge of the sun.

Earth

D If you observed a total solar eclipse, that is where the moon blocks all sunlight from shining on Earth, would you be within the umbra or penumbra?

A Rare Event

Although a rare and dramatic event, a solar eclipse can be dangerous to careless observers. You should never look directly at the sun, particularly during a solar eclipse. The sun's radiation can damage your eyes and cause blindness. A solar eclipse should be viewed indirectly by projecting the image of the eclipse onto a sheet of white paper. If you can't witness the event firsthand, you now have the option of live and taped video coverage of such events.

Solar eclipses do not happen every time the moon travels around Earth, however. This is because the path of the moon's revolution is tilted at about a 5° angle to Earth's path around the sun. Because of this difference, the moon usually passes above or below the sun and not directly in front of it.

While between two and seven solar eclipses occur every year, they can be seen in only a few areas on Earth at any one time. A total solar eclipse can be seen only once every 450 years from any one location. Often, total solar eclipses occur in remote regions such as Siberia and the middle of the Atlantic Ocean. So unless you are able to travel, and depending on the weather once you get there, your chances of seeing a total eclipse are not very good.

If you do the following Investigate, however, you will see exactly how solar eclipses—as well as moon phases—occur.

INVESTIGATE!

Eclipses and Moon Phases

You know that moon phases and solar eclipses result from the relative positions of the sun, the moon, and Earth. In this activity, you will demonstrate the positions of these bodies during certain phases and eclipses. You will also see why only a very small portion of Earth sees a total solar eclipse.

Problem

How can you demonstrate moon phases and solar eclipses?

Materials

- pencil
- unshaded light source
- polystyrene ball
- globe

Safety Precautions

Be careful, the exposed bulb will be hot.

What To Do

1. Copy the data table *into your Journal.*
2. Stick the pencil into the polystyrene ball, ***making a model*** moon with a handle.
3. Set the globe and the lamp on the table about 0.5 m apart and turn on the light.

Data and Observations

Moon Phase	Observations
New	
First Quarter	
Full	
Third Quarter	

A

B

4 Holding the model moon by its pencil handle, move it around the globe to duplicate the position that will cause a solar eclipse. Record your observations *in your Journal.*

5 Use this sun-Earth-moon model to duplicate the phases of the moon. During which phase(s) of the moon could a solar eclipse occur? How can you use the model to observe the umbra and penumbra of the moon?

Analyzing

1. During which phase(s) of the moon is it possible for a solar eclipse to occur?
2. ***Determine the effect*** that a small change in the distance between Earth and the moon would have on the size of the shadow during an eclipse.
3. As seen from Earth, how does the apparent size of the moon ***compare*** with the apparent size of the sun? How can an eclipse be used to confirm this?

Concluding and Applying

4. Why doesn't a solar eclipse occur every month? Explain your answer.
5. Suppose you wanted to make a more accurate model of the movement of the moon around Earth. How might you adjust the distance between the light source and the globe? How would you adjust the size of the moon model in comparison with the globe you are using?
6. **Going Further** ***Hypothesize*** what would happen if the sun, the moon, and Earth were lined up with Earth directly in between the sun and the moon.

Figure 19-13

A During a lunar eclipse, the moon gradually becomes darker as it moves into Earth's shadow.

B A lunar eclipse can last up to one hour and forty-four minutes. During this time, the moon may appear reddish. Unless clouds hide the view, most people on the nighttime side of Earth can see the lunar eclipse.

■ Lunar Eclipses

In the Investigate, did you conclude that a shadow can also be cast on the moon? When this happens, a lunar eclipse occurs.

Earth casts a shadow on the side of the moon facing the sun. Once every 29 days, in its revolution around Earth, the moon moves near this shadow. When the moon does pass through Earth's shadow, we see a **lunar eclipse**. At this time, Earth is directly between the sun and the moon. **Figure 19-13** will help you understand how a lunar eclipse occurs.

In this section, you learned that moon phases and eclipses are a result of the way Earth, the sun, and the moon line up. In the next section, you'll discover one more interesting effect their positions can produce.

Lunar eclipse

Penumbra

Earth

Umbra

Moon

Sun

C A total lunar eclipse occurs when the moon passes completely into Earth's umbra.

check your UNDERSTANDING

1. Draw the relative positions of the sun, the moon, and Earth during a full moon phase.
2. Which type of eclipse can occur during a full moon?
3. **Apply** Why does only a small percentage of Earth's population witness a solar eclipse, while people on the entire nighttime side of Earth can see a lunar eclipse?

Tides

Earth, Moon, and Ocean

Have you ever been to an ocean beach? Many people unfamiliar with the ocean will place their towels and sandals at what seems a safe distance from the water and then return to find them floating away. What happened? The lifeguard on duty will tell you that the tide came in.

Do you remember what you learned about waves and wavelengths in Chapter 17? **Tides** are slow-moving water waves with long wavelengths. They produce an alternate rise and fall of the surface level of the oceans. **Figure 19-14** shows the difference in water levels during high and low tides.

Section Objectives

- Describe the changes you might observe along a coastline during high and low tides.
- Diagram the relative positions of the sun, the moon, and Earth during the highest tides.

Key Terms

tides

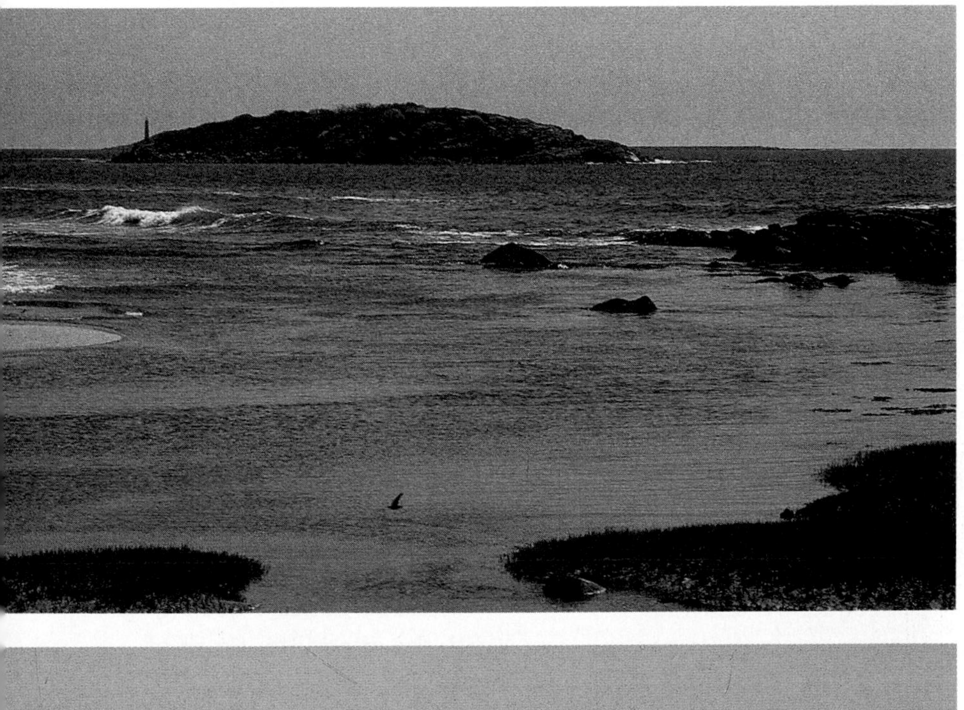

Figure 19-14

A At high tide, the surface level of the ocean is at its highest point. Once this high point is reached, the water level begins to drop. This photograph of the shoreline at Cape Ann, Massachusetts, was taken during high tide.

B Over a period of several hours, the water recedes, and more and more land is exposed. This photograph was taken at low tide, which is when the surface of the ocean reaches its lowest level.

Figure 19-15

The sun, the moon, and Earth have gravitational forces acting between them. These gravitational forces actually pull on Earth's oceans.

A When the sun and the moon line up with Earth, the high tides are very high and the low tides are very low.

B When the sun and the moon are not lined up with Earth, they pull in different directions, and the tides are not as high and not as low.

When the tide comes in, the water level rises, and the waves break farther and farther inland. At high tide, the surface level of the ocean is at its highest point. At low tide, the surface of the ocean has reached its lowest level.

High tides occur about every $12\frac{1}{2}$ hours. A low tide occurs about $6\frac{1}{4}$ hours after every high tide. In other words, there are two high tides and two low tides every day. High and low tides occur about six hours apart along much of the East Coast of the United States.

You may be asking yourself, "What do tides have to do with this chapter?" **Figure 19-15** and the next activity will show you.

Life Science CONNECTION

Life in an Intertidal Zone

As you learned in the chapter, the gravitational pull of the moon causes tides in the oceans of Earth. You know that tides can affect the daily activities of people who fish and other people who rely on the sea. But did you also know that tides affect the activities of some of the many organisms that inhabit Earth's oceans?

If you were on a boat in the middle of the ocean, you would not be able to see the effects of tides. However, if you were on shore, you would see the changes in water level due to tides. The area near shore that is alternately covered and uncovered by tides is known as the intertidal zone, and it is home to a variety of organisms.

The continuously changing environment of the intertidal zone presents quite a challenge to the many organisms that live there. One of the toughest tasks for the many tiny animals living in intertidal zones is dealing with the intermittent rush of water and waves. Many of these animals, such as barnacles and mussels, survive by attaching themselves to large rocks. Other animals, such as crabs, lugworms, and shelled mollusks, avoid crashing waves by burrowing into the ground.

Another challenge in an intertidal zone is the dry

Fiddler crab

Find Out! ACTIVITY

What is the relationship between tides and the moon?

What To Do

1. Study **Table 19-1**, a chart that lists the range of tidal heights for 2 weeks and also the observed moon phases for this same time period.
2. Identify the time during these 2 weeks that the tide difference or range was the greatest. What phase of the moon corresponds to this date? What other phase might cause a similar range?

Conclude and Apply

1. Sketch the way the sun, the moon, and Earth are positioned when the tide difference was greatest.
2. How would you change the sketch for dates when the tidal difference was the lowest?
3. What relation do you see between tide movement and moon position?

Table 19-1

Date	Height of high tide (meters)	Height of low tide (meters)
1	1.4	0.5
2	1.5	0.4
3	1.7	0.2
4	1.8	–0.1
5	2.1	–0.3
6	2.2	–0.5
7	2.3	–0.6
8	2.3	–0.6
9	2.3	–0.6
10	2.1	–0.5
11	1.9	–0.2
12	1.6	–0.1
13	1.6	0.2
14	1.6	0.4

condition of the zone when the tide is out. Many marine organisms require a moist environment to survive. Seaweeds often attach to cracks and crevices in large beach rocks where water collects. The barnacle, shown here, can close its shell, sealing in moisture and protecting itself from predators and the sun's rays.

Feeding habits of animals are also affected by tides. Barnacles close up during low tide, but as soon as the sea covers them again, their shells open, and they use leg-like structures for feeding. Another animal, the limpet, while fixed to one spot during low tide, is known to travel long distances when the tide is in. As the tide goes out, limpets travel back to their original rock homes.

Mussels

Barnacles

What Do You Think?

The intertidal zone represents one example of how physical factors affect living organisms. How are the organisms of the intertidal zone adapted to their changing environment? Can you think of other animals or plants that are adapted to continuously changing environmental conditions?

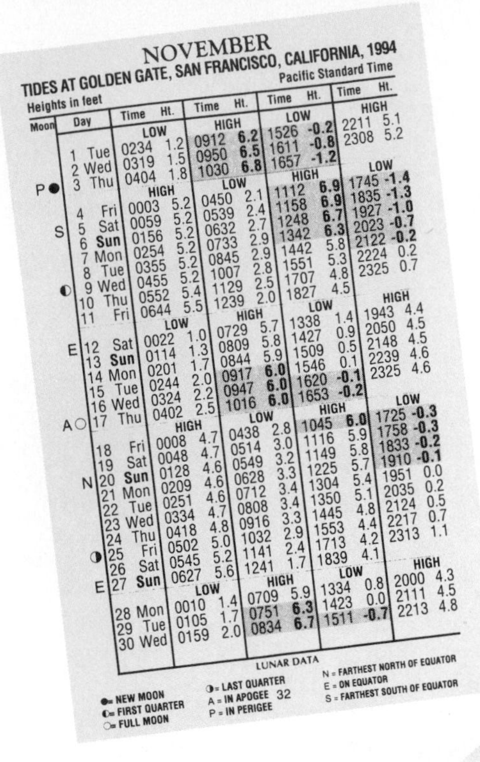

NOVEMBER

TIDES AT GOLDEN GATE, SAN FRANCISCO, CALIFORNIA, 1994

Heights in feet — Pacific Standard Time

Moon	Day	Time	Ht.	Time	Ht.	Time	Ht.	Time	Ht.
		LOW		HIGH		LOW		HIGH	
	1 Tue	0234	1.2	0912	6.2	1526	-0.2	2211	5.1
	2 Wed	0319	1.5	0950	6.5	1611	-0.8	2308	5.2
P●	3 Thu	0404	1.8	1030	6.8	1657	-1.2		
		HIGH		LOW		HIGH		LOW	
	4 Fri	0003	5.2	0450	2.1	1112	6.9	1745	-1.4
S	5 Sat	0059	5.2	0539	2.4	1158	6.9	1835	-1.3
	6 Sun	0156	5.2	0632	2.7	1248	6.7	1927	-1.0
	7 Mon	0254	5.2	0733	2.9	1342	6.3	2023	-0.7
	8 Tue	0355	5.2	0845	2.9	1442	5.8	2122	-0.2
◐	9 Wed	0455	5.2	1007	2.8	1551	5.3	2224	0.2
	10 Thu	0552	5.4	1129	2.5	1707	4.8	2325	0.7
	11 Fri	0644	5.5	1239	2.0	1827	4.5		
		LOW		HIGH		LOW		HIGH	
E	12 Sat	0022	1.0	0729	5.7	1338	1.4	1943	4.4
	13 Sun	0114	1.3	0809	5.8	1427	0.9	2050	4.5
	14 Mon	0201	1.7	0844	5.9	1509	0.5	2148	4.5
	15 Tue	0244	2.0	0917	6.0	1546	0.1	2239	4.6
	16 Wed	0324	2.2	0947	6.0	1620	-0.1	2325	4.6
A○	17 Thu	0402	2.5	1016	6.0	1653	-0.2		
		HIGH		LOW		HIGH		LOW	
	18 Fri	0008	4.7	0438	2.8	1045	6.0	1725	-0.3
	19 Sat	0048	4.7	0514	3.0	1116	5.9	1758	-0.3
N	20 Sun	0128	4.6	0549	3.2	1149	5.8	1833	-0.2
	21 Mon	0209	4.6	0628	3.3	1225	5.7	1910	-0.1
	22 Tue	0251	4.6	0712	3.4	1304	5.4	1951	0.0
	23 Wed	0334	4.7	0808	3.4	1350	5.1	2035	0.2
	24 Thu	0418	4.8	0916	3.3	1445	4.8	2124	0.5
◑	25 Fri	0502	5.0	1032	2.9	1553	4.4	2217	0.7
	26 Sat	0545	5.2	1141	2.4	1713	4.2	2313	1.1
E	27 Sun	0627	5.6	1241	1.7	1839	4.1		
		LOW		HIGH		LOW		HIGH	
	28 Mon	0010	1.4	0709	5.9	1334	0.8	2000	4.3
	29 Tue	0105	1.7	0751	6.3	1423	0.0	2111	4.5
	30 Wed	0159	2.0	0834	6.7	1511	-0.7	2213	4.8

LUNAR DATA

●= NEW MOON
◐= FIRST QUARTER
○= FULL MOON
◑= LAST QUARTER
A = IN APOGEE 32
P = IN PERIGEE
N = FARTHEST NORTH OF EQUATOR
E = ON EQUATOR
S = FARTHEST SOUTH OF EQUATOR

Figure 19-16

People who work on the sea must take the tides into consideration. Tide charts, like the one shown here from San Francisco, California, help them plan their work.

As you could see from the Find Out activity, the moon has a great effect on tides. But why does the moon have a greater effect than the sun? That's because it is about 400 times closer to Earth than the sun.

What effect might tides have on people living along an ocean coast? What other people might make use of our knowledge of tides? **Figure 19-16** describes the importance knowledge of tides can have for some people.

Now you know why you've studied tides with the moon. Tides are caused by the gravitational pull of the sun and moon on the oceans. The range of the tides depends on how the moon, the sun, and Earth are lined up.

Ⓐ People who fish have discovered that the best time to fish is when the ocean tides are about to turn: about one hour before and after both high tide and low tide. According to the chart above when are the best times to fish?

Ⓑ Oyster harvesters in Cancale, France, take advantage of the tides in making their living. At high tide, their oyster beds are covered by water. At low tide, the beds are uncovered, making them easily accessible to harvest.

check your UNDERSTANDING

1. Compare and contrast a beach at high tide and a beach at low tide.
2. Diagram the relative positions of the sun, the moon, and Earth during the highest tides of the month.
3. **Apply** Suppose you want to search for shells along a beach. How would a knowledge of tides help you in your search?

Science and Society

Spin-Offs from the Space Program

From the beginning of space exploration, some people have wondered why so much time and money have been devoted to the pursuit of knowledge about space. Aren't there more important concerns than learning about space? Wouldn't money be better spent on improving the quality of life on Earth?

The space program has benefited many people right here on Earth. Much of the technology developed for space exploration is adapted and used to make our lives better. These technologies are called spin-offs. Let's look at some of the spin-offs from the United States space program.

Medical science has gained much from space research. Patients with internal bleeding may wear astronaut-type pressure suits that temporarily alter blood flow to promote healing. Heart attack victims benefit from heart monitoring techniques. Pacemakers, which help to regulate the heartbeats of some heart patients, use tiny batteries first developed for spacecraft.

Movable artificial limbs, designed for NASA's robots, are available for use by amputees and victims of paralysis of the legs (paraplegics) or of all four limbs (quadriplegics). Lasers, used as an improved "vision" for spacecraft by NASA, provide an alternative method of performing delicate eye and brain surgery.

Many of our clothes are made from fabrics originally created for astronauts. Our digital clocks evolved from NASA's timepieces. We can wear sunglasses that change tint with changes in the light around us. Even in the kitchen, we can find cookware coated with heat-resistant substances, plastic film and aluminum foil for preserving food, and freeze-dried foods—all originally developed for the space program.

Science Journal

Considering the amount and types of spin-offs from the space program, is all the time and money devoted to the program worth it? *In your Science Journal,* write a few paragraphs giving your opinions.

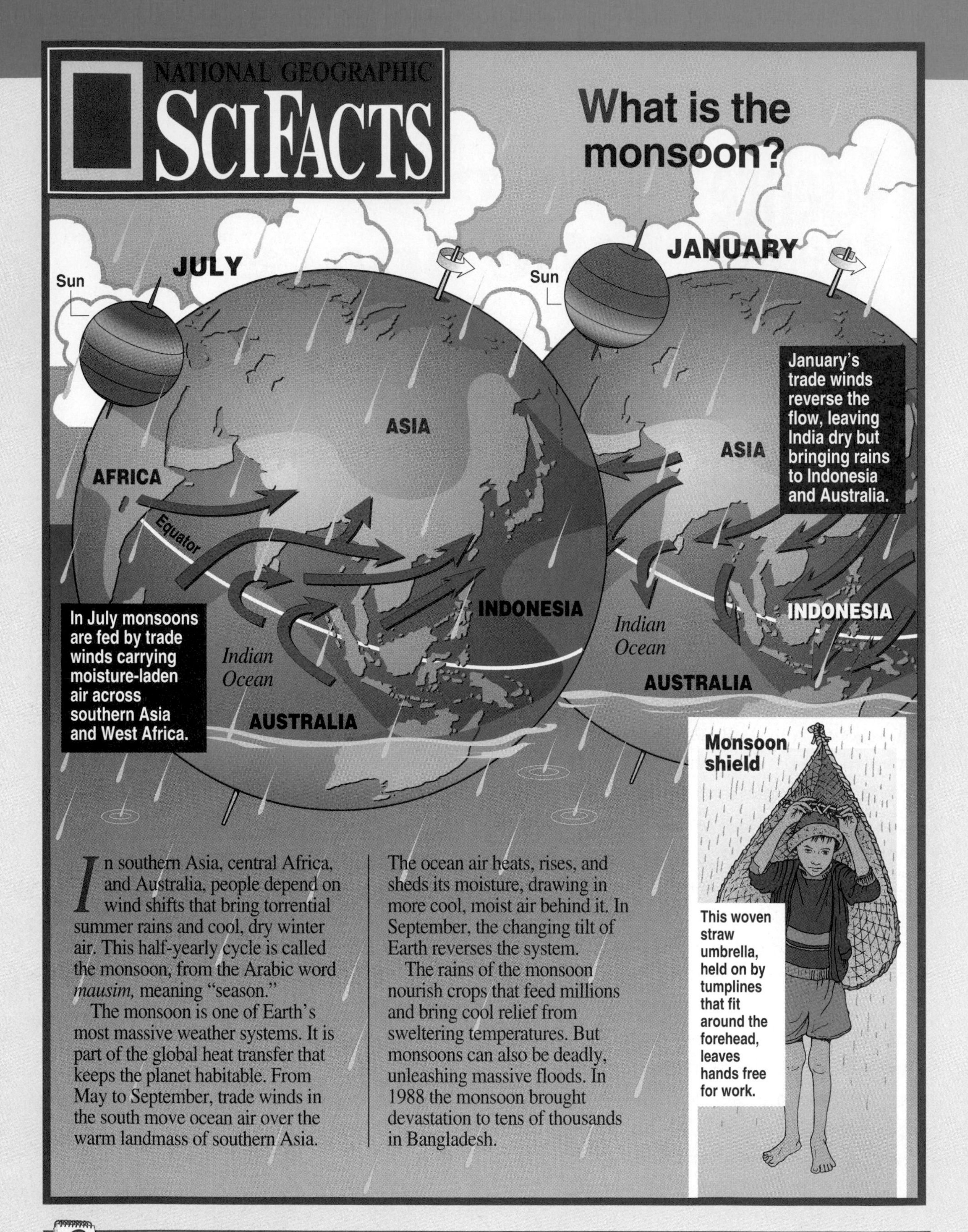

What is the monsoon?

In southern Asia, central Africa, and Australia, people depend on wind shifts that bring torrential summer rains and cool, dry winter air. This half-yearly cycle is called the monsoon, from the Arabic word *mausim,* meaning "season."

The monsoon is one of Earth's most massive weather systems. It is part of the global heat transfer that keeps the planet habitable. From May to September, trade winds in the south move ocean air over the warm landmass of southern Asia. The ocean air heats, rises, and sheds its moisture, drawing in more cool, moist air behind it. In September, the changing tilt of Earth reverses the system.

The rains of the monsoon nourish crops that feed millions and bring cool relief from sweltering temperatures. But monsoons can also be deadly, unleashing massive floods. In 1988 the monsoon brought devastation to tens of thousands in Bangladesh.

Science Journal

In your Science Journal, describe what might happen if the monsoon ceased to take place. Be sure to discuss the monsoon's impact on Earth's weather patterns, as well as its impact on people.

Teens in SCIENCE

Reaching for the Stars

Have you ever experienced a solar eclipse? Some people describe eclipses as being eerie or strange. But Natalie Sanchez, who experienced an eclipse when she was a freshman at Valley High School in Albuquerque, New Mexico, described an eclipse in a completely different way.

"I was on a field trip with the Math and Engineering Club at school," Natalie said. "We had gone to the observatory to watch the eclipse. The staff had given us really good glasses to protect our eyes. I thought it was the most beautiful thing I had ever seen. As it grew dark, everyone started cheering. But I was very quiet. I was completely in awe. On the bus ride home, I made up my mind that I want to be an astronomer."

Natalie soon discovered that her school did not offer any in-depth classes about astronomy. But she did not let that stop her from finding out more about her new hobby.

"After school, I spent a lot of time doing research at the library," Natalie explained. "I read everything about astronomy that I can get my hands on—and that's a lot. But the more I read, the more I wanted to know. Sure, I'm curious about our solar system. But I'm also trying to decide for myself whether or not it is possible that other solar systems are out there, too. Before I saw that eclipse, when I looked at the night sky I thought it was very pretty. But now when I look up at the stars, I feel like I'm looking at the biggest mystery in the universe."

What Do You Think?

Observing the eclipse changed the course of Natalie Sanchez's life. Have you ever had an experience that affected your plans for the future?

Below, the Mayall telescope at Kitt Peak, Arizona

chapter 19
REVIEWING MAIN IDEAS

Science Journal

Review the statements below about the big ideas presented in this chapter, and answer the questions. Then, re-read your answers to the Did You Ever Wonder questions at the beginning of the chapter. *In your Science Journal,* write a paragraph about how your understanding of the big ideas in the chapter has changed.

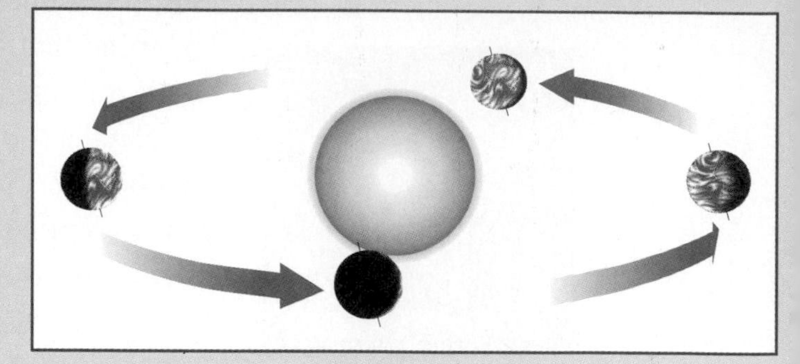

1. The motions and relative positions of Earth, the moon, and the sun are responsible for night and day, the change of seasons, the phases of the moon, eclipses, and tides. ***What would be different on Earth if it weren't tilted on its axis?***

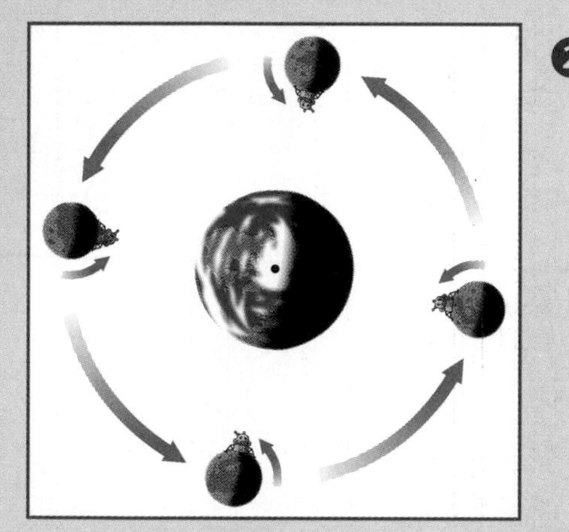

2. The moon rotates once during its month-long revolution around Earth. During this time, different portions of the side of the moon facing Earth are lighted. ***What would appear different about the moon if it rotated twice during each revolution?***

3. During a solar eclipse, the moon passes between the sun and Earth and casts a shadow on Earth. During a lunar eclipse, Earth passes between the sun and moon, casting a curved shadow on the moon. ***What parts of Earth experience a total solar eclipse when the moon passes between the sun and Earth?***

4. Tides are the alternate rise and fall of the surface level of the oceans and are directly related to the gravitational force of the moon and the sun on Earth. ***Why aren't tides as noticeable in the middle of the ocean as they are along the shore?***

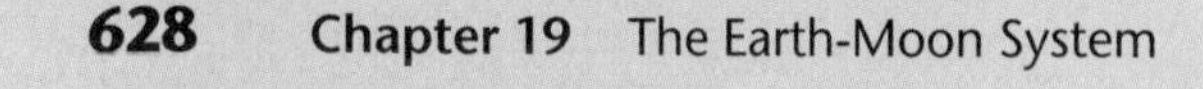

chapter 19

CHAPTER REVIEW

Using Key Science Terms

equinox
lunar eclipse
revolution
rotation
solar eclipse
solstice
sphere
tide

For each set of terms below, choose the one term that does not belong and explain why it does not belong.

1. equinox, lunar eclipse, solstice
2. revolution, rotation, equinox
3. sphere, rotation, tide
4. solar eclipse, lunar eclipse, rotation
5. lunar eclipse, tide, equinox

Use one of the terms to complete each sentence.

6. Earth's movement around the sun is called a __________.
7. Earth's spinning on its axis is called __________.
8. In the Northern Hemisphere, the summer __________ occurs on June 21 or 22, when the North Pole is tilted toward the sun.

Understanding Ideas

Answer the following questions in your Journal *using complete sentences.*

1. What causes the change in seasons?
2. At the time of an equinox, the sun is directly over what point on Earth?
3. What causes the moon's phases?
4. Compare and contrast a solar and a lunar eclipse.
5. When does the greatest range between high and low tides occur?

Developing Skills

Use your understanding of the concepts developed in this chapter to answer each of the following questions.

1. **Concept Mapping** Create and label a diagram illustrating the moon phases and why they occur.
2. **Making Models** Use the lamp and globe from the Find Out activity on page 605 to show how the rays of the sun change location with the beginning of the summer and winter solstices and the spring and fall equinoxes.
3. **Observing and Inferring** After doing the Explore activity on page 614, use two different-sized balls and line them up so they appear to be the same size. Which ball is farther away from you? How do the results of this activity compare with the results of the original activity?
4. **Making Models** Use the model from the Investigate on pages 618-619 to show the position of the sun, Earth, and the moon during a lunar eclipse.

chapter 19
CHAPTER REVIEW

Critical Thinking

In your Journal, *answer each of the following questions.*

1. Why do the sun and moon appear to move westward in the sky? Why are the terms sunrise and sunset misleading?
2. Imagine that Earth is not tilted on its axis, as shown in the illustration. What effect would this have on the seasons and the number of hours of daylight and darkness throughout the year?

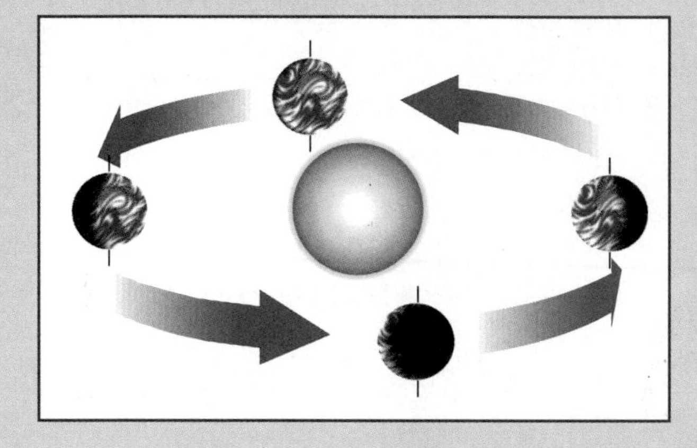

3. Earth is actually closest to the sun during the Northern Hemisphere's winter. Explain how this can be so.

Problem Solving

Read the following problem and discuss your answers in a brief paragraph.

Imagine you and your friends will be spending the coming year traveling throughout the world! Your friends want to arrange a schedule allowing you always to be someplace warm.

Using a globe, describe the route you and your friends would take to make sure that over the course of the year you are always someplace that is experiencing the summer season. Be specific. Give dates, locations, and explanations for your choices.

CONNECTING IDEAS

Discuss each of the following in a brief paragraph.

1. **Theme—Systems and Interactions** Explain the moon's revolution around Earth in terms of a satellite's motion. What force holds the moon in its path around Earth? What keeps it from crashing into Earth?
2. **Theme—Systems and Interactions** Explain why a lunar eclipse can occur only during a full moon phase.
3. **Theme—Scale and Structure** If the moon were transparent instead of opaque, what effect would this have on the occurrence of solar eclipses? What if it were translucent?
4. **Science and Society** Summarize the technological benefits we have received from the space program.
5. **A Closer Look** At which phase of the moon do you think you can best see the maria and craters from Earth?

unit 5

UNIT REVIEW

In this unit, you investigated mechanical waves and found that they may be longitudinal or transverse, depending on how particles within a wave move.

You also learned that movements of Earth and the moon cause tides, moon phases, and lunar and solar eclipses to occur. In addition to this, you learned how humans are affected by the motion caused by earthquakes and volcanoes.

Try the exercises and activity that follow—they will challenge you to use and apply some of the ideas you learned in this unit.

CONNECTING IDEAS

1. Do you think that a transverse wave can pass through water? When you send a transverse wave through rope, the particles of rope move side to side. Would water particles move side to side to allow a transverse wave to pass? What do you think would happen to transverse waves generated by earthquakes when they encountered liquid rock material inside Earth?
2. How do waves at Earth's surface cause buildings to crumble during an earthquake? In what way are these waves similar to waves generated in water?

Exploring Further ACTIVITY

1. Design and construct a moving model that demonstrates the cause of eclipses.
2. Demonstrate it for the class.

Table of Contents

International System of Units

The International System (SI) of Measurement is accepted as the standard for measurement throughout most of the world. Three base units in SI are the meter, kilogram, and second. Frequently used SI units are listed below.

Table A-1: Frequently used SI Units	
Length	1 millimeter (mm) = 1000 micrometers (µm) 1 centimeter (cm) = 10 millimeters (mm) 1 meter (m) = 100 centimeters (cm) 1 kilometer (km) = 1000 meters (m) 1 light-year = 9 460 000 000 000 kilometers (km)
Area	1 square meter (m^2) = 10 000 square centimeters (cm^2) 1 square kilometer (km^2) = 1 000 000 square meters (m^2)
Volume	1 milliliter (mL) = 1 cubic centimeter (cm^3) 1 liter (L) = 1000 milliliters (mL)
Mass	1 gram (g) = 1000 milligrams (mg) 1 kilogram (kg) = 1000 grams (g) 1 metric ton (g) = 1000 kilograms (kg)
Time	1 s = 1 second

Temperature measurements in SI are often made in degrees Celsius. Celsius temperature is a supplementary unit derived from the base unit kelvin. The Celsius scale (°C) has 100 equal graduations between the freezing temperature (0°C) and the boiling temperature of water (100°C). The following relationship exists between the Celsius and kelvin temperature scales:

$$K = °C + 273$$

Several other supplementary SI units are listed below.

Table A-2: Supplementary SI Units

Measurement	Unit	Symbol	Expressed in Base Units
Energy	Joule	J	$kg \cdot m^2/s^2$ or $N \cdot m$
Force	Newton	N	$kg \cdot m/s^2$
Power	Watt	W	$kg \cdot m^2/s^3$ or J/s
Pressure	Pascal	Pa	$kg/(m \cdot s^2)$ or N/m^2

APPENDIX B

°F: 210, 200, 190, 180, 170, 160, 150, 140, 130, 120, 110, 100, 90, 80, 70, 60, 50, 40, 30, 20, 10, 0, -10

°C: 100, 90, 80, 70, 60, 50, 40, 30, 20, 10, 0, -10, -20

Table B-1: SI/Metric to English Conversions

	When You Want to Convert:	Multiply By:	To Find:
Length	inches	2.54	centimeters
	centimeters	0.39	inches
	feet	0.30	meters
	meters	3.28	feet
	yards	0.91	meters
	meters	1.09	yards
	miles	1.61	kilometers
	kilometers	0.62	miles
Mass and Weight	ounces	28.35	grams
	grams	0.04	ounces
	pounds	0.45	kilograms
	kilograms	2.2	pounds
	tons	0.91	tonnes (metric tons)
	tonnes (metric tons)	1.10	tons
	pounds	4.45	newtons
	newtons	0.23	pounds
Volume	cubic inches	16.39	cubic centimeters
	cubic centimeters	0.06	cubic inches
	cubic feet	0.03	cubic meters
	cubic meters	35.3	cubic feet
	liters	1.06	quarts
	liters	0.26	gallons
	gallons	3.78	liters
Area	square inches	6.45	square centimeters
	square centimeters	0.16	square inches
	square feet	0.09	square meters
	square meters	10.76	square feet
	square miles	2.59	square kilometers
	square kilometers	0.39	miles
	hectares	2.47	acres
	acres	0.40	hectares
Temperature	Fahrenheit	5/9 (°F – 32)	Celsius
	Celsius	9/5 °C + 32	Fahrenheit

Safety in the Science Classroom

1. Always obtain your teacher's permission to begin an investigation.
2. Study the procedure. If you have questions, ask your teacher. Understand any safety symbols shown on the page.
3. Use the safety equipment provided for you. Goggles and a safety apron should be worn when any investigation calls for using chemicals.
4. Always slant test tubes away from yourself and others when heating them.
5. Never eat or drink in the lab, and never use lab glassware as food or drink containers. Never inhale chemicals. Do not taste any substances or draw any material into a tube with your mouth.
6. If you spill any chemical, wash it off immediately with water. Report the spill immediately to your teacher.
7. Know the location and proper use of the fire extinguisher, safety shower, fire blanket, first aid kit, and fire alarm.
8. Keep materials away from flames. Tie back hair and loose clothing.
9. If a fire should break out in the classroom, or if your clothing should catch fire, smother it with the fire blanket or a coat, or get under a safety shower. NEVER RUN.
10. Report any accident or injury, no matter how small, to your teacher.

Follow these procedures as you clean up your work area.

1. Turn off the water and gas. Disconnect electrical devices.
2. Return all materials to their proper places.
3. Dispose of chemicals and other materials as directed by your teacher. Place broken glass and solid substances in the proper containers. Never discard materials in the sink.
4. Clean your work area.
5. Wash your hands thoroughly after working in the laboratory.

Table C-1: First Aid

Injury	Safe Response
Burns	Apply cold water. Call your teacher immediately.
Cuts and bruises	Stop any bleeding by applying direct pressure. Cover cuts with a clean dressing. Apply cold compresses to bruises. Call your teacher immediately.
Fainting	Leave the person lying down. Loosen any tight clothing and keep crowds away. Call your teacher immediately.
Foreign matter in eye	Flush with plenty of water. Use eyewash bottle or fountain. Call your teacher immediately.
Poisoning	Note the suspected poisoning agent and call your teacher immediately.
Any spills on skin	Flush with large amounts of water or use safety shower. Call your teacher immediately.

Table D-1: Safety Symbols			
	**Disposal Alert** This symbol appears when care must be taken to dispose of materials properly.		**Animal Safety** This symbol appears whenever live animals are studied and the safety of the animals and the students must be ensured.
	**Biological Hazard** This symbol appears when there is danger involving bacteria, fungi, or protists.		**Radioactive Safety** This symbol appears when radioactive materials are used.
	**Open Flame Alert** This symbol appears when use of an open flame could cause a fire or an explosion.		**Clothing Protection Safety** This symbol appears when substances used could stain or burn clothing.
	**Thermal Safety** This symbol appears as a reminder to use caution when handling hot objects.		**Fire Safety** This symbol appears when care should be taken around open flames.
	**Sharp Object Safety** This symbol appears when a danger of cuts or punctures caused by the use of sharp objects exists.		**Explosion Safety** This symbol appears when the misuse of chemicals could cause an explosion.
	**Fume Safety** This symbol appears when chemicals or chemical reactions could cause dangerous fumes.		**Eye Safety** This symbol appears when a danger to the eyes exists. Safety goggles should be worn when this symbol appears.
	**Electrical Safety** This symbol appears when care should be taken when using electrical equipment.	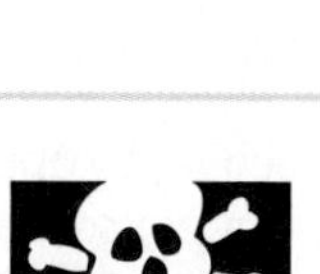	**Poison Safety** This symbol appears when poisonous substances are used.
	**Skin Protection Safety** This symbol appears when use of caustic chemicals might irritate the skin or when contact with microorganisms might transmit infection.		**Chemical Safety** This symbol appears when chemicals used can cause burns or are poisonous if absorbed through the skin.

Diversity of Life: Classification of Living Organisms

Scientists use a five kingdom system for the classification of organisms. In this system, there is one kingdom of organisms, Kingdom Monera, which contains organisms that do not have a nucleus and lack specialized structures in the cytoplasm of their cells. The members of the other four kingdoms have cells each of which contains a nucleus and structures in the cytoplasm that are surrounded by membranes. These kingdoms are Kingdom Protista, Kingdom Fungi, the Plant Kingdom, and the Animal Kingdom.

Kingdom Monera

Phylum Cyanobacteria one celled prokaryotes; make their own food, contain chlorophyll, some species form colonies, most are blue-green

Bacteria one-celled prokaryotes; most absorb food from their surroundings, some are photosynthetic; many are parasites; round, spiral, or rod shaped

Kingdom Protista

Phylum Euglenophyta one-celled; can photosynthesize or take in food; most have one flagellum; euglenoids

Phylum Chrysophyta most are one-celled; make their own food through photosynthesis; golden-brown pigments mask chlorophyll; diatoms

Phylum Pyrrophyta one-celled; make their own food through photosynthesis; contain red pigments and have two flagella; dinoflagellates

Phylum Chlorophyta one-celled, many-celled, or colonies; contain chlorophyll and make their own food; live on land, in fresh water or salt water; green algae

Phylum Rhodophyta most are many-celled and photosynthetic; contain red pigments; most live in deep saltwater environments; red algae

Phylum Phaeophyta most are many-celled and photosynthetic; contain brown pigments; most live in saltwater environments; brown algae

Phylum Myxomycota
Pretzel slime mold
× 5

Bacteria
Clostridium botulinum
× 13 960

Phylum Chlorophyta
Desmids × 50

Phylum Sarcodina one-celled; take in food; move by means of pseudopods; free-living or parasitic; amoebas

Phylum Mastigophora one-celled; take in food; have two or more flagella; free-living or parasitic; flagellates

Phylum Ciliophora one-celled; take in food; have large numbers of cilia; ciliates

Phylum Sporozoa one-celled; take in food; no means of movement; parasites in animals; sporozoans

Phyla Myxomycota and Acrasiomycota one- or many-celled; absorb food; change form during life cycle; cellular and plasmodial slime molds

Kingdom Fungi

Phylum Zygomycota many-celled; absorb food; spores are produced in sporangia; zygote fungi; bread mold

Phylum Ascomycota one- and many-celled; absorb food; spores produced in asci; sac fungi; yeast

Phylum Basidiomycota many-celled; absorb food; spores produced in basidia; club fungi; mushrooms

Phylum Deuteromycota members with unknown reproductive structures; imperfect fungi; penicillin

Lichens organisms formed by symbiotic relationship between an ascomycote or a basidiomycote and a green alga or a cyanobacterium

Plant Kingdom

Spore Plants

Division Bryophyta nonvascular plants that reproduce by spores produced in capsules; many-celled; green; grow in moist land environments; mosses and liverworts

Division Lycophyta many-celled vascular plants; spores produced in cones; live on land; are photosynthetic; club mosses

Division Sphenophyta vascular plants with ribbed and jointed stems; scalelike leaves; spores produced in cones; horsetails

Division Pterophyta vascular plants with feathery leaves called fronds; spores produced in clusters of sporangia called sori; live on land or in water; ferns

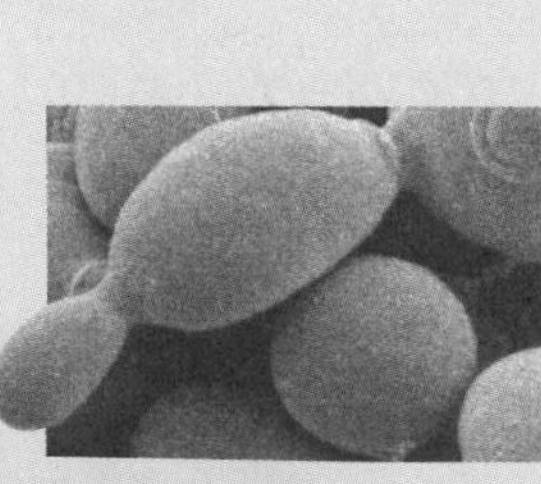

Phylum Ascomycota
Yeast × 7800

Lichens
Old Man's Beard lichen

Division Bryophyta
Liverwort

Seed Plants

Division Ginkgophyta deciduous gymnosperms; only one living species called the maiden hair tree; fan-shaped leaves with branching veins; reproduces with seeds; ginkgos

Division Cycadophyta palmlike gymnosperms; large compound leaves; produce seeds in cones; cycads

Division Coniferophyta deciduous or evergreen gymnosperms; trees or shrubs; needlelike or scalelike leaves; seeds produced in cones; conifers

Division Gnetophyta shrubs or woody vines; seeds produced in cones; division contains only three genera; gnetum

Division Anthophyta dominant group of plants; ovules protected at fertilization by an ovary; sperm carried to ovules by pollen tube; produce flowers and seeds in fruits; flowering plants

Animal Kingdom

Phylum Porifera aquatic organisms that lack true tissues and organs; they are asymmetrical and sessile; sponges

Phylum Cnidaria radially symmetrical organisms with a digestive cavity with one opening; most have tentacles armed with stinging cells; live in aquatic environments singly or in colonies; includes jellyfish, corals, hydra, and sea anemones

Phylum Platyhelminthes bilaterally symmetrical worms with flattened bodies; digestive system has one opening; parasitic and free-living species; flatworms

Division Coniferophyta
Slash Pine cones

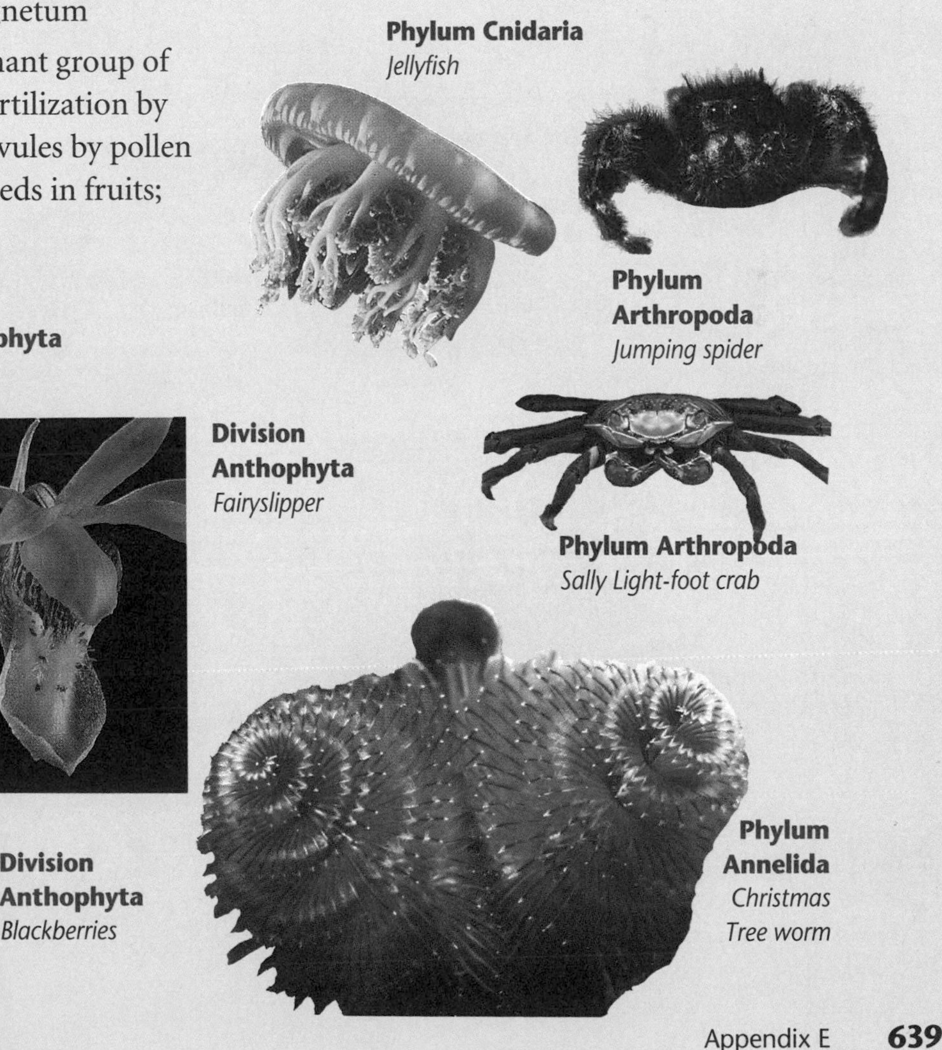

Phylum Cnidaria
Jellyfish

Phylum Arthropoda
Jumping spider

Division Anthophyta
Fairyslipper

Phylum Arthropoda
Sally Light-foot crab

Phylum Annelida
Christmas Tree worm

Division Anthophyta
Blackberries

APPENDIX E

Phylum Nematoda round bilaterally symmetrical body; digestive system with two openings; some free-living forms but mostly parasitic; roundworms

Phylum Mollusca soft-bodied animals, many with a hard shell; a mantle covers the soft body; aquatic and terrestrial species; includes clams, snails, squid, and octopuses

Phylum Annelida bilaterally symmetrical worms with round segmented bodies; terrestrial and aquatic species; includes earthworms, leeches, and marine polychaetes

Phylum Arthropoda very large phylum of organisms that have segmented bodies with pairs of jointed appendages, and a hard exoskeleton; terrestrial and aquatic species; includes insects, crustaceans, spiders, and horseshoe crabs

Phylum Echinodermata saltwater organisms with spiny or leathery skin; water-vascular system with tube feet; radial symmetry; includes starfish, sand dollars, and sea urchins

Phylum Chordata organisms with internal skeletons, specialized body systems, and paired appendages; all at some time have a notochord, dorsal nerve cord, gill slits, and a tail; includes fish, amphibians, reptiles, birds, and mammals

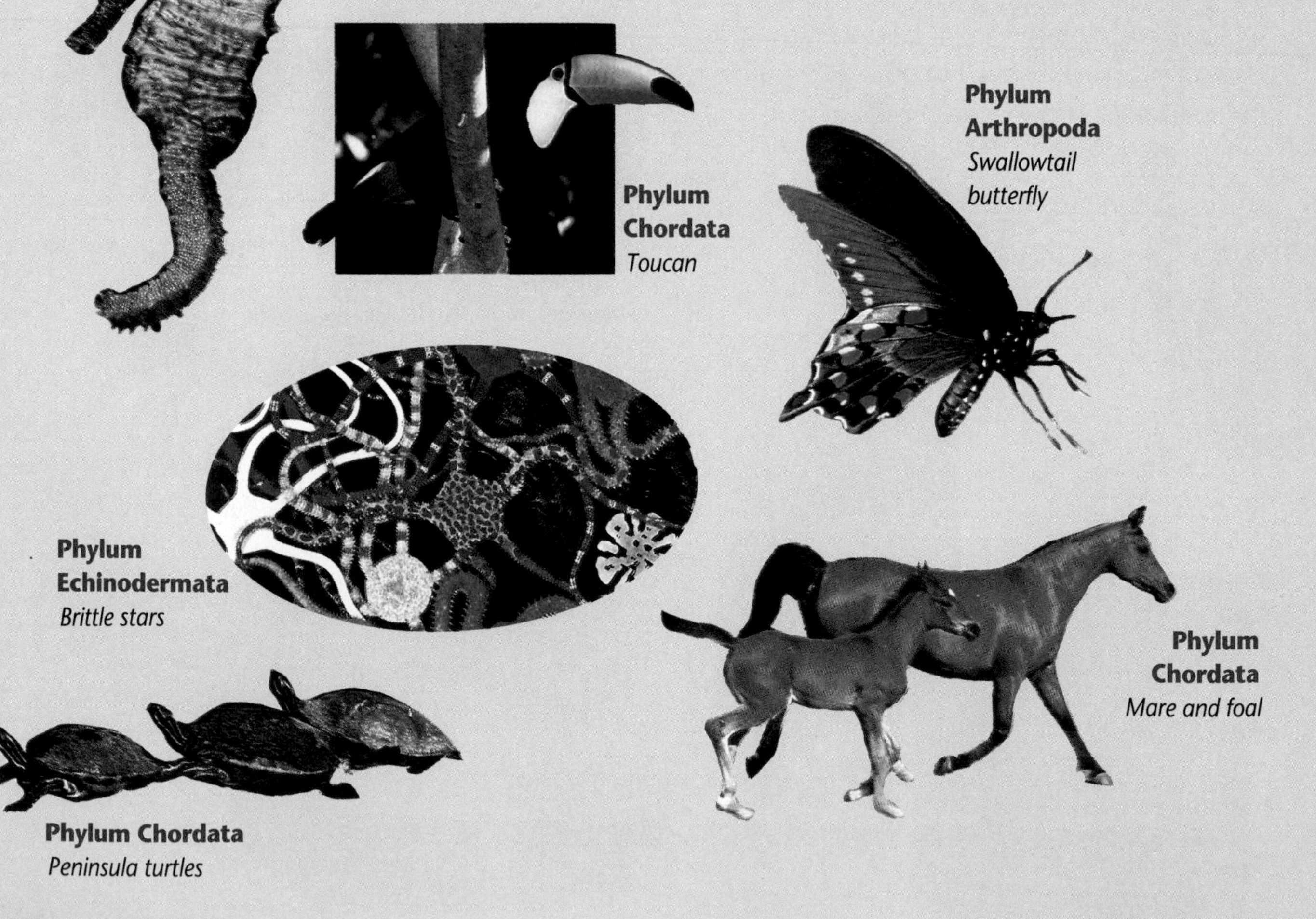

Phylum Chordata *Seahorse*

Phylum Chordata *Toucan*

Phylum Arthropoda *Swallowtail butterfly*

Phylum Echinodermata *Brittle stars*

Phylum Chordata *Mare and foal*

Phylum Chordata *Peninsula turtles*

Topographic Map Symbols

Primary highway, hard surface
Secondary highway, hard surface
Light-duty road, hard or improved surface
Unimproved road
Railroad: single track and multiple track
Railroads in juxtaposition

Buildings
School, church, and cemetery — cem
Buildings (barn, warehouse, etc.)
Wells other than water (labeled as to type) — oil gas
Tanks: oil, water, etc. (labeled only if water) — water
Located or landmark object; windmill
Open pit, mine, or quarry; prospect

Marsh (swamp)
Wooded marsh
Woods or brushwood
Vineyard
Land subject to controlled inundation
Submerged marsh
Mangrove
Orchard
Scrub
Urban area
Spot elevation — × 7369
Water elevation — 670

Index contour
Supplementary contour
Intermediate contour
Depression contours

Boundaries: National
State
County, parish, municipal
Civil township, precinct, town, barrio
Incorporated city, village, town, hamlet
Reservation, National or State
Small park, cemetery, airport, etc.
Land grant
Township or range line, United States land survey
Township or range line, approximate location

Perennial streams
Elevated aqueduct
Water well and spring
Small rapids
Large rapids
Intermittent lake
Intermittent streams
Aqueduct tunnel
Glacier
Small falls
Large falls
Dry lake bed

APPENDIX G

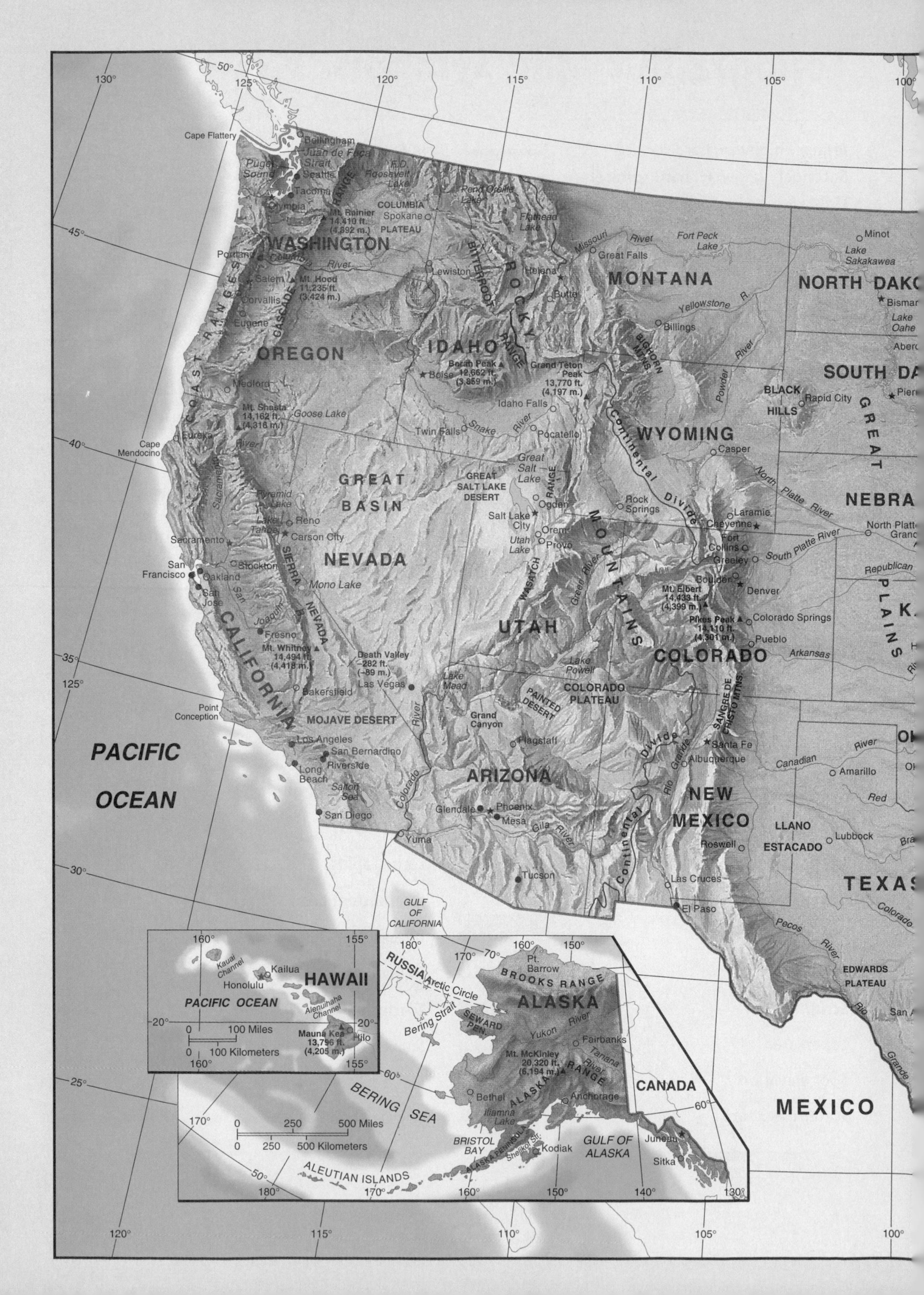

WASHINGTON
OREGON
IDAHO
MONTANA
WYOMING
NEVADA
UTAH
COLORADO
CALIFORNIA
ARIZONA
NEW MEXICO
NORTH DAKO
SOUTH DA
NEBRA
TEXAS
MEXICO
PACIFIC OCEAN
GREAT BASIN
GREAT SALT LAKE DESERT
COLUMBIA PLATEAU
COLORADO PLATEAU
PAINTED DESERT
MOJAVE DESERT
LLANO ESTACADO
EDWARDS PLATEAU
BLACK HILLS
GREAT PLAINS
ROCKY MOUNTAINS
CASCADE RANGE
COAST RANGES
SIERRA NEVADA
WASATCH RANGE
BITTERROOT RANGE
BIGHORN MTNS.
SANGRE DE CRISTO MTNS.
Continental Divide
Mt. Rainier 14,410 ft. (4,392 m.)
Mt. Hood 11,235 ft. (3,424 m.)
Mt. Shasta 14,162 ft. (4,316 m.)
Borah Peak 12,662 ft. (3,859 m.)
Grand Teton Peak 13,770 ft. (4,197 m.)
Mt. Whitney 14,494 ft. (4,418 m.)
Death Valley -282 ft. (-89 m.)
Mt. Elbert 14,433 ft. (4,399 m.)
Pikes Peak 14,110 ft. (4,301 m.)
Cape Flattery
Cape Mendocino
Point Conception
Puget Sound
Juan de Fuca Strait
Seattle
Tacoma
Olympia
Bellingham
Spokane
Portland
Salem
Corvallis
Eugene
Medford
Eureka
Boise
Lewiston
Idaho Falls
Twin Falls
Pocatello
Helena
Butte
Great Falls
Billings
Casper
Rock Springs
Laramie
Cheyenne
Fort Collins
Greeley
Boulder
Denver
Colorado Springs
Pueblo
Salt Lake City
Ogden
Orem
Provo
Reno
Carson City
Sacramento
San Francisco
Oakland
San Jose
Stockton
Fresno
Bakersfield
Los Angeles
San Bernardino
Riverside
Long Beach
San Diego
Las Vegas
Yuma
Glendale
Phoenix
Mesa
Tucson
Flagstaff
Grand Canyon
Santa Fe
Albuquerque
Las Cruces
El Paso
Roswell
Amarillo
Lubbock
Minot
Bismar
Rapid City
Pierr
North Platt
Columbia River
Snake River
Missouri River
Yellowstone R.
Powder River
North Platte River
South Platte River
Arkansas
Republican
Canadian River
Red
Green River
Colorado River
Rio Grande
Gila River
Pecos River
Sacramento River
San Joaquin R.
Great Salt Lake
Utah Lake
Lake Powell
Lake Mead
Lake Tahoe
Pyramid Lake
Mono Lake
Goose Lake
Salton Sea
Flathead Lake
Pend Oreille Lake
F.D. Roosevelt Lake
Fort Peck Lake
Lake Sakakawea
Lake Oahe
GULF OF CALIFORNIA
HAWAII
PACIFIC OCEAN
Kauai Channel
Alenuihaha Channel
Kailua
Honolulu
Hilo
Mauna Kea 13,796 ft. (4,205 m.)
100 Miles
100 Kilometers
ALASKA
RUSSIA
CANADA
Pt. Barrow
BROOKS RANGE
Arctic Circle
SEWARD PEN.
Bering Strait
BERING SEA
Yukon River
Tanana River
Fairbanks
Mt. McKinley 20,320 ft. (6,194 m.)
ALASKA RANGE
Anchorage
Bethel
Iliamna Lake
BRISTOL BAY
ALASKA PENINSULA
Shelikof Str.
Kodiak
GULF OF ALASKA
Juneau
Sitka
ALEUTIAN ISLANDS
250 500 Miles
250 500 Kilometers

APPENDIX G

UNITED STATES
National capital
State capital
Major city
Other city
International boundary
State boundary
0 150 300 Miles
0 150 300 Kilometers
Projection: Albers Equal Area
CANADA
ATLANTIC
OCEAN
GULF OF MEXICO
Straits of Florida
THE
BAHAMAS
CUBA
N
90°
85°
80°
75°
70°
65°
50°
45°
40°
35°
30°
25°
MAINE
Moosehead Lake
Bangor
Mt. Washington
6,288 ft.
(1,905 m.)
Augusta
Lewiston
Portland
N.H.
VT.
Concord
Manchester
MASS.
Boston
Worcester
Springfield
Cape Cod
Providence
R.I.
Hartford
New Haven
CONN.
NEW YORK
Lake Champlain
Burlington
Montpelier
ADIRONDACK MTNS.
Hudson R.
Utica
Albany
Syracuse
Rochester
Buffalo
Niagara Falls
Binghamton
Yonkers
New York
Lake Ontario
Lake Erie
Lake Huron
Lake Superior
Lake Michigan
St. Lawrence River
PENNSYLVANIA
Erie
Susquehanna River
Allentown
Newark
N.J.
Trenton
Philadelphia
Harrisburg
Pittsburgh
Camden
Wilmington
Dover
MD.
DEL.
DELAWARE BAY
Baltimore
Annapolis
Washington
D.C.
Arlington
CHESAPEAKE BAY
Newport News
Norfolk
Richmond
VIRGINIA
WEST VIRGINIA
Charleston
Huntington
Wheeling
Parkersburg
Roanoke
Roanoke River
NORTH CAROLINA
Durham
Raleigh
Greensboro
Winston-Salem
Cape Hatteras
Mt. Mitchell
6,684 ft.
(2,037 m.)
Charlotte
APPALACHIAN MOUNTAINS
APPALACHIAN PLATEAU
SOUTH CAROLINA
Spartanburg
Greenville
Columbia
Charleston
GEORGIA
Augusta
Atlanta
Macon
Columbus
Albany
Savannah
COASTAL PLAIN
FLORIDA
Jacksonville
Tallahassee
Pensacola
Orlando
Cape Canaveral
Tampa
St. Petersburg
Lake Okeechobee
Palm Beach
Miami Beach
Miami
Cape Sable
Key West
ALABAMA
Birmingham
Tuscaloosa
Montgomery
Mobile
Huntsville
Alabama R.
Chattahoochee R.
CUMBERLAND PLATEAU
TENNESSEE
Nashville
Knoxville
Chattanooga
Memphis
Tennessee R.
Cumberland River
KENTUCKY
Frankfort
Lexington
Louisville
Owensboro
Evansville
OHIO
Toledo
Cleveland
Youngstown
Akron
Canton
Columbus
Dayton
Cincinnati
Ohio River
INDIANA
Indianapolis
Muncie
Fort Wayne
South Bend
Gary
Hammond
Wabash R.
MICHIGAN
Grand Rapids
Flint
Lansing
Detroit
Ann Arbor
ILLINOIS
Chicago
Rockford
Aurora
Joliet
Peoria
Springfield
Decatur
East St. Louis
CENTRAL LOWLAND
WISCONSIN
Green Bay
Appleton
Milwaukee
Madison
Racine
Duluth
St. Paul
Rochester
Mississippi River
Dubuque
Cedar Rapids
Davenport
Des Moines
MISSOURI
St. Louis
Jefferson City
Independence
Harry S. Truman Res.
Springfield
OZARK PLATEAU
ARKANSAS
Fort Smith
Little Rock
North Little Rock
Hot Springs
Pine Bluff
MISSISSIPPI
Jackson
Meridian
Hattiesburg
Greenville
Biloxi
Lake Pontchartrain
LOUISIANA
Shreveport
Toledo Bend Res.
Baton Rouge
Lafayette
Lake Charles
New Orleans

APPENDIX H

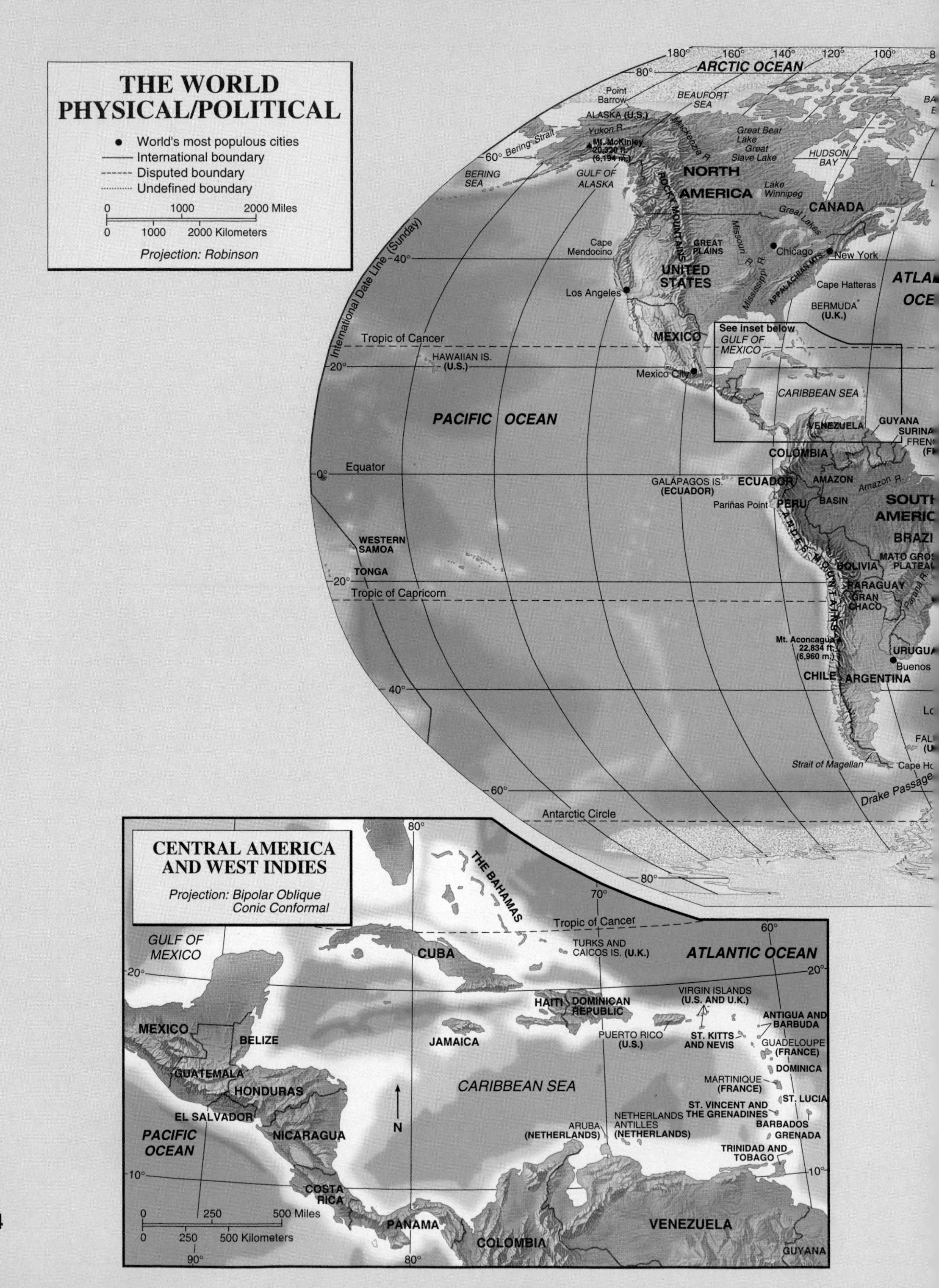
THE WORLD
PHYSICAL/POLITICAL
World's most populous cities
International boundary
Disputed boundary
Undefined boundary
0 1000 2000 Miles
0 1000 2000 Kilometers
Projection: Robinson
180°
160°
140°
120°
100°
80°
ARCTIC OCEAN
Point Barrow
BEAUFORT SEA
ALASKA (U.S.)
Yukon R.
Mackenzie R.
Great Bear Lake
Great Slave Lake
HUDSON BAY
Bering Strait
60°
Mt. McKinley 20,320 ft. (6,194 m.)
BERING SEA
GULF OF ALASKA
NORTH AMERICA
ROCKY MOUNTAINS
Lake Winnipeg
CANADA
Great Lakes
Missouri R.
Cape Mendocino
GREAT PLAINS
Chicago
New York
International Date Line (Sunday)
40°
UNITED STATES
Mississippi R.
APPALACHIAN MTS.
Cape Hatteras
Los Angeles
BERMUDA (U.K.)
See inset below
Tropic of Cancer
MEXICO
GULF OF MEXICO
HAWAIIAN IS. (U.S.)
20°
Mexico City
CARIBBEAN SEA
PACIFIC OCEAN
VENEZUELA
GUYANA
COLOMBIA
0°
Equator
GALÁPAGOS IS. (ECUADOR)
ECUADOR
AMAZON BASIN
Amazon R.
Pariñas Point
PERU
ANDES MOUNTAINS
WESTERN SAMOA
BOLIVIA
TONGA
PARAGUAY
GRAN CHACO
Paraná R.
Tropic of Capricorn
Mt. Aconcagua 22,834 ft. (6,960 m.)
Buenos
CHILE
ARGENTINA
Strait of Magellan
60°
Drake Passage
Antarctic Circle
80°
CENTRAL AMERICA AND WEST INDIES
Projection: Bipolar Oblique Conic Conformal
80°
70°
60°
THE BAHAMAS
Tropic of Cancer
GULF OF MEXICO
CUBA
TURKS AND CAICOS IS. (U.K.)
ATLANTIC OCEAN
20°
VIRGIN ISLANDS (U.S. AND U.K.)
HAITI
DOMINICAN REPUBLIC
ANTIGUA AND BARBUDA
MEXICO
BELIZE
JAMAICA
PUERTO RICO (U.S.)
ST. KITTS AND NEVIS
GUADELOUPE (FRANCE)
DOMINICA
GUATEMALA
HONDURAS
CARIBBEAN SEA
MARTINIQUE (FRANCE)
ST. LUCIA
EL SALVADOR
N
ST. VINCENT AND THE GRENADINES
BARBADOS
PACIFIC OCEAN
NICARAGUA
ARUBA (NETHERLANDS)
NETHERLANDS ANTILLES (NETHERLANDS)
GRENADA
TRINIDAD AND TOBAGO
10°
COSTA RICA
0 250 500 Miles
0 250 500 Kilometers
PANAMA
VENEZUELA
COLOMBIA
GUYANA
90°

APPENDIX H

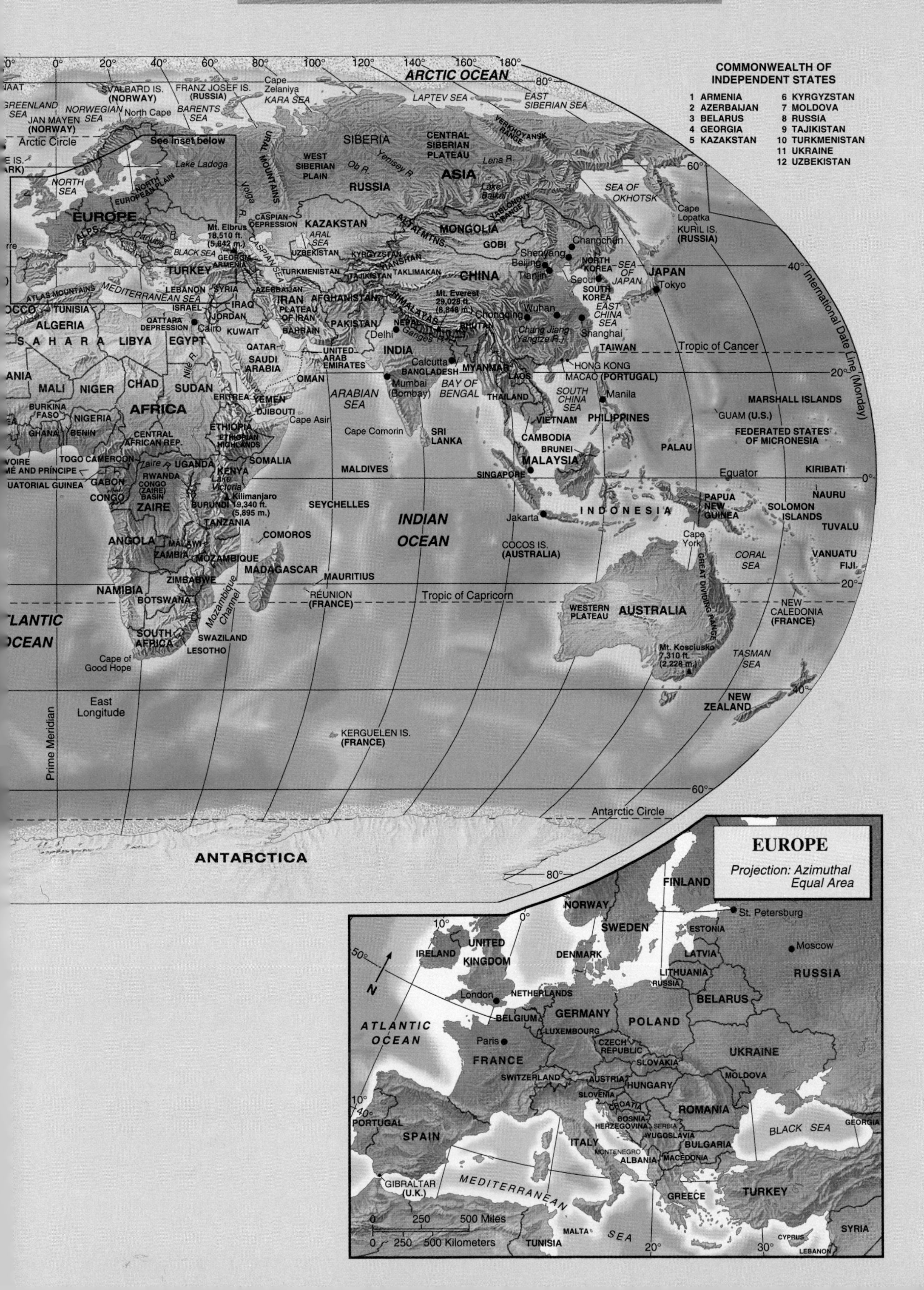
COMMONWEALTH OF INDEPENDENT STATES
1 ARMENIA
2 AZERBAIJAN
3 BELARUS
4 GEORGIA
5 KAZAKSTAN
6 KYRGYZSTAN
7 MOLDOVA
8 RUSSIA
9 TAJIKISTAN
10 TURKMENISTAN
11 UKRAINE
12 UZBEKISTAN
ARCTIC OCEAN
LAPTEV SEA
EAST SIBERIAN SEA
KARA SEA
BARENTS SEA
NORWEGIAN SEA
GREENLAND SEA
SVALBARD IS. (NORWAY)
FRANZ JOSEF IS. (RUSSIA)
JAN MAYEN (NORWAY)
North Cape
Cape Zelaniya
Arctic Circle
See inset below
Lake Ladoga
NORTH SEA
NORTH EUROPEAN PLAIN
EUROPE
ALPS
Danube
BLACK SEA
CASPIAN SEA
CASPIAN DEPRESSION
Mt. Elbrus 18,510 ft. (5,642 m.)
URAL MOUNTAINS
Volga R.
SIBERIA
WEST SIBERIAN PLAIN
CENTRAL SIBERIAN PLATEAU
Ob R.
Yenisey R.
Lena R.
VERKHOYANSK RANGE
RUSSIA
ASIA
Lake Baikal
YABLONOVY RANGE
SEA OF OKHOTSK
Cape Lopatka
KURIL IS. (RUSSIA)
KAZAKSTAN
ARAL SEA
UZBEKISTAN
KYRGYZSTAN
TURKMENISTAN
TAJIKISTAN
ALTAI MTNS.
TIAN SHAN
MONGOLIA
GOBI
TAKLIMAKAN
CHINA
Changchun
Shenyang
Beijing
Tianjin
NORTH KOREA
SOUTH KOREA
Seoul
SEA OF JAPAN
JAPAN
Tokyo
EAST CHINA SEA
Shanghai
Wuhan
Chongqing
Chang Jiang (Yangtze R.)
TAIWAN
HONG KONG
MACAO (PORTUGAL)
Tropic of Cancer
International Date Line (Monday)
TURKEY
GEORGIA
ARMENIA
AZERBAIJAN
LEBANON
SYRIA
ISRAEL
JORDAN
IRAQ
IRAN
PLATEAU OF IRAN
AFGHANISTAN
PAKISTAN
HIMALAYAS
Mt. Everest 29,028 ft. (8,848 m.)
NEPAL
BHUTAN
Delhi
Ganges R.
INDIA
Calcutta
BANGLADESH
MYANMAR
LAOS
THAILAND
VIETNAM
CAMBODIA
Mumbai (Bombay)
ARABIAN SEA
BAY OF BENGAL
Cape Comorin
SRI LANKA
MALDIVES
SOUTH CHINA SEA
Manila
PHILIPPINES
BRUNEI
MALAYSIA
SINGAPORE
Jakarta
INDONESIA
PALAU
GUAM (U.S.)
MARSHALL ISLANDS
FEDERATED STATES OF MICRONESIA
Equator
KIRIBATI
NAURU
PAPUA NEW GUINEA
SOLOMON ISLANDS
TUVALU
VANUATU
FIJI
Cape York
CORAL SEA
GREAT DIVIDING RANGE
WESTERN PLATEAU
AUSTRALIA
Mt. Kosciusko 7,310 ft. (2,228 m.)
TASMAN SEA
NEW CALEDONIA (FRANCE)
NEW ZEALAND
ATLAS MOUNTAINS
MEDITERRANEAN SEA
TUNISIA
ALGERIA
LIBYA
EGYPT
Cairo
QATTARA DEPRESSION
SAHARA
Nile R.
KUWAIT
BAHRAIN
QATAR
SAUDI ARABIA
UNITED ARAB EMIRATES
OMAN
YEMEN
ERITREA
DJIBOUTI
Cape Asir
MALI
NIGER
CHAD
SUDAN
AFRICA
BURKINA FASO
NIGERIA
GHANA
BENIN
TOGO
CAMEROON
CENTRAL AFRICAN REP.
ETHIOPIA
ETHIOPIAN HIGHLANDS
SOMALIA
UGANDA
KENYA
Lake Victoria
Zaire R.
RWANDA
BURUNDI
CONGO (ZAIRE) BASIN
GABON
CONGO
ZAIRE
Kilimanjaro 19,340 ft. (5,895 m.)
TANZANIA
SEYCHELLES
COMOROS
MALAWI
ANGOLA
ZAMBIA
MOZAMBIQUE
Mozambique Channel
MADAGASCAR
MAURITIUS
RÉUNION (FRANCE)
ZIMBABWE
NAMIBIA
BOTSWANA
SOUTH AFRICA
SWAZILAND
LESOTHO
Cape of Good Hope
INDIAN OCEAN
COCOS IS. (AUSTRALIA)
Tropic of Capricorn
KERGUELEN IS. (FRANCE)
East Longitude
Prime Meridian
Antarctic Circle
ANTARCTICA
EUROPE
Projection: Azimuthal Equal Area
FINLAND
NORWAY
SWEDEN
St. Petersburg
ESTONIA
LATVIA
LITHUANIA
RUSSIA
Moscow
IRELAND
UNITED KINGDOM
London
DENMARK
NETHERLANDS
BELGIUM
GERMANY
POLAND
BELARUS
LUXEMBOURG
CZECH REPUBLIC
SLOVAKIA
UKRAINE
MOLDOVA
ATLANTIC OCEAN
Paris
FRANCE
SWITZERLAND
AUSTRIA
HUNGARY
SLOVENIA
CROATIA
BOSNIA-HERZEGOVINA
SERBIA
YUGOSLAVIA
ROMANIA
BLACK SEA
GEORGIA
PORTUGAL
SPAIN
ITALY
MONTENEGRO
ALBANIA
MACEDONIA
BULGARIA
GIBRALTAR (U.K.)
MEDITERRANEAN SEA
GREECE
TURKEY
MALTA
TUNISIA
CYPRUS
SYRIA
LEBANON
0 250 500 Miles
0 250 500 Kilometers

Animal Cell

Refer to this diagram of an animal cell as you read about cell parts and their jobs.

Nucleus *ultimately controls cell activity*

Cytoplasm *contains cell parts*

Mitochondrion *releases energy*

Chromosomes *carry information that determines traits*

Digestive sacs *destroy worn out parts and get rid of bacteria*

Nuclear membrane *controls what moves into and out of nucleus*

Canal network *moves certain materials within cell*

Nucleolus *helps make ribosomes*

Cell membrane *controls what moves into and out of cell*

Ribosome *where proteins are made*

Plant Cell

Refer to this diagram of a plant cell as you read about cell parts and their jobs.

Nucleus *ultimately controls cell activity*

Chromosomes *carry information that determines traits*

Nucleolus *helps make ribosomes*

Nuclear membrane *controls what moves into and out of nucleus*

Vacuole *stores food water and minerals*

Ribosome *where proteins are made*

Digestive sacs *destroy worn out parts and get rid of bacteria*

Cell wall *protects and supports some cells*

Cytoplasm *contains cell parts*

Chloroplast *contains chlorophyll; place where food is made in plants*

Cell membrane *controls what moves into and out of cell*

Mitochondrion *releases energy*

Star Charts

Shown here are star charts for viewing stars in the Northern Hemisphere during the four different seasons. These charts are drawn from the night sky at about 35° north latitude, but they can be used for most locations in the Northern Hemisphere. The lines on the charts outline major constellations. The dense band of stars is the Milky Way. To use, hold the chart vertically, with the direction you are facing at the bottom of the map.

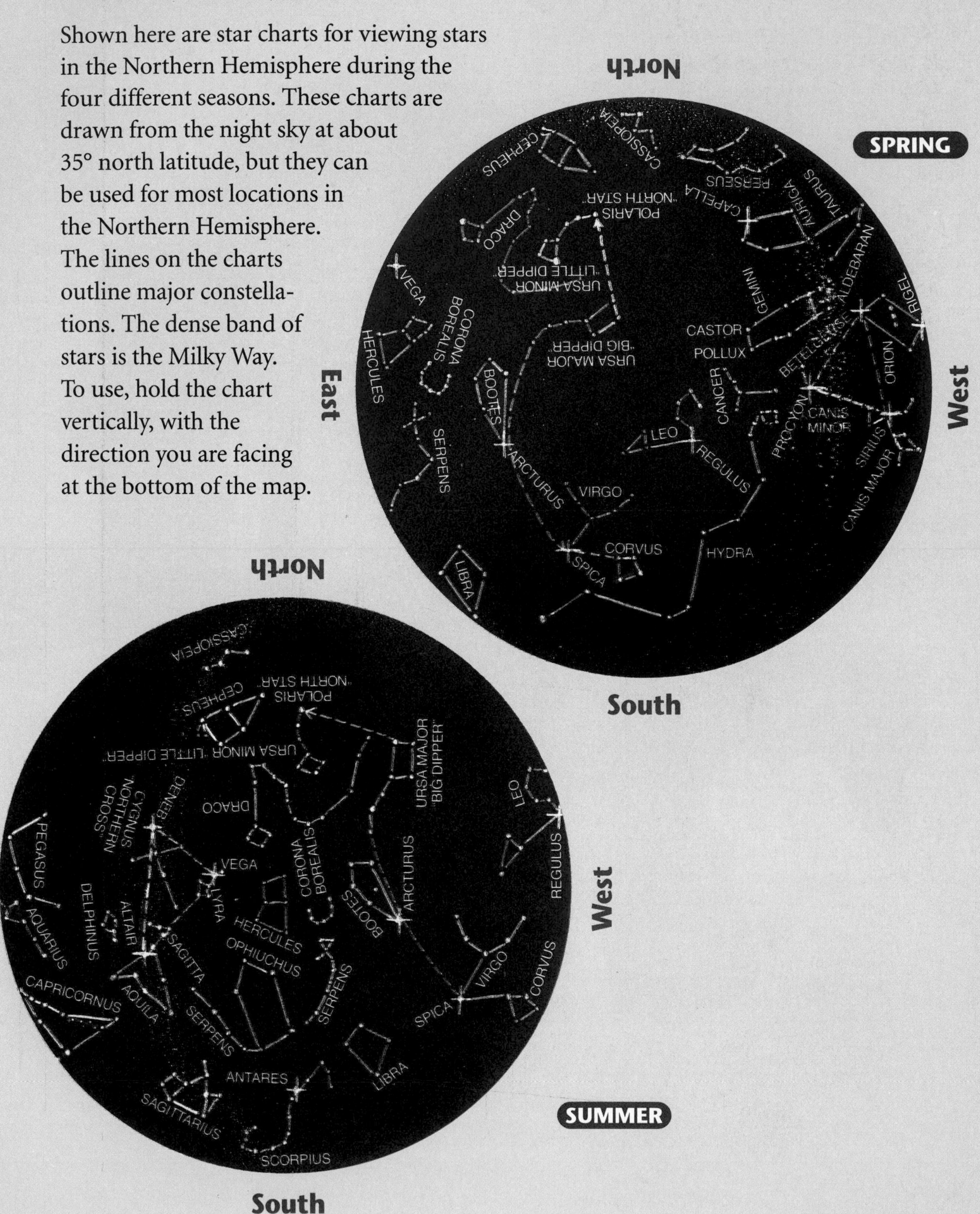

APPENDIX J

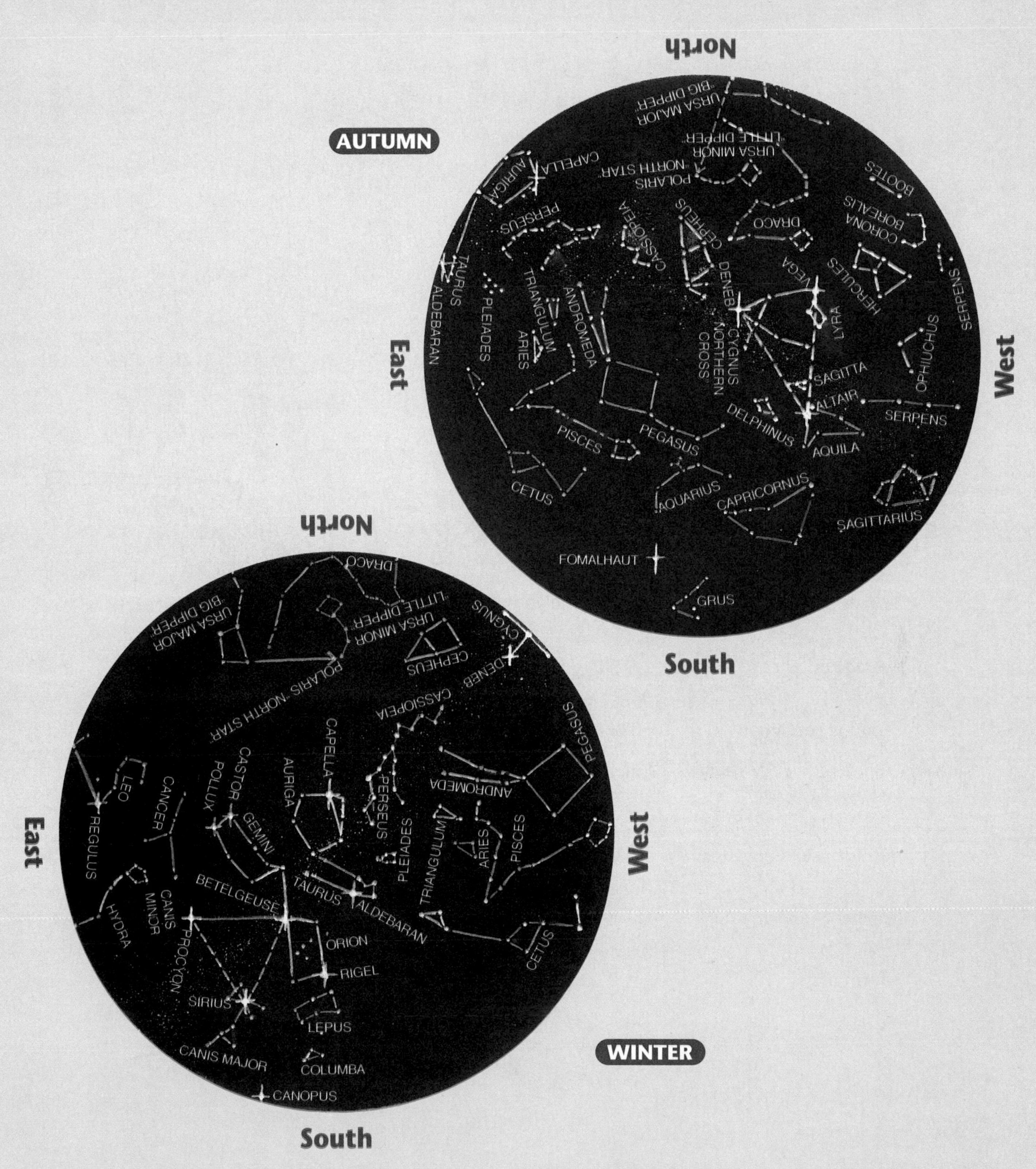
AUTUMN
North
East
West
South
URSA MAJOR
"BIG DIPPER"
URSA MINOR
"LITTLE DIPPER"
POLARIS
"NORTH STAR"
CAPELLA
AURIGA
PERSEUS
CASSIOPEIA
CEPHEUS
DRACO
BOOTES
CORONA BOREALIS
HERCULES
SERPENS
VEGA
LYRA
DENEB
CYGNUS
"NORTHERN CROSS"
TAURUS
ALDEBARAN
PLEIADES
TRIANGULUM
ARIES
ANDROMEDA
SAGITTA
ALTAIR
OPHIUCHUS
SERPENS
DELPHINUS
AQUILA
PEGASUS
PISCES
CETUS
AQUARIUS
CAPRICORNUS
SAGITTARIUS
FOMALHAUT
GRUS
WINTER
North
East
West
South
DRACO
URSA MAJOR
"BIG DIPPER"
URSA MINOR
"LITTLE DIPPER"
CYGNUS
DENEB
CEPHEUS
POLARIS "NORTH STAR"
CASSIOPEIA
PEGASUS
CAPELLA
AURIGA
CASTOR
POLLUX
LEO
CANCER
GEMINI
ANDROMEDA
PERSEUS
PLEIADES
TRIANGULUM
ARIES
PISCES
REGULUS
TAURUS
ALDEBARAN
BETELGEUSE
CANIS MINOR
HYDRA
PROCYON
ORION
RIGEL
SIRIUS
LEPUS
CETUS
CANIS MAJOR
COLUMBA
CANOPUS

APPENDIX K

Solar System Information

Table K-1: Solar System Information

Planet	Mercury	Venus	Earth	Mars	Jupiter	Saturn	Uranus	Neptune	Pluto
Diameter (km)	4878	12104	12756	6794	142796	120660	51118	49528	2290
Diameter (E = 1.0)*	0.38	0.95	1.00	0.53	11.19	9.46	4.01	3.88	0.18
Mass (E = 1.0)*	0.06	0.82	1.00	0.11	317.83	95.15	14.54	17.23	0.002
Density (g/cm^3)	5.42	5.24	5.50	3.94	1.31	0.70	1.30	1.66	2.03
Period of rotation									
days	58	243	00	00	00	00	00	00	06
hours	15	00	23	24	09	10	17	16	09
minutes	28	14_R	56	37	55	39	14_R	03	17
R = retrograde									
Surface gravity (E = 1.0)*	0.38	0.90	1.00	0.38	2.53	1.07	0.92	1.12	0.06
Average distance to sun (AU)	0.387	0.723	1.000	1.524	5.203	9.529	19.191	30.061	39.529
Period of revolution	87.97d	224.70d	365.26d	686.98d	11.86y	29.46y	84.04y	164.79y	248.53y
Eccentricity of orbit	0.206	0.007	0.017	0.093	0.048	0.056	0.046	0.010	0.248
Average orbital speed (km/s)	47.89	35.03	29.79	24.13	13.06	9.64	6.81	5.43	4.74
Number of known satellites	0	0	1	2	16	18	15	8	1
Known rings	0	0	0	0	1	thousands	11	4	0

* Earth = 1.0

Care and Use of a Microscope

Coarse Adjustment *Focuses the image under low power*

Fine Adjustment *Sharpens the image under high and low magnification*

Arm *Supports the body tube*

Low-power objective *Contains the lens with low-power magnification*

Stage clips *Hold the microscope slide in place*

Base *Provides support for the microscope*

Eyepiece *Contains a magnifying lens you look through*

Body tube *Connects the eyepiece to the revolving nosepiece*

Revolving nosepiece *Holds and turns the objectives into viewing position*

High-power objective *Contains the lens with the highest magnification*

Stage *Platform used to support the microscope slide*

Diaphragm *Regulates the amount of light entering the body tube*

Light source *Allows light to reflect upward through the diaphragm, the specimen, and the lenses*

Care of a Microscope

1. Always carry the microscope holding the arm with one hand and supporting the base with the other hand.
2. Don't touch the lenses with your finger.
3. Never lower the coarse adjustment knob when looking through the eyepiece lens.
4. Always focus first with the low-power objective.
5. Don't use the coarse adjustment knob when the high-power objective is in place.
6. Store the microscope covered.

Using a Microscope

1. Place the microscope on a flat surface that is clear of objects. The arm should be toward you.
2. Look through the eyepiece. Adjust the diaphragm so that light comes through the opening in the stage.
3. Place a slide on the stage so that the specimen is in the field of view. Hold it firmly in place by using the stage clips.
4. Always focus first with the coarse adjustment and the low-power objective lens. Once the object is in focus on low power, turn the nosepiece until the high-power objective is in place. Use ONLY the fine adjustment to focus with the high-power objective lens.

Making a Wet Mount Slide

1. Carefully place the item you want to look at in the center of a clean glass slide. Make sure the sample is thin enough for light to pass through.
2. Use a dropper to place one or two drops of water on the sample.
3. Hold a clean coverslip by the edges and place it at one edge of the drop of water. Slowly lower the coverslip onto the drop of water until it lies flat.
4. If you have too much water or a lot of air bubbles, touch the edge of a paper towel to the edge of the coverslip to draw off extra water and force air out.

Table of Contents

Organizing Information

▶ Classifying

You may not realize it, but you make things orderly in the world around you. If you hang your shirts together in the closet, if your socks take up a particular corner of a dresser drawer, or if your favorite CDs are stacked together, you have used the skill of classifying.

Classifying is the process of sorting objects or events into groups based on common features. When classifying, first observe the objects or events to be classified. Then, select one feature that is shared by most members in the group but not by all. Place those members that share the feature into a subgroup. You can classify members into smaller and smaller subgroups based on characteristics.

How would you classify a collection of CDs? You might classify those you like to dance to in one subgroup and CDs you like to listen to in the next column, as in the diagram. The CDs you like to dance to could be subdivided into a rap subgroup and a rock subgroup. Note that for each feature selected, each CD only fits into one subgroup. Keep selecting features until all the CDs are classified. The diagram above shows one possible classification.

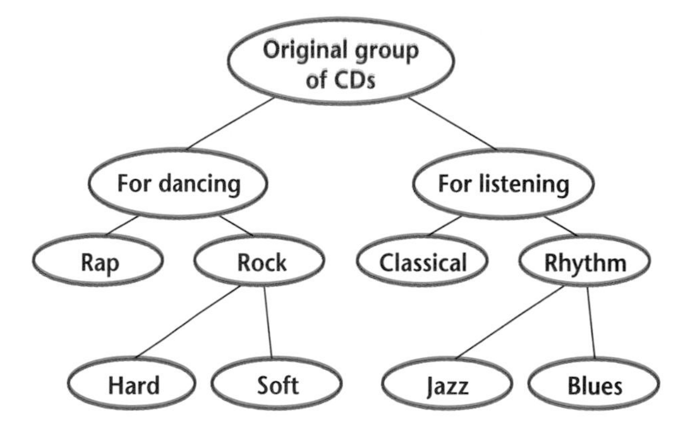

Remember, when you classify, you are grouping objects or events for a purpose. Keep your purpose in mind as you select the features to form groups and subgroups.

▶ Sequencing

A sequence is an arrangement of things or events in a particular order. A sequence with which you are most familiar is the use of alphabetical order. Another example of sequence would be the steps in a recipe. Think about baking chocolate chip cookies. Steps in the recipe have to be followed in order for the cookies to turn out right.

When you are asked to sequence objects or events within a group, figure out what comes first, then think about what should come second. Continue to choose objects or events until all of the objects you started out with are in order. Then, go back over the sequence to make sure each thing or event in your sequence logically leads to the next.

▶ Concept Mapping

If you were taking an automobile trip, you would probably take along a road map. The road map shows your location, your destination, and other places along the way. By looking at the map and finding where you are, you can begin to understand where you are in relation to other locations on the map.

A concept map is similar to a road map. But, a concept map shows relationships among ideas (or concepts) rather than places. A concept map is a diagram that visually shows how concepts are related. Because the concept map shows relationships among ideas, it can make the meanings of ideas and terms clear, and help you understand better what you are studying.

Network Tree Look at the concept map about Protists. This is called a network tree. Notice how some words are circled while others are written across connecting lines. The circled words are science concepts. The lines in the map show related concepts. The words written on the lines describe the relationships between concepts.

When you are asked to construct a network tree, write down the topic and list the major concepts related to that topic on a piece of paper. Then look at your list and begin to put them in order from general to specific. Branch the related concepts from the major concept and describe the relationships on the lines. Continue to write the more specific concepts. Write the relationships between the concepts on the lines until all concepts are mapped. Examine the concept map for relationships that cross branches, and add them to the concept map.

Events Chain An events chain is another type of concept map. An events chain map, such as the one on the effects of gravity, is used to describe ideas in order. In science, an events chain can be used to describe a sequence of events, the steps in a procedure, or the stages of a process.

When making an events chain, first find the one event that starts the chain. This event is called the initiating event. Then, find the

Events Chain

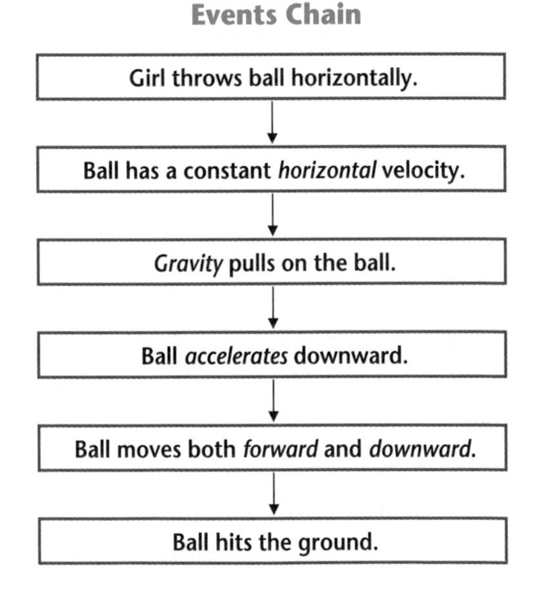

Network Tree

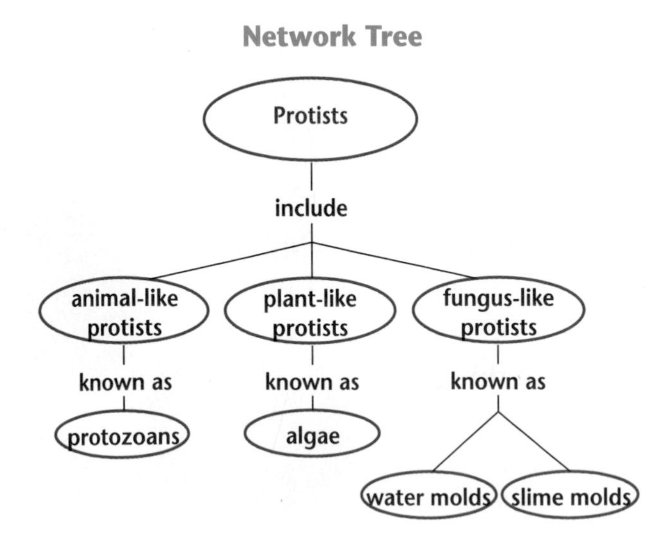

next event in the chain and continue until you reach an outcome. Suppose you are asked to describe what happens when someone throws a ball horizontally. An events chain map describing the steps might look like the one on page 654. Notice that connecting words are not necessary in an events chain.

Cycle Map A cycle concept map is a special type of events chain map. In a cycle concept map, the series of events does not produce a

Cycle Map

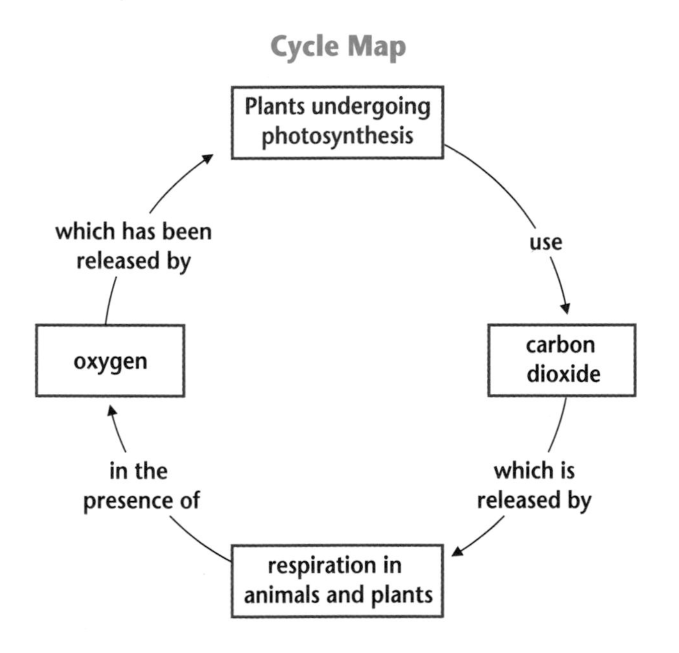

final outcome. Instead, the last event in the chain relates back to the initiating event.

As in the events chain map, you first decide on an initiating event and then list each event in order. Since there is no outcome and the last event relates back to the initiating event, the cycle repeats itself. Look at the cycle map for photosynthesis shown above.

Spider Map A fourth type of concept map is the spider map. This is a map that you can use for brainstorming. Once you have a central idea, you may find you have a jumble of ideas that relate to it, but are not necessarily clearly related to each other. By writing these

Spider Map

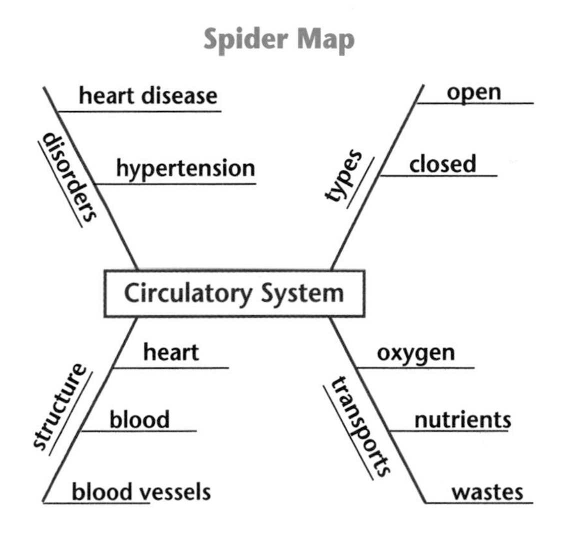

ideas outside the main concept, you may begin to separate and group unrelated terms so that they become more useful.

There is usually not one correct way to create a concept map. As you construct one type of map, you may discover other ways to construct the map that show the relationships between concepts in a better way. If you do discover what you think is a better way to create a concept map, go ahead and use the new way. Overall, concept maps are useful for breaking a big concept down into smaller parts, making learning easier.

▶ Making and Using Tables

Browse through your textbook, and you will notice tables in the text and in the activities. In a table, data or information is arranged in such a way that makes it easier for you to understand. Activity tables help organize the data you collect during an activity so that results can be interpreted more easily.

Parts of a Table Most tables have a title. At a glance, the title tells you what the table is about. A table is divided into columns and rows. The first column lists items to be compared. In the table shown to the right, different magnitudes of force are being compared. The row across the top lists the specific characteristics being compared. Within the grid of the table, the collected data is recorded. Look at the features of the table in the next column.

What is the title of this table? The title is "Earthquake Magnitude." What is being compared? The distance away from the epicenter that tremors are felt and the average number of earthquakes expected per year are being compared for different magnitudes on the Richter scale.

Using Tables What is the average number of earthquakes expected per year for an earthquake with a magnitude of 5.5 at the focus? Locate the column labeled "Average number expected per year" and the row "5.0 to 5.9." The data in the box where the column and row intersect is the answer. Did you answer "800"? What is the distance away from the epicenter for an earthquake with a magnitude of 8.1? If you answered "720 km," you understand how to use the parts of a table.

Earthquake Magnitude

Magnitude at Focus	Distance from Epicenter that Tremors are Felt	Average Number Expected Per Year
1.0 to 3.9	24 km	>100 000
4.0 to 4.9	48 km	6200
5.0 to 5.9	112 km	800
6.0 to 6.9	200 km	120
7.0 to 7.9	400 km	20
8.0 to 8.9	720 km	<1

Making Tables To make a table, list the items to be compared down in columns and the characteristics to be compared across in rows. Make a table and record the data comparing the mass of recycled materials collected by a class. On Monday, students turned in 4 kg of paper, 2 kg of aluminum, and 0.5 kg of plastic. On Wednesday, they turned in 3.5 kg of paper, 1.5 kg of aluminum, and 0.5 kg of plastic. On Friday, the totals were 3 kg of paper, 1 kg of aluminum, and 1.5 kg of plastic. If your table looks like the one shown below, you are able to make tables to organize data.

Recycled Materials

Day of Week	Paper (kg)	Aluminum (kg)	Plastic (kg)
Mon.	4	2	0.5
Wed.	3.5	1.5	0.5
Fri.	3	1	1.5

Making and Using Graphs

After scientists organize data in tables, they may display the data in a graph. A graph is a diagram that shows how variables compare. A graph makes interpretation and analysis of data easier. There are three basic types of graphs used in science—the line graph, the bar graph, and the pie graph.

Line Graphs A line graph is used to show the relationship between two variables. The variables being compared go on two axes of the graph. The independent variable always goes on the horizontal axis, called the *x*-axis. The dependent variable always goes on the vertical axis, called the *y*-axis.

Suppose a school started a peer study program with a class of students to see how science grades were affected.

Average Grades of Students in Study Program

Grading Period	Average Science Grade
First	81
Second	85
Third	86
Fourth	89

You could make a graph of the grades of students in the program over the four grading periods of the school year. The grading period is the independent variable and is placed on the *x*-axis of your graph. The average grade of the students in the program is the dependent variable and would go on the *y*-axis.

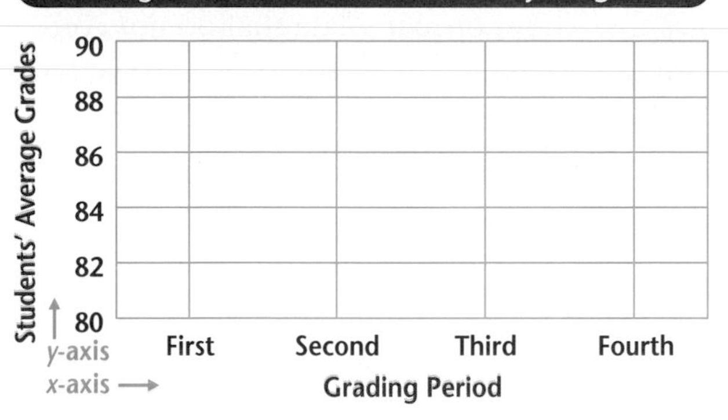

After drawing your axes, you would label each axis with a scale. The *x*-axis simply lists the four grading periods. To make a scale of grades on the *y*-axis, you must look at the data values. Since the lowest grade was 81 and the highest was 89, you know that you will have to start numbering at least at 81 and go through 89. You decide to start numbering at 80 and number by twos through 90.

Next, plot the data points. The first pair of data you want to plot is the first grading period and 81. Locate "First" on the *x*-axis and locate "81" on the *y*-axis. Where an imaginary vertical line from the *x*-axis and an imaginary horizontal line from the *y*-axis would meet, place the first data point. Place the other data points the same way. After all the points are plotted, connect them with straight lines.

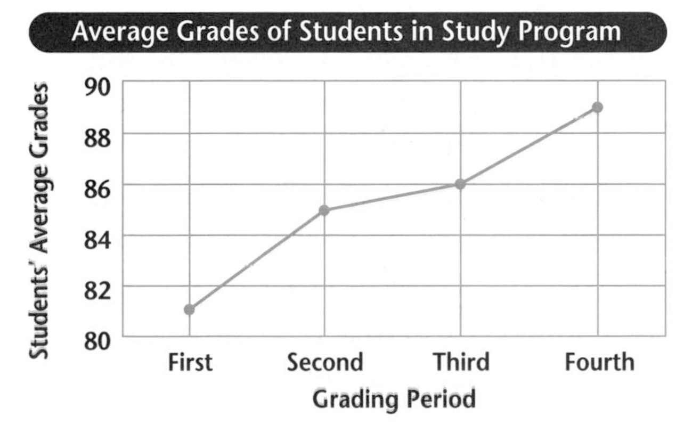

Bar Graphs Bar graphs are similar to line graphs. They compare data that do not continuously change. In a bar graph, vertical bars show the relationships among data.

To make a bar graph, set up the *x*-axis and *y*-axis as you did for the line graph. The data is plotted by drawing vertical bars from the *x*-axis up to a point where the *y*-axis would meet the bar if it were extended.

Look at the bar graph comparing the masses lifted by an electromagnet with different numbers of dry cell batteries. The *x*-axis is the number of dry cell batteries, and the *y*-axis is the mass lifted.

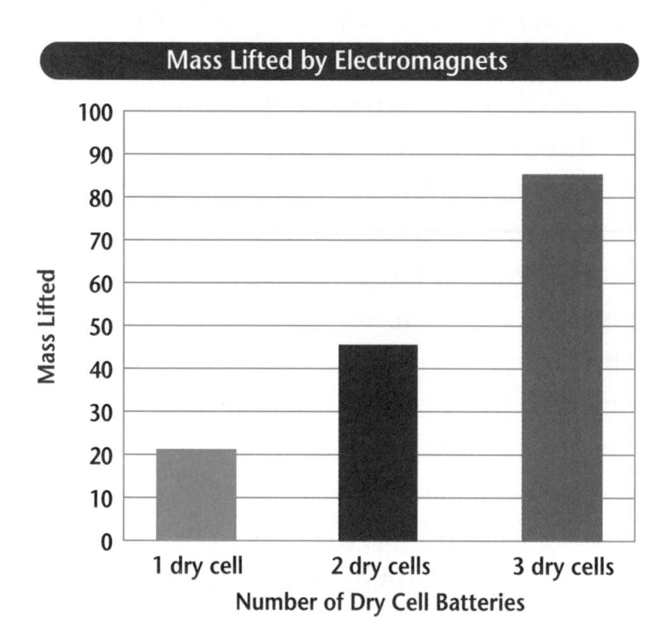

Pie Graphs A pie graph uses a circle divided into sections to display data. Each section represents part of the whole. All the sections together equal 100 percent.

Suppose you wanted to make a pie graph to show the number of seeds that germinated in a package. You would have to count the total number of seeds and the number of seeds that germinated out of the total.

You find that there are 143 seeds in the package. This represents 100 percent, the whole pie.

You plant the seeds, and 129 seeds germinate. The seeds that germinated will make up one section of the pie graph, and the seeds that did not germinate will make up the remaining section.

Seeds Germinated

Not germinating
35 degrees

Germinating
325 degrees

To find out how much of the pie each section should take, divide the number of seeds in each section by the total number of seeds. Then multiply your answer by 360, the number of degrees in a circle, and round to the nearest whole number. The section of the pie graph in degrees that represents the seeds germinated is figured below.

$$\frac{129}{143} \times 360 = 324.75 \text{ or } 325 \text{ degrees}$$

Plot this group on the pie graph using a compass and a protractor. Use the compass to draw a circle. Then, draw a straight line from the center to the edge of the circle. Place your protractor on this line and use it to mark a point on the edge of the circle at 325 degrees. Connect this point with a straight line to the center of the circle. This is the section for the group of seeds that germinated. The other section represents the group of 14 seeds that did not germinate. Label the sections of your graph and title the graph.

Thinking Critically

Observing and Inferring

Imagine that you have just finished a volleyball game. At home, you open the refrigerator and see a jug of orange juice on the back of the top shelf. The jug feels cold as you grasp it. Then you drink the juice, smell the oranges, and enjoy the tart taste in your mouth.

As you imagined yourself in the story, you used your senses to make observations. You used your sense of sight to find the jug in the refrigerator, your sense of touch when you felt the coldness of the jug, your sense of hearing to listen as the liquid filled the glass, and your senses of smell and taste to enjoy the odor and tartness of the juice. The basis of all scientific investigation is observation.

Scientists try to make careful and accurate observations. When possible, they use instruments such as microscopes and thermometers or a pan balance to make observations. Measurements with a balance or thermometer provide numerical data that can be checked and repeated.

When you make observations in science, you'll find it helpful to examine the entire object or situation first. Then, look carefully for details. Write down everything you observe.

Scientists often make inferences based on their observations. An inference is an attempt to explain or interpret observations or to say what caused what you observed. For example, if you observed a CLOSED sign in a store window around noon, you might infer the owner is taking a lunch break. But, it's also possible that the owner has a doctor's appointment or has taken the day off to go fishing. The only way to be sure your inference is correct is to investigate further.

When making an inference, be certain to use accurate data and observations. Analyze all of the data that you've collected. Then, based on everything you know, explain or interpret what you've observed.

Comparing and Contrasting

Observations can be analyzed by noting the similarities and differences between two or more objects or events that you observe. When you look at objects or events to see how they are similar, you are comparing them. Contrasting is looking for differences in similar objects or events.

Suppose you were asked to compare and contrast the planets Venus and Earth. You would start by looking at what is known about these planets. Arrange this information in a table, making two columns on a piece of paper and listing ways the planets are similar in one column and ways they are different in the other.

Comparison of Venus and Earth		
Properties	Earth	Venus
Diameter (km)	12 756	12 104
Average density (g/cm^3)	5.5	5.3
Percentage of sunlight reflected	39	76
Daytime surface temperature (degrees)	300	750
Number of satellites	1	0

Similarities you might point out are that both planets are similar in size, shape, and mass. Differences include Venus having a hotter surface temperature that reflects more sunlight than Earth reflects. Also, Venus lacks a moon.

Recognizing Cause and Effect

Have you ever watched something happen and then made suggestions as to why it happened? If so, you have observed an effect and inferred a cause. The event is an effect, and the reason for the event is the cause.

Suppose that every time your teacher fed the fish in a classroom aquarium, she or he tapped the food container on the edge of the aquarium. Then, one day your teacher just happened to tap the edge of the aquarium with a pencil while making a point about an ecology lesson. You observed the fish swim to the surface of the aquarium to feed. What is the effect, and what would you infer to be the cause? The effect is the fish swimming to the surface of the aquarium. You might infer the cause to be the teacher tapping on the edge of the aquarium. In determining cause and effect, you have made a logical inference based on your observations.

Perhaps the fish swam to the surface because they reacted to the teacher's waving hand or for some other reason. When scientists are unsure of the cause of a certain event, they design controlled experiments to determine what causes the event. Although you have made a logical conclusion about the behavior of the fish, you would have to perform an experiment to be certain that it was the tapping that caused the effect you observed.

▶ Measuring in SI

The metric system is a system of measurement developed by a group of scientists in 1795. It helps scientists avoid problems by providing standard measurements that all scientists around the world can understand. A modern form of the metric system, called the International System, or SI, was adopted for worldwide use in 1960.

Metric Prefixes

Prefix	Symbol	Meaning	
kilo-	k	1000	thousand
hecto-	h	100	hundred
deka-	da	10	ten
deci-	d	0.1	tenth
centi-	c	0.01	hundreth
milli-	m	0.001	thousandth

The metric system is convenient because unit sizes vary by multiples of 10. When changing from smaller units to larger units, divide by 10. When changing from larger units to smaller, you multiply by 10. For example, to convert millimeters to centimeters, divide the millimeters by 10. To convert 30 millimeters to centimeters, divide 30 by 10 (30 millimeters equals 3 centimeters).

Prefixes are used to name units. Look at the table for some common metric prefixes and their meanings. Do you see how the prefix *kilo-* attached to the unit *gram* is *kilogram*, or 1000 grams? The prefix *deci-* attached to the unit *meter* is *decimeter*, or one-tenth (0.1) of a meter.

Length You have probably measured lengths or distances many times. The meter is the SI unit used to measure length. A baseball bat is about one meter long. When measuring smaller lengths, the meter is divided into smaller units called centimeters and millimeters. A centimeter is one-hundredth (0.01) of a meter, which is about the size of the width of the fingernail on your ring finger. A millimeter is one-thousandth of a meter (0.001), about the thickness of a dime.

Most metric rulers have lines indicating centimeters and millimeters. The centimeter lines are the longer, numbered lines, and the shorter lines are millimeter lines. When using a metric ruler, line up the 0 centimeter mark with the end of the object being measured, and read the number of the unit where the object ends.

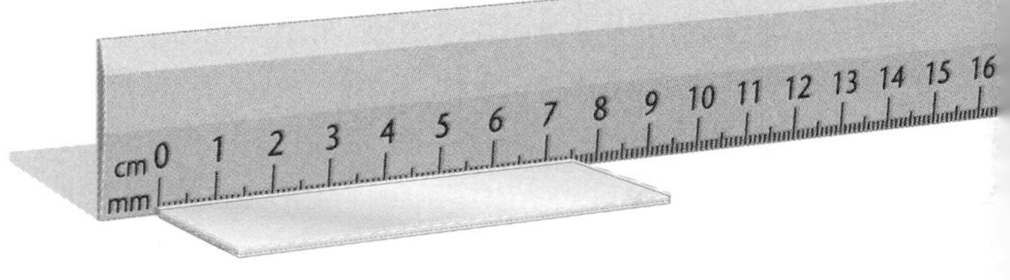

Surface Area Units of length are also used to measure surface area. The standard unit of area is the square meter (m^2). A square that's one meter long on each side has a surface area of one square meter. Similarly, a square centimeter (cm^2) is one centimeter long on each side. The surface area of an object is determined by multiplying the length times the width.

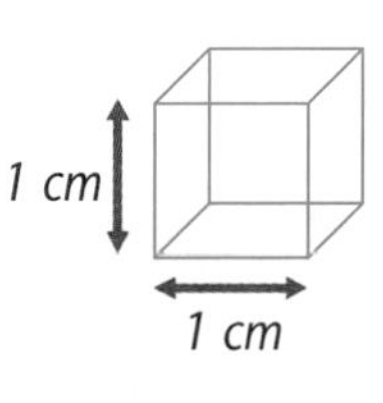

Volume The volume of a rectangular solid is also calculated using units of length. The cubic meter (m^3) is the standard SI unit of volume. A cubic meter is a cube one meter on each side. You can determine the volume of rectangular solids by multiplying length times width times height.

Liquid Volume During science activities, you will measure liquids using beakers and graduated cylinders marked in milliliters. A graduated cylinder is a cylindrical container marked with lines from bottom to top.

Liquid volume is measured using a unit called a liter. A liter has the volume of 1000 cubic centimeters. Since the prefix *milli-* means thousandth (0.001), a milliliter equals one cubic centimeter. One milliliter of liquid would completely fill a cube measuring one centimeter on each side.

Mass Scientists use balances to find the mass of objects in grams. You will use a beam balance similar to the one illustrated. Notice that on one side of the balance is a pan and on the other side is a set of beams. Each beam has an object of a known mass called a *rider* that slides on the beam.

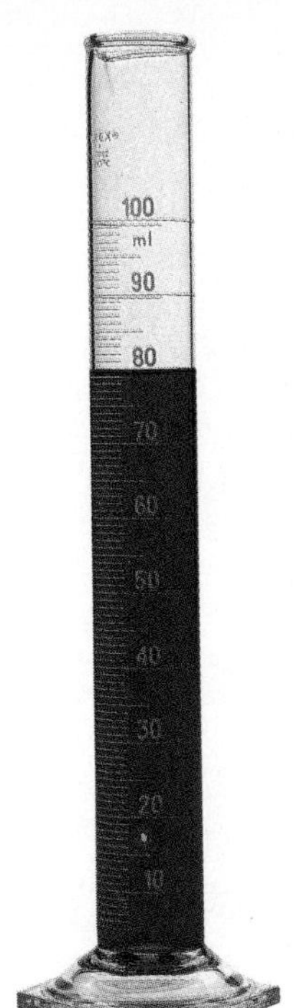

Before you find the mass of an object, set the balance to zero by sliding all the riders back to the zero point. Check the pointer on the right to make sure it swings an equal distance above and below the zero point on the scale. If the swing is unequal, find and turn the adjusting screw until you have an equal swing.

Place an object on the pan. Slide the rider with the largest mass along its beam until the pointer drops below zero. Then move it back one notch. Repeat the process on each beam until the pointer swings an equal distance above and below the zero point. Add the masses on each beam to find the mass of the object.

You should never place a hot object or pour chemicals directly on the pan. Instead, find the mass of a clean beaker or a glass jar. Place the dry or liquid chemicals in the container. Then find the combined mass of the container and the chemicals. Calculate the mass of the chemicals by subtracting the mass of the empty container from the combined mass.

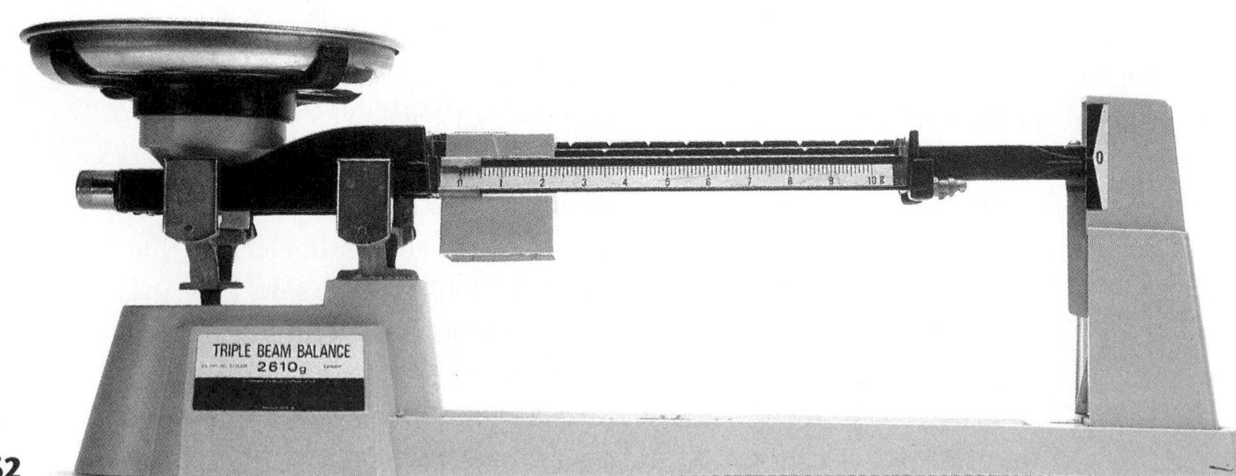

Practicing Scientific Processes

You might say that the work of a scientist is to solve problems. But when you decide how to dress on a particular day, you are doing problem solving, too. You may observe what the weather looks like through a window. You may go outside and see if what you are wearing is warm or cool enough.

Scientists use an orderly approach to learn new information and to solve problems. The methods scientists may use include observing, forming a hypothesis, testing a hypothesis, separating and controlling variables, and interpreting data.

▶ Observing

You observe all the time. Any time you smell wood burning, touch a pet, see lightning, taste food, or hear your favorite music, you are observing. Observation gives you information about events or things. Scientists try to observe as much as possible about the things and events they study so that they can know that what they say about their observations is reliable.

Some observations describe something using only words. These observations are called qualitative observations. If you were making qualitative observations of a dog, you might use words such as furry, brown, short-haired, or short-eared.

Other observations describe how much of something there is. These are quantitative observations and use numbers as well as words in the description. Tools or equipment are used to measure the characteristic being described. Quantitative observations of a dog might include a mass of 45 kg, a height of 76 cm, ear length of 14 cm, and an age of 283 days.

▶ Using Observations to Form a Hypothesis

Suppose you want to make a perfect score on a spelling test. Begin by thinking of several ways to accomplish this. Base these possibilities on past observations. If you put each of these possibilities into sentence form, using the words if and then, you can form a hypothesis. All of the following are hypotheses you might consider to explain how you could score 100 percent on your test:

If the test is easy, then I will get a perfect score.

If I am intelligent, then I will get a perfect score.

If I study hard, then I will get a perfect score.

Scientists make hypotheses that they can test to explain the observations they have made. Perhaps a scientist has observed that plants that receive fertilizer grow taller than plants that do not. A scientist may form a hypothesis that says: If plants are fertilized, then their growth will increase.

Designing an Experiment to Test a Hypothesis

Once you state a hypothesis, you probably want to find out if it explains an event or an observation or not. This requires a test. A hypothesis must be something you can test. To test a hypothesis, you design and carry out an experiment. Experiments involve planning and materials. Let's figure out how to conduct an experiment to test the hypothesis stated before about the effects of fertilizer on plants.

First, you need to write out a procedure. A procedure is the plan that you follow in your experiment. A procedure tells you what materials to use and how to use them. In this experiment, your plan may involve using ten bean plants that are each 15-cm tall (to begin with) in two groups, Groups A and B. You will water the five bean plants in Group A with 200 mL of plain water and no fertilizer twice a week for three weeks. You will treat the five bean plants in Group B with 200 mL of fertilizer solution twice a week for three weeks.

You will need to measure all the plants in both groups at the beginning of the experiment and again at the end of the three-week period. These measurements will be the data that you record in a table. A sample table has been done for you. Look at the data in the table for this experiment. From the data, you can draw a conclusion and make a statement about your results. If the conclusion you draw from the data supports your hypothesis, then you can say that your hypothesis is

Growing Bean Plants

Plants	Treatment	Height 3 Weeks Later
Group A	no fertilizer added to soil	17 cm
Group B	3 g fertilizer added to soil	31 cm

reliable. Reliable means that you can trust your conclusion. If it did not support your hypothesis, then you would have to make new observations and state a new hypothesis, one that you could also test.

Separating and Controlling Variables

In the experiment with the bean plants, you made everything the same except for treating one group (Group B) with fertilizer. In any experiment, it is important to keep everything the same, except for the item you are testing. In the experiment, you kept the type of plants, their beginning heights, the soil, the frequency with which you watered them, and the amount of water or fertilizer all the same, or constant. By doing so, you made sure that at the end of three weeks any change you saw was the result of whether or not the plants had been fertilized. The only thing that you changed, or varied, was the use of fertilizer. In an experiment, the one factor that you change (in this case, the fertilizer), is called the independent variable. The factor that changes (in this case, growth) as a result of the independent variable is called the dependent variable. Always make sure that there is only one independent variable. If you allow more than one, you will not know what causes the changes you observe in the dependent variable.

Many experiments also have a control, a treatment that you can compare with the results of your test groups. In this case, Group A was the control because it was not treated with fertilizer. Group B was the test group. At the end of three weeks, you were able to compare Group A with Group B and draw a conclusion.

▶ Interpreting Data

The word *interpret* means to explain the meaning of something. Information, or data, needs to mean something. Look at the problem originally being explored and find out what the data shows. Perhaps you are looking at a table from an experiment designed to test the hypothesis: If plants are fertilized, then their growth will increase. Look back to the table showing the results of the bean plant experiment.

Identify the control group and the test group so you can see whether or not the variable has had an effect. In this example, Group A was the control and Group B was the test group. Now you need to check differences between the control and test groups. These differences may be qualitative or quantitative. A qualitative difference would be if the leaf colors of plants in Groups A and B were different. A quantitative difference would be the difference in numbers of centimeters of height among the plants in each group. Group B was in fact taller than Group A after three weeks.

If there are differences, the variable being tested may have had an effect. If there is no difference between the control and the test groups, the variable being tested apparently had no effect. From the data table in this experiment on page 664, it appears that fertilizer does have an effect on plant growth.

▶ What is Data?

In the experiment described on these pages, measurements have been taken so that at the end of the experiment, you had something concrete to interpret. You had numbers to work with. Not every experiment that you do will give you data in the form of numbers. Sometimes, data will be in the form of a description. At the end of a chemistry experiment, you might have noted that one solution turned yellow when treated with a particular chemical, and another remained clear, like water, when treated with the same chemical. Data therefore, is stated in different forms for different types of scientific experiments.

▶ Are All Experiments Alike?

Keep in mind as you perform experiments in science, that not every experiment makes use of all of the parts that have been described on these pages. For some, it may be difficult to design an experiment that will always have a control. Other experiments are complex enough that it may be hard to have only one dependent variable. Real scientists encounter many variations in the methods that they use when they perform experiments. The skills in this handbook are here for you to use and practice. In real situations, their uses will vary.

Representing and Applying Data

Interpreting Scientific Illustrations

As you read this textbook, you will see many drawings, diagrams, and photographs. Illustrations help you to understand what you read. Some illustrations are included to help you understand an idea that you can't see easily by yourself. For instance, we can't see atoms, but we can look at a diagram of an atom and that helps us to understand some things about atoms. Seeing something often helps you remember more easily. The text may describe the surface of Jupiter in detail, but seeing a photograph of Jupiter may help you to remember that it has cloud bands. Illustrations also provide examples that clarify difficult concepts or give additional information about the topic you are studying. Maps, for example, help you to locate places that may be described in the text.

Captions and Labels Most illustrations have captions. A caption is a comment that identifies or explains the illustration. Diagrams, such as the one of the feather, often have labels that identify parts of the item shown or the order of steps in a process.

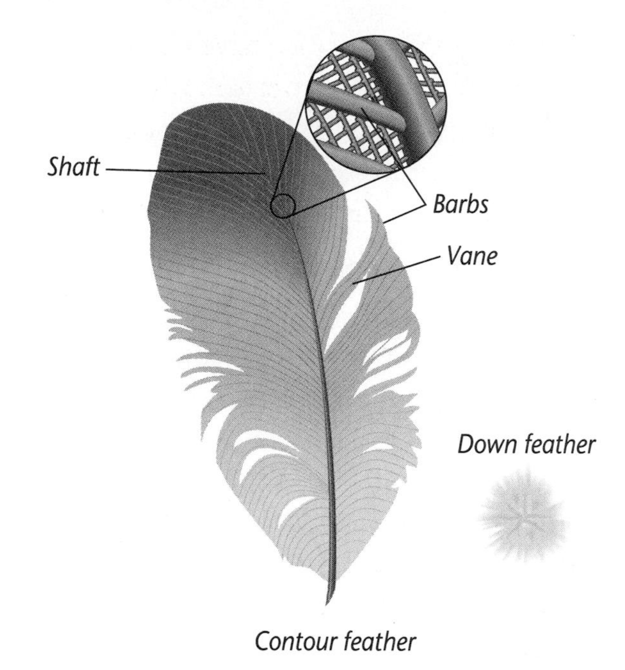

Learning with Illustrations An illustration of an organism shows that organism from a particular view or orientation. In order to understand the illustration, you may need to identify the front (anterior) end, tail (posterior) end, the underside (ventral), and the back (dorsal) side of the organism shown.

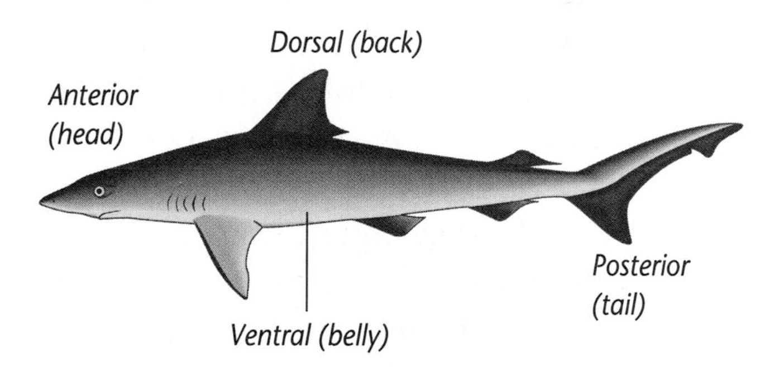

You might also check for symmetry. Look at the illustration on the following page. A shark has bilateral symmetry. This means that drawing an imaginary line through the center of the animal from the anterior to posterior end forms two mirror images.

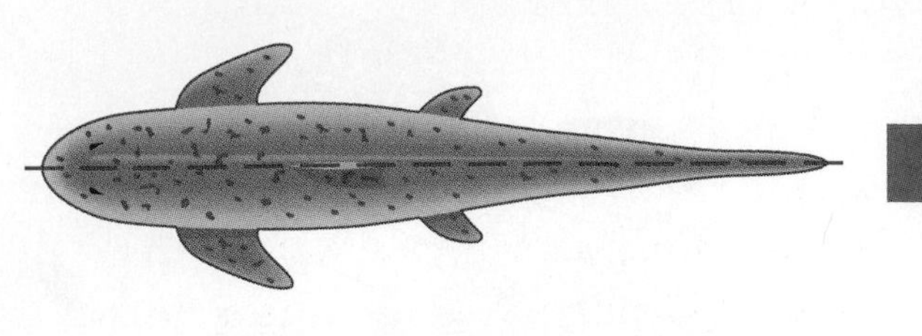

Bilateral symmetry

Two sides exactly alike

Radial symmetry is the arrangement of similar parts around a central point. An object or organism such as a hydra can be divided anywhere through the center into similar parts.

Some organisms and objects cannot be divided into two similar parts. If an organism or object cannot be divided, it is asymmetrical. Regardless of how you try to divide a natural sponge, you cannot divide it into two parts that look alike.

Some illustrations enable you to see the inside of an organism or object. These illustrations are called sections.

Look at all illustrations carefully. Read captions and labels so that you understand exactly what the illustration is showing you.

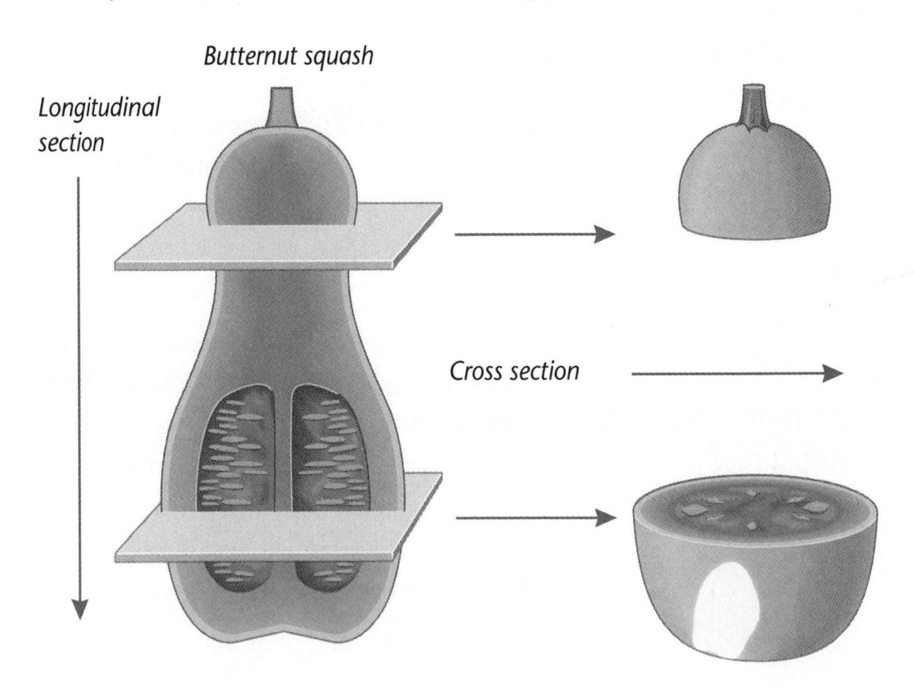

▶ Making Models

Have you ever worked on a model car or plane or rocket? These models look, and sometimes work, just like the real thing, but they are usually much smaller than the real thing. In science, models are used to help simplify large processes or structures that may be difficult to understand. Your understanding of a structure or process is enhanced when you work with materials to make a model that shows the basic features of the structure or process.

In order to make a model, you first have to get a basic idea about the structure or process involved. You decide to make a model to show the differences in size of arteries, veins, and capillaries. First, read about these structures. All three are hollow tubes. Arteries are round and thick. Veins are flat and have thinner walls than arteries. Capillaries are very small.

Now, decide what you can use for your model. Common materials are often best and cheapest to work with when making models. Different

kinds and sizes of pasta might work for these models. Different sizes of rubber tubing might do just as well. Cut and glue the different noodles or tubing onto thick paper so the openings can be seen. Then label each. Now you have a simple, easy–to–understand model showing the differences in size of arteries, veins, and capillaries.

What other scientific ideas might a model help you to understand? A model of a molecule can be made from gumdrops (using different colors for the different elements present) and toothpicks (to show different chemical bonds). A working model of a volcano can be made from clay, a small amount of baking soda, vinegar, and a bottle cap. Other models can be devised on a computer.

▶ Predicting

When you apply a hypothesis, or general explanation, to a specific situation, you predict something about that situation. First, you must identify which hypothesis fits the situation you are considering. People use prediction to make everyday decisions. Based on previous observations and experiences, you may form a hypothesis that if it is wintertime, then temperatures will be lower. From past experience in your area, temperatures are lowest in February. You may then use this hypothesis to predict specific temperatures and weather for the month of February in advance. Someone could use these predictions to plan to set aside more money for heating bills during that month.

▶ Sampling and Estimating

When working with large populations of organisms, scientists usually cannot observe or study every organism in the population. Instead, they use a sample or a portion of the population. Sampling is taking a small portion of organisms of a population for research. By making careful observations or manipulating variables with a portion of a group, information is discovered and conclusions are drawn that might then be applied to the whole population.

Scientific work also involves estimating. Estimating is making a judgment about the size of something or the number of something without actually measuring or counting every member of a population.

Suppose you are trying to determine the effect of a specific nutrient on the growth of black-eyed Susans. It would be impossible to test the entire population of black-eyed Susans, so you would select part of the population for your experiment. Through careful experimentation and observation on a sample of the population, you could generalize the effect of the chemical on the entire population.

Here is a more familiar example. Have you ever tried to guess how many beans were in a sealed jar? If you did, you were estimating. What if you knew the jar of beans held one liter (1000 mL)? If you knew that 30 beans would fit in a 100-milliliter jar, how many beans would you estimate to be in the one-liter jar? If you said about 300 beans, your estimate would be close to the actual number of beans.

Scientists use a similar process to estimate populations of organisms from bacteria to buffalo. Scientists count the actual number of organisms in a small sample and then estimate the number of organisms in a larger area. For example, if a scientist wanted to count the number of microorganisms in a petri dish, a microscope could be used to count the number of organisms in a one square millimeter sample. To determine the total population of the culture, the number of organisms in the square millimeter sample is multiplied by the total number of millimeters in the culture.

This glossary defines each key term that appears in bold type in the text. It also indicates the chapter number and page number where you will find the word used.

acceleration: rate of change of velocity; acceleration takes place whenever you speed up, slow down, move in a circle, or go around a corner. (Chap. 12, p. 397)

acceleration due to gravity: acceleration on or near Earth that is the same for any free falling object; can be expressed as $g = 9.8/s^2$; satellites remain orbiting around Earth because of horizontal velocity and acceleration due to gravity. (Chap. 13, p. 418)

acids: sour-tasting, corrosive compounds that may release hydrogen gas when reacting with some metals; examples include nitric and sulfuric acids in acid rain, and hydrochloric acid in your stomach. (Chap. 6, p. 188)

adaptation: inherited trait that helps an organism survive; the better adapted a living thing is, the greater its chances to reproduce. (Chap. 7, p. 221)

amplitude: measure of the distance from the top of a crest or the bottom of a trough to the middle level; the energy carried by mechanical waves depends on their amplitude. (Chap. 17, p. 550)

aquifer: layer of permeable rock or soil that allows groundwater to move in and out freely; aquifers provide water for many communities. (Chap. 14, p. 461)

average acceleration: the change in velocity divided by the time interval during which this change occurred; the acceleration of an object at any one instant will most probably be different from its average acceleration. (Chap. 12, p. 400)

average speed: measure of motion that can be found by dividing the total distance traveled by the total time needed to travel that distance; tells how rapidly an object travels but does not describe the direction of the motion. (Chap. 12, p. 387)

average velocity: measure of motion that tells how fast an object moved over a specific displacement; can be found by the following equation: average velocity = total displacement/time interval. (Chap. 12, p. 392)

bases: bitter-tasting, usually solid compounds that feel slippery when dissolved in water; blood and some other body fluids are mildly basic; soaps, antacids, drain cleaners, and household ammonia are common bases. (Chap. 6, p. 193)

cellular respiration: chemical change occurring inside body cells in which oxygen combines with digested food and energy is released. (Chap. 9, p. 297)

centripetal acceleration: acceleration experienced by an object when it is moving in a circle at a constant speed. (Chap. 12, p. 404)

chemical change: materials do not keep their identity after a chemical change; for example, when iron and sulfur are heated, they are chemically changed to iron sulfide, which has properties different from either iron or sulfur; some signs that a chemical change has taken place include smoke, foaming, smell, and sound. (Chap. 4, p. 137)

chemical property: any characteristic of a substance that allows it to undergo a chemical change; chemical properties such as flammability and sensitivity to light can be used to describe and identify materials. (Chap. 4, p. 138)

chlorophyll: green pigment in plants that traps light from the sun, enabling plants to carry out the process of photosynthesis, which changes water and carbon dioxide into sugar and oxygen in a series of chemical reactions. (Chap. 10, p. 336)

cilia: short hairlike structures covering the body of some protists, such as paramecia; cilia are used by this protozoan group for movement and to sweep food into their mouths. (Chap. 8, p. 261)

classification: any organizational grouping system; living things are classified by scientists according to their traits and given names, which helps us understand how organisms are related. (Chap. 7, p. 225)

climax community: final stage of succession in which the plants and animals of a community are well adapted and make up a balanced ecosystem; a mature oak and maple forest is an example. (Chap. 16, p. 510)

colloid: mixture whose medium-sized particles do not settle out of solution upon standing and are large enough to scatter light; milk, gelatin, and fog are colloids. (Chap. 5, p. 174)

commensalism: symbiotic relationship in which one species benefits and the other species is neither harmed nor benefited; for example, Spanish moss receives support from its host trees but the trees are neither harmed nor helped. (Chap. 16, p. 518)

community: all of the populations that live together in the same space and interact with one another; for example, a community could include grasses and various plants and a variety of animals such as hippos, zebras, and birds. (Chap. 11, p. 348)

compound: material made of two or more elements that are chemically combined; the same compound always has the same composition; a compound cannot be separated into its separate parts by physical means, and the substances making up a compound do not retain their own properties; iron sulfide is a compound. (Chap. 4, p. 123)

compression: area of bunched-up air particles created by an object's vibrations, which push the air particles in front of its movements closer together; compressions and rarefactions spread out from the vibrating object in all directions and pass through a medium to produce sound. (Chap. 3, p. 88)

concentrated: solution containing a large amount of solute in a solvent; chocolate milk made with 6 tablespoons of syrup is more concentrated than if made with 2 tablespoons of syrup. (Chap. 5, p. 171)

cones: light-detecting nerve cells in the retina; respond to bright light, resulting in color images; the three types of cones—red, green, and blue—allow you to see the entire spectrum; the brain produces a single image from the information sent by both rods and cones. (Chap. 2, p. 76)

constellation: pattern formed by a group of stars; star maps can help you find where constellations are at different times of year; examples are the Big Dipper, the Little Dipper, and Pegasus. (Chap. 1, p. 44)

consumer: organism such as an animal or a fungus that is unable to make its own food and must feed on other organisms. (Chap. 8, p. 250)

continental glaciers: thick ice that covers very large land areas near Earth's polar regions and makes up 96 percent of Earth's glacial ice; continental glaciers and valley glaciers contain about 75 percent of the world's supply of fresh water; much of Earth's landscape has been shaped by glacier movement. (Chap. 15, p. 487)

contour lines: thin lines that show the shape of three-dimensional landforms on two-dimensional topographic maps; the closer the contour lines, the steeper the change in elevation. (Chap. 1, p. 32)

creep: slow, downhill movement of soil in response to freezing and thawing and the pull of gravity; over time creep can help reshape such landforms as hills, which become more rounded and less steep. (Chap. 15, p. 475)

crest: high point or hill of a wave; for example, when a crest strikes a floating object, it moves slightly forward, exhibiting longitudinal motion, and slightly upward, exhibiting transverse motion. (Chap. 17, p. 548)

D

decomposer: organism such as a mold, mushroom, or bacterium that obtains food by breaking down dead organic material; decomposers are valuable consumers that recycle nutrients back into the environment. (Chap. 11, p. 353)

delta: triangular-shaped land area formed when a river empties into another body of water and deposits sediments; for example, the fertile Mekong Delta, which is Southern Vietnam's chief agricultural area, was formed by the Mekong River depositing topsoil and mineral sediments into the South China Sea. (Chap. 15, p. 481)

density: measure of an object's or material's mass compared to its volume; density is a physical property that can be used to identify unknown materials and can be measured in g/cm^3. (Chap. 4, p. 131)

deposition: accumulation of eroded sediments; for example, the formation of the fertile Mississippi Delta is the result of deposition. (Chap. 15, p. 474)

dilute: solution with a small amount of solute in a solvent; for example, a drink containing 10% fruit juice in water is more dilute than one containing 90% fruit juice. (Chap. 5, p. 171)

displacement: difference between the starting position of an object and its ending position, noting whether the path is straight or curved; for example, round trips produce a displacement of zero because the object ends up where it started. (Chap. 12, p. 391)

distance: length of the path an object travels in changing its position; science uses the meter, or m, for measuring distance, but distance can also be measured in many other units such as blocks or number of steps. (Chap. 12, p. 384)

diversity: presence of many different species within a community; diversity helps ecosystems recover from volcanic eruptions, fires, and floods and is an important factor in succession. (Chap. 16, p. 512)

Doppler effect: apparent change in the pitch and frequency of a sound as the source moves with respect to the observer; a train's horn sounds higher pitched as it moves toward you and lower pitched as it moves away from you. (Chap. 17, p. 563)

GLOSSARY

drainage basin: land area whose runoff is drained into one stream; in the United States, the largest is the Mississippi drainage basin, which is fed by rains falling between the Rocky Mountains and the Appalachians. (Chap. 14, p. 454)

dune: mound of wind-eroded loose sediments or sand particles that are blown by wind and deposited in another location; sand dunes themselves can move by building up a slope on the windward side until the sand falls down the steeper, opposite side; dunes can be found on a beach or in a desert. (Chap. 15, p. 494)

E

ecosystem: a community of organisms interacting with each other and with the nonliving things in their environment; examples of ecosystems are oceans, cities, and pine forests. (Chap. 11, p. 351)

element: substance that cannot be broken down further by ordinary physical or chemical methods; elements are the building blocks of matter; examples are calcium, iron, and phosphorus. (Chap. 4, p. 122)

elevation: height above sea level or depth below sea level; on a topographic map, elevation describes the shape of an area by telling us how high or low specific landforms are. (Chap. 1, p. 32)

endoskeleton: internal skeleton that provides body support for all vertebrates and is made of bone or, in some fish, is made of cartilage. (Chap. 9, p. 287)

equinox: occurs twice yearly when the sun is directly above the equator, with the result that day and night are the same length all over the world; in the Northern Hemisphere, the spring equinox occurs March 20 or 21 and the fall equinox occurs September 22 or 23. (Chap. 19, p. 608)

erosion: movement of weathered materials from where they formed to a new location; gravity, running water, glaciers, and wind are the four major agents of erosion; erosion can be reduced by such measures as planting vegetation, constructing terraces, and building retaining walls. (Chap. 15, p. 474)

exoskeleton: hardened external covering of many invertebrates that provides protection from fluid loss, protects internal organs, and provides a support system for the body. (Chap. 9, p. 288)

extinction: local or global disappearance of a species either by natural processes such as climate changes or through destruction of habitats or introduction of competing species; dinosaurs and the dodo are examples of extinct species. (Chap. 16, p. 524)

F

fertilization: sexual reproductive process of organisms (both plants and animals); in external fertilization in some animals, eggs are released into water and fertilized by free-swimming sperm; in internal fertilization, the male deposits sperm-containing fluid into the female's body. (Chap. 9. p. 290)

firn: small, thick granules formed from snow that has survived for one year without melting; firn contains about 50 percent air—as it becomes still more compressed, it will contain less than 20 percent air and become glacial ice. (Chap. 15, p. 486)

flagella: whiplike structures of some protozoans propel animal-like protists through water. (Chap. 8, p. 261)

floodplain: land area beyond the river channel over which fine, light sediments are deposited by a flooding river; floodplains are excellent for planting crops because the sediments contain minerals and rich topsoil. (Chap. 15, p. 481)

food chain: model of how energy in food passes through an ecosystem; for example, energy is passed when plants are eaten by animals, who are then eaten by other animals. (Chap. 11, p. 356)

food web: model that shows the interconnection of food chains in an ecosystem; organisms in a large food web have a better chance of survival than those with a limited diet. (Chap. 11, p. 357)

frequency: number of times an object vibrates in 1 second; frequency is measured in hertz and is recognized by your ears as differences in pitch. (Chap. 3, p. 95)

genus: subgroup of a family; genera are further divided into species; genus is the first part of the organism's scientific name and is always capitalized and italicized. (Chap. 7, p. 231)

groundwater: water that soaks into the ground and accumulates in connecting pores beneath Earth's surface. (Chap. 14, p. 455)

habitat: the particular place in which an organism lives; for example, the ocean is the habitat of an octopus, your neighborhood is your habitat, and an eagle's habitat includes both land and air. (Chap. 11, p. 347)

GLOSSARY

hertz (Hz): unit that measures frequency; 1 hertz is a frequency of 1 vibration/second or 1 cycle/second; for example, dolphins hear sounds up to about 155,000 hertz (Hz) and humans hear sounds up to about 20,000 Hz. (Chap. 3, p. 95)

heterogeneous mixture: mixture containing various particles of different substances that are scattered unevenly throughout; many heterogeneous mixtures can be separated into their component substances by filtration or by hand-separating on the basis of size, color, or shape; examples are paper and pita bread. (Chap. 4, p. 119)

homogeneous mixture: mixture in which the individual particles of the combined substances are evenly distributed throughout and are too small to be seen; two methods of separating homogeneous mixtures into their component substances are by boiling and evaporation; iced tea is a homogeneous mixture. (Chap. 4, p. 119)

hydrologic cycle: system of water circulation at Earth's surface and above Earth's surface; evaporation changes water into water vapor that rises into the air, cools back into liquid by condensation and falls back to Earth's surface, where it evaporates or runs off or soaks into the ground. (Chap. 14, p. 445)

indicator: substance used to determine pH; an acid-base indicator has one color in one pH range and a different color in a different pH range—for example, cabbage juice, an indicator, turns green in a medium base and red in a medium acid; two types of indicators are solutions or indicator paper such as litmus paper. (Chap. 6, p. 202)

interference: occurs when two or more waves cross at one point and their crests and troughs add or subtract; for example, when two reflected light waves from a CD meet, constructive interference allows you to see bright colors, whereas destructive interference prevents colors from being seen. (Chap. 17, p. 556)

invertebrate: animal without a backbone; invertebrates make up the largest part of the animal kingdom—for example, flies, clams, and spiders. (Chap. 9, p. 285)

kingdom: largest group in the scientific classification system of organisms; kingdoms are subdivided into phyla, and in the case of plants, into divisions instead of phyla; the five kingdoms are plant, fungus, moneran, protist, and animal. (Chap. 7, p. 227)

landforms: surface land features; three common landforms are low, mostly flat coastal and interior plains; raised, rather flat plateaus; and craggy or rounded mountains. (Chap. 1, p. 22)

latitude: angular distance north or south of the equator; lines of latitude are parallel to each other and measure distance in degrees from 0° latitude at the equator to 90° north or south latitude at the poles; lines of latitude and longitude were developed by mapmakers to help us locate places on Earth's surface. (Chap. 1, p. 35)

lava: molten rock at Earth's surface that can erupt quietly or explosively, forming shield volcanoes, cinder cone volcanoes, or composite volcanoes. (Chap. 18, p. 577)

limiting factor: any living or nonliving factor that influences the survival of an organism or species; weather conditions, food and shelter, and predator-prey relationships. (Chap. 11, p. 364)

longitude: angular distance east and west of the prime meridian; lines of longitude measure distance in degrees—the prime meridian is 0° longitude, places east of the prime meridian are located from 0° to 180° E longitude and places west of the prime meridian are located from 0°to 180° W longitude. (Chap. 1, p. 36)

longitudinal wave: mechanical wave that travels in the same direction as the disturbance; sound waves are a type of longitudinal wave that travels through the air in a pattern of compressions and rarefactions. (Chap. 17, p. 542)

lunar eclipse: occurs when Earth passes between the moon and sun and casts a curved shadow on the moon; a total lunar eclipse takes place when the moon passes totally into Earth's umbra, or dark inner shadow. (Chap. 19, p. 620)

magma: molten rock deep beneath Earth's surface that rises slowly through cracks in rock or by melting through rock; when magma reaches Earth's surface, it is called lava. (Chap. 18, p. 577)

magnitude: measure of an earthquake's strength; the Richter scale describes magnitude in terms of the amounts of energy released by an earthquake—for example, an earthquake measuring 7.5 on the Richter scale is 1000 times stronger than one measuring 5.5. (Chap. 18, p. 588)

meander: curves or bends in a river; meanders are formed by fast-moving channels of deep water, which are not affected by friction from the stream bottom, wearing away the sides of the streambed. (Chap. 14, p. 451)

medium: any sound-conducting liquid, solid, or gas; for example, you hear most sounds through the medium of air, which conducts the sound produced by a vibrating object to your ears. (Chap. 3, p. 89)

metabolism: total of all the chemical changes that take place in an organism. (Chap. 9, p. 299)

metamorphosis: hormonally controlled process of organisms such as as frogs and insects during which they undergo extensive changes in form as they grow from egg to adult; metamorphosis in insects can be complete (egg, larva, pupa, adult) or incomplete (egg, nymph, adult). (Chap. 9, p. 292)

microorganism: organism that is too small to be seen with the unaided eye; examples include protists, bacteria, and many fungi. (Chap. 8, p. 249)

mixture: any material made of a combination of two or more substances that are combined in such a way that each substance keeps its own properties; mixtures can be heterogeneous or homogeneous and can be physically separated into simpler substances; examples are air and brass. (Chap. 4, p. 119)

mudflow: mass movement of heavy, water-saturated layers of sediments that flow easily downhill, move anything in their path, and can be highly destructive. (Chap. 15, p. 476)

mutualism: symbiotic relationship in which both species benefit; for example, algae living inside the coral polyp produce oxygen and food used by the polyp, which in turn gives the algae nutrients and a home. (Chap. 16, p. 517)

neutralization: chemical reaction during which acidic and basic properties are canceled, resulting in the production of a salt plus water. (Chap. 6, p. 203)

niche: specific role played by an organism within its community; niches allow many populations to share an area because no two plants or animals meet their needs, such as producing or consuming food, in exactly the same way. (Chap. 11, p. 350)

nonvascular plant: spore-producing plant without xylem, phloem, roots, stems, or leaves; nonvascular plants are unable to transport water efficiently; usually live close to water; mosses and liverworts are examples. (Chap. 10, p. 316)

opaque: property of a material that allows it to absorb or reflect all of the light hitting it; light does not pass through an opaque object. (Chap. 2, p. 59)

organism: any living thing; organisms are made up of cells, need water and food and produce wastes, reproduce, grow and develop, respond to stimuli, and adapt to their environment. (Chap. 7, p. 219)

P

parasite: organism that lives on or in another organism and obtains its food from that living thing; some parasitic fungi cause athlete's foot, ringworm, and plant diseases such as corn smut. (Chap. 8, p. 265)

parasitism: symbiotic relationship in which one species benefits and the other is harmed or, less often, may be killed; mosquitoes, ticks, and lice are examples of parasites. (Chap. 16, p. 520)

period: amount of time it takes for a pendulum bob to swing back and forth once; period is determined by pendulum length, regardless of mass or amplitude. (Chap. 13, p. 430)

pH: scale that indicates how acidic a solution is; ranges from 0 to 14, with 0 being the most acidic and 14 being the most basic; a pH of 7 indicates that the solution is neither acidic nor basic but is neutral. (Chap. 6, p. 199)

phase: cycle in which the moon appears to change its shape, going from full moon to new moon to full moon in about four weeks. (Chap. 1, p. 43)

phloem: tubelike vessels of vascular plants that transport sugar made during photosynthesis, from the leaves to other plant parts. (Chap. 10, p. 314)

photosynthesis: food-producing process in which plants use the energy from sunlight, which is trapped by chlorophyll, to change water and carbon dioxide into sugar and oxygen. (Chap. 10, p. 336)

phylum: subgroup of a kingdom; phyla are divided into smaller categories—classes. (Chap. 7, p. 230)

physical change: substances keep their identity after physical changes, which may include boiling, freezing, breaking, and melting; for example, when pieces of chalk are broken up, resulting in physical changes in length and mass, they are still the same substance. (Chap. 4, p. 136)

physical property: characteristic that can be used to identify and describe materials; examples include color, shape, brittleness, density, length, width, height, mass, and volume. (Chap. 4, p. 127)

pioneer species: the first species to live in a new ecosystem; lichens, which are able to live in barren places and begin the breakdown of rock into soil, are one of many types of pioneer species. (Chap. 16, p. 507)

pitch: the highness or lowness of a sound; the slower the vibration of an object, the lower its pitch, and the faster its vibration, the higher its pitch. (Chap. 3, p. 96)

pollination: in flowering plants, the transfer of sperm-containing pollen grains from the male stamen to the female stigma. (Chap. 10, p. 326)

population: any group of individuals of the same species that occupies a specific area at the same time; the following are all populations: a herd of zebras, a pride of lions, and a group of Cape May warblers. (Chap. 11, p. 348)

position: place at which you or an object is located compared to a reference point; when position is changed, you experience motion. (Chap. 12, p. 382)

producer: organism that uses light energy to make food from water and carbon dioxide in the presence of chlorophyll; examples are green plants, cyanobacteria, and certain algae. (Chap. 8, p. 250)

projectile motion: motion experienced by an object that is launched into the air horizontally or at an angle and then falls back to Earth; projectiles all move forward and downward at the same time. (Chap. 13, p. 422)

R

rarefaction: area of spread-out air particles—created by an object's vibrations—that occurs opposite an area of compression; sound is produced by patterns of compressions and rarefactions traveling through a medium. (Chap. 3, p. 88)

receptors: light-sensitive structures in the retina that allow you to respond to color and light changes; also called rods and cones. (Chap. 2, p. 76)

reflection: bouncing back of light from a surface; most things are visible because light bounces off objects and is reflected back to your eyes; smooth surfaces produce regular reflections, and rough surfaces produce diffuse reflections. (Chap. 2, p. 54)

refraction: process that occurs when light moves through materials with different densities, resulting in the light changing speed and refracting, or bending; for example, refraction causes the image of an object in water to appear closer to the surface than it really is. (Chap. 2, p. 64)

regeneration: formation of a missing body part; also, may be a form of asexual reproduction that occurs when entire new individuals grow from a piece of the original organism. (Chap. 9, p. 291)

relative velocity: motion that depends on your frame of reference, or what you're comparing your motion to; for example, when you stand still, your velocity relative to Earth is zero, even though Earth is rotating and you are moving along with it. (Chap. 12, p. 393)

reproduction: ability of an organism to produce more organisms of the same kind; process that ensures the survival of that specific type of organism. (Chap. 7, p. 220; see also plant reproduction, Chap. 10)

resonance: an object's tendency to vibrate at the same frequency as another sound source; the frequency at which an object resonates is affected by such factors as its shape and the type of material from which it is made. (Chap. 3, p. 103)

retina: light-sensitive tissue in the back of the eye; receives light from the lens; contains rods and cones, which send messages through the optic nerve to the brain, resulting in image formation. (Chap. 2, p. 75)

revolution: elliptical trip of Earth around the sun, which takes about 365.25 days, or one year, to complete; Earth's revolution on its tilted axis around the sun is responsible for the change in seasons. (Chap. 19, p. 604)

rockslide: sudden mass movement of falling rocks; rockslides are most likely to occur on the steep, rocky slopes of mountains and happen most often during earthquakes or after heavy rain. (Chap. 15, p. 476)

rods: light-detecting nerve cells in the retina of the eye; respond to dim light, resulting in black-and-white images. (Chap. 2, p. 76)

rotation: spinning motion of Earth in space, responsible for day and night; Earth rotates around its axis, which is an imaginary line running through the North and South Poles, and takes 24 hours to complete one rotation. (Chap. 19, p. 604)

runoff: rainwater that flows off a land surface and does not soak in; usually results when land is hard, steep, or barren, or can result when rain falls too hard and fast. (Chap. 14, p. 446)

salts: compounds formed as part of neutralization; examples include sodium chloride, which is used in food preparation and chemical manufacture, and potassium permanganate, which is used to tan leather and purify water. (Chap. 6, p. 203)

saturated: a solution is saturated when solutes will no longer dissolve in it at a given temperature; when heated to higher temperatures, saturated solutions may become unsaturated and able to hold more solute. (Chap. 5, p. 166)

seismograph: instrument used to record earthquake vibrations, which are recorded as wavy lines whose peaks indicate the magnitude, or strength, of the earthquake. (Chap. 18, p. 588)

slump: slow slippage of rock layers or a large mass of loose material; occurs when its underlying material gives way and the overlying material slips downslope in a single mass; over time slumps can help reshape such landforms as valleys. (Chap. 15, p. 475)

solar eclipse: occurs when the moon passes directly between the sun and Earth, casting shadow on Earth; the dark inner shadow, or umbra, is experienced as a total eclipse; the lighter, outer shadow, or penumbra, is experienced as a partial eclipse. (Chap. 19, p. 615)

solstice: occurs twice yearly when the sun is directly over the northernmost or southernmost edges of the tropics; in the Northern Hemisphere, the winter solstice (December 21 or 22) has the fewest daylight hours and the summer solstice (June 21 or 22) has the most daylight hours. (Chap. 19, p. 608)

solubility: number of grams of solute that will dissolve in 100 g of a solvent at a given temperature; for example, at room temperature, table salt has a solubility of 36.0 g/100 g water and sugar has a solubility of 204.0 g/100 g water. (Chap. 5, p. 166)

solute: any substance that dissolves in a solvent and forms a solution; solutes dissolve in solvents at different rates depending on such factors as the size of the particles, shaking or stirring, and temperature. (Chap. 5, p. 156)

solution: mixture made up of tiny, evenly mixed particles that do not settle out on standing and cannot be separated by mechanical means; solutions can be made up of solids, gases, and liquids; for example, air is a gas-gas solution, soft drinks are gas-liquid solutions, and sterling silver is a solid-solid solution. (Chap. 5, p. 156)

solvent: the substance in which a solute is dissolved, forming a solution; water is known as a universal solvent because it can dissolve so many different solutes. (Chap. 5, p. 156)

species: subgroup of a genus; in Linnaeus's two-part naming system, the second name always lower case and italicized. (Chap. 7, p. 231)

spectrum: separate bands of colors produced when white light, which is a mixture of all colors of light, passes through a prism; colors usually listed are red, orange, yellow, green, blue, indigo, and violet. (Chap. 2, p. 67)

sphere: three-dimensional, round object such as a volleyball or basketball whose surface at all points is equidistant from its center; Earth's sphere is slightly flattened at the poles and bulges slightly at the equator. (Chap. 19, p. 603)

stationary satellite: type of satellite that moves in its daily orbit around Earth's equator at the same rate as Earth rotates, so to a person on Earth the satellite has no motion and always appears at the same place in the sky. (Chap. 13, p. 429)

stimulus: anything that produces a change in how an organism responds to its environment; stimuli can include changes in sound, light, touch, or taste. (Chap. 7, p. 221)

substance: anything that is made of only one kind of material; the identity of a substance changes after a chemical change but not after a physical change; examples of substances are sugar, water, and chalk. (Chap. 4, p. 118)

succession: gradual process of change through which new environments become populated, or one community slowly replaces another community, or an ecosystem recovers from such disasters as flooding or volcanic eruption. (Chap. 16, p. 507)

suspension: liquid-containing mixture whose unevenly mixed particles settle out of solution upon standing, are large enough to scatter light, and can be separated by filter paper. (Chap. 5, p. 175)

symbiosis: cooperative relationship between members of two or more species; mutualism, parasitism, and commensalism are three types. (Chap. 16, p. 516)

GLOSSARY

T

tides: slow-moving water waves with long wavelengths that produce the alternate rise, or high tides, and fall, or low tides, of the surface levels of oceans; the gravitational forces acting between the moon, sun, and Earth produce two high tides and two low tides daily. (Chap. 19, p. 621)

translucent: property of a material that allows light to pass through it, but bends the light, causing fuzzy images to be seen on its other side; examples of translucent objects are frosted glass and waxed paper. (Chap. 2, p. 59)

transparent: property of a material that allows enough light to pass through it so that objects can be clearly seen on its other side; examples of transparent objects are plate glass and pair of reading glasses. (Chap. 2, p. 59)

transpiration: process of water loss in plants during which water vapor from inside the leaves moves out through the stomata. (Chap. 10, p. 332)

transverse wave: mechanical wave in which wave disturbance travels at right angles to the direction of the wave itself; the up-and-down pulse traveling along a stretched and shaken rope is an example of a transverse wave. (Chap. 17, p. 541)

trough: low point or valley of a wave; for example, when a trough strikes an object floating in water, the object moves slightly backward, exhibiting longitudinal motion, and slightly downward, exhibiting transverse motion. (Chap. 17, p. 548)

tsunami: giant wave that may travel thousands of kilometers in all directions as quickly as a jet plane, reach heights of over 50 km, and cause destruction in coastal areas; tsunamis are caused by earthquakes under the ocean floor, volcanic eruptions in the sea, or by underwater landslides. (Chap. 18, p. 585)

unsaturated: qualitative term describing the fact that an unsaturated solution can hold any amount of solute as long as the amount is less than the amount that would make it saturated at that temperature. (Chap. 10, p. 338)

valley glaciers: small glaciers found at higher elevations in mountainous regions; valley glaciers erode land as they move down mountain slopes, typically creating U-shaped valleys. (Chap. 15, p. 487)

vascular plant: plant with xylem and phloem; most vascular plants reproduce by seeds and some reproduce by spores; vascular plants can grow taller and thicker and live in drier areas than nonvascular plants; examples are ferns, pines, and flowering plants. (Chap. 10, p. 318)

vertebrate: animal with a backbone; vertebrates are chordates; humans, birds, fish, and amphibians are examples of vertebrates. (Chap. 9, p. 285)

viruses: nonliving, submicroscopic structures with a DNA or RNA core surrounded by a protein coat; uses the cell's energy and materials to duplicate itself; viruses cause diseases such as AIDS, rabies, and chicken pox. (Chap. 8, p. 251)

water table: upper limit of the underground area that is saturated with groundwater; springs can be found where the water table meets Earth's surface. (Chap. 14, p. 462)

wavelength: measure of the distance between the crest of one wave and the crest of the next wave or between the trough of one wave and the trough of the next wave; wavelength gets smaller as frequency increases. (Chap. 17, p. 551)

weightlessness: state experienced during a free-fall as you accelerate toward Earth, regardless of the direction of your velocity; in space, biological effects of weightlessness include loss of calcium in the bones and loss of body mass. (Chap. 13, p. 428)

xylem: specialized tubelike vessels of vascular plants; xylem transports minerals and water absorbed by roots up the stem to the leaves. (Chap. 10, p. 314)

SPANISH GLOSSARY

This glossary defines each key term that appears in bold type in the text. It also indicates the chapter number and page number where you will find the word used.

A

acceleration/aceleración ritmo al cual cambia la velocidad (Cap. 12, pág. 397)

acceleration due to gravity/aceleración por gravedad aceleración que es la misma para cualquier objeto que cae hacia la tierra (Cap. 13, pág. 418)

acids/ácidos compuestos que contienen hidrógeno, tienen un sabor agrio y son corrosivos (Cap. 6, pág. 188)

adaptation/adaptación cualquier rasgo que posee un organismo y que lo ayuda a sobrevivir en su ambiente (Cap. 7, pág. 221)

amplitude/amplitud distancia desde la cresta o el seno de una onda hasta el nivel intermedio de la misma onda (Cap. 17, pág. 550)

aquifer/acuífero capa de suelo o de roca permeable que le permite al agua infiltrarse y fluir libremente (Cap. 14, pág. 461)

average acceleration/aceleración promedio cambio en la velocidad dividido entre el intervalo de tiempo durante el cual ocurre el cambio (Cap. 12, pág. 400)

average speed/rapidez promedio se obtiene al dividir la distancia total viajada entre el tiempo total requerido para viajar esa distancia (Cap. 12, pág. 387)

average velocity/velocidad promedio la rapidez con que un objeto se mueve sobre un desplazamiento (Cap. 12, pág. 392)

B C

bases/bases compuestos de sabor amargo, por lo general, sólidos, que se sienten resbaladizos cuando se disuelven en agua (Cap. 6, pág. 193)

cellular respiration/respiración celular proceso que ocurre dentro de las células del cuerpo cuando el oxígeno se combina con el alimento digerido para liberar energía de los enlaces químicos en el alimento (Cap. 9, pág. 298)

centripetal acceleration/aceleración centrípeta la dirección de la aceleración de un objeto que se mueve a lo largo de una trayectoria circular, la cual tiende a moverlo hacia el centro del círculo (Cap. 12, pág. 404)

chemical change/cambio químico cambio durante el cual una de las sustancias de una materia se transforma en una sustancia diferente (Cap. 4, pág. 137)

chemical property/propiedad química cualquier característica que permite que una sustancia sufra un cambio químico (Cap. 4, pág. 138)

chlorophyll/clorofila pigmento verde de las plantas que atrapa la luz solar (Cap. 10, pág. 336)

cilia/cilios estructuras filamentosas cortas que poseen algunos protozoos por todo su cuerpo (Cap. 8, pág. 261)

classification/clasificación cualquier sistema que se usa para agrupar ideas, información u objetos, basándose en sus semejanzas (Cap. 7, pág. 225)

climax community/comunidad clímax comunidad que se establece después de que un ecosistema alcanza su última etapa de sucesión (Cap. 16, pág. 510)

colloid/coloide mezcla que, al igual que una solución, no se asienta (Cap. 5, pág. 174)

commensalism/comensalismo relación en la cual un organismo se beneficia y el otro ni se beneficia ni se perjudica (Cap. 16, pág. 518)

community/comunidad la interacción de poblaciones en un área determinada (Cap. 11, pág. 348)

compound/compuesto sustancia cuya unidad más pequeña está formada por más de un elemento (Cap. 4, pág. 123)

compression/compresión la parte del patrón de partículas amontonadas que forman las vibraciones en un objeto que vibra (Cap. 3, pág. 88)

concentrated/concentrada solución que contiene una gran cantidad de soluto en un disolvente (Cap. 5, pág. 171)

cones/conos receptores sensibles a todos los colores del espectro visible de la luz (Cap. 2, pág. 76)

constellations/constelaciones patrones que forman los grupos de estrellas (Cap. 1, pág. 44)

consumer/consumidor organismo que no puede producir su propio alimento (Cap. 8, pág. 250)

continental glaciers/glaciares continentales masas de hielo y nieve que cubren áreas extensas de terreno cerca de las regiones polares de la Tierra (Cap. 15, pág. 487)

contour lines/curvas de nivel líneas con la misma elevación que muestran las formas o contornos de los accidentes geográficos (Cap. 1, pág. 32)

SPANISH GLOSSARY

creep/corrimiento movimiento lento del suelo cuesta abajo (Cap. 15, pág. 475)

crest/cresta punto más alto o cima de una onda (Cap. 17, pág. 548)

decomposer/descomponedor organismo que obtiene su alimento al descomponer organismos muertos y transformarlos en nutrimientos (Cap. 11, pág. 353)

delta/delta área de terreno triangular formada por sedimentos que se depositan cuando un río desemboca en otro cuerpo de agua (Cap. 15, pág. 481)

density/densidad es la cantidad de masa, o de material, que un objeto posee comparada con su volumen (Cap. 4, pág. 131)

deposition/deposición acumulación de sedimentos erosionados (Cap. 15, pág. 474)

dilute/diluida solución que contiene una pequeña cantidad de soluto en un disolvente (Cap. 5, pág. 171)

displacement/desplazamiento cambio neto en la posición de un objeto (Cap. 12, pág. 391)

distance/distancia la lejanía al viajar a lo largo de una ruta, mientras se cambia la posición (Cap. 12, pág. 384)

diversity/diversidad la presencia de muchas especies diferentes dentro de una comunidad (Cap. 16, pág. 512)

Doppler effect/efecto Doppler cambio aparente en la frecuencia de una onda producida por un objeto que se acerca o que se aleja del observador (Cap. 17, pág. 563)

drainage basin/cuenca hidrográfica área desaguada por un río o un arroyo (Cap. 14, pág. 454)

dune/duna montecillo de arena o de sedimentos sueltos formado por la acción del viento (Cap. 15, pág. 494)

E

ecosystem/ecosistema una comunidad de organismos que interactúan entre sí y con el ambiente (Cap. 11, pág. 351)

element/elemento sustancia que no se puede descomponer en sustancias más simples por medios físicos o químicos comunes (Cap. 4, pág. 122)

elevation/elevación la altura sobre el nivel del mar o la profundidad bajo el nivel del mar (Cap. 1, pág. 32)

endoskeleton/endoesqueleto esqueleto que se encuentra dentro del cuerpo del animal (Cap. 9, pág. 287)

equinox/equinoccio cada uno de los dos momentos cada año en que el Sol se encuentra directamente sobre el ecuador (Cap. 19, pág. 608)

erosion/erosión movimiento de los productos de la meteorización desde el lugar en donde se formaron, a un lugar diferente (Cap. 15, pág. 474)

exoskeleton/exoesqueleto sistema de soporte en la parte externa del cuerpo de muchos invertebrados (Cap. 9, pág. 288)

extinction/extinción el desaparecimiento de una especie (Cap. 16, pág. 524)

fertilization/fecundación proceso por el cual el espermatozoide de un macho se une con uno o más óvulos producidos por una hembra (Cap. 9, pág. 290)

firn/nieve granular nieve que no se derrite después de un año y que se vuelve más dura y más densa (Cap. 15, pág. 486)

flagella/flagelos estructuras en forma de látigo que poseen algunos protozoos para poder moverse en el agua (Cap. 8, pág. 261)

floodplain/llanura aluvial área formada por sedimentos finos y livianos que viajan más allá del canal de un río (Cap. 15, pág. 481)

food chain/cadena alimenticia modelo que muestra la manera en que la energía de los alimentos pasa de un organismo a otro en un ecosistema (Cap. 11, pág. 356)

food web/red alimenticia combinación de todas las cadenas alimenticias superpuestas en un ecosistema (Cap. 11, pág. 357)

frequency/frecuencia el número de veces que un objeto vibra en un segundo (Cap. 3, pág. 95)

genus/género subdivisión de una familia de organismos (Cap. 7, pág. 231)

groundwater/agua subterránea agua que se infiltra en el suelo y que se acumula en los poros (Cap. 14, pág. 455)

habitat/hábitat el lugar particular en donde vive un organismo (Cap. 11, pág. 347)

hertz (Hz)/hertz (Hz) un hertz es la frecuencia de una vibración por segundo o un ciclo por segundo (Cap. 3, pág. 95)

heterogeneous mixture/mezcla heterogénea una mezcla en la cual las distintas sustancias están distribuidas irregularmente (Cap. 4, pág. 119)

homogeneous mixture/mezcla homogénea una mezcla en la cual las distintas sustancias están distribuidas uniformemente (Cap. 4, pág. 119)

hydrologic cycle/ciclo hidrológico ciclo en el cual el agua cambia de vapor en el aire a líquido en la Tierra y desde la Tierra regresa al aire (Cap. 14, pág. 445)

indicator/indicador sustancia que muestra un color en una gama del pH y otro color en otra gama (Cap. 6, pág. 202)

interference/interferencia interacción de dos o más ondas en un punto determinado (Cap. 17, pág. 556)

invertebrate/invertebrado cualquier animal que no posee una columna vertebral (Cap. 9, pág. 285)

kingdom/reino el grupo de organismos más grande y general en el sistema de clasificación (Cap. 7, pág. 227)

landforms/accidentes geográficos las características naturales de las superficies terrestres (Cap. 1, pág. 22)

latitude/latitud la distancia en grados ya sea al norte o al sur del ecuador (Cap. 1, pág. 35)

lava/lava nombre que recibe el magma una v ez que alcanza la superficie terrestre (Cap. 18, pág. 577)

limiting factor/factor limitativo cualquier condición que influye el crecimiento o la supervivencia de un organismo o de una especie (Cap. 11, pág. 364)

longitude/longitud la distancia en grados al este o al oeste del primer meridiano (Cap. 1, pág. 36)

longitudinal waves/ondas longitudinales ondas que viajan en la misma trayectoria o dirección de la perturbación (Cap. 17, pág. 542)

lunar eclipse/eclipse lunar ocurre cuando la Luna atraviesa por la sombra que proyecta la Tierra en el lado de la Luna que mira al Sol (Cap. 19, pág. 620)

magma/magma material rocoso derretido que se encuentra debajo de la superficie terrestre (Cap. 18, pág. 577)

magnitude/intensidad medida de la potencia de un terremoto (Cap. 18, pág. 588)

meander/meandro curva de un río que se forma debido a que la velocidad del agua varía dependiendo del ancho del canal (Cap. 14, pág. 451)

medium/medio cualquier sólido, líquido o gas que transporta el patrón de un sonido (Cap. 3, pág. 89)

metabolism/metabolismo es el total de todos los cambios químicos que ocurren en un organismo (Cap. 9, pág. 299)

metamorphosis/metamorfosis cambios de forma que sufren los organismos durante sus ciclos de vida (Cap. 9, pág. 292)

microorganisms/microorganismos organismos tales como las bacterias, los protistas y una gran variedad de hongos que son demasiado pequeños para poder observarlos a simple vista (Cap. 8, pág. 249)

mixture/mezcla cualquier material hecho de dos o más sustancias (Cap. 4, pág. 119)

mudflow/corriente de lodo capas gruesas y espesas de sedimentos que se deslizan fácilmente cuesta abajo (Cap. 15, pág. 476)

mutualism/mutualismo relación en la cual dos especies se benefician (Cap. 16, pág. 517)

neutralization/neutralización reacción química que ocurre entre un ácido y una base (Cap. 6, pág. 203)

niche/nicho es el papel que desempeña un organismo dentro de su comunidad (Cap. 11, pág. 350)

nonvascular plant/planta no vascular planta que carece de vasos tubulares para transportar agua, minerales y alimento (Cap. 10, pág. 316)

opaque/opaco objeto que refleja o absorbe la luz pero que no deja pasarla (Cap. 2. pág. 59)

organism/organismo ser viviente (Cap. 7, pág. 219)

parasites/parásitos organismos que viven fuera o dentro de otros organismos, de los cuales obtienen su alimento (Cap. 8, pág. 265)

parasitism/parasitismo relación en la cual una de las especies perjudica o destruye a la otra (Cap. 16, pág. 520)

period/período (de un péndulo) el tiempo que tarda la lenteja del péndulo en oscilar de ida y vuelta una vez (Cap. 13, pág. 430)

pH/pH una medida que muestra el grado de acidez o de basicidad de una solución (Cap. 6, pág. 199)

phase/fase cada etapa del ciclo lunar (Cap. 1, pág. 43)

phloem/floema vasos tubulares que mueven el alimento desde las hojas hacia otras partes de una planta (Cap. 10, pág. 314)

photosynthesis/fotosíntesis proceso en el cual las plantas usan la luz para producir su alimento (Cap. 10, pág. 336)

phylum/fílum subgrupo en que se divide un reino (Cap. 7, pág. 230)

physical change/cambio físico cambio en las propiedades físicas de una sustancia pero sin alterar la sustancia misma (Cap. 4, pág. 136)

physical property/propiedad física cualquier característica de un material que puede observarse o medirse (Cap. 4, pág. 127)

pioneer species/especies pioneras las primeras especies que viven en un ecosistema (Cap. 16, pág. 507)

pitch/tono se refiere al grado de elevación o de bajo nivel de un sonido (Cap. 3, pág. 96)

pollination/polinización la transferencia de granos de polen del estambre al estigma (Cap. 10, pág. 326)

population/población grupo de individuos de la misma especie que viven en un área al mismo tiempo (Cap. 11, pág. 348)

position/posición lugar donde se encuentra un objeto con relación a un punto de referencia (Cap. 12, pág. 382)

producer/productor plantas verdes que usan la energía luminosa para producir alimento del dióxido de carbono y del agua (Cap. 8, pág. 250)

projectile motion/movimiento de un proyectil el que describe el movimiento de cualquier objeto que es lanzado hacia adelante (horizontalmente) y que luego cae de regreso a la Tierra (Cap. 13, pág. 422)

rarefaction/rarefacción la parte del patrón de partículas separadas que forman las vibraciones en un objeto que vibra (Cap. 3, pág. 88)

receptors/receptores estructuras sensibles a la luz que se encuentran en la retina (Cap. 2, pág. 76)

reflection/reflejo luz que rebota de algo (Cap. 2, pág. 54)

refraction/refracción proceso de doblar la luz cuando pasa de un medio a otro (Cap. 2, pág. 64)

regeneration/regeneración proceso que ocurre cuando un animal vuelve a desarrollar una parte del cuerpo que ha perdido (Cap. 9, pág. 291)

relative velocity/velocidad relativa la velocidad de un objeto, la cual se determina desde el marco de referencia de otro objeto (Cap. 12, pág. 393)

reproduction/reproducción proceso mediante el cual los organismos producen más organismos de la misma especie (Cap. 7, pág. 220; Cap. 10, pág. 322)

resonance/resonancia la tendencia de un objeto a vibrar en la misma frecuencia que otra fuente sonora (Cap. 3, pág. 103)

retina/retina tejido ocular sensible a la luz (Cap. 2, pág. 75)

revolution/revolución movimiento elíptico de la Tierra alrededor del Sol, el cual dura 365 1/4 días, o un año (Cap. 19, pág. 604)

rockslide/deslizamiento de rocas movimiento de una masa de rocas que caen (Cap. 15, pág. 476)

rods/bastones receptores sensibles a la luz y a la oscuridad (Cap. 2, pág. 76)

rotation/rotación movimiento de un cuerpo alrededor de un eje (Cap. 19, pág. 604)

runoff/desagüe de aguas aguas que fluyen y que no se infiltran en la tierra (Cap. 14, pág. 446)

salt/sal un tipo de compuesto que se forma como parte de la neutralización (Cap. 6, pág. 203)

saturated/saturada solución que ha disuelto todo el soluto que le es posible a una temperatura dada (Cap. 5, pág. 166)

SPANISH GLOSSARY

seismograph/sismógrafo se utiliza para registrar las vibraciones de los terremotos (Cap. 18, pág. 588)

slump/desprendimiento movimiento lento de una masa de material suelto (Cap. 15, pág. 475)

solar eclipse/eclipse solar ocurre cuando la Luna pasa directamente entre la Tierra y el Sol (Cap. 19, pág. 615)

solstice/solsticio **cuando** el Sol se encuentra directamente sobre el extremo norte o el extremo sur de los trópicos (Cap. 19, pág. 608)

solubility/solubilidad cantidad de una sustancia que puede disolverse en 100 g de disolvente a una temperatura dada (Cap. 5, pág. 166)

solute/soluto cualquier sustancia que parece desaparecer en una mezcla (Cap. 5, pág. 156)

solution/solución cualquier mezcla formada por partículas pequeñísimas mezcladas uniformemente, las cuales no se asientan (Cap. 5, pág. 156)

solvent/disolvente sustancia en la cual se disuelve un soluto (Cap. 5, pág. 156)

species/especie la categoría más pequeña en la que se subdivide un género (Cap. 7, pág. 231)

spectrum/espectro bandas separadas de color que emergen al pasar la luz a través de un prisma (Cap. 2, pág. 67)

sphere/esfera objeto redondo y tridimensional cuya superficie se encuentra equidistante de un punto llamado centro (Cap. 19, pág. 603)

stationary satellite/satélite fijo satélite que se coloca en órbita alrededor de la Tierra a una altitud y una velocidad precisas con el fin de que gire alrededor de su órbita una vez al día (Cap. 13, pág. 429)

stimulus/estímulo cualquier cosa a la que responde un organismo (Cap. 7, pág. 221)

substance/sustancia cualquier cosa que contiene una sola clase de materia (Cap. 4, pág. 118)

succession/sucesión proceso de cambio que ocurre cuando una comunidad es reemplazada lentamente por otra (Cap. 16, pág. 507)

suspension/suspensión mezcla que contiene un líquido en la cual las partículas visibles se asientan (Cap. 5, pág. 175)

symbiosis/simbiosis estrecha asociación de dos o más especies (Cap. 16, pág. 516)

tide/marea movimiento lento de las olas de mar con longitudes de onda largas (Cap. 19, pág. 621)

translucent/translúcido dícese del cuerpo que deja pasar la luz, pero que no permite ver claramente lo que hay detrás de él (cap. 2, pág. 59)

transparent/transparente dícese de los cuerpos que dejan que la luz pase a través de ellos y que permiten divisar claramente los objetos a través de su espesor (Cap. 2, pág. 59)

transpiration/transpiración pérdida de vapor de agua por los estomas de una hoja (Cap. 10, pág. 332)

transverse waves/ondas transversales ondas en que la perturbación se mueve en ángulo recto a la trayectoria de la onda misma (Cap. 17, pág. 541)

trough/seno punto más bajo o valle de una onda (Cap. 17, pág. 450)

tsunami/maremoto inmensas olas provocadas por terremotos o avalanchas submarinas o erupciones volcánicas en el mar (Cap. 18, pág. 584)

unsaturated/no saturada solución que puede contener más soluto a una temperatura dada (Cap. 5, pág. 170)

valley glaciers/glaciares de valle glaciares pequeños que se encuentran a grandes alturas en valles de regiones montañosas (Cap. 15, pág. 487)

vascular plant/planta vascular planta que posee xilema y floema (Cap. 10, pág. 318)

vertebrate/vertebrado animal que posee una columna vertebral (Cap. 9, pág. 285)

viruses/virus partículas submicroscópicas formadas por un centro de DNA o de RNA, rodeado de un forro proteico (Cap. 8, pág. 251)

water table/nivel hidrostático parte superior del nivel donde se han juntado aguas subterráneas en el suelo (Cap. 14, pág. 462)

wavelength/longitud de onda distancia entre crestas de ondas (Cap. 17, pág. 551)

weightlessness/ingravidez falta de peso; la aceleración hacia la Tierra en caída libre (Cap. 13, pág. 428)

xylem/xilema vasos tubulares que transportan agua y minerales desde las raíces, a través del tallo y hasta llegar a las hojas de una planta (Cap. 10, pág. 314)

The Index for *Science Interactions* will help you locate major topics in the book quickly and easily. Each entry in the Index is followed by the numbers of the pages on which the entry is discussed. A page number given in **boldface type** indicates the page on which that entry is defined. A page number given in *italic type* indicates a page on which the entry is used in an illustration or photograph. The abbreviation *act.* indicates a page on which the entry is used in an activity.

A

D

E

F

G

INDEX

INDEX

Q R

U

V

W

X Y Z

Credits

Illustrations

Jonathan Banchick 424; **Cende Courtney-Hill** 285, 414-415, 510, 532; **John Edwards** 144, 460-461, (t) 542, 543, 547, 556, 561, (r) 569, 575, 583, 594, 595, (t) 603; **Chris Forsey/Morgan-Cain & Associates** 444-445, 446-447, 450-451, 457, 462, 469; **Rolin Graphics** 525-532; **Tonya Hines** 92-93; **JAK Graphics/John Walters & Associates** 23, 24, 27, 28-29, 193, 392, 454; **Deborah Morse/Morgan-Cain & Associates** 475, 490-491, 576-577, 585, (c,b) 597; **Laurie O'Keefe** 100, 348-349, 350, 366, 374, 509; **Sharron O'Neil/Morgan-Cain & Associates** 324-325, 339, (l) 341, 351; **Felipe Passalacqua** (b) 65, 258, 262, 265, 278-279, 298, (t) 307, 478-479; **Bill Pitzer (National Geographic SciFacts)** 48, 209, 304, 497, 626; **Pond and Giles/Morgan-Cain & Associates** 238, 263, 294, 357; **Precision Graphics** 35, 36-37, 43, 45, 49, 51, 57, (t) 65, 66-67, 69, 71, 76, 81, 88, (b) 91, 95, 97, 101, 129, 147, 160-161, 170, 187, 191, 249, 253, 254, 261, 284, 287, 289, 290-291, 293, (b) 307, 314-315, 327, 333, 336, (r) 341, 359, 383, 385, 386-387, 396-397, 400-401, 403, 405, 409, 410, 416, 419, 423, 425, 426, 429, 430-431, 434, 435, 439, 440, 464, 467, 471, 486-487, 500, 504-505, (b) 542, 562-563, 564, (tl,b) 569, 579, 587, 601, (bl) 603, 604, 605, 608, 611, 613, 616-617, 620, 622, 628, 630, 641, 646-647, 667, 668

Photographs

Mark Thayer Studio **5, 7, 13, 14, 26, 44,** (b) **52, 53,** (t) **59, 61, 68,** (t) **74, 75, 76, 81,** (b) **85,** (t) **87,** (t) **88, 90,** (t) **95, 96,** (t) **97, 102,** (b) **103, 110, 116, 117,** (t) **119, 120, 121, 123, 126, 129, 130, 134, 135,** (t) **136, 137, 138, 140,** (br, cr, tl, tr) **141, 143,** (t) **149,** (b, cb, ct, tr) **152, 153** (l) **157, 160, 162,** (t) **166,** (br, l) **171,** (t) **172, 174, 176,** (br) **181,** (t, cl, cr, br) **185, 198-199, 204-205, 205, 206, 209, 210,** (t, c, br) **217, 218, 229,** (cheese) **232,** (c) **242, 246, 255, 257,** (t) **258,** (br) **264,** (b) **277,** (t) **288,** (b) **307,** (t) **310,** (t, b) **311,** (t) **321,** (b) **323** (l, tc) **329, 330,** (t) **341,** (t) **352, 359, 373, 385, 392, 402, 406,** (t) **413, 420,** (t) **456,** (t) **473, 539,** (t) **543, 546, 554,** (bc) **557,** (c, b) **584,** (t) **596**; RMIP/Richard Haynes **2, 4, 6, 8, 10, 11, 21,** (r) **22, 30, 31, 34, 39,** (t) **40, 53, 54, 55,** (t) **56, 58, 60,** (t) **62, 64, 66,** (t) **73, 85,** (c) **87,** (b) **89, 92, 94, 99, 104, 105, 113, 115, 117,** (c) **118, 122, 124, 132, 133, 135,** (b) **139, 149,** (tl) **153,** (r) **155,** (b) **158, 159,** (t) **161, 163,** (t) **165,** (t) **168, 169, 173, 175, 185,** (c) **186, 192, 193, 194, 195, 196, 200, 201, 210,** (bl) **213, 215, 217, 221,** (b) **222, 223, 225, 226,** (b) **229,** (b) **236, 247, 248,** (b) **252, 263, 266, 268, 277,** (b) **279, 282, 283, 289, 293,** (t) **300, 301, 311,** (b) **313,** (t) **318, 322, 328, 331, 334, 335, 345,** (b) **354, 360, 362, 363, 374,** (c) **377, 379, 381, 388, 398, 399, 403, 413, 415, 422,** (t) **432, 433, 439,** (b) **443, 444, 452, 455, 458, 459, 473, 479, 482, 483, 488, 489, 491,** (t) **493, 505, 507,** (t) **508, 509, 514, 523, 527,** (r) **535, 537, 539,** (b) **544, 545, 549, 552, 553, 555, 559, 561, 562, 569,** (b) **573, 574, 578, 582, 590, 591, 601, 602, 605, 606, 607, 610, 614, 618, 619, 631, Cover,** (bk) Tom & Pat Leeson, (tl) NASA/Photo Researchers, (others) ; xiii Tony Stone Images; XIX Color-Pic; xvii J. Azel/Woodfin Camp & Assoc.; xxi World Perspectives; xxiii Superstock; **12,** Steven E. Sutton/Duomo; **17,** Wendy Shattil/Bob Rozinski/Tom Stack & Assoc.; **18-19,** National Geographic Journeys, (c.) National Geographic Society Philip Sharpe/Oxford Scientific Films; **20,** John Bova/Photo Researchers; **21,** (tl) Eunice Harris/Photo Researchers, (bl) John Cleare; **23,** (l) Grant Heilman Photography, (r) Tom Bean; **24,** (l) Barrie Rokeach, (r) David Cavagnaro/Peter Arnold, Inc.; **25,** (t) Tom Till/Photographer, (c) George Ranalli/Photo Researchers, (b) Ric Ergenbright Photography; **27,** (t) Tom Till Photography; (b) Superstock; **28,** (t) Robert Frerck/Odyssey/Chicago, (b) Larry Ulrich Photography; **32-33,** USGS; **33,** Ken Ferguson; **35,** Joel Simon/Allstock; **36,** Comstock/Greg Gerster; **37,** Jeffrey Howe/Visuals Unlimited; **38,** (t) MonTresor/Panoramic Images, (bl) Tim Davis/Photo Researchers, (br) W.G. MacDonald/Photo Researchers; **39,** (b) Color-Pic; **41,** Francois Gohier/Photo Researchers; **42,** (t) NASA/Photri, (c, b) World Perspectives; **43,** NASA/Peter Arnold, Inc.; **44,** (t) Susan McCartney/Photo Researchers; **46,** (l) Ray Pfortner/Peter Arnold, Inc., (r) Ray Pfortner/Peter Arnold, Inc.; **47,** NASA; **48,** (t) Courtesy Jessica Flintoft, (b) Joanne Lotter/Tom Stack & Assoc.; **49,** (t) David Cavagnaro/Peter Arnold, Inc., (b) World Perspectives; **55,** (b) Color-Pic; **61,** (l) Leo de Wys Inc./Fridmar Damm; **63,** Chris Sorensen; **65,** Claude Charlier/The Stock Market; **66,** (b) H.R. Bramaz/Peter Arnold, Inc.; **68,** (b) Galen Rowell/Peter Arnold, Inc.; **69,** Color-Pic; **72,** Doug Martin; **77,** Igaku-Shoin; **78,** (l) Scott Frances, (r) Scott Frances\Esto; **79,** Superstock; **80,** Courtesy of Dr. Adriann Ocampa; **81,** (t) RMIP/Richard Haynes, (c) Claude Charlier/The Stock Market; **85,** (b) Rafael Macia/Photo Researchers; **86,** Chris Sorensen; **90,** (b) Zigy Kaluzny/TSI; **96,** (b) John Harrington/Black Star; **98, 99,** Doug Martin; **102,** (t) Courtesy Feingarsh; **106,** Superstock; **107,** Bob Daemmrich/ Stock Boston; **108,** (l) Terence A. Gili/FPG, (r) E. Hartmann/Magnum; **109,** Courtesy of Torey Verts; **110,** (bl) Courtesy Feingarsh; **112,** StudiOhio; **114-115,** National Geographic Journeys, (c.) National Geographic Society/Breton Littlehales; **117,** (bl) W. Frerck/Odyssey; **125,** Doug Martin; **127, 131,** Ralph Brunke; **140,** (cl) Adam Woolfitt/Woodfin Camp & Assoc., (bl) Bruce Forster/Allstock; **142,** (t) Ken Ferguson, (c) Visuals Unlimited, (b) NASA/Mark Marten/Photo Researchers; **143,** (c) Frank Rossotto/Tom Stack & Assoc., (b) Fred Ward/Black Star; **145,** Custom Medical Stock Photo; **146,** (t) Pascal Quittemelle/Stock Boston, (b) Otto Rogge/The Stock Market; **148,** (t) Art Resource, NY, (b) National Museum of American Art, Washington DC/Art Resource, NY; **154,** Ken Ferguson; **155,** (t) Bob Daemmrich/Tony Stone Images; **156,** (b) Earth Scenes/H. & J. Beste; **157,** (t) Bruce McNitt/Panoramic Images, (bl) Steven Underwood; **159,** (b) Chris Sorensen; **162,** (b) Color-Pic; **163,** (bl, br) Chris Sorensen; **164,** Chris Sorensen; **166,** (l), (tr) Chris Sorensen; **171,** (b) Adam Hart-Davis/SPL/Photo Researchers; **176,** (tl) The Avery Brundage Collection/Asian Art Museum of San Francisco, (tr) Ed Pritchard/Tony Stone Images, (bl) Skip Moody/Dembinsky Photo Assoc., (bc) Thomas Braise/The Stock Market; **177,** Frederica Georgia/Photo Researchers; **178,** Michael Baytoff/Black Star; **179,** Catherine Karnow/Woodfin Camp & Assoc.; **180,** D. Newman/Visuals Unlimited; **181,** (bl) Ed Pritchard/Tony Stone Images; **182,** Kenji Kernis; **185,** (tr, bl) Robert Frerck/Odyssey Productions; **187,** Gernot Huber/Woodfin Camp & Assoc.; **188,** S.J. Krasemann/Peter Arnold, Inc.; **189,** Carr Clifton; **190,** Color-Pic; **197,** Color-Pic; **202,** Matt Meadows; **204,** Courtesy of Griffith Laboratories; **207,** (t) Ray Pfortner/Peter Arnold, Inc., (b) Kevin Horan/Stock Boston; **208,** (t) Roland Birke/Peter Arnold, Inc., (b) Archive Photos; **212,** (t) Grant Heilman Photography, (b) Kenji Kerins; **214-215,** National Geographic Journeys, (c) National Geographic Society/David Doubilet; **216,** George Holton/Photo Researchers, **216-217,** Tim Davis/Photo Researchers; **219,** (l) Christopher Talbot Frank, (r) National Audubon Society/Photo Researchers, Inc.; **220,** (t) Nigel Dennis/Photo Researchers, (c) David M. Phillips/Visuals Unlimited, (b) BBH Fotografie/OKAPIA/Photo Researchers, Inc.; **221,** (t) Tim Davis/Photo Researchers, (c) F. Gohier/Photo Researchers; **224,** (t) Stephen Dalton/Photo Researchers, (b) Gary Milburn/Tom Stack & Assoc.; **226,** (tl) Stephen Holt/Academy of Natural Sciences/VIREO, (tr) P. Gadsby/Natural Academy of Sciences/Vireo; **227,** C.H. Greenholt Academy of Natural Sciences/VIREO; **228,** (t) Manfred Kage/Peter Arnold, Inc., (cl) CNRI/SPL/Photo Researchers, (cr) Tom E. Adams/Peter Arnold, Inc., (b) Professor David Hall/Science Photo Library/Photo Researchers, Inc.; **229,** (t, tc) David M. Dennis/Tom Stack & Assoc., (cheese), (cl) Kevin Schafer, (cr) John Cancalosi/Peter Arnold, Inc.; **230,** R.S. Michaud/Woodfin Camp & Assoc.; **231,** (t) Tom & Pat Leeson/Photo Researchers, (b) Robert Frerck/Odyssey/Chicago; **232,** (t) Kevin Schafer & Martha Hill, (b) Tom Stack & Assoc.; **234,** (t) K. Scholz/H. Armstrong Roberts, (c) Frans Lanting/Allstock, (bl) Fredrik D. Bodin, (bc) Bios (Pu Tao) /Peter Arnold, Inc., (br) Barbara Gerlach/Dembinsky Photo Assoc.; **237,** (t) Animals, Animals, Inc./Robert Lubeck; (b) Leonard Lee Rue/Photo Researchers; **239,** SPL/Photo Researchers; **240,** Superstock; **241,** (t) Sharon Cummings/ Dembinsky Photo Assoc., (b) Thomas D. Mangelsen/Peter Arnold, Inc.; **243,** (bear) Fredrik D. Bodin, (flower) Tierbild Okapia/Photo Researchers, Inc., (fox) Nigel Dennis/Photo Researchers, (panda) Bios (Pu Tao) /Peter Arnold, Inc., (racoon) Barbara Gerlach/Dembinsky Photo Assoc., (student) RMIP/Richard Hatnes, (wolf) Tom Leeson/Photo Researchers, Inc.; **246,** (t) DCRT/NIH/Custom Medical Stock; **247,** (t) Matt Meadows; **248,** (t) Cabisco/Visuals Unlimited, (c) Eric Grave/Phototake, NYC; **249,** Eric Grave/Photo Researchers; **250,** (l) T. Brain/Photo Researchers, (c) David M. Phillips/Visuals Unlimited, (r) Ray Coleman/Photo Researchers; **251,** (t) Dr. O. Bradfute/Peter Arnold, Inc., (c) SPL/Photo Researchers, Inc., (b) Institut Pasteur/CNRI/Phototake; **256,** David Scharf/Peter Arnold, Inc.; **257,** (b) Leon J. LeBeau/Biological Photo Service; **258,** (c) Charles W. Stratton/Visuals Unlimited; **259,** (t, cl, bl) Eric Grave/Photo Researchers, (br) Manfred Kage/Peter Arnold, Inc., (cr) Ward's Natural Science Establishment; **260,** Robert Brons/BPS; **262,** (t) Patrick Grace/Photo Researchers, (b) Ed Reschke/Peter Arnold, Inc.; **264,** (tl) Maslowski Photo/Visuals Unlimited, (tr) Andrew McClengahan/SPL/Photo Researchers; **265,** Hans Pfletschinger/Peter Arnold, Inc.; **267,** Grant Heilman Photography; **269,** Zeva Delbaum/Peter Arnold, Inc.; **270,** (t) James Aronsovsky, illustrattion by James Crumble/ Discover Magazine, (b) NIBSC/SPL/Photo Researchers; **271,** Courtesy Audrey Cruz; **272,** Ken Graham; **273,** (t) David Scharf/Peter Arnold, Inc., (cl) Eric Grave/Photo Researchers, (c) Manfred Kage/Peter Arnold, Inc., (cr) Ray Coleman/Photo Researchers, (b) Phototake; **276,** Color-Pic; **276-277,** Ron Kimball; **281,** Anthony Mercieca Photo/Photo Researchers, Inc.; **284,** Animals, Animals, Inc./Adrienne T. Gibson; **286,** (t) Biophoto Assoc./Photo Researchers, Inc., (cl) James H. Robinson/Photo Researchers, (cr) Thomas Dimock/The Stock Market, (b) E.R. Degginger/Photo Researchers; **288,** (t) David M. Dennis/Tom Stack & Assoc.; **291,** Comstock/Gwen Fidler; **292,** (ltc, lbc, lb) Color-Pic, (others) Dwight Kuhn; **293,** (cr) Color-Pic, (cl, b) Dwight Kuhn; **294,** (l) Animals, Animals, Inc./Breck P. Kent, (others) Harry Rogers/Photo Researchers; **295,** (l) Harry Rogers/Photo Researchers; (r) Color-Pic; **296,** (t) Christine M. Douglas/Photo Researchers, (c) Luiz C. Marigo/Peter Arnold, (bl) Stephen Krasemann/Peter Arnold, (br) Colin Prior/Tony Stone Inter.; **297,** Steven Underwood; **298,** Dennis Stock/Magnum; **299,** Ron Spomer/Visuals Unlimited; **302,** (l) Renee Lynn/Allstock, (r) E. R. Degginger/Photo

Credits

Researchers; **303,** (t) R. Andrew Odum/Peter Arnold, Inc., (c) Nick Bergkessel/ Photo Researchers, (b) Stan Wayman/Photo Researchers, Inc.; **304,** Glencoe file photo; **305,** Chris Noble/Allstock; **306,** (t) Courtesy of Jessica Knight, (b) T. E. Adams/Visuals Unlimited; **307,** (c) Steven Underwood, (b) Steven Underwood; **309,** Gerry Davis/Phototake; **312,** Steven Underwood; **313,** (b) Steven Underwood; **314,** Steven Underwood; **316-317,** Rick Ergenbright Photography; **317,** Color-Pic; **319,** (c, bl) Matt Meadows, (others) Steven Underwood; **320,** (t) Mary Lou Uttermohlen, (bl) Tom Bean/Allstock, (br) Pat O'Hara/Allstock; **321,** (tr) Steven Underwood; **323,** (r) E.A. Janes/NHPA, (b) Steven Underwood; **326,** Anthony Mercieca Photo/Photo Researchers; **327,** Cesar Paredes/The Stock Market; **330,** (bl) Kerry T. Givens/Tom Stack & Assoc.; **332,** Lindsay Hebberd/Woodfin Camp & Assoc.; **337,** (t) David Hiser/Tony Stone Images, (b) NASA; **338,** Michael J. Balick/Peter Arnold; **339,** Overseas/Phototake; **340,** Courtesy of the DuSable Museum of African American History; **341,** (b) Color-Pic; **343,** (l) Kim Heacox/Peter Arnold, (c) William Grenfell/Visuals Unlimited, (r) Ian Murphy/Tony Stone Inter.; **344,** (t) Comstock/Bob Grant; **344-345,** Ron Sanford/Panoramic Images; **345,** (t) Kevin McCarthy; **346,** (t) Stephen McBrady/PhotoEdit, (b) Richard Hutchings/ PhotoEdit; **347,** (tl) Stan Osolinski/Dembinsky Photo Assoc., (tr) Tom & Pat Leeson/Photo Researchers, (bl) Fred Bavendam/Peter Arnold, Inc., (br) David Frazier Photolibrary; **353,** (t) Ernest Manewal/Alaska Stock, (c) Kevin Schafer/Martha Hill/Tom Stack & Assoc., (b) Scott Camazine/Photo Researchers; **355,** Stephen Dalton/Photo Researchers; **356,** (t) Willard Clay/Dembinsky Photo Assoc., (tc) Superstock, (b) M. H. Sharp/Photo Researchers, , (bc) Animals, Animals, Inc./Ziggy Leszczynski; **358,** Willard Clay/Dembinsky Photo Assoc.; **361,** (tl) Steven Underwood, (tr) Sharon Cummings/Dembinsky Photo Assoc., (bl) Wiley Wales/Profiles West, (br) Nathan Benn/Woodfin Camp & Assoc.; **364,** (t) Jose Azell/Woodfin Camp & Assoc., (tc) Kevin Schafer, (bc) Roy Morsch/The Stock Market, (b) David Muench; **365,** (t) Bill Gallery/Stock Boston, (c) William Johnson/Stock Boston, (b) Robert Rathe/Stock Boston; **367,** (t) Gunter Ziesler/Peter Arnold, Inc., (bl) Color-Pic, (br) Superstock; **368,** Paul Drummond/Bryan and Cherry Alexander; **369,** (t) Tim Davis/Photo Researchers, (b) James Martin; **370,** Toni Angermayer/Photo Researchers; **371,** Aaron Haupt; **372,** M. H. Sharp/Photo Researchers; **372-373,** Robert Llewellyn; **374,** (t) Stephen Dalton/Photo Researchers, Inc., (b) Toni Angermayer/Photo Researchers; **378-379,** National Geographic Journeys, (c) National Geographic Society/Dewitt Jones; **380-381,** Thomas Del Braise/The Stock Market; **380,** Dick Young/Unicorn Stock Photos; **382,** Doug Brown/Panoramic Images; **384,** (l) Comstock/Boyd Norton, (tr) Bruce Iverson/Visuals Unlimited, (br) David C. Fritts/Allstock; **389,** David Madison; **390,** (l) Suzanne & Joseph Collins/Photo Researchers, (c) Jean Marc Barey/Photo Researchers, (r) Thomas Kitchin/Tom Stack & Assoc.; **391,** Christoper Brown/Stock Boston; **393,** Ken Ferguson; **394,** (t) NASA/Science Source/Photo Researchers, (b) Richard E. Hill/Visuals Unlimited; **395,** NASA/Science Source/Photo Researchers; **404,** Jeff Persons/Stock Boston; **406,** (b) National Maritime Museum, London/The Bridgeman Art Library; **407,** Chad Slattery; **408,** Albright-Knox Art Gallery; **409,** (t) David Madison, (b) Jeff Persons/Stock Boston; **412,** Mark Marten/NASA/Photo Researchers; **412-413,** David Madison; **414,** David Ball/The Stock Market; **417,** Vandystadt/Photo Researchers; **418,** (l) Photri/The Stock Market, (r) Tom Sanders/Photri/The Stock Market; **419,** William Johnson/Stock Boston; **420,** (c) John Bova/Photo Researchers, (b) Kofk, Inc./Allstock; **421,** Brian Stablyk/Allstock; **423,** Richard Menga/Fundamental Photographs; **425,** Science Photo Library/Photo Researchers, Inc.; **426, 427,** NASA/Photo Researchers; **428,** (t) Chris Sorensen, (b) Steven Underwood; **436,** NASA/Photri; **437,** (t) European Space Agency/SPL/Photo Researchers, (b) Photri; **438,** (t) The Royal Society, (bl) Mary Evans Picture Library, (br) D.A. Calvert, Royal Greenwich Observatory/Science Photo Library/Photo Researchers; **439,** (t) Tom Sanders/The Stock Market; **442,** Tom Bean; **442-443,** Renee Lynn/David Madison; **447,** Jim Richardson; **448,** (l) Willard Clay/Dembinsky Photo Assoc., (r) Dale Jorgenson/Tom Stack and Assoc.; **449,** Ralph Brunke; **450,** Superstock; **451,** Carr Clifton; **453,** (t) Doug Bryant, (b) Jennifer Jones/Profiles West; **454,** (l) James Blank/The Stock Market; (tr) Frederica Georgia/Photo Researchers, (br) James Blank/The Stock Market; **456,** (b) Frederica Georgia/Photo Researchers; **460,** (l) Earth Scenes/E. R. Degginger, (r) Earth Scenes/Breck P. Kent; **462,** (t) Earth Scenes/John Lemker, (b) Earth Scenes/R. Ingo Riepl; **463,** (l) Earth Scenes/Ken Cole, (r) John Kieffer/Peter Arnold, Inc.; **464,** Alexander Lowry/Photo Researchers, Inc.; **464-465,** Gene Marshall/Tom Stack & Assoc.; **465,** (t) Chuck Savage/The Stock Market; (c) David Frazier Photolibrary, (b) Steven Underwood; **466, 467,** Gillette Liaison/ Gamma Liaison; **468,** (t) H. Abernathy/H. Armstrong Roberts, (b) Courtesy of JoAnna Gott; **472,** Carr Clifton; **472-473,** Tom Till Photography; **474,** (t, cr) Color-Pic, (cl) Carr Clifton, (cr) Color-Pic, (b) Marvin L. Dembinsky, Jr./Dembinsky Photo Assoc.; **475,** (t) David Frazier/Photolibrary, (b) McCutcheon\Visuals Unlimited; **476,** (t) Jeff Foott/Tom Stack & Assoc., (b) Color-Pic; **477,** (t) Earth Scenes/Jack Wilburn, (b) D. Cavagnaro/Visuals Unlimited; **480,** (t) Aaron Haupt/David Frazier Photolibrary, (b) Stephen Krasemann/Photo Researchers; **481,** (t) Michael S. Yamashita, (b) Peter M. Fisher/The Stock Market; **484,** (l) Robert Cushman Hayes; (c) Alex S. MacLean/Peter Arnold, Inc., (r) Color-Pic; **485,** Byron Crader/Ric Ergenbright Photography; **487,** (t) Bryan and Cherry Alexander, (b) Steve Kraseman/Photo Researchers; **489,** Doug Martin; **490,** (t) Thomas Kitchin/Tom Stack and Assoc., (b) Susan Heady/Ohio Sea Grant Program; **491,** (b) John & Ann Mahan; **492,** (l) Bryan and Cherry Alexander, (r) Color-Pic; **494,** (t) Color-Pic, (b) Dr. Gene Feldman, NASA GSFC/Science Photo Library/Photo Researchers; **495,** (l) EOSAT, (r) Kerstin Geier/Anthony Bannister Photo Library; **496,** (t) Douglas R. Shane/Photo Researchers, (b) Paul Solomon/Woodfin Camp & Assoc.; **497,** (t) E.R.I.M./Tony Stone Images; (b) NASA/Photri; **498,** Superstock; **499,** (l) Superstock, (r) W. Kleck/Terraphotogaphics/BPS; **500,** Sharon Cummings/ Dembinsky Photo Assoc.; **501,** (tl) Stephen Krasemann/Photo Researchers, (tr) Jeff Foott/Tom Stack & Assoc., (bl, br) Color-Pic; **503,** Mike Yamashita/ Westlight; **504,** Jeff Foott/Tom Stack & Assoc.; **504-505,** Nubar Alexanian/ Woodfin Camp & Assoc.; **506,** Tom Bean; **507,** (b) Howard Garrett/Dembinsky Photo Assoc.; **511,** (t) Milton Rand/Tom Stack & Assoc., (c) Color-Pic, (b) Comstock/Michael S. Thompson; **512,** Carr Clifton; **513,** (t) Joe McDonald/ Visuals Unlimited, (c) David Austen/Tony Stone Images, (b) ABPL; **515,** (l) Arthur Morris/Visuals Unlimited, (r) Animals, Animals, Inc./Zig Leszczynski; **516,** (t) Joe McDonald/Visuals Unlimited, (c) Animals, Animals, Inc./B. G. Murray, (b) Marty Snyderman/Visuals Unlimited; **517,** (l) Joe McDonald/Tom Stack & Assoc., (tr) Nigel Dennis/ABPL, (br) Clem Haagner/ABPL; **518,** (l) Mike Bacon/Tom Stack & Assoc., (c) Keith Gillett/Tom Stack & Assoc., (r) C. Garoutte/Tom Stack & Assoc.; **519,** (t) Matt Bradley/Tom Stack & Assoc., (b) Brian Parker/Tom Stack & Assoc.; **520,** (t) Rod Planck/Tom Stack & Assoc., (bl) Eric A. Soder/Tom Stack & Assoc., (br) John D. Cunningham/Visuals Unlimited; **521,** (t) Bill Beatty/Visuals Unlimted; (b) Rod Allin/Tom Stack & Assoc.; **522,** (t) Gary Milburn/Tom Stack & Assoc., (b) Rod Allin/Tom Stack & Assoc.; **524,** Patrice Ceisel/Visuals Unlimited; **526,** (tl) Tom McHugh/Photo Researchers, (tr) Larry Tackett/Tom Stack & Assoc., (c) Animals, Animals, Inc./Maresa Pryor, (bl) Sharon Cummings/Dembinsky Photo Assoc., (br) Animals, Animals, Inc./Zig Leszczynski; **527,** (l) Kevin Schafer/Tom Stack and Assoc., (c) Johan Elzenga/Tony Stone Images; **528,** Earth Scenes/Patty Murray; **528-529,** Robert Frerck/Odyssey/Chicago; **529,** (t) Animals, Animals, Inc./ Patti Murray, (c) Tom McHugh/Photo Researchers; **530,** (t) Seth Resnick/Stock Boston, (b) Glencoe file; **531,** Courtesy of the BioGeography Lab, UC at Santa Rosa; **532,** (tl) Marty Snyderman/Visuals Unlimited; (tr) Larry Tackett/Tom Stack & Assoc., (lc) John D. Cunningham/Visuals Unlimited, (rc) Animals, Animals, Inc./Maresa Pryor, (bl) Matt Bradley/Tom Stack & Assoc., (br) Animals, Animals, Inc./Zig Leszczynski; **533,** Luis Villota/The Stock Market; **534,** (t) Color-Pic, (b) Mike Severns/Tom Stack & Assoc.; **536-537,** National Geographic Journeys, (c.) National Geographic Society/Devon Jacklin; **538,** Chris Kapolka/ TSI; **538-539,** Karen R. Preuss; **540,** Reuters/Bettmann; **541,** Martin Dohrn/ SPL/Photo Researchers; **542,** James Sugar/Black Star; **548,** (t) George Munday/Leo de Wys, (b) David Madison; **550-551,** Arnulf Husmo/Tony Stone Images; **554,** (t) Arthur Tilley/FPG, (tc) Color-Pic, (b) Dick Luria/FPG; **557,** (t) Color-Pic; **558,** (l) Ken Sherman/Phototake, (r) W. Banaszewski/Visuals Unlimited; **560,** (t) Superstock, (b) Tom Pantages; **565,** Earth Scenes/Stefan Meyers; **567,** (l) Bernd Witich/Visuals Unlimited, (r) Chris Sorensen; **568,** Courtesy of Jason Cobb; **569,** (t) Matin Dohrn/SPL/Photo Researchers; **572,** Art Resource, NY; **572-573,** Superstock; **576, 577,** Underwood Photo Archives; **580,** (t) Greg Vaughn/Tom Stack & Assoc., (b) Tony Stone Images; **581,** (t) Color-Pic, (c) Krafft/Explorer/Science Source/Photo Researchers, (b) Greg Probst/Stock Boston; **583,** (t) Underwood Photo Archives; (b) Emmons/ PhotoReporters; **584,** (b) The NOAA Geophysical Lab; **586,** Francois Gohier/Photo Researchers; **586-587,** Milton Rand/Tom Stack & Assoc.; **587,** Leonard Von Matt/Photo Researchers; **588,** Vince Streano/Tony Stone Images; **588-589,** The Natural History Museum Picture Library, London; **596,** (t) Courtesy of Deena Strobman; **597,** (t) Color-Pic, (b) John Emmons/ Photoreporters; **600,** Earth Satellite Corporation/SPL/Photo Researchers; **600-601,** World Perspectives; **609,** (t) Christopher Talbot Frank, (b) Joe MacDonald/Visuals Unlimited; **611,** World Perspectives; **612,** NASA/Photri; **613,** World Perspectives; **615,** Tom Pantages; **616,** University of California Regents; **620,** Guillermo Gonzalez/Visuals Unlimited; **621,** Color-Pic; **622,** Stephen Krasemann/Photo Researchers; **623,** (t) G. Carleton Ray/Photo Researchers, (b) Copr. F. Stuart Westmorland/Photo Researchers; **624,** (t) The Tidebook Company, (c) Momatiuk/Eastcott/Woodfin Camp & Assoc., (b) Bryan and Cherry Alexander Photography; **625,** Steven Underwood; **626,** (l) Steve Kaufman/Peter Arnold, Inc., (r) Cameramann International, Ltd.; **627,** (t) Courtesy of Natalie Sanchez, (b) Ray Nelson/ Phototake; **628,** (l) Steve Kaufman/Peter Arnold, Inc., (r) Guillermo Gonzalez/Visuals Unlimited; **637,** (l) A.B. Dowsett/Photo Researchers, (r) David Dennis/Tom Stack & Assoc.; **638,** (l) Lynn Stone, (c) David Scharf/Peter Arnold, Inc., (r) Alton Biggs; **639,** (l-r) James Westwater, Joey Jacques, Lynn Stone (3), Aaron Haupt, William D. Popejoy; **640,** (tl) Al Grotell, (tc) Jim Rorabaugh, (tr) Hutchins, (c) Kjell Sandved, (bl) Wolfgang Kaehler, (br) Jean Wentworth; **653, 659,** Ken Frick; **660,** Janet L. Adams; **662, 663,** Doug Martin; **667,** NASA; **670,** Keith Turpie.

PERIODIC TABLE OF THE ELEMENTS

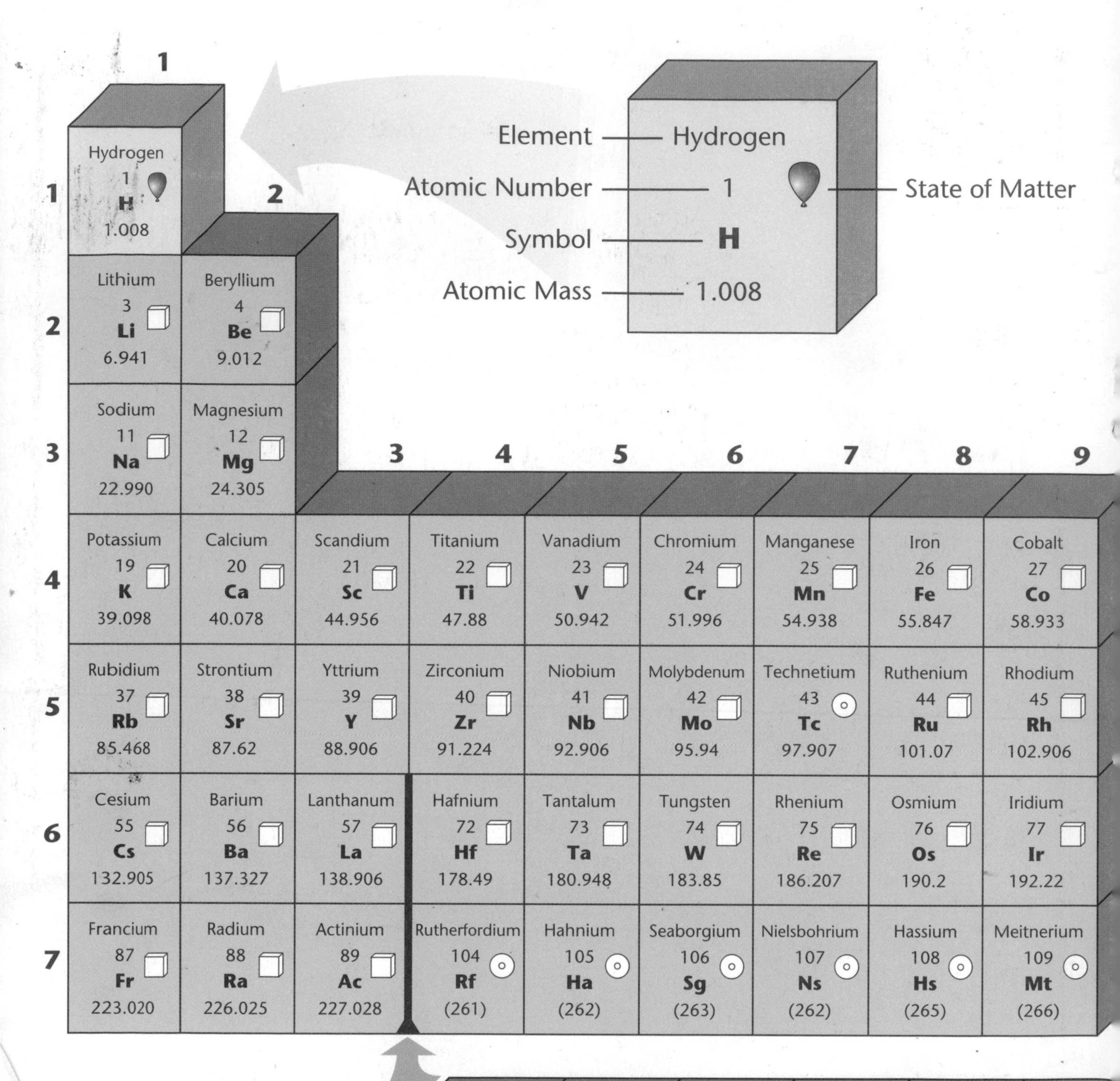

	1	2	3	4	5	6	7	8	9
1	Hydrogen 1 H 1.008								
2	Lithium 3 Li 6.941	Beryllium 4 Be 9.012							
3	Sodium 11 Na 22.990	Magnesium 12 Mg 24.305							
4	Potassium 19 K 39.098	Calcium 20 Ca 40.078	Scandium 21 Sc 44.956	Titanium 22 Ti 47.88	Vanadium 23 V 50.942	Chromium 24 Cr 51.996	Manganese 25 Mn 54.938	Iron 26 Fe 55.847	Cobalt 27 Co 58.933
5	Rubidium 37 Rb 85.468	Strontium 38 Sr 87.62	Yttrium 39 Y 88.906	Zirconium 40 Zr 91.224	Niobium 41 Nb 92.906	Molybdenum 42 Mo 95.94	Technetium 43 Tc 97.907	Ruthenium 44 Ru 101.07	Rhodium 45 Rh 102.906
6	Cesium 55 Cs 132.905	Barium 56 Ba 137.327	Lanthanum 57 La 138.906	Hafnium 72 Hf 178.49	Tantalum 73 Ta 180.948	Tungsten 74 W 183.85	Rhenium 75 Re 186.207	Osmium 76 Os 190.2	Iridium 77 Ir 192.22
7	Francium 87 Fr 223.020	Radium 88 Ra 226.025	Actinium 89 Ac 227.028	Rutherfordium 104 Rf (261)	Hahnium 105 Ha (262)	Seaborgium 106 Sg (263)	Nielsbohrium 107 Ns (262)	Hassium 108 Hs (265)	Meitnerium 109 Mt (266)

Lanthanide Series	Cerium 58 Ce 140.115	Praseodymium 59 Pr 140.908	Neodymium 60 Nd 144.24	Promethium 61 Pm 144.913	Samarium 62 Sm 150.36	Europium 63 Eu 151.965
Actinide Series	Thorium 90 Th 232.038	Protactinium 91 Pa 231.036	Uranium 92 U 238.029	Neptunium 93 Np 237.048	Plutonium 94 Pu 244.064	Americium 95 Am 243.061